ALBA's
medical technology

BOARD EXAMINATION REVIEW

Volume II

ALBA's
medical technology

BOARD EXAMINATION REVIEW

Volume II

Thousands of Representative Questions and
Answers from Recent Examinations PLUS
*Practical Math for Clinical Chemistry, Board
Examination Tips* and other unusual features

Fourth Edition

Revised and Updated by Authorities
in the Various Subjects

BERKELEY SCIENTIFIC PUBLICATIONS
DRAWER 160
WESTLAKE, OREGON 97493

PUBLISHER'S FOREWORD

We have just acquired a new address, an old name, and a new section. Beginning January 2, 1978, mail orders for our medical technology board examination review manuals should be directed to **Berkeley Scientific Publications, Drawer 160, Westlake, OR 97493.** Any mail addressed to our former (Berkeley, CA) address will still reach us but, for fastest service, this new address should be used. Additional information on how to obtain our manuals will be found on the last pages of this book.

In the past few years, the need to permanently identify our medical technology board examination review (presently available as a two-volume set) has become more imperative. Therefore, beginning with the present edition of Volume II, the name of the original author is again being used and subsequent editions and reprints will continue to bear his name.

For the first time in our books, a formal section (or "supersection") on microbiology has been formed and, for this edition of Volume II, questions in all areas of diagnostic microbiology have been brought up to date. The greatest update involved nomenclature and currently used diagnostic tests. On the other hand, questions denoting concepts are paramount and have been left intact. Anaerobic bacteriology, venereal diseases, and mycobacteriology, among other subjects, have been updated. A number of questions were eliminated and replaced with more current questions and errors in past editions have been corrected and/or eliminated. We have tried to provide information that would not only be helpful in medical technology examinations but in clinical microbiology examinations (notably the National Registry of Microbiologists of the American Academy of Microbiology) as well. In the parasitology subsection, questions on serological and immunodiagnosis and questions on parasites of current significance (e.g., *Toxocara canis*) were introduced. And, in this same subsection, the terminology has been updated and the medical entomology questions modified and expanded.

In the clinical hematology section, modern terminology has now replaced older terminology. Older forms of testing have given way to more modern interpretations. For example, the multiple methods of performing the erythrocyte sedimentation rate are much less important at the present time than they were when the ESR was the sole indicator of inflammatory or neo-plastic process. Questions regarding newer diagnostic tests have been included—specifically these are in the areas of understanding of the neutropenias and marrow function. Additionally, there have been many new concepts raised by recent studies in the field of coagulation and thrombosis and new questions will be found concerning them. Platelet function has been the object of concerted study and our concepts are vastly altered and new questions are included in this regard. In a recent communication, Dr. Schrier observes that the clinical laboratory is now required to be responsible to the clinician in another sense. In the past, diagnosis was what was required. Now the clinical laboratory must also help the clinician with his therapy. This is particularly true in the management of patients with malignant disorders where the use of chemotherapeutic agents results in selective depression of certain blood counts. For that reason, particular attention has been devoted to questions dealing with pancytopenia, aplasia or cytopenia of one cell line.

With the chief exception of "Practical Math for Clinical Chemistry" (which required no change), similar updates have been carried out in the subject matter of other sections and features of this book. Overall, there has been an increase in the number of questions and, hopefully, an improvement in quality of coverage.

January, 1978

TABLE OF CONTENTS

Section I — CLINICAL CHEMISTRY

Section II – HEMATOLOGY

Hematology Examination

Section III – MICROBIOLOGY

Subsection I – Parasitology

Subsection II — Bacteriology and Allied Fields

Subsection III — Serology and Immunology

Section IV — REVIEW OF HISTOLOGY TECHNIQUE

Section V   MISCELLANEOUS EXAM QUESTIONS

Section VI — BOARD EXAMINATION TIPS

Section I
CLINICAL CHEMISTRY

1.

PRACTICAL MATH FOR CLINICAL CHEMISTRY

Edited by Edith Zak Helman, M.S., Scientific Newsletters, Anaheim, California

This text has been written for students and laboratory workers to help them understand the fundamentals necessary for solving math problems in the clinical chemistry laboratory. Since this work is in the form of a programmed text, each question is immediately followed by the correct answer, and an explanation of how the problem is solved. To use this text, the reader covers up the page and slides the cover downward as he progresses from question to question. It is recommended that the reader *write down* the answers to the questions as he progresses throughout the text. A review test is provided at the end of every chapter. If difficulty is encountered it is recommended that the chapter be reviewed. The material herein is presented in such a form that the reader can study it completely on his own, or it may be used as a classroom text. A table of atomic weights is provided on page 28.

$-$I$-$
MOLARITY

1. The molecular weight (M.W.) of a compound is obtained by adding the atomic weights (At. wts.) of the component elements in the proportions indicated in the formula.

   Thus: M.W. HCl = At. wt. of H + At. wt. of Cl

   M.W. HCl =   1   +   35.5

   M.W. HCl =   36.5

   Thus: M.W. H_2SO_4 = 2 (At. wt. H) + At. wt. S + 4 (At. wt. O)

   M.W. H_2SO_4 = 2 (1.0)   +   32.1   + 4 (16.0)

   M.W. H_2SO_4 = 2   +   32.1 +   64

   M.W. H_2SO_4 = 98.1

   What is the molecular weight of NaCl?

   What is the molecular weight of H_3PO_4?

   Answer: M.W. NaCl $-$ 23.0 + 35.5 = 58.5

   M.W. H_3PO_4 = 3 (1.0) + 31.0 + 4 (16) = 98

2. What is the M.W. of $Ca_3(PO_4)_2$?

   Answer: M.W. $Ca_3(PO_4)_2$ = 3 (40.1) + 2 (31.0 + 64) = 310.3

3. M.W. of NaCl = 58.5
   Gram molecular weight (G.M.W.) of NaCl = 58.5 grams
   What are the molecular and gram molecular weights of Na_2SO_4?

   Answer: M.W. Na_2SO_4 = 142.1
   G.M.W. = 142.1 grams

4. A mole represents one gram molecular weight of a substance:

   $$\frac{Gms.}{M.W.} = Moles$$

   How many moles in 252 gms. of $NaHCO_3$?

   Answer: 3 moles   *Solution:*

   M.W. $NaHCO_3$ = 84

   $$\frac{Gms.}{M.W.} = \frac{252}{84} = 3$$

5. A one molar (1M) solution contains 1 gram molecular weight (G.M.W.)
   or a mole of solute per liter of solution.

   Thus: 1 M = 1 mole/liter   = 1 G.M.W./liter
   0.1 M = 0.1 mole/liter = 0.1 G.M.W./liter

   How many grams of NaCl does 1 liter of a 1 M NaCl solution contain?

   Answer: 58.5 grams   G.M.W. = 58.5 grams
   1M = 58.5 gms./liter

6. How many grams does 1 liter of a 0.2M solution of NaCl contain?

   Answer: 11.7 grams   *Solution:*

   1 G.M.W. NaCl = 58.5 grams = 1 mole
   1 liter of a 1M NaCl = 58.5 gms.
   a liter of a 0.2M NaCl = 58.5 $\times$ 0.2 = 11.7 gms.

7. a. How many milliliters in 1 liter?
   b. 1 ml. = ? liters

Answers: a. 1000 ml.

b. $\dfrac{1}{1000}$ = .001 liter

---

8. How many grams of NaCl are required to make 250 ml. of a 0.4M solution?

Answer: 5.85 grams   *Solution:*

G.M.W. NaCl = 58.5
1 liter of 1M NaCl = 58.5 gm./liter
1 liter of 0.4M = 58.5 × 0.4 = 23.4 gm./liter

$23.4 \times \dfrac{250}{1000}$ = gms. in 250 ml. = 5.85

---

9. How many grams of NaCl are required to make 1500 ml. of 0.3M solution?

Answer: 26.32 grams   *Solution·*

1500 ml. = 1.5 liters
M.W. NaCl = 58.5
58.5 × 0.3 × 1.5 = 26.32 gms.

---

10. What is the molarity of a solution of Na_2SO_4 in which 284.2 gms. of this salt are placed in a liter volumetric flask and made up to volume with water?

Answer: 2M   *Solution:*

M.W. Na_2SO_4 = 142.1

Moles = $\dfrac{gm.}{M.W.}$ = $\dfrac{284.2}{142.1}$ = 2

2 Moles/liter = 2 molar solution

---

11. Define "molecular weight," "gram molecular weight," "mole," a "1 molar solution."

Answers: The molecular weight of a compound is the sum of the atomic weights of its elements in their proper proportions. A gram molecular weight is the molecular weight expressed in grams.

Mole = $\dfrac{gm.}{M.W.}$

A 1 molar solution contains 1 G.M.W./liter or 1 mole/liter

12.   Describe fully how you would prepare a 1M solution of Na_2SO_4.

Answer: Weigh out 142.1 of Na_2SO_4 (G.M.W. Na_2SO_4 = 142.1). Place in liter flask and add about 800 ml. of H_2O. Swirl until salt is dissolved. Add distilled water to 1000 ml. mark. Stopper, invert, shake, upright and repeat 10 times.

----

13.   Outline steps you would use in preparing 500 ml. of a 0.5 $NaHCO_3$ solution.

Answer: M.W. $NaHCO_3$ = 84.0
0.5M $NaHCO_3$ = 42 gm./liter = 21 gm./500 ml.

Place 21 grams $NaHCO_3$ in a 500 ml. flask. Fill flask about ¾ full with distilled water. Swirl until salt dissolves. Make up to 500 ml. mark with distilled water. Stopper, invert, shake, upright and repeat 10 times.

Practice Problems

1.   How many grams of each of the following are necessary to make 1 liter of a 1m solution?
   a. KCl
   b. $CaCO_3$
   c. Al_2O_3
   d. $Ca_3(PO_4)_2$

Answers:
   a.   74.6
   b.   100.1
   c.   102.0
   d.   310.3

----

2.   What is the molar concentration of each of these:
   a.   40 gm. of NaOH diluted to 1 liter
   b.   116.7 gm. of $BaSO_4$ diluted to 1 liter
   c.   58.5 gm. NaCl diluted to 500 ml.

Answers:
   a. 1M
   b. 0.5M
   c. 2M

—II—
WATER OF HYDRATION

1. Some salts are available with a certain number of water molecules attached to each molecule of salt. This is called "water of hydration." The water of hydration must be included in determining the molecular weight of the salt.

    What is the molecular weight of $CuSO_4$?
    What is the molecular weight of $CuSO_4.H_2O$?

    _____

    Answer: 159.6
                   177.6 (159.6 + 18)

2. How many grams of $CuSO_4.5H_2O$ are needed to make 1 liter of a 1M solution of copper sulfate?

    _____

    Answer: 249.6 gm.   *Solution:*
    $$M.W.\ CuSO_4.5H_2O = 63.5 + 32.1 + 64 + 5(18)$$
    $$= 249.6$$

3. How many grams of $Co(NO_3)_2.6H_2O$ are needed in preparing 1 liter of a .05M solution?

    _____

    Answer: 14.545 gm.   *Solution:*
    $$M.W. = 290.9$$
    $$290.9 \times .05 = 14.545\ gm.$$

4. The hydrate used should be specified when the directions call for a certain salt, since different quantities of salts are present in different hydrates.

    A 5% $CuSO_4$ (anhydrous) solution is made up by dissolving 5 gms. of anhydrous $CuSO_4$ in 100 ml. of solution.
    How is a 5% $CuSO_4.5H_2O$ made up?

    _____

    Answer: Dissolve 5 gm. of $CuSO_4.5H_2O$ in 100 ml. of solution.

5. Do a 5% $CuSO_4$ solution and 5% $CuSO_4.5H_2O$ contain the same quantities of $CuSO_4$?
    Which one has more?

    _____

Answer: No.

The 5% $CuSO_4$ has a greater quanity of $CuSO_4$ since only 64% of $CuSO_4.5H_2O$ is $CuSO_4$.

$$\frac{\text{M.W. } CuSO_4}{\text{M.W. } CuSO_4.5H_2O} \times 100 = \frac{159.6}{249.6} \times 100 = 64\%$$

---

6. Do a 5M $CuSO_4$ and a 5M $CuSO_4.5H_2O$ contain the same quantities of $CuSO_4$?
   Why?

   Answer: Yes

   Each contains 5 moles of $CuSO_4$ per liter.

---

7. How many grams of $CuSO_4$ or $CuSO_4.H_2O$ or $CuSO_4.5H_2O$ are required to make 500 ml. of a 2% solution of each of these salts?

   Answer: 10 gms. of these salts make up to 500 ml.

   Solution: $2\% = \dfrac{2 \text{ gm.}}{100 \text{ ml.}} = \dfrac{10 \text{ gm.}}{500 \text{ ml.}}$

Practice Problems

1. How many grams are required to make a liter of a 0.2M solution of each of these:
   a. $CuSO_4$
   b. $CuSO_4.H_2O$
   c. $CuSO_4.5H_2O$

   Answers:
   a. 31.92
   b. 35.52
   c. 49.92

---

2. How many grams are required to make 50 ml. of a 3% solution of:
   a. $CuSO_4$
   b. $CuSO_4.5H_2O$

   Answers:
   a. 1.5 grams
   b. 1.5 grams

$-III-$
NORMALITY

1. Valence is the combining power of one atom of an element (or radical) using the hydrogen atom as the unit of comparison.
    Thus in HCl, chloride is monovalent (valence = 1). In $CaCl_2$, the calcium is divalent. In NH_3 what valence does N possess?

    _____

    Answer: 3

---

2. An equivalent weight of an element is that weight of an element which will combine or replace 1 gram of hydrogen.

    $$\text{Equivalent Weight (E.W.)} = \frac{M.W.}{\text{Valence}}$$

    What is the molecular weight of NaCl?

    _____

    Answers: M.W. = 58.5
    E. W. = 58.5 (valence is 1)

---

3. What is the molecular weight of H_2SO_4?
    What is the equivalent weight of H_2SO_4?

    _____

    Answers: M.W. 98.1   M.W. = 98.1
    E. W. 49.05   E.W. $= \dfrac{98.1}{2} = 49.05$

---

4. What is the molecular weight of H_3PO_4?
    What is the equivalent weight of H_3PO_4?

    _____

    Answers: M.W. = 98   M.W. H_3PO_4 = 98
    E.W. = 32.66   E.W. $H_3PO_4 = \dfrac{98}{3} = 32.66$

---

5. The normality of a solution indicates the number of equivalent weights of a substance contained in 1 liter of solution.

    Thus a 1N HCl solution contains 1 equivalent weight of HCl per liter of solution.

    $$\text{E.W.} = \frac{M.W.}{\text{Valence}} = \frac{36.5}{1} = 36.5$$

$$1N\ HCl = \frac{1\ E.W.}{liter} = 36.5\ gm./liter$$

How many grams of solute does a 5N HCl solution contain?

Answer: 182.5 gms. $1N\ HCl = 36.5\ gm./liter$
                                                     $5N\ HCl = 5 \times 36.5 = 182.5$

6.   How many grams does a liter of a 2N solution of Na_2CO_3 contain?

Answer: 106 gm./liter   *Solution:*

   M.W. $Na_2CO_3 = 106$

   $E.W. = \dfrac{M.W.}{Valence} = \dfrac{106}{2} = 53$

   $1N\ Na_2CO_3 = 1\ E.W./liter = 53\ gm./liter$
   $2N\ Na_2CO_3 = 53 \times 2 = 106\ gm./liter$

7.   How many grams of solute does a liter of a 0.05N H_3PO_4 solution contain?

Answer: 1.63 gm./liter   *Solution:*

   M.W. $H_3PO_4 = 98$
   E.W. $H_3PO_4 = 98/3 = 32.67$
   $1N\ H_3PO_4 = 32.67\ gm./liter$
   $.05N\ H_3PO_4 = 32.67 \times .05 = 1.63$

8.   How many grams of solute does a 0.05M H_3PO_4 solution contain?

Answer: 4.9 gm./liter   *Solution:*

   $1M\ H_3PO_4 = \dfrac{1\ G.M.W.}{liter} = 98\ gm./liter$

   $.05M\ H_3PO_4 = 98 \times .05 = 4.9\ gm./liter$

9.   Normality = Molarity $\times$ Valence: N = M $\times$ Valence
        What is the normality of a 0.3M H_3PO_4?

Answer: 0.9N   *Solution:*

   N = M $\times$ Valence
   N = $0.3 \times 3 = 0.9$

10. What is the molarity of a 0.3N H_2SO_4 solution?

——————————————————————————

Answer: .15M

Solution:

N = M X Valence

.3 = M X 2

$M = \dfrac{.3}{2} = .15$

———————————————————————————————————————

11. Calculate the amount of $CaCl_2.2H_2O$ necessary to prepare 300 ml. of a 0.4N solution of $CaCl_2$.

——————————————————————————

Answer: 8.8 gm.

Solution:

M.W. $CaCl_2.2H_2O$ = 147.1

E.W. = $\dfrac{147.1}{2}$ = 73.6

0.4N = 73.6 X 0.4 = 29.44 gm./liter

$\dfrac{29.44\ \text{gm.}}{\text{liter}} = \dfrac{29.44\ \text{gm.}}{1000\ \text{ml.}}$ X 300 = 8.8 gm./300 ml.

Practical Problems

1. How many grams of each of these substances are needed to make a liter of 1 1N solution:
   a. $AgNO_3$
   b. Na_2CO_3
   c. NH_4OH
   d. H_3PO_4

——————————————————————————

Answers:
   a. 169.9
   b. 53
   c. 35
   d. 32.7

———————————————————————————————————————

2. Express the following in terms of normality:
   a. 2M NaOH
   b. 0.3M NaCl
   c. 0.5M H_3PO_4
   d. 0.1M $CuSO_4$

——————————————————————————

Answers:
    a. 2N
    b. 0.3N
    c. 1.5N
    d. 0.2N

---

3.   Express the following in terms of molarity:
    a. 0.2N NaOH
    b. 0.3N NaCl
    c. 0.5N H_3PO_4
    d. 0.1N $CuSO_4$

Answers:
    a. 0.2M NaOH
    b. 0.3M NaCl
    c. 0.17M H_3PO_4
    d. 0.05M $CuSO_4$

−IV−
CONCENTRATION RELATIONSHIPS

1.   One milligram (mg.) is equal to $\dfrac{1}{1000}$, (.001) of a gram.

    Thus: $gm. = \dfrac{mg.}{1000}$ −or− $mg. = gm. \times 1000$

    How many milligrams in 5 grams?

Answer: 5000 mg. $Mg. = gm. \times 1000 = 5 \times 1000$

---

2.   How many grams does 60 mg. represent?

Answer: 0.06 grams $Gm. = \dfrac{mg.}{1000} = \dfrac{60}{1000}$

---

3.   A milliequivalent weight is $\dfrac{1}{1000}$ of an equivalent weight; therefore, 1000 milliequivalents (mEq.) = 1 Equivalent (Eq.).

    How many milliequivalents in a liter of a 5N HCl solution?

Answer: 5000 mEq.   *Solution:*

$$5N = 5 \text{ equivalents} = 5 \times 1000 =$$
5000 milliequivalents

---

4.   # Equivalents = $\dfrac{gm.}{Eq.\ Wt.}$ and #mEquivalents = $\dfrac{mg.}{Eq.\ Wt.}$

How many milliequivalents are there in 213 mg. of Na_2SO_4?

Answer: 3   *Solution:*

Eq. Wt. Na_2SO_4 = $\dfrac{M.W.}{Valence}$ = $\dfrac{142}{2}$ = 71 gm.

#mEq. = $\dfrac{mg.}{Eq.\ Wt.}$ = $\dfrac{213}{71}$ = 3 mEq.

---

5.   How many milliequivalents are contained in .213 gms. of Na_2SO_4?

Answer: 3 mEq.   *Solution:*

Equiv. Wt. Na_2SO_4 = $\dfrac{M.W.}{Valence}$ = $\dfrac{142}{2}$ = 71 gms.

#mEq. = $\dfrac{mg.}{Eq.\ Wt.}$ = $\dfrac{213^*}{71}$ = 3 mEq.

*.213 gms. = 213 mg. (see question #4).

---

6.   A 10% (W/V) solution contains 10 gms. of solute dissolved in 100 ml. of solution.

Convert 10% to gm./liter.

Answer: 100 gm./liter   *Solution:*

$$10\% = \dfrac{10\ gm.}{100\ ml.} = \dfrac{100\ gm.}{1000\ ml.} = \dfrac{100\ gm.}{liter}$$

---

7.   A 10 mg.% solution contains 10 mg. of solute/100 ml. of solution.

Convert 10 mg.% to mg./liter and then gm./liter.

Answer: 100 mg./liter or 0.1 gm./liter

Solution:

$$10\ mg.\% = \dfrac{10\ mg.}{100\ ml.} = \dfrac{100\ mg.}{1000\ ml.} = \dfrac{0.1\ gm.}{liter}$$

8.   A sodium concentration is reported as 345 mg.%. What is the concentration in mg./liter?

Answer: 3450 mg./liter   *Solution:*

$$\frac{345 \text{ mg.}}{100 \text{ ml.}} = \frac{3450 \text{ mg.}}{1000 \text{ ml.}} = \frac{3450 \text{ mg.}}{\text{liter}}$$

9.   In problem #8 it was found that the sodium concentration reported as 345 mg.% is the same as 3450 mg./liter.

What is the concentration in mEq./liter?

Answer: 150 mEq./liter   *Solution:*

$$\text{mEq./liter} = \frac{\text{mg./l.}}{\text{Eq. Wt.}} = \frac{3450}{23} =$$

150 mEq./liter

10.   A magnesium concentration is reported as 2.3 mEq./liter.

What is its concentration in mg./100 ml.?

Answer: 2.8 mg./100 ml.   *Solution:*

$$\text{Eq. Wt. of Mg} = \frac{\text{M.W.}}{\text{Valence}} = \frac{24.3}{2} = 12.15 \text{ gm.}$$

1mEq. Wt. of Mg. = 12.15 mg.
2.3 mEq./liter = .23 mEq./100 ml.
.23 × 12.15 = 2.8 mg./100 ml.

11.   Express a 5% NaCl solution in terms of Molarity and Normality.

Answers: 0.85M and 0.85N

Solution:

M.W. NaCl = Eq. Wt. = 58.5 (since valence is 1)

$$5\% = \frac{5 \text{ gm.}}{100 \text{ ml.}} = \frac{50 \text{ gm.}}{\text{liter}} = \frac{50 \text{ gm./liter}}{58.5} = 0.85M \text{ or } 0.85N$$

12.   What is the molarity of a 15% K_2CO_3 solution?

Answer: 1.08M

Solution:

M.W. K_2CO_3 = 138.2

$$15\% = \frac{15 \text{ gm.}}{100 \text{ ml.}} = \frac{150 \text{ gm.}}{\text{liter}}$$

$$\frac{150 \text{ gm./liter}}{138.2} = 1.08M$$

---

13. What is the normality of a 15% K_2CO_3 solution?

- -

Answer: 2.17N

Solution:

$$\text{Eq. Wt. } K_2CO_3 = \frac{\text{M.W.}}{2} = \frac{138.2}{2} = 69.1$$

$$15\% = \frac{15 \text{ gm.}}{100 \text{ ml.}} = \frac{150 \text{ gm.}}{\text{liter}}$$

$$\frac{150 \text{ gm./liter}}{69.1} = 2.17$$

---

14. What is the normality of a 0.05M H_2SO_4 solution?

- -

Answer: 0.1N

Solution:

$$N = M \times \text{valence} = 0.05 \times 2 = 0.1$$

---

15. What is the molarity of a 2N H_3PO_4 solution?

- -

Answer: .67

Solution:

$N = M \times \text{valence}$
$2 = M \times 3$
$M = 2/3 = 0.67$

---

16. A commercial solution of concentrated nitric acid has a density of 1.42 and contains 70% HNO_3. What is the *molarity* of the acid?

- -

Answer: 15.8M

Solution:

$$\text{Density} = \frac{\text{gm.}}{\text{ml.}} = \frac{1.42 \text{ gm.}}{\text{ml.}} = \frac{1420 \text{ gm.}}{\text{liter}}$$

Since only 70% of the solution is HNO_3:

$$\frac{1420 \text{ gm.}}{\text{liter}} \times .70 = 994 \text{ gm. } HNO_3/\text{liter}$$

$$\text{M.W. HNO}_3 = 63$$

$$M = \frac{\text{Moles}}{\text{liter}} = \frac{994/63}{\text{liter}} = 15.8$$

---

17. What is the molarity of a commercial solution of H_2SO_4 having a density of 1.84 and containing 95% H_2SO_4?

Answer: 17.8M

Solution:

$$\text{Density} = \frac{1.84 \text{ gm.}}{\text{ml.}} = \frac{1840 \text{ gm.}}{\text{liter}}$$

$$\frac{1840 \text{ gm.}}{\text{liter}} \times 0.95 = 1748 \text{ gm. } H_2SO_4/\text{liter}$$

M.W. $H_2SO_4 = 98.1$

$$\text{Molarity} = \frac{\text{Moles}}{\text{liter}} = \frac{1748/98.1}{\text{liter}} = 17.8$$

---

18. To prepare a standard solution with a certain concentration with respect to one of the elements in the formula, one must take into account how much of this element is contained in a gram-molecular weight of the compound.

Thus, $(NH_4)_2SO_4$ which has a M.W. of 132 has 2 nitrogen atoms each having an atomic weight of 14. Therefore.

$\frac{28}{132}$ of the weight of ammonium sulfate is nitrogen.

This means that for every unit of nitrogen desired $\frac{132}{28}$ of ammonium sulfate are needed.

How many milligrams of $(NH_4)_2SO_4$ are needed to make a liter of a 5 mg. per 100 ml. nitrogen standard?

Answer: 236

Solution:

$$\frac{5 \text{ mg.}}{100 \text{ ml.}} = \frac{50 \text{ mg.}}{1000 \text{ ml.}} = \text{nitrogen}$$

$$50 \times \frac{132}{28} = 236 \text{ mg. ammonium sulfate}$$

Practice Problems

1. Express 0.5% $CaCl_2$ in terms of molarity and normality.

Answers:
a. .045M
b. .09N

---

2.   Express the following in terms of mEq./liter:
a. 0.9% NaCl
b. 2.8 mg.% $CaCl_2$
c. .02% KCl

$\dfrac{\% \text{ in gms}}{} \times 1000$

Answers:
a. 154
b.   0.5
c.   2.7

---

3.   Express the following in mg.%.:
a. 150 mEq./liter of Cl
b.   2.3 mEq./liter of Mg

Answers:
a. 532.5
b.   2.79

---

4.   What is the molarity of a commercial H_3PO_4 solution having a density of 1.7 and containing 85% H_3PO_4?

Answer: 14.7

---

5.   How many mg. of urea $CO(NH_2)_2$ are needed to make 1 liter of solution containing 4 mg. of nitrogen/100 ml.?

Answer: 85.7 mg. urea   *Solution:*

M.W. urea = 60

$\dfrac{28}{60}$ of urea is nitrogen; therefore,

$40 \times \dfrac{60}{28} = 85.7$

–V–
DILUTIONS

1.   Dilutions are usually expressed as 1 unit of original solution to the total units of the final solution. A 1:10 dilution means that 1 unit of concentrated solution is diluted to a total volume of 10 units, resulting in a solution which is 1/10 the concentration of the original solution.

How would you dilute a 12% aqueous solution 1:10?

What is the concentration of the resulting solution?

Answer: Pipette 1 ml. of 12% solution into a 10 ml. volumetric flask. Make up to mark with distilled water. Stopper, invert, shake, upright, and repeat 10 times.

Final concentration = 1.2% $(12 \times \frac{1}{10} = 1.2)$

---

2.   A 2% solution is diluted 1:100. What is the final concentration?

Answer: .02% $(2\% \times \frac{1}{100} = .02\%)$

---

3.   A solution of 10 mg./100 ml. is diluted 1:10. What is the final concentration?

Answer: 1 mg./100 ml. = 1 mg.%

Solution:

$$\frac{10 \text{ mg.}}{100 \text{ ml.}} \times \frac{1}{10} = 1 \text{ mg./100 ml.}$$

---

4.   A total of 300 ml. of a 1:3 dilution is to be prepared. How much of the concentrated solution is to be used?

Answer: 100 ml.   *Solution:*

$$\frac{1}{3} = \frac{X}{300} : X = 100$$

---

5.   If 0.5 ml. of serum is diluted to 75 ml., what is the resulting dilution?

Answer: 1/150   *Solution:*

$$\frac{0.5}{75} = \frac{1}{150}$$

---

6. If more than one dilution (serial dilution) is performed with a given solution, the concentration of the final dilution is found by multiplying the dilutions by each other and by the starting concentration.

    A 3N solution is diluted 1:10, rediluted 1:5, and rediluted 1:25. What is the concentration of the final solution?

    What is the volume of the final solution?

    Answers: .0024 and 25 ml.   *Solution:*

    $$3 \times \frac{1}{10} \times \frac{1}{5} \times \frac{1}{25} = .0024$$

---

7. One ml. of serum is added to a tube containing 9 ml. saline; 1 ml. of the resulting solution is diluted 1:100. How much serum is there in the final solution?

    Answer: .001 ml. serum/ml.   *Solution:*

    $$1 \times \frac{1}{10} \times \frac{1}{100} = .001 \text{ ml./ml.}$$

Practice Problems

1. 5 ml. of urine is diluted to 100 ml. One ml. of this solution is diluted 1:10. What is the final concentration of urine in the solution?

    Answer: $\dfrac{5}{1000} = \dfrac{1}{200}$

---

2. 5 ml. of 5% TCA is added to 5 ml. of urine. One ml. of this solution is diluted to 50 ml. with water and 3 ml. of this is used for the analysis. How many ml. of urine are in the analysis sample?

    Answer: .03 ml.

---

3.   A 5N solution is diluted 1:20 and then rediluted 1:100. What is the final concentration?

_____

Answer: .0025N

−VI−
VOLUME-CONCENTRATION

1.   One relationship frequently used in the clinical laboratory is:

$volume_1 \times concentration_1 = volume_2 \times concentration_2$

This formula can be used to solve any problem where more dilute solutions are made from more concentrated solutions, and where 3 of the 4 pieces of information are given. However, the two volumes as well as the two concentrations must be in the same units.

How much 85% alcohol is needed to make 500 ml. of 60% alcohol?

_____

Answer: 352.9 ml.   *Solution:*

$$Vol._1 \times Conc._1 = Vol._2 \times Conc._2$$
$$(X) \times 85 = 500 \times 60$$
$$X = 352.9 \; ml.$$

---

2.   How much 0.3M solution can be made from 60 ml. of a 1M solution?

_____

Answer: 200 ml.   *Solution:*

$$(X)\,(.3) = (60)\,(1)$$
$$.3X = 60$$
$$X = 200 \; ml.$$

---

3.   How would you make 1 liter of a 0.04 solution from an 0.8N solution?

_____

Answer: Place 50 ml. of the 0.8N solution in a liter volumetric flask and make up to volume with water, etc.

Solution: $(X)\,(0.8) = (0.04)\,(1000)$
$$X = 50 \; ml.$$

---

4.   In acid-base titrations:

$$Vol. \; Acid \times Conc. \; Acid = Vol. \; Base \times Conc. \; Base$$

The units of volume and concentration must be the same.

A total of 7.2 ml. of base are needed to neutralize 10 ml. of 0.03N acid. What is the normality of the base?

Answer: .042N   *Solution:*

$$ml._a \times N_a = ml._b \times N_b$$
$$10 \times 0.03 = 7.2 \times N_b$$
$$N = .042$$

---

5.   How much 0.2N acid is needed to neutralize 50 ml. of 0.6N base?

Answer: 150 ml.   *Solution:*

$$(X)(0.2) = 50(0.6)$$
$$X = 150 \text{ ml.}$$

Practice Problems

1.   10 ml. of 1N HCl will neutralize how many ml. of 0.1N NaOH?

Answer: 100 ml.

---

2.   The normality of an HCl solution is 6N. How much water must be added to 25 ml. of this solution to make a 1.5N solution?

Answer: 75 ml.

---

3.   25 ml. of 250 ml. stock solution of H_2SO_4 is neutralized by 25.25 ml. of 1N NaOH. How much water must be added to the remainder of the H_2SO_4 to make it 1N?

Answer: 2.25 ml.

—VII—
pH

1.   The greater the hydrogen-ion concentration $[H^+]$ of a solution, the more acid it is.

The greater the hydroxyl-ion concentration [OH⁻], the more _____ the solution.

_____

Answer: Basic

---

2.   A pH of 7 indicates that the solution is neutral, i.e., $[H^+]$ = $[OH^-]$. A pH of less than 7 indicates that the $[H^+]$ is greater than the $[OH^-]$ and therefore the solution is acidic; whereas a pH greater than 7 indicates that the $[OH^-]$ concentration is greater than the $[H^+]$ and therefore the solution is basic.

True or False: The higher the pH the greater the acidity.

_____

Answer: False

---

3. $pH = \log \dfrac{1}{[H^+]} = -\log [H^+]$

Thus if the $[H^+]$ = 1×10^{-5} M

$pH = -\log 10^{-5} = -5$: therefore, $pH = -(-5) = 5$

What is the pH of a solution with $[H^+]$ of 1×10^{-6}

_____

Answer: pH = 6

---

4.   From problem #3 it is seen that a solution of pH 5 has _____ as many hydrogen-ions as a solution of pH 6. Therefore, the lower the pH, the greater the _____ of the solution.

_____

Answer: 10 times
              acidity

---

5.   Each pH unit represents a multiple of 10; therefore, a solution of pH 9 has _____ as many hydrogen-ions as does neutral water.

_____

Answer: $\dfrac{1}{100}$

---

6.   What is the pH of a .01M HCl?

_____

Answer: pH = 2   *Solution:*

$$pH = -\log [H^+] = -\log 1 \times 10^{-2} = -(-2)$$
$$= 2$$

---

7.   What is the pH of a .03M HCl? (log 3 = 0.5)

- -

Answer: pH = 1.5   *Solution:*

$$pH. = -\log (3 \times 10^{-2}) = -\log 3$$
$$-\log 10^{-2} = -0.5 + 2 = 1.5$$

---

8.   pH + pOH = 14

If the pH of a solution = 7 (neutrality), the pOH is also 7.

$$pOH = \log \frac{1}{[OH^-]} = -\log [OH^-]$$

What is the pOH of a 0.1M NaOH solution?

- -

Answer: pOH = 1   *Solution:*

$$pOH = -\log 10^{-1}$$
$$pOH = 1$$

---

9.   What is the pH of a solution having a OH⁻ of .01M?

- -

Answer: pH 12   *Solution:*

$$pOH = \frac{\log 1}{[OH^-]} = -\log [OH^-]$$
$$pOH = -\log 1 \times 10^{-2} - 2$$
$$pH + pOH = 14$$
$$pH + 2 = 14$$
$$pH = 12$$

---

10.   A buffer is a solution composed of a weak acid plus the salt anion of the weak acid which buffers or resists changes in pH.

What is a buffer composed of? What is its function?

- -

Answers: A buffer is composed of a weak acid and a salt of the weak acid. Its function is to resist change in pH.

11.   An efficient buffer should have equal concentrations of salt and acid. When is the buffering capacity of a buffer the greatest?

Answer: When the concentration of the acid = the concentration of the salt. [Salt] = [Acid]

---

12.   The relationship between the pH of a buffer and the relative concentrations of the weak acid and salt can be expressed by the Henderson-Hasselbach equation:

$$pH = pK + \log \frac{[Salt]}{[Acid]}$$ (pK = −log of dissociation constant for the weak acid)*

*Can be found in *Handbook of Chemistry*

What is the pH of a buffer solution containing equal concentrations of salt and acid?

Answer: pH = pK $pH = pK + \log \frac{[Salt]}{[Acid]}$ therefore, pH = pK

---

13.   The buffering capacity of a buffer is greatest when the pH = ____ ?

Answer: pH = pK

---

14.   Give the formula for the Henderson-Hasselbach equation.

Answer: $pH = pK + \log \frac{[Salt]}{[Acid]}$

Practice Problems

1.   The $[H^+]$ of a solution is 1×10^{-6}. What is the pH of the solution?

Answer: pH = 6

---

2.   What is the pH of a solution with a $[H^+]$ of 5×10^{-6}? (log 5 = 0.7)

Answer: 5.3

---

3.   What is the pH of a .001M NaOH solution?

Answer: 11.0

---

4.   What is the Henderson-Hasselbach equation?

Answer: $pH = pK + \log \dfrac{[Salt]}{[Acid]}$

---

5.   For maximal buffer capacity, the [Salt] should _____ the [Acid], so that the pH = _____.

Answers: equal
            pK

−VIII−
MISCELLANEOUS

1.   The optical density (O.D.) or absorbance (A) of a substance is proportional to the amount of light of a certain wavelength (λ) which it absorbs. The greater the O.D. or A, the more light it absorbs and the less it will transmit.

The relationship between Absorbance (O.D.) and %Transmission is:

$$A = 2 - \log \%T$$

Thus if the %T of a solution is 100, the Absorbance is 0, since

$$A = 2 - \log \%T = 2 - \log 100 = 2 - 2 = 0$$

What is the A of a solution having an 80%T? ($\log 80 = 1.9$)

Answer: 0.1   *Solution:*

$$A = 2 - \log 80 = 2 - 1.9 = 0.1$$

---

2.   For analyses that follow Beer's law, absorbance (A) or O.D. is directly related to concentration (C).

Thus: $\dfrac{A_{unknown}}{A_{standard}} = \dfrac{C_{unknown}}{C_{standard}}$

Therefore, $C_{unknown} = \dfrac{A_{unknown}}{A_{standard}} \times C_{standard}$

The absorbance of an unknown is .16, the absorbance of the standard is .14. The concentration of the standard $= 100\mu g.\%$.

What is the concentration of the unknown?

_____

Answer: $114\,\mu g.\%$ *Solution:*

$$C_{unknown} = \dfrac{A_{unknown}}{A_{standard}} \times C_{standard}$$

$$C_{unknown} = \dfrac{.16}{.14} \times 100 = 114.3\,\mu g.\%$$

---

3.   The percent transmission of an unknown solution is 50%. What is the concentration of this solution if a standard solution of $100\,\mu g.\%$ of this substance has an 80%T?

(Log 80 = 1.9   Log 50 = 1.7)

_____

Answer: $300\,\mu g.\%$ *Solution:*

%T is not directly related to concentration and must be converted to A or O.D.

A = 2−log %T
A = 2−log 50 = 2−1.7 = 0.3
A = 2−log 80 = 2−1.9 = 0.1

$$C_{unknown} = \dfrac{A_{unknown}}{A_{standard}} \times C_{standard}$$

$$C_{unknown} = \dfrac{0.3}{0.1} \times 100 = 300\,\mu g.\%$$

Usually a standard curve relating %T and concentration is plotted on semilog paper so that when %T is read from the spectrophotometer, the concentration can be read directly from the graph.

---

4.   The relationship between degrees centigrade and degrees Fahrenheit is given by this formula:

$$C = \dfrac{5}{9}\,(F - 32)$$

Substitute whatever value is given and solve for the unknown.

For example: The temperature of water is $212°F$. What is the temperature in degrees centigrade?

$$C = \frac{5}{9} (F - 32) = \frac{5}{9} (212 - 32) = \frac{5}{9} (180) = 100°$$

What is the temperature in degrees Fahrenheit if the centigrade temperature is 70 degrees?

Answer: 158°F   *Solution:*

$$C = \frac{5}{9} (F - 32)$$

$$70 = \frac{5}{9} (F - 32) = \frac{5F - 160}{9}$$

$$5F = 790$$

$$F = 158°$$

Practice Problems

1. A solution of 100 μg.% of ammonia nitrogen has an A (O.D.) of .15. The A (O.D.) of an unknown blood sample is .11. What is the ammonia concentration of the blood sample?

Answer: 73.3 μg.%

---

2. The temperature of an oven is 132°F. What is the temperature in degrees centigrade?

Answer: 58.5°C

---

3. The temperature of a room is 25°C. What is the temperature in degrees Fahrenheit?

Answer: 77°F

ATOMIC WEIGHTS

Aluminum	Al	27.0
Barium	Ba	137.3
Calcium	Ca	40.1
Carbon	C	12.0
Chlorine	Cl	35.5
Cobalt	Co	58.9
Copper	Cu	63.5
Hydrogen	H	1.0
Magnesium	Mg	24.3
Nitrogen	N	14.0
Oxygen	O	16.0
Phosphorus	P	31.0
Potassium	K	39.1
Silver	Ag	107.9
Sodium	Na	23.0
Sulfur	S	32.1

2.

CLINICAL CHEMISTRY EXAMINATION

Edited by Dr. Richard C. Dale

REVIEW OF STRUCTURE OF MATTER

1. Atomic weights are absolute weights.   T   F | F

2. The element currently in use as a standard of comparison for establishing atomic weights is _____. | Carbon isotope weight of 12.000

3. What are isotopes? | See p. 129

4. What is Deuterium? | See p. 129

5. Explain briefly Radioactivity. | See p. 129

6. What are Gamma rays? | See p. 129

7. What is an electron? | See p. 129

8. What is the electron shell (or cloud)? | See p. 129

9. Describe ionic bonding. | See p. 129

10. Indicate atomic weight of potassium:
    a. 16.0000
    b. 22.991
    c. 39.100 | c
    d. 35.457

11. Indicate atomic weight of sodium:
    a. 16.000
    b. 22.991 | b
    c. 39.100
    d. 1.0080

12. Indicate atomic weight of sulfur:
    a. 74.91
    b. 209.00
    c. 40.08
    d. 32.066 | d

13. Indicate atomic weight of chlorine:
    a. 12.011
    b. 35.457 | b
    c. 63.54
    d. 19.00

14. What is an atom? | See p. 129

15. What is a compound? | See p. 129

16. What is a molecule? | See p. 129

17. Define ion. | See p. 129

18.	Define Angstrom unit (Å).	1×10^{-8} cm. (the approx. diameter of atoms)
19.	Define a liter.	See p. 129
20.	What do the initials S.I. stand for?	See p. 129

CLASSICAL LABORATORY INSTRUMENTATION

21. The rate a substance travels upon ultracentrifugation is expressed in terms of:
    a. S units   a
    b. Svedberg units   b
    c. R_f units
    d. DEAE units

22. On ultracentrifugation, serum proteins fall into three categories according to their sedimentation rate:
    _____.   4S, 7S, 19S

23. The 4S proteins have the (lowest, highest) molecular   lowest
    weight and the 19S have the (lowest, highest) molecular highest
    weight.

24. With the exception of low density lipoproteins, there is an inverse relationship between increasing molecular weight and increasing Svedberg number.   T   F   F

25. Indicate whether each of these proteins is an 4S, 7S, or 19S protein:
    a. Albumin   4S
    b. Immunoglobulin G (IgG)   7S
    c. Immunoglobulin M (IgM)   19S

26. The movement of small charged particles, usually ions, through a buffered electrolyte subjected to an electric   electro-
    field is known as _____.   phoresis

27. At pH commonly used (pH 8.6) the plasma proteins are mostly:
    a. positively charged
    b. negatively charged   b
    c. uncharged

28. Plasma proteins in standard procedure move toward:
    a. anode   a
    b. cathode
    c. either
    d. neither

29. Electrophoresis using a homogeneous solution is called:
    a. Liquid electrophoresis
    b. Moving boundary electrophoresis   b

     c. Homogeneous electrophoresis
     d. Liquid-solid electrophoresis

30. Electrophoresis using a solid support medium such as paper or cellulose acetate is known as:
     a. Discrete electrophoresis
     b. Horizontal strip electrophoresis
     c. Disc electrophoresis
     d. Zone electrophoresis   d

31. Starch gel and acrylamide gel electrophoresis give better resolution than cellulose acetate electrophoresis. T   F   T

32. Type of supporting medium used in the separation of isozymes:
     a. Paper
     b. Cellulose acetate   b
     c. Agar gel   c
     d. Starch gel

33. A combination of electrophoresis and immunodiffusion is called:
     a. Zone electrophoresis
     b. Moving boundary electrophoresis
     c. Immuno-electrophoresis   c

34. _____ is the name given to technique by which the members of a group of similar substances are separated by a continuous redistribution between two phases, stationary and liquid.   Chromotography

35. Separation of mixture of solute molecules by chromotography is achieved by differences in migration rates through a porous support medium called:
     a. Sorbent   a
     b. Moving phase
     c. Ultracentrifugation resins

36. Dowex, Amberlite IRC, DEAE-cellulose are names of:
     a. Electrophoretic membranes
     b. Ion-exchange resins   b
     c. Ultracentrifugation resins

37. Alumina in a column is most often used in what type of chromatography in clinical chemistry:
     a. Adsorption   a
     b. Two-dimensional
     c. Thin-layer
     d. Descending

38. The two most important general categories of chromatography are:
     a. _____   Column
     b. _____   Thin Layer
                                       (T.L.C.)

39. Gas column chromatography is best used to separate which
     substances:
     a. Steroids   a
     b. Proteins
     c. Carbohydrates
     d. Lipids   d
     e. Toxic substances   e

40. _____ chromatography is a powerful technique for
     the separation of any mixtures which are volatile in their   Gas
     natural state or after the formation of derivatives.   column

41. In partition chromatography, e.g. paper chromatography,
     one form of thin-layer chromatography (TLC), the ratio
     of the distance travelled by the substance to the distance
     travelled by the solvent front is known as the:
     a. TLC value
     b. R_f value   b
     c. S_f value
     d. Relative fraction   d

42. The relation between optical density and concentration
     of the standard and unknown depends on the following
     law being obeyed:
     a. Boyle's
     b. Charles'
     c. Beer's   c
     d. Coleman Jr.'s

43: An instrument for measuring the amount of incident light
     scattered by suspended particles in a solution is a:
     a. Colorimeter
     b. Spectrophotometer
     c. Nephelometer   c
     d. Flame photometer

44. In photoelectric colorimeters the intensity of a trans-
     mitted light beam is measured by its effect on a photo-
     electric cell.   T   F   T

45. A transmittance (T) of 100% represents the following
     optical density (OD):
     a. 0.000   a
     b. 0.097
     c. 1.000
     d. 2.000

46. A transmittance (T) of 1.0 represents the following
     optical density (OD):
     a. 1.000
     b. 0.000
     c. 2.000   c
     d. 0.097

47. When Beer's law is obeyed, the O.D. is directly proportional to concentration.   T   F

    T

48. Beer's law gives a straight line using what graph paper?
    a. Concentration vs. O.D. with linear graph paper
    b. Concentration vs. absorbance using linear graph paper
    c. Concentration vs. O.D. using semi-log paper
    d. Concentration vs. absorbance using semi-log paper
    e. Concentration vs. log. %T with semi-log graph paper

    a
    b

    e

49. If Beer's law is not obeyed, the concentrations of the standard and unknown should be close.   T   F

    T

50. What is the relationship between %T (transmittance) and O.D. (optical density)?

    O.D. = $2-\log\%T$

51. In principle a spectrophotometer operates very much like the photoelectric colorimeter. However, in the former a prism or diffractive grating is employed instead of a filter to break up white light to its visible components.   T   F

    T

52. The function of a filter in a photoelectric colorimeter is the same as that of a _____ in a spectrophotometer.

    prism or diffraction grating

53. The blue filter of a photoelectric colorimeter possesses a wave-length within the following range of the visible spectrum:
    a. 400–440 millimicrons
    b. 440–490 millimicrons
    c. 490–560 millimicrons
    d. 560–600 millimicrons

    b

54. The green filter of a photoelectric colorimeter possesses a wave-length within the following range of the visible spectrum:
    a. 440–490 millimicrons
    b. 490–560 millimicrons
    c. 560–600 millimicrons
    d. 600–730 millimicrons

    b

55. Na^+ may be measured at the following wavelength:
    a. 589 millimicrons
    b. 768 millimicrons
    c. either a or b
    d. Neither a nor b

    a

56. K^+ may be measured at the following wavelength:
    a. 589 millimicrons
    b. 768 millimicrons
    c. 440 millimicrons
    d. 130 millimicrons

    b

57. A blood sugar determination is read at suitable wavelength using a photoelectric colorimeter. The standard's
reading is 92 and the unknown's 128. The concentration of standard is 100 mg.%. Therefore, the % concentration of the unknown is:
    a. 112 mg.%
    b. 128 mg.%
    c. 139 mg.%   c
    d. 184 mg.%

58. One can quickly examine a supernatant fluid for the
Tyndall effect by means of:
    a. A spectrograph
    b. A hand spectroscope
    c. Wood's light
    d. A spotlight   d

59. A nephelometer, which measures reflected light at right
angles to the incident beam of light, is used to measure:
    a. Optical density
    b. Fluorescence
    c. Turbidity   c
    d. Specific gravity

60. When a substance absorbs ultraviolet light and emits light
at a longer (visible) wavelength it is said to be _____.   fluorescent

61. Explain the difference between emission photometry and
atomic absorption spectrophotometry.   See p. 130

62. In atomic absorption spectrophotometry, the atoms in the
_____ state absorb energy. The energy released by   ground
these atoms in the flame is absorbed by hollow cathode
lamps of the same composition as the atoms being determined.

63. The atomic absorption spectrophotometer is more sensitive
than emission flame photometer because:
    a. AAS provides better wave length selection
    b. AAS involves double beam instruments
    c. No need for internal standards with AAS
    d. Atoms in the ground state are activated in AAS   d

64. In the AutoAnalyzer, the need for protein free filtrates is
obviated by the use of:
    a. Dialyzers   a
    b. Microchemical reactions
    c. Chelator

65. A combination of precipitation, filtration, distillation and
centrifugation is accomplished by the _____ module   dialyzer
of the AutoAnalyzer.

66. In serum and urine, two main groups of compounds affect
the osmolality:
    a. Proteins   a

b. Phosphates
c. Fatty acids
d. Electrolytes |d

67. Determination of osmolality of serum or urine by freezing point measurement is based on the theory that the more concentrated a solution is, the (lower, higher) will be its freezing point. | lower

68. Match the man associated with the technique:
1. Tswett   a. Electrophoresis | 1—b
2. Tiselius   b. Chromatography | 2—a
3. Svedberg   c. Ultracentrifugation | 3—c
               d. NMR (Nuclear Magnetic Resonance

69. A new technique which combines the specificity of immunology with the sensitivity of radiochemistry is known as: _____. | radioimmuno-chemistry

70. Radioimmunoassay (RIA) enables detection of nanogram or picogram quantities of hormones, vitamins and drugs in biological fluids.   T   F | T

71. Competitive binding is the basis for RIA.   T   F | T

72. Only gamma emitting isotopes are used in radioimmunoassay.   T   F | F

73. The following are needed for radioimmunoassay (RIA):
a. Antigen | a
b. Labeled antigen | b
c. Antibody | c
d. Scintillation counter | d
e. Geiger-Muller counter
f. Substance to separate bound from free isotope | f

MECHANIZATION AND AUTOMATION OF THE CLINICAL LABORATORY

74. Give the main reason for automation in the clinical laboratory. | See p. 130

75. No matter what automation you have, it is not possible to insure quality results without skilled, dedicated, motivated personnel.   T   F | T

76. Differentiate between "mechanization" and automation. | See p. 130

77. Define "feedback." | See p. 130

78. Is "modern automation" always a "good thing"? | See p. 130

79. Name the commonest problem related to laboratory instrumentation. | Instrument susceptibility to line voltage problems

80. In this day of power shortages, is this problem likely to increase?

Yes—power "brownouts" can cause terrible problems

81. Name three major directions automation has taken in the clinical laboratory.

See p. 130

82. Differentiate between "continuous flow" analysis and "discrete" analysis.

See p. 130

"Automatic" Analyzers

83. Several steps are common to most analyses—whether manual or automated. See how many of these you can list.

See p. 130

84. The term AutoAnalyzer refers appropriately only to the continuous flow equipment manufactured by the Technicon Company of Tarrytown, New York.   T   F. Why?

T. The name is a registered trademark of the company.

85. In the AutoAnalyzer, the flowing stream of samples and reagents are segmented by _____ thereby maintaining sample integrity and eliminating cross-mixing of samples.

air bubbles

86. In the AutoAnalyzer, the walls of the tubing are continuously scrubbed by:
    a. Wash liquid between each sample
    b. Air bubbles
    c. Physiological saline
    d. AutoAnalyzer detergent

a
b

87. It is not necessary to run controls with the AutoAnalyzer if carefully prepared standards are used at frequent intervals.   T   F

F

88. SMA is an abbreviation for _____.

Sequential Multiple Analysis

89. It is important that all tubing on the AutoAnalyzer be the same width.   T   F

F

90. In the AutoAnalyzer, the samples and reagents are moved by:
    a. Air bubbles
    b. Hydrostatic pressure
    c. Peristaltic proportioning pump
    d. Sampler

c

91. Fundamental to the AutoAnalyzer techniques is the exposure of known standards to exactly the same reaction steps as the unknown samples.   T   F

T

92. Reactions on the AutoAnalyzer need not be carried to
equilibrium.   T   F

T

93. To determine sodium and potassium on the AutoAnalyzer,
the colorimeter is often replaced by a _____.

flame
photometer

94. Another way the AutoAnalyzer can be set up to measure
sodium and potassium is with an _____.

ion-selective
electrode

95. Which of the following would result in inability to stabilize the baseline measurements of a spectrograph?
    a. A blown fuse
    b. Inadequate grounding
    c. A scratched filter
    d. Broken winding in isolation transformer

b

96. Carry-over is a problem to be watched for when using:
    a. Hycel Mark X
    b. DuPont Automatic Clinical Analyzer
    c. Technicon AutoAnalyzer

c

97. The DuPont Automatic Clinical Analyser is a discrete
specimen analyzer.   T   F

T

98. Describe briefly the reaction chamber for DuPont A.C.A.

See p. 130

99. The test to be carried out by the DuPont A.C.A. is identified by the means of a binary code on the test pack (envelope) header.   T   F

T

100. The DuPont A.C.A. does not need any calibration.   T   F

F

101. The DuPont A.C.A. employs two photometric readings
for every test.   T   F

T

102. Outline the operating set-up of the Centrifugal Fast Analyzers.

See p. 130

103. Centrifugal Fast Analyzers can be calibrated easily by the
use of pure chemicals.   T   F.

T

104. One of the important features of Centrifugal Fast Analyzers is that it uses microspecimens $(2-100 \lambda)$.   T   F

T

105. Centifugal Fast Analyzers are especially useful in monitoring kinetic or rate reactions.   T   F

T

QUALITY CONTROL

106. The extent to which repeated determinations on an individual specimen vary using a particular technique is known
as:
    a. Accuracy
    b. Precision
    c. Reproducibility
    d. Reliability

b
c

107. The degree of correspondence between a given laboratory determination and the true or absolute value is known as:
    a. Accuracy   a
    b. Precision
    c. Reproducibility
    d. Reliability

108. Reliability depends on:
    a. Accuracy alone
    b. Precision alone
    c. Both accuracy and precision   c

109. Precision is the same as reproducibility.   T   F   T

110. How does the continuous flow system of the Technicon AutoAnalyzer replace the pipetting steps in manual procedures? See p. 130

111. The number of different analyzers on the market today attest to the fact that there is no one answer to the work load problem of the clinical laboratory.   T   F   T

Laboratory Quality Control

112. Give six objectives of laboratory quality control. See p. 130

113. The following factors must be considered part of a quality control program in the clinical laboratory:
    a. Purity of water   a
    b. Purity of reagents   b
    c. Preventive maintenance   c
    d. Instrument calibration   d
    e. Personnel accuracy   e

114. What is the formula for calculation of standard deviation? See p. 131

115. _____% of the value are included between ±1 Standard Deviation.   68
    _____% of the values is included between ±2 Standard Deviations.   95.5
    _____% of the values is included between ±3 Standard Deviations.   99.7

116. What formula is used to calculate the coefficient of variation? See p. 131

117. Standards can often be substituted for serum controls. T   F   F

118. Advantage of the "cusum" plot. (Abbreviation for cumulative sum technique.) Method keeps track of daily values where most values will fall within normal range (Na^+ and K^+ for example). (Robinson—1971) See p. 131

119. Why should quality control charts be displayed and kept up to date? See p. 131

120. Selection of control sera.	See p. 131
121. Use of selected control sera.	See p. 131
122. If the normal serum control stays within the two Standard Deviation limits of confidence it is not necessary to run abnormal controls. T F	F
123. Controls used to monitor qualitative reactions include: a. Positive control b. Negative control c. Both positive and negative controls	c

LABORATORY GLASSWARE AND PLASTIC WARE

124. Match the following:

1. It should be rinsed out after delivery of liquid.
2. It has a bulb near the bottom of the tip. The last drop is blown out.
3. It has an etched ring at the top.
4. 5–500 μl. (microliter) pipette calibrated "to deliver."
5. It has a bulb midway between the tip. It is calibrated "to deliver."
6. Contains markings to permit delivery of different volumes
7. Serological pipette graduated to tip having a double line at top.

a. Serological pipette
b. TC (to contain) pipette
c. Ostwald pipette
d. To blow out pipette
e. Lang-Levy
f. Volumetric pipette

1—b

2—c
3—d
4—e

5—f

6—a

7—d

125. Which of the following tubes is long, slender, and has a constricted portion near its bulb-like base:
    a. NPN tube
    b. Folin-Wu sugar tube
    c. BUN tube
    d. Addis tube

b

126. A flask possessing a flat bottom and inwardly sloping sides is a:
    a. Volumetric flask
    b. Erlenmeyer flask

b

127. Quartz glass cuvets for spectrophotometers must never be cleaned or rinsed with organic solvents such as acetone.
    T   F

T

128. Recommended cleaning method for removing blood or other protein residues from glassware is:

See p. 131

129. Cleaning for glassware to be used with enzymes.

See p. 131

130. Give a visual test that can reassure the worker about cleanliness of glassware.

See p. 131

131. Why can teflon be used as a stopcock without grease? See p. 131
132. Indicate advantages of polystyrene specimen cups over glass. See p. 131
133. What is the importance of non-wettable plastic surfaces in analytical chemistry? See p. 131

LABORATORY SAFETY

134. How should all biological materials including whole blood serum, plasma, urine, and containers which have held them, be disposed of? See p. 131
135. Mouth pipeting is allowed in the laboratory.   T   F   F
136. Lyophilized control materials should be treated exactly like serum or plasma—as potentially hazardous.   T   F   T
137. Eating and smoking are all right in the laboratory. T   F   F
138. Laboratory surfaces which come in contact with biological substances should be cleaned at least once a week with _____.   0.5% hypochlorite solution
139. _____ should be available for washing hands which come in contact with serum materials.   Bacteriostatic soap
140. All materials containing heavy metals must be disposed of in appropriate containers.   T   F   T
141. It is all right to stop and talk with people involved with running equipment or in handling chemicals.   T   F   F
142. It is mandatory that you know where all emergency equipment is located in your area.   T   F   T

URINALYSIS
Routine, Microscopic, and Special Chemical Tests

143. Give three principal factors affecting the kidneys' availability to produce urine and its composition: See p. 131
144. Urine leaves the body through the:
    a. Urethra   a
    b. Bladder
    c. Ureters
    d. Glomeruli
145. Which of the following urinary constituents could not be suspected as being the cause of cloudiness or a urine specimen:
    a. Pus cells

b. Amorphous urates
c. Albumin   c
d. Epithelial cells
e. Amorphous phosphates

146. The average total volume of urine passed by a normal adult every 24 hours is approximately:
   a.   750 ml.
   b. 1,200 ml.   b
   c. 2,000 ml.
   d. 2,400 ml.
   e. 3,500 ml.

147. Give briefly the reasons for collection of a 24 hour urine specimen. See p. 131

148. What do we mean by a "random" urine specimen? See p. 132

149. Describe the proper way to collect a 24 hour urine specimen. See p. 132

150. "Diuretics" are medicines which:
   a. Are used in the treatment of hypertension
   b. Decrease the secretion of urine
   c. Increase the production of insulin
   d. Decrease the production of insulin
   e. Increase the secretion of urine   e

151. Freshly voided urine usually has the following pH:
   a. Above 7.0
   b. 7.0
   c. Below 7.0   c

152. Specific gravity of night adult urine (if 8:00 P.M. and 8:00 A.M. are the divisions) is normally not below 1.018.
T   F   T

153. Volume of night urine is normally more than 75% of total day urine volume.   T   F   F

154. The volume of night urine in adults (if 8:00 P.M. and 8:00 A.M. are the divisions) normally exceeds 500–700 ml.
T   F   F

155. An abnormal decrease in the secretion of urine is called:
   a. Anuria
   b. Oliguria   b
   c. Polyuria
   d. Glycosuria
   e. Uremia

156. Anuria, the complete absence of urinary secretion, may occur in the following condition:
   a. Uremia
   b. Diabetes mellitus
   c. Diabetes insipidus
   d. Renal insufficiency
   e. Acute yellow atrophy of liver   d

157. Poisoning by mercury bichloride may cause:
    a. Anuria   a
    b. Chlorosis
    c. Mycetoma
    d. Nocturia
    e. Generalized edema

158. Normal range of specific gravity of 24 hour urine:
    a. 1.003–1.010
    b. 1.003–1.030
    c. 1.010–1.015
    d. 1.015–1.025   d
    e. 1.025–1.050

159. Most urinometers are calibrated to give accurate readings
    at the following temperature:
    a. 15°C.
    b. 22°C.   b
    c. 30°C.
    d. 18°C.
    e. 100°C.

160. The higher the specific gravity of a fluid the deeper a
    hydrometer will sink in it.   T   F   F

161. Urinometers are calibrated to give accurate readings at a
    specified temperature. Therefore, when specific gravity
    readings are taken at different temperature a proper cor-
    rection must be made by adding or subtracting (for every
    3°C. that the urine is above or below the calibration tem-
    perature) the following figure:
    a. 0.010
    b. 0.001   b
    c. 0.101
    d. 0.003
    e. 0.303

162. A refractometer instead of a urinometer, can be used to
    measure the specific gravity of urine.   T   F   T

163. A refractometer (total solids meter) is preferable to a uri-
    nometer because it requires one drop of urine for a spe-
    cific gravity.   T   F   T

164. Specific gravity measurements are of most use to pedia-
    tricians because of the danger of dehydration in small
    children.   T   F   T

165. In healthy persons the specific gravity of the urine varies
    greatly during the day.   T   F   T

166. The color of the urine affords a better indication of the
    degree of its concentration than does its specific gravity.
    T   F   F

167. An acid urine is usually darker than an alkaline one.
     T   F   T

168. Freshly voided urine is usually acid. This acidity is due to:
     a. Acid phosphates   a
     b. Free hydrochloric acid
     c. Free organic acids   c
     d. Acetic acid
     e. Oxalic acid

169. The color of concentrated urine is usually lighter than the
     color of diluted urine.   T   F   F

170. According to Long's coefficient, to estimate the amount
     of total solids per liter of urine present you would multiply
     the last two figures of the specific gravity by:
     a. 1.28
     b. 1.96
     c. 2.66   c
     d. 3.14
     e. 5.50

171. What are the urine parameters most often investigated by
     "dipstick."?   See p. 132

172. Why do we advocate "dipsticks"?   See p. 132

Proteinuria

173. Albuminuria which appears after a person has been in the
     erect position for some time and disappears with rest in
     bed is called:
     a. Orthostatic albuminuria   a
     b. Accidental albuminuria
     c. Pathologic albuminuria
     d. Physiologic albuminuria

174. When dipstick spot for protein is positive, it should be con-
     firmed and quantitated with 10% w/v sulfosalicylic acid in
     50% methanol by layering and checking interface for pre-
     cipitate.   T   F   T

175. Only if albumin is present will urine become cloudy upon
     heating.   T   F   F

176. Pathologic proteinuria ("albuminuria") indicates kidney
     failure.   T   F   T

177. Dissolved protein in urine can be detected by means of
     visual inspection.   T   F   F

178. True of pathologic albuminuria is caused by the passage
     of protein from the blood into the urine.   T   F   T

179. Presence of as little as 0.01% albumin in the urine is suf-
     ficient to cause definite cloudiness in heat and nitric acid
     test.   T   F   T

180. The presence of only 0.5% albumin in the urine is sufficient to produce a heavy cloud in heat and nitric acid test.
T   F
    T

181. True albuminuria may be due to the presence of pus in the urine.   T   F
    F

182. True albuminuria is caused by loss of blood protein via the urine.   T   F
    T

183. In cases of true albuminuria, globulin may be present in the urine. Therefore it is more correct to speak of proteinuria.   T   F
    T

184. The presence of qualitatively detectable albumin in the urine is abnormal.   T   F
    T

185. Indicate reagents or tests which cannot be used to test for protein ("albumin") in urine:
    a. 20% sulfosalicylic acid
    b. 10% ferric chloride
    b
    c. Combistix
    d. Benedict's solution
    d
    e. Robert's reagent

186. Which of the following is not a method for quantitative protein in urine:
    a. Tsuchiya
    b. Esbach
    c. Ehrlich
    c
    d. Kingsbury

187. Robert's reagent is used to test for:
    a. Sugar
    b. Protein ("albumin")
    b
    c. Calcium
    d. Chloride
    e. Occult blood

188. Epsom salts are needed to prepare the following reagent:
    a. Obermayer's
    b. Ehrlich's diazo
    c. Ehrlich's benzaldehyde
    d. Robert's
    d

189. Of what significance is proteinuria in a diabetic person?   See p. 132

190. Briefly explain the difference between true and false albuminuria.   See p. 132

191. By dissolving 4 grams of ferric chloride in 1,000 ml. of concentrated HCl, the following reagent is prepared:
    a. Pandy's reagent
    b. Obermayer's reagent
    b
    c. Tsuchiya's reagent
    d. Fouchet's reagent

Urine Glucose

192. Glucose is a reducing sugar.   T   F

    T

193. Glucose is the only reducing substance that may be present in the urine.   T   F

    F

194. Which of the following sugars will not reduce alkaline copper solution:
    a. Maltose
    b. Glucose
    c. Sucrose
    d. Levulose

    c

195. What two enzymes are present in the glucose "spot" on the dipstick?

    Glucose oxidase and Peroxidase

196. Is the presence of Ketones in urine only important in the diabetic syndrome?

    See p. 132

197. Clinitest tablets are glucose-specific.   T   F

    F

198. If cane sugar (sucrose) is added to a normal urine a positive Benedict's test or a positive Clinitest will be obtained.   T   F

    F

199. A qualitative Benedict's test turns orange. The urine contains the following amount of sugar:
    a. 0.5%
    b, 1,0%
    c. 1.5%
    d. Over 2%

    d

200. In late pregnancy, a positive Clinitest or a positive Benedict's test may be obtained. This is frequently due to the presence in the urine of the following reducing sugar:
    a. Glucose
    b. Levulose
    c. Galactose
    d. Lactose

    b

    d

201. The basis for differentiating glucose from lactose is that _____ is fermentable.

    glucose

202. The Clinistix dip-and-read test is specific for glucose.   T   F

    T

203. False positives and false negatives are not encountered with the Clinistix test for glucose.   T   F

    F

204. The reaction of glucose with Clinistix is an enzymatic reaction.   T   F

    T

205. A positive Clinitest (or Benedict's) and a negative Clinistix or enzyme test on the same speciment is usually due to the presence of _____ reducing substances.

    nonglucose

206. If the enzyme test for glucose (Clinistix) is positive and the Clinitest is negative on the same specimen, it may be due to the presence of glucose in urine in a concentration below the sensitivity range for which Clinitest is designed.
T   F   T

207. The lowest blood glucose concentration which will produce glycosuria is called the _____ for glucose.   renal
                                                                          threshold

208. The renal threshold point for glucose remains constant from person to person.   T   F   F

Ketone Bodies in Urine

209. With faulty carbohydrate metabolism, large quantities of fat are metabolized, resulting in the formation of _____ bodies.   ketone

210. Metabolic acidosis may be detected by testing the urine for presence of:
    a. Protein
    b. Glucose
    c. Uric acid
    d. Ketone bodies   d
    e. Bile

211. Ketone bodies are excreted in the urine in ketosis. The disease most commonly responsible for this condition is:
    a. Leukemia
    b. Diabetes mellitus   b
    c. Acute pancreatitis
    d. Multiple myeloma
    e. Gout

212. If the urinary glucose test is positive a test for ketone bodies should be performed.   T   F   T

213. The color reaction given by acetone to sodium nitroprusside is:
    a. Green to blue
    b. Purple to red   b
    c. Green to yellow
    d. Light brown
    e. Orange

214. Which of the following tests for ketone bodies will detect both acetone and diacetic (aceto-acetic) acid:
    a. Hart's test
    b. Lange's test   b
    c. Gerhardt's test
    d. Rothera's test   d

215. Lange's test (for acetone in urine) uses the following reagent:
    a. 20% sulfosalicylic acid
    b. Saturated sodium nitroprusside solution   b
    c. 10% ferric chloride
    d. 10% barium chloride
    e. Absolute alcohol

216. Which of the following tests for ketone bodies will detect only diacetic (aceto-acetic) acid:
    a. Hart's test
    b. Gerhardt's test   b
    c. Rothera's test
    d. Lange's test

217. Gerhardt's test for diacetic (aceto-acetic) acid in the urine uses the following reagent:
    a. 10% ferric chloride   a
    b. 20% sulfosalicylic acid
    c. 10% barium chloride
    d. Saturated sodium nitroprusside solution
    e. Glycerin

218. Which of the following tests for ketone bodies will detect betahydroxybutyric acid:
    a. Lange's test
    b. Rothera's test
    c. Hart's test   c
    d. Gerhardt's test

219. Acetone is never present in the urine unless sugar (glucose) is also present.   T   F   F

Urine Urea

220. What substance in particular would you test for in an unknown fluid in order to determine whether or not such fluid is urine?   urea

221. Urea is removed from the blood by the:
    a. Liver
    b. Lung
    c. Kidney   c
    d. Spleen
    e. Thyroid gland

222. Urea diffuses with great difficulty across the glomerular membrane.   T   F   F

223. The end-product of protein decomposition in the body is:
    a. Creatinine
    b. Urea   b
    c. Acetone
    d. Urease

224. The chief *organic* urinary constituent is:
    a. Uric acid
    b. Ammonia
    c. Urea   c
    d. Creatinine

225. The urine becomes alkaline upon standing. This is due to
    decomposition of _____ with liberation of _____.   urea; ammonia

226. In urea nitrogen in urine determination, permutit pow-
    der is added to urine in order to:
    a. Clarify the specimen
    b. Remove ammonia   b
    c. Precipitate calcium
    d. Dissolve any casts and cells that might
       be present

227. A Conway cell can be used to determine urine urea by the
    following method:
    a. Evaporation
    b. Heat distillation
    c. Diffusion   c

Hematuria & Hemoglobinuria

228. Male urine containing fresh blood in macroscopic amount
    is always pathological.   T   F   T

229. Female urine containing fresh blood in macroscopic
    amount is always pathological.   T   F   F

230. The presence of free hemoglobin in the urine can be deter-
    mined by means of the microscopic examination.   T   F   F

231. Which of the following is not a test for occult blood in
    urine:
    a. Guaiac test
    b. Benzidine test
    c. Lange's nitroprusside test   c
    d. Pyramidone ring test
    e. Reduced phenolphthalein test
    f. Orthodolidine test
    g. Microscopic examination of the sediment   g

232. Porphyrins do not give a positive benzidine reaction.
    T   F   T

233. A compound related to hemoglobin that can be found in
    the urine of individuals who have much muscular tissue
    breakdown is _____.   myoglobin

234. The most sensitive test for the presence of red blood cells
    in the urine is _____ _____.   microscopic
                                                               inspection

235. Presence of free homoglobin in the urine is known as
_____.

hemoglobi-
nuria

236. Presence of red blood cells in the urine is known as
_____.

hematuria

Microscopic Urine Examinations

237. Amorphous phosphates (of calcium, magnesium) may be
dissolved by heat.   T   F

F

238. Which are the chief organized structures which may be
present in a urine specimen?

See p. 132

239. What amorphous and crystalline sediments might one find
in acid urine?

See p. 132

240. What amorphous and crystalline sediments might one find
in alkaline urine?

See p. 132

241. The presence of a few pus cells in the urine is abnormal.
T   F

F

242. An accurate method for counting the cells and casts
which are present in a 12-hour specimen of urine was developed by the following worker:
   a. Kolmer
   b. Benedict
   c. Addis
   d. Van Slyke
   e. Wintrobe

c

243. An Addis count may yield valuable data in:
   a. Nephritis
   b. Hepatitis
   c. Multiple myeloma
   d. Lupus erythematosus
   e. Typhoid fever

a

244. Which of the following urinary constituents are normally
absent:
   a. Squamous epithelial cells
   b. Urochrome
   c. Granular casts
   d. Chyle

c
d

245. A few segmented neutrophils may normally be present in
urine.   T   F

T

246. Polymorphonuclear leukocytes which contain refractive
granules on brownian motion are called _____.

glitter
cells

247. Fat globules usually occur in alkaline urine.   T   F

F

248. Red cells appear small or crenated if the urine is:
    a. Hypertonic   a
    b. Hypotonic
    c. Isotonic

249. Desquamated epithelial cells which have undergone fatty
    degeneration are known as _____.   oval fat
                                                              bodies

250. Renal tubular cells in large numbers are seen in _____ glomerulo-
    _____.   nephritis

251. Hyaline casts and cylindroids are the result of _____ protein
    precipitation within the renal tubules.

252. Hyaline casts dissolve in urine that has become alkaline
    through standing.   T   F   T

253. Coarse and finely granular casts are rarely seen in normal
    urine.   T   F   T

254. Cylindroids have the same significance as casts.   T   F   T

255. Normal people may, particularly after strenuous exercise,
    show a small number of hyaline casts in the urine.   T   F   T

256. Amorphous materials in urine are of little importance.
    T   F   T

257. Amorphous urates dissolve upon addition of acetic acid.
    T   F   F

258. Crystals of calcium oxalate may occur in acid urine only.
    T   F   F

259. Amorphous phosphates (of calcium, magnesium) dissolve
    upon addition of acetic acid.   T   F   T

260. Amorphous urates may be dissolved by heat or by NaOH.
    T   F   T

261. Every urine specimen, if kept acid, will in time deposit
    the following crystal:
    a. Uric acid   a
    b. Cystine
    c. Calcium phosphate
    e. Triple phosphate
    e. Tyrosine

262. The following are also known as "envelop crystals":
    a. Triple phosphate
    b. Uric acid
    c. Calcium oxalate   c
    d. Cystine

263. Tyrosine crystals are needle-like.   T   F   T

264. Talcum resembles what crystals?   calcium
                                                             oxalate

265. Which of the following is not a urine preservative:
    a. Thymol
    b. Calcium chloride   b
    c. Formaldehyde
    d. Toluene

266. The best preservative of urinary *chemical* constituents is:
    a. Thymol
    b. Toluol   b
    c. Formalin
    d. Boric acid.

267. The following normal blood constituents are seldom present in detectable qualitative amounts in normal urine:
    a. Protein   a
    b. Chloride
    c. Glucose   c
    d. Calcium

268. Which of the following items is not tested for in a "routine" urinalysis:
    a. Protein
    b. Diacetic acid   b
    c. Glucose
    d. Casts
    e. Red blood cells

269. Urine that has been diluted with water can safely be used for routine chemical testing provided a correction for this dilution is made before results are given to the physician.
    T   F   F

270. Define "polyuria." See p. 132

Urine Calcium

271. Urinary calcium is precipitated as calcium oxalate by ammonium oxalate in the following tests:
    a. Obermayer's test
    b. Sulkowitch's test   b
    c. Robert's test
    d. Gmelin's test
    e. Harrison's spot test

272. Sulkowitch's test for urinary calcium level employs the following reagent:
    a. A mixture of potassium and ammonium oxalate
    b. A solution of 1 part HNO_3 and 5 parts of saturated ammonium sulfate
    c. A mixture of oxalic acid, ammonium oxalate and acetic acid   c
    d. A solution of 2 grams of ferric chloride in 1 liter of HCl
    e. 70% alcohol

273. The renal threshold for calcium is approximately:
    a.   7.5 mg.%
    b.   9.5 mg.%
    c. 10.0 mg.%
    d. 11.5 mg.%
    e. 40.0 mg.%

a

274. In tetany there is a marked (increase, decrease) in the excretion of urinary calcium.

decrease

Bile In Urine

275. The presence of qualitatively detectable bilirubin in the urine always results from the presence of an excessive amount of bilirubin in the serum.   T   F

T

276. Bilirubin (unchanged chief bile pigment) is usually excreted in the urine when direct-reading serum bilirubin exceeds about:
    a.   0–0.1 mg.%
    b.   0.1–0.2 mg.%
    c.   0.2–0.4 mg.%
    d.   0.08–0.15 mg.%

c

277. When a physician requests that a specimen of urine or feces be examined for "bile," one should test for:
    a. Urobilin
    b. Urobilinogen
    c. Bilirubin
    d. Occult blood
    e. Porphyrins

c

278. Which of the following reagents will not react with bilirubin (unchanged chief bile pigment):
    a. Yellow nitric acid
    b. Ethyl alcohol solution of iodine
    c. Ictotest
    d. Ehrlich's aldehyde reagent

d

279. Ictotest tablets may be employed in testing urine for:
    a. Bilirubin
    b. Urobilinogen
    c. Urobilin
    d. Diacetic acid
    e. Occult blood

a

280. Urine normally contains a small amount of bilirubin.
    T   F

F

281. Gmelin's modified test for bile (bilirubin) in urine utilizes the following reagent:
    a. Barium chloride
    b. Yellow nitric acid
    c. 20% sulfosalicylic acid

a
b

    d. Obermayer's reagent
    e. Lugol's iodine solution

282. Bilirubin and bile are present in urine in various _____ diseases.

> liver

283. Fouchet's reagent is used in _____ spot test for urinary bile pigments.

> Harri-
> son's

284. Which of the following will not detect bilirubin in urine:
    a. Foam test
    b. Gmelin's test
    c. Diagnex blue test
    d. Harrison's spot test
    e. Smith test
    f. Ictotest

> c

Porphyrins

285. Four pyrrole molecules connected cyclically by methylene groups comprising the heme portion of the hemoglobin molecule are known as _____.

> porphyrins

286. The iron-free porphin-ring-containing pyrrole derivatives which form the basis for the respiratory pigments of plants and animals are known as _____.

> porphyrins

287. What is a porphyrin? What is porphyria? What porphyrins are important from the clinical laboratory standpoint?

> See p. 132

288. Increased levels occur in the urine of patients with congenital porphyria, liver damage, and heavy metal poisoning:
    a. Hemoglobin
    b. ALA
    c. Protoporphyrin
    d. Total porphyrins
    e. Uroporphyrins

> d

289. Congenital porphyria is a common disease.   T   F

> F

290. Small amounts of porphyrin may normally be present in the urine.   T   F

> T

291. When a large amount of porphyrin is present in the urine the color is frequently:
    a. Dark brown
    b. Pale yellow
    c. Port-wine
    d. Greenish-blue
    e. Pink

> c

292. The benzidine test will detect urinary porphyrin.   T   F

> F

293. Porphyrins, when excited by _____, emit visible light and therefore fluoresce.

> ultraviolet
> light

294. In certain liver and hematological disorders and in lead
     poisoning, the following is primarily increased in the
     urine:
     - a. Coproporphyrin   a
     - b. Uroporphyrin
     - c. Protoporphyrin
     - d. Hemoglobin

295. Coproporphyrins are ether-soluble, while uroporphyrins
     are not.   T   F   T

296. In porphyria the following may be increased:
     - a. Uroporphyrin   a
     - b. Coproporphyrin   b
     - c. Porphobilinogen
     - d. Urobilinogen
     - e. Urobilin

297. Bile is soluble in ether.   T   F   T (slightly)

298. Which of the following is not a bile product:
     - a. Urobilinogen
     - b. Porphobilinogen   b
     - c. Urobilin
     - d. Bilirubin
     - e. Stercobilin

299. The colorless chromogen precursor of uroporphyrin,
     coproporphyrin, and protoporphyrin/ is called:
     - a. Porphobilinogen   a
     - b. Urobilinogen
     - c. Urobilin

300. Porphobilinogen is (soluble, insoluble) in ether and bu-   insoluble
     tanol.

301. A solution containing paramethylaminobenzaldehyde in
     hydrochloric acid is known as _____ _____   Ehrlich's
     reagent and is used in the test for porphobilinogen.   benzaldehyde

302. A procedure using Ehrlich's aldehyde reagent and fre-
     quently employed in testing urine for porphobilinogen is
     that of:
     - a. Siebold and Bradbury
     - b. Watson and Schwartz   b
     - c. Shank and Hoagland
     - d. Wang

303; When a porphobilinogen determination is carried out on a
     specimen of urine which has stood for some time, the re-
     sults are unreliable.   T   F   T

304. Porphobilinogen is formed from _____   ALA (delta-
     _____.   aminolevulinic
                                                                  acid)

Urobilinogen

305. Urobilinogen is normally formed from bilirubin by the action of bacteria in the bowel.   T   F | T

306. In complete biliary duct obstruction large amounts of urobilinogen can be found in urine and feces.   T   F | F

307. When a urobilinogen determination is carried out on a specimen of urine or feces which has been standing for some time, the results are unreliable.   T   F | T

308. The total absence of urobilinogen from the urine is abnormal.   T   F | T

309. Which of the following tests will detect urobilinogen:
    a. Fouchet's test
    b. Ehrlich's aldehyde reagent
    c. Nitric acid test
    d. Schlesinger's test
    e. Obermayer's test
    | b

310. Two reagents used to test for urobilinogen are _____ _____ and _____ _____. | Ehrlich's reagent & sodium acetate

311. Ehrlich's aldehyde reagent is specific for urobilinogen.   T   F | F

312. _____ interferes with the Watson test for urobilinogen and must be removed with $BaCl_2$. | Bile

313. Since both porphobilinogen and urobilinogen react with Ehrlich's aldehyde reagent, they are distinguished from one another by their differential solubility of the aldehyde product of these two compounds in _____ and _____. | water; chloroform

314. The following substances are used as color standards for urobilinogen determinations:
    a. Pontacyl dyes
    b. Carmine dyes
    c. BSP dye
    d. Phenol red
    | a

315. Eventually most of the urobilinogen is excreted in the feces and oxidized to orange-colored _____. | urobilin

316. The results of the urobilinogen test are reported in _____ units. | Ehrlich

Kidney Function Tests

317. Explain why urea clearance (C_u) is a better indicator of renal function than blood urea nitrogen (BUN). | See p. 132

318. The normal range for urea clearance (C_u) is:
     a. 60–90%
     b. 75–120%   b
     c. 2–16%
     d. 98–200%

319. Maximal urea clearance takes place when volume of urine   2 ml./min.;
     is over _____ . Standard urea clearance takes   <2 ml./min.
     place when volume of urine is _____ .

320. Why is a creatinine clearance preferred to urea clearance?   See p. 132

321. Both urine and blood creatinine must be determined for
     creatinine clearance test.   T   F   T

322. The urea clearance test is less influenced by rate of urine
     flow than the creatinine clearance.   T   F   F

323. Urea and creatinine clearance are used as guides to
     _____ _____ rate.   glomerular
                                                                 filtration

324. Three quite frequently performed tests of kidney function
     are:
         a. _____   Mosenthal
         b. _____   PSP
         c. _____   Creatinine
                                                                 clearance

325. The PSP test is primarily a test for _____ secretory   tubular
     function.

326. Briefly explain how urine which is to be examined for PSP
     dye content may be clarified when it is contaminated with
     blood.   See p. 132

327. When PSP is given to a normal person the dye is rapidly
     removed from the blood by the:
         a. Liver
         b. Pancreas
         c. Kidney   c
         d. Thyroid gland
         e. Spleen

328. An exceptionally high PSP excretion may occur in the
     urine of patients suffering from disease of the:
         a. Liver   a
         b. Kidney
         c. Pancreas
         d. Gall bladder
         e. Small intestine

329. The chemical name for phenol red indicator is:
         a. Dihydroxyphthalophenone
         b. Phenolsulphonphthalein   b
         c. Chlorophenol red
         d. Phenolphthalein

330. The PSP dose used for kidney function testing is 6 mg. and this amount of dye is contained in the following volume of the commercially obtainable dye solution:
    a. 0.6 ml.
    b. 1.0 ml.   b
    c. 2.0 ml.
    d. 3.0 ml.
    e. 6.0 ml.

331. PSP dye is colorless in alkaline urine.   T   F   F

332. The normal amount of PSP excreted in the urine in two hours after I.V. injection of 1 ml. (6 mg.) of the dye is:
    a. 20–30%
    b. 0–25%
    c. Over 65%   c
    d. 35–55%

333. A true test of glomerular filtration rate is inulin clearance because inulin is filtered at the glomeruli only and is neither _____ nor _____ during its passage along the tubules.   reabsorbed nor excreted

334. Inulin is employed for:
    a. Kidney function tests   a
    b. Liver function tests
    c. Thyroid function tests
    d. Extracellular fluid (ECF) volume determinations   d

335. Inulin is:
    a. An amino acid
    b. A polysaccharide-polymer of fructose   b
    c. A lipid
    d. A conjugated protein

336. Describe calculation of Glomerular Filtration Rate using the inulin method.   See p. 132

337. How can problem of incomplete urine collections in inulin clearance be solved?   See p. 133

938. In the Mosenthal test the volume and specific gravity of urine are measured at specified intervals.   T   F   T

339. Substances such as diodrast and p-aminohippuric acid are a measure of _____ flow.   renal plasma

Bence-Jones Protein

340. Upon boiling Bence-Jones protein will:
    a. Precipitate
    b. Redissolve   b

341. Which of the following urinary constituents will give rise to a precipitate at about 60°C.:

a. Porphobilinogen
b. Bence-Jones protein   b
c. Diazo substances
d. Alkapton bodies
e. Indican

342. Bence-Jones proteinuria is usually present in:
a. Typhoid fever
b. Porphyria
c. Multiple myeloma   c
d. Scarlet fever
e. Gonorrhea

343. The tests which are often requested in suspected cases of
multiple myeloma include:
a. Bence-Jones protein   a
b. Blood proteins   b
c. 17-ketosteroids
d. Bone marrow studies   d
e. Catecholamines

344. On protein electrophoresis of urine, the presence of Bence-
Jones protein is indicated by a single sharp peak in the
_____ region.   globulin

345. Myeloma protein in the urine is known as the _____   Bence-
protein.   Jones

Abnormal Urinary Constituents
(Indican, Melanin, Alkapton Bodies, Hemosiderin)

346. Indole is produced by bacterial action on _____.   tryptophan

347. Normally, no more than a trace of indican is found in the
urine.   T   F   T

348. Increased intestinal putrefaction or a high protein diet
may result in a positive _____ test.   indican

349. What chemical takes blue color in positive test for indican? indigo
blue

350. Melanin is a pigment derived from _____ and is in-   tyrosine
creased in cases of melanotic tumors.

351. Melanin reduces copper.   T   F   F

352. Tests for melanin are based upon oxidation of melanogen
(a colorless chromogen) to black melanin by either ferric
chloride or bromine.   T   F   T

353. Homogentisic acid, the chief alkapton body, will reduce
copper but not bismuth.   T   F   T

354. In alkaptonuria homogentisic acid is excreted in the urine.
On exposure to air the latter turns:
a. Green

b. Pink
c. Brown
d. Black   d
e. Red

355. Phenolic acids resulting from abnormal metabolism of
phenylalanine and tyrosine are known as _____   alkapton
bodies.

356. The chief alkapton body is _____.   homogentisic
acid.

357. In melanuria and alkaptonuria the urine usually darkens
upon standing.   T   F   T

358. The occurrence of hemosiderin crystals in the urine is
called:
    a. Urinary siderosis   a
    b. Hemochromatosis
    c. Hemoglobinuria
    d. Kidney siderosis
    e. None of these

359. Urinary siderosis occurs in hemoglobinuria or in hemochromatosis.   T   F   T

360. Hemosiderin is an iron-containing pigment, a product of
the decomposition of _____.   hemoglobin

361. The _____ reaction is used to demonstrate   Prussian blue
hemosiderin.   (ferrocyanide)

362. Urine of patients with phenylketonuria (PKU) have an increase in the following amino acid:
    a. Cystine
    b. Phenylalanine   b
    c. Cysteine
    d. Homocystine
    e. Phosphoethanolamine

363. An excessive excretion of valine, leucine, and isoleucine
and their keto-acids and hydroxy-acids in the urine is seen
in:
    a. Maple syrup urine disease   a
    b. Homocystinuria
    c. General aminoaciduria

364. Determinations of toxic metals (such as lead or mercury)
are usually carried out on:
    a. Blood
    b. Urine   b
    c. Feces
    d. Gastric contents
    e. Seminal fluid

365. In acidosis the urinary excretion of ammonia:
    a. Is increased   a

b. Is decreased
c. Remains unchanged

366. The presence of chyle in the urine ("chyluria") is most
frequently associated with:
    a. A high fat diet
    b. Bright's disease
    c. Multiple myeloma
    d. Filarial infection   d
    e. Trichomonas vaginitis

367. In acute pancreatitis urinary amylase and lipase levels are:
    a. Increased   a
    b. Decreased
    c. Normal

368. After an attack of gout the uric acid content of the urine
is:
    a. Increased   a
    b. Decreased
    c. Neither a nor b

ANTICOAGULANTS & PROTEIN-FREE FILTRATES
Anticoagulants for Chemistry Specimens

369. As an anticoagulant sodium fluoride acts by:
    a. Removal of calcium by chelation
    b. Forming weakly dissociated calcium component   b
    c. Forming double salt with calcium
    d. Combining with calcium to form insoluble calcium
       oxalate

370. As an anticoagulant EDTA acts by:
    a. Combining with calcium to form insoluble calcium
       oxalate
    b. Removing calcium by chelation   b
    c. Forming double salt with calcium
    d. Forming weakly dissociated calcium component

371. Heparin is:
    a. A synthetic anticoagulant
    b. A physiological anticoagulant   b
    c. Neither of these.

372. Heparin is believed to prevent clotting by:
    a. Removing calcium by chelation
    b. Inhibiting thrombin   b
    c. Forming weakly dissociated calcium component
    d. Forming double salt with calcium

373. The use of ammonium oxalate as anticoagulant will invali-
date the results of any analysis requiring:
    a. Bloor's reagent

b. Folin-Ciocalteu's reagent
c. Nessler's reagent   c
d. Ehrlich's diazo reagent

374. Which of the following will preserve blood but not prevent
it from clotting:
    a. Heparin
    b. Thymol   b
    c. Lithium oxalate
    d. EDTA

375. Which anticoagulant also preserves? Why?   See p. 133

376. EDTA is also known as "sequestrene" or "versene."   T   F   T

377. Serum and plasma can be used interchangeably in automated equipment.   T   F   F

378. Anticoagulants affect mainly the following:
    a. Total protein
    b. Bilirubin
    c. Serum enzymes   c
    d. Cholesterol
    e. T_3

379. Sodium oxalate is used as an anticoagulant for a blood
specimen. Later requests are made for the following determinations: Na^+ and K^+, S.G.O.T., Calcium, and amylase.
Which determinations could be carried out on this specimen? K^+ only

Protein-Free Filtrates

380. Which of the following reagents are used in the preparation of a classic Folin-Wu protein-free filtrate:
    a. 10% Na tungstate   a
    b. 1/12N HCl
    c. 10% Na bicarbonate
    d. 2/3N H_2SO_4 d

381. Every ml. of Folin-Wu protein-free filtrate contains the
following amount of blood:
    a. 0.1 ml.   a
    b. 0.2 ml.
    c. 0.5 ml.
    d. 0.75 ml.

382. A brownish Folin-Wu filtrate may be saved by refiltering
it after pouring filtrate back into mixture and adding
(drop-by-drop until a slight tinge of blue is given to Congo
red paper) the following reagent:
    a. 10% sodium tungstate
    b. 1N NaOH
    c. 0.1N NaOH
    d. 10% sulfuric acid   d

383. A brownish protein-free filtrate is never due to the use of impure tungstate.   T   F   F

384. A brownish protein-free filtrate may be due to the use of insufficient acid.   T   F   T

385. A brownish protein-free filtrate may be caused by excessive oxalate in blood protein.   T   F   T

386. Which of the following is not a method for the preparation of a blood protein-free filtrate:
    a. Folin-Wu
    b. Looney and Walsh   b
    c. Benedict-Newton
    d. Greenwald

387. Unless a protein-free filtrate is absolutely water-clear it should not be used for a test to be read on spectrophotometer.   T   F   T

388. The final blood dilution in most protein-free filtrates is:
    a. 1:2
    b. 1:5
    c. 1:10   c
    d. 1:8

389. The protein precipitant used in the determination of inorganic phosphorus by the Fiske-Subbarow method is ____ _____.   TCA (trichloracetic acid)

390. Trichloroacetic acid protein-free filtrates have a pH close to one.   T   F   T (They are very stable)

391. In the Somogyi-Nelson glucose method, equal volumes of $0.3N$ $Ba(OH)_2$ and 5% $ZnSO_4$ are used as the protein precipitants.   T   F   T

CLASSICAL BLOOD CHEMISTRY
Glucose in Blood; Glucose Tolerance

392. Levulose (fruit sugar) rotates polarized light to the right.   T   F   F

393. Which of the following is not a carbohydrate:
    a. Galactose
    b. Globulin   b
    c. Pentose
    d. Levulose
    e. Glucose

394. The end-product of carbohydrate digestion is:
    a. Protein

    b. Starch
    c. Glucose   c
    d. Sucrose
    e. Alcohol

395. Insulin is secreted by:
    a. Liver
    b. Thyroid
    c. Pancreas   c
    d. Adrenals
    e. Spleen

396. The clinical symptoms of hypoglycemia begin to appear
    when the blood sugar level drops below:
    a. 120 mg.%
    b. 90 mg.%   b
    c. 60 mg.%
    d. 24 mg.%
    e. 12 mg.%

397. When the blood sugar level is low the condition is referred
    to as:
    a. Hyperglycemia
    b. Glucose tolerance
    c. Hypoglycemia   c
    d. Glucosuria
    e. Diabetic acidosis

398. Hyperinsulinism is the same as diabetes.   T   F   F

399. Excess glucose is stored by liver as:
    a. Levulose
    b. Maltose
    c. Glycogen   c
    d. Starch
    e. Sucrose

400. The majority of older methods of glucose determination
    are based upon:
    a. Production of reducing sugar from starch by amylase
    b. Reduction of glucose by alkaline copper solution
    c. Fermentation of glucose by yeast
    d. Reduction of alkaline copper by glucose   d

401. Which of the following is not a procedure for blood sugar:
    a. Somogyi-Nelson
    b. Benedict
    c. Folin-Wu
    d. Whitehorn   d

402. The condition characterized by body failure to oxidize
    carbohydrates at a normal rate is:
    a. Diabetes mellitus   a
    b. Uremia
    c. Gout

      d. Yellow atrophy of liver

      e. Glycogen storage disease

403. The normal (true sugar technique) range of fasting blood glucose is:
      a. 40–60 mg.%
      b. 70–92 mg.%   b
      c. 90–120 mg.%
      d. 120–150 mg.%
      e. 150–165 mg.%

404. The normal (Folin-Wu method) range of fasting blood glucose is:
      a. 25–35 mg.%
      b. 70–92 mg.%
      c. 80–120 mg.%   c
      d. 120–150 mg.%
      e. 150–165 mg.%

405. Because it employs a _____ protein-free filtrate, the Folin-Wu method includes nonglucose reducing substances, in addition to blood glucose, in all blood glucose determinations carried out by this method.   *tungstic acid*

406. In the Somogyi-Nelson method for blood glucose the nonprotein filtrate formed by $BaSO_4$ and $Zn(OH)_2$ excludes non-sugar reducing substances and therefore measures _____ glucose.   *true*

407. In the enzymatic method of glucose determination, glucose is converted to gluconic acid and hydrogen peroxide in the presence of the enzyme _____. In the presence of peroxidase, the peroxide _____ orthodianisidine to an orange color (or o-toluidine to a blue color).   *glucose-oxidase; oxidizes*

408. The glucose tolerance test is based upon the principle that a diabetic person (because of insulin deficiency) will remove glucose from the blood stream at a rate _____ than that of a normal individual.   *slower*

409. The normal fasting blood glucose by the Folin-Wu method is 80–120 mg.%. One-half hour after administration of standard test dose of glucose it should go no higher than _____ mg.% in a normal person. At the end of ____ hours it should have dropped to the fasting level or less.   *160–170 mg.%; 2 hours*

410. In a diabetic, the peak after glucose administration is higher than in a normal person and the return to fasting blood level is prolonged.   T F   *T*

411. If 2 hours after a meal containing 50–100 gm. of sugar the blood sugar content is found to be normal, diabetes mellitus can be ruled out without further testing.   T F   *T*

412. Injection of tolbutamide in a patient with no diabetes should result in an increased secretion of _____ and a decrease in blood _____.

insulin; sugar (glucose)

BUN

413. The chief waste product resulting from protein metabolism is:
    a. Creatinine
    b. Urea
    c. Uric acid
    d. None of these

b

414. The amount of NPN (total nonprotein nitrogen) normally represented by BUN (blood urea nitrogen) is approximately:
    a. 5%
    b. 10%
    c. 50%
    d. 12%
    e. 3%

c

415. The concentration of urea nitrogen in the blood of healthy adults ranges between _____ mg.%.

10-20 mg.%

416. The importance of urea level in the blood lies in its value as an indicator of:
    a. Liver function
    b. Kidney function
    c. Pancreatic function
    d. Adrenal function
    e. Protein digestion

b

417. The blood pH is always low in metabolic acidosis.   T   F

F

418. In metabolic acidosis CO_2 combining power of plasma is:
    a. Increased
    b. Decreased
    c. Normal

b

419. Diacetyl monoxime reacts with _____ with subsequent formation of color.

urea

420. Diacetyl monoxime heated in acid solution releases diacetyl which in turn reacts with _____ to form colored Schiff's base.

urea

421. The reaction between ammonia and phenol-hypochlorite using sodium nitroprusside as a catalyst is called the:
    a. Conway reaction
    b. Van Slyke ammonia reaction
    c. Berthelot reaction
    d. Jaffé reaction
    e. Nessler reaction

c

422. Briefly describe analytical principle involved in Karr's
urease method for BUN determination   See p. 133

423. The use of sodium fluoride-thymol as an anticoagulant
and a preservative is contraindicated in the following determination:
a. Creatinine
b. Urea by urease methods   b
c. NPN (total nonprotein nitrogen)
d. Sugar (glucose)

424. In direct nesslerization determinations of nitrogen gum
ghatti is used to:
a. Develop the color
b. Stop the reaction
c. Prevent cloudiness by forming a protective colloid   c
d. Split ammonia compounds

425. When urea is acted upon by urease the former is converted
to:
a. Ammonium oxalate
b. Uric acid
c. Ammonium carbonate   c
d. Ammonium sulfate
e. Uricase

426. Urea by urease method is not affected by ammonia fumes
in atmosphere.   T   F   F

427. Urease is:
a. A trade name for commercial urea
b. An urealytic enzyme from the jack bean   b
c. A differential medium for Proteus sp.
d. A salt of uric acid

428. Nessler's reagent is:
a. An alkaline potassium mercuric iodide   a
b. A saturated solution of picric acid
c. A saturated solution of sodium nitroprusside
d. A saturated solution of ammonium sulfate

429. "Urease" and "uricase" are two different names of the
same enzyme.   T   F   F

Uric Acid & Creatinine

430. A condition in which the metabolism of uric acid (but not
that of other nitrogenous urinary constituents) is impaired is:
a. Uremia
b. Azotemia
c. Diabetes mellitus
d. Gout   d
e. Nephritis

431. The nitrogenous waste product of nucleic acid or purine metabolism is:
    a. NPN
    b. Creatinine
    c. Uric acid   c
    d. Ammonia
    e. BUN

432. Uric acid is a more reliable indicator of renal insufficiency than either urea or creatinine.   T   F   F

433. The cyanide-urea solution used in uric acid determinations will keep indefinitely provided it is stored in a refrigerator.   T   F   F

434. When uric acid reacts with arsenotungstate solution (Newton's uric acid reagent) in the presence of cyanide and urea, the arsenotungstate is:
    a. Reduced   a
    b. Oxidized
    c. Neither

435. Most chemical methods for the quantitative determination of uric acid are based on the:
    a. Reducing properties of uric acid   a
    b. Oxidizing properties of uric acid
    c. Catalytic properties of uric acid

436. Briefly explain the advantages of using serum or plasma rather than whole blood in uric acid determinations.   See p. 133

437. Which of the following methods for uric acid is based upon the decrease in the optical density of specimen after incubating with specific (destroys uric acid only) enzyme "uricase":
    a. Brown
    b. Blauch and Koch   b
    c. Folin
    d. Newton

438. Uricase converts uric acid to _____.   allantoin

439. As uricase breaks uric acid down to allantoin, serum UV absorption:
    a. Increases
    b. Decreases   b
    c. Remains the same

440. Normal uric acid ranges from ___ to ___ mg.%.   3 to 7

441. The serum creatinine level is most useful in the diagnosis of late stages of:
    a. Renal disease   a
    b. Liver disease
    c. Pancreatic disease
    d. Thyroid gland disease
    e. Hodgkin's disease

442. Creatinine reacts with strong alkaline picrate to form a red colored compound. This reaction is called:
    a. Nessler's reaction
    b. Liebermann-Burchard reaction
    c. Ehrlich's benzaldehyde reaction
    d. Jaffé reaction   d
    e. Ehrlich's diazo reaction

443. The Jaffé reaction is specific for creatinine.   T   F   F

444. The specificity of the Jaffé reaction can be increased by the use of:
    a. NaOH-dilute
    b. Lloyd's reagent   b
    c. Acetic acid
    d. Oxalic acid
    e. Ammonium sulfate

445. In colorimetric methods of creatinine determination the unknown must closely approximate the color of the standard in order to prevent appreciable error from the color of the picrate.   T   F   T

446. In determination of creatinine by Jaffé reaction, hemolyzed blood is acceptable.   T   F   F

447. The normal range of serum creatinine is:
    a.   1–2 mg.%   a
    b.   2–4 mg.%
    c.   4–8 mg.%
    d.   8–10 mg.%
    e.   12–20 mg.%

448. The constancy of the daily creatinine excretion may be used as a verification of the completeness of a 24-hour urine collection.   T   F   T

449. It is more meaningful to express creatinine excretion in terms of body size since creatinine excretion is related to
    _____.   muscle
                                                          mass

450. Creatinine is the anhydride of _____.   creatine

NPN

451. Which of the following substances does not belong to the NPN group of blood constituents:
    a. Urea
    b. Uric acid
    c. Creatinine
    d. Ammonia
    e. Cholesterol   e
    f. Amino acids

452. The NPN would not be elevated in the following (uncomplicated) condition:
    a. Uremia
    b. Acute pancreatitis   b
    c. Severe glomerulonephritis
    d. Mercury bichloride poisoning

453. Explain briefly why copper is added to digestion mixture of sulfuric and phosphoric acid employed in NPN determinations.   See p. 133

454. Briefly describe analytical principle involved in micro-Kjeldahl NPN determination.   See p. 133

Protein

455. Which of the following substances is not a protein:
    a. Globulin
    h. Urea   b
    c. Fibrinogen
    d. Albumin

156. Total protein in plasma minus total protein in serum equals _____.   fibrinogen

457. Blood serum contains fibrinogen.   T   F   F

458. Methods of determining total protein include:
    a. Refractometer   a
    b. Biuret   b
    c. Macro-Kjeldahl   c
    d. Folin-Ciocalteu   d

459. When protein solutions are treated with a very dilute solution of alkalinized copper sulfate a violet colored compound is formed. This reaction is called:
    a. Nessler's reaction
    b. Liebermann-Burchard reaction
    c. Ehrlich's diazo reaction
    d. Jaffé reaction
    e. Biuret reaction   e

460. A compound formed by combination of two urea molecules with the elimination of one molecule of ammonia is called _____.   biuret

461. The biuret reaction used to quantitate proteins employs biuret as one of the reagents.   T   F   F

462. A tripeptide is the smallest peptide that gives a positive biuret reaction.   T   F   T

463. The protein method in which a phenol reagent is added to alkalinized protein solution is the:
    a. Greenberg method
    b. Biruet method   b

c. Looney and Walsh method

464. A protein is a large molecule consisting of various _____ _____ linked together by _____ bonds.

amino-acids; peptide

465. The —CONH group is called a _____ bond.

peptide

466. The —CONH linkage is also an _____ linkage.

amide

467. Amino acids form internal salts that are called _____ .

zwitter-ions

468. Normal blood contains no methemalbumin.   T   F

F

469. Another name for methemalbumin if ferrihemalbumin.   T   F

T

470. Haptoglobin is an alpha-2 globulin which binds _____ .

hemoglobin

471. The acidic and basic groups present in protein molecules are capable of acting as buffers in the body.   T   F

T

472. Amino acids are broken down ("deamination") and the amino groups converted to urea by the:
    a. Pancreas
    b. Kidney
    c. Liver
    d. Spleen
    e. Adrenal gland

b

473. Albumins and globulins are the chief proteins in plasma.   T   F

T

474. Which of the following is not a method for serum proteins:
    a. Kingsley's biuret method
    b. Looney and Walsh
    c. Van Slyke
    d. Greenberg

c

475. Fibrinogen, prothrombin, albumin and perhaps some of the globulins (except gamma globulin) are formed in the:
    a. Kidney
    b. Liver
    c. Pancreas
    d. Thyroid
    e. Spleen

b

476. Which proteins constituents of the serum may be recognized through electrophoretic analysis?

See p. 133

477. One would expect the plasma specific gravity to be raised in conditions with a high total protein.   T   F

T

478. A severe loss of albumin could bring about a serious reduction in the plasma colloidal osmotic pressure.   T   F

T

479. Albumin synthesis is decreased in _____ dysfunction.   hepatic

480. Precipitation of proteins by neutral salts, such as ammonium sulfate, is called _____.   salting out

481. The A/G ratio may remain normal despite an abnormal amount of albumin and/or globulin.   T   F   T

482. In healthy adults the normal serum protein ranges from ____ to ____ gm.%   6.5 to 8.0

483. When the plasma osmotic pressure ("oncotic pressure") falls below the capillary blood pressure, _____ results.   edema

484. The normal range of serum albumin is:
  a. 1.5–3.4 Gm.%
  b. 4.5–5.5 Gm.%   b
  c. 4–8 mg.%
  d. 6–8 Gm.%
  e. 10–20 mg.%

485. Albumin is water-soluble.   T   F   T

486. Low plasma albumin values favor formation of:
  a. Edema   a
  b. Malignant neoplasms
  c. Systemic lupus erythematosus
  d. Antibodies
  e. Gallbladder stones

487. An increase in the amount of albumin in the plasma or the serum seldom takes place.   T   F   T

488. Globulins which are insoluble in water but soluble in saline solutions are called:
  a. Alpha globulins
  b. Beta globulins
  c. Euglobulins   c
  d. Pseudoglobulins

489. Globulins are water-soluble.   T   F   F

490. Globulins are soluble in dilute salt solutions   T   F   T

491. A serum globulin which precipitates on cooling is called:
  a. Euglobulin
  b. Cryoglobulin   b
  c. Pseudoglobulin
  d. Gamma globulin
  e. Alpha globulin

492. Which of the following reagents will cause serum to gel when globulin content is increased (as in Kala-azar or multiple myeloma):
  a. 40% formaldehyde   a
  b. 95% ethyl alcohol
  c. 70% ethyl alcohol
  d. 0.1N H_2SO_4
  e. Carbolic acid

493. An inversion of A/G ratio may actually occur in conditions, such as lipoid nephrosis, which are accompanied by marked:
    a. Hypoglobulinemia
    b. Anemia
    c. Hyperglobulinemia   c
    d. Hyperprothrombinemia

494. Parfentjev's method is used to determine:
    a. Creatinine
    b. Glucose
    c. Total protein
    d. BUN
    e. Fibrinogen   e

495. The Sia water test is used in the diagnosis of:
    a. Macrocytic anemia
    b. Lupus erythematosus
    c. Waldenström's macroglobulinemia   c
    d. Pernicious anemia
    e. Leukemia

496. Determination of protein by the macro-Kjeldahl method is one of the most accurate methods available.   T   F   T

497. In the Kjeldahl method the _____ is subtracted from the total nitrogen in order to obtain protein nitrogen.   NPN

498. In the Kjeldahl method for protein determination, copper sulfate is used as a boiling point (elevator, depressor) and mercuric oxide as a _____.   elevator   catalyst

499. Dyes used to measure albumin include:
    a. Methyl orange   a
    b. HABA   b
    c. Phenol red
    d. Biuret
    e. PSP

500. Electrophoresis is based on the fact that ionized particles in a suitable medium under the influence of an electrical current will migrate at velocities proportional to the _____ _____ of the particles.   net   charges

Lipids

501. An increase in fat and fatty acids in the blood is called:
    a. Hyperphospholipidemia
    b. Hyperlipemia   b
    c. Hyperphosphatasemia
    d. Hypercholesterolemia
    e. Hyperacidity

502. Simple lipids or simple fat are esters of fatty acids and _____.   glycerol

503. Waxes are esters of fatty acids and some alcohol other than _____ .   glycerol

504. The sterols (e.g., cholesterol) are often classified among the lipids although they contain no _____ acid.   fatty

505. Phospholipids differ markedly from fats and waxes in composition and structure because they contain _____ .   phosphorus

506. Lecithins, cephalin, and sphingomyelins are classified as _____ .   phospholipids

507. Bloor's reagent (alcohol and ether) is used in the gravimetric method for determining total lipids.   T   F   T

508. In plasma, the lipids are soluble due to their combination with _____ .   protein

509. Proteins that combine with lipids and aid in their transport are called _____ .   lipoproteins

510. Triglycerides are classified as _____ fats.   neutral

511. Triglycerides are not appreciably affected by the diet. T   F   F

512. The fat fraction of serum which, when present in increased amounts, imparts a lactescent (milky) appearance to serum is _____ .   triglyceride

513. Ultracentrifugation and electrophoresis are two techniques used to characterize and measure _____ .   lipoproteins

514. In lipoprotein electrophoresis, the _____ fraction remains at the origin.   chylomicron

515. The type of hyperlipoproteinemia (Lee and Fredrickson) which has been most commonly associated with atherosclerosis and vascular complications is _____ .   Type II

516. In addition to protein electrophoretic pattern, the classification and management of hyperlipoproteinemia is aided by the following measurements:
    a. Free fatty acids
    b. Cholesterol   b
    c. Chylomicrons
    d. Total lipids
    e. Triglycerides   e

517. β-lipoproteins contain a high proportion of:
    a. Free fatty acid
    b. Cholesterol   b
    c. Triglyceride
    d. Chylomicrons

518. Pre-β-lipoproteins contain a high percentage of:
    a. Free fatty acid
    b. Cholesterol
    c. Triglyceride   c
    d. Chylomicrons

Cholesterol

519. The normal range of total serum cholesterol is:
    a. 15–25 mg.%
    b. 1.5–2.5 mg.%
    c. 150–250 mg.%
    d. 50–150 mg.%
    e. 20–40 mg.%

c

520. Cholesterol is an alcohol.   T   F

T

521. Cholesterol ester is normally about:
    a. 18% of total cholesterol
    b. 50% of total cholesterol
    c. 70% of total cholesterol
    d. 98% of total cholesterol
    e. 5% of total cholesterol

c

522. Total cholesterol minus ester cholesterol equals _____
_____.

free
cholesterol

523. In ester cholesterol determination the alcohol-ether mixture extract of total cholesterol is treated with an alcoholic solution of _____ which then combines with the ____ _____, forming petroleum ether-insoluble _____ _____.

digitonin;
free choles-
terol; chol-
esterol-digi-
tonide

524. Ester cholesterol is free cholesterol in combination with:
    a. Glycerol
    b. Fatty acid
    c. Lactic acid
    d. Nucleic acid
    e. Alanine

b

525. To prepare a standard, cholesterol is usually dissolved in:
    a. Water
    b. Acetic acid
    c. Ethyl alcohol
    d. Methyl alcohol
    e. None of these

b

526. An organ important in cholesterol metabolism is the:
    a. Liver
    b. Pancreas
    c. Thyroid
    d. Parathyroid
    e. Spleen

a

527. Cholesterol metabolism is intimately associated with:
    a. Carbohydrate metabolism
    b. Protein metabolism
    c. Lipid metabolism

c

528. The ingestion of food has great effect on the plasma level of cholesterol.   T   F   F

529. The deposit of cholesterol on the lining of arteries is called:
   a. Atherosclerosis   a
   b. Hypertension
   c. Arteriosclerosis
   d. Hypercholesteronemia
   e. Collagen disease

530. Both free cholesterol and ester cholesterol react with acetic anhydride and concentrated sulfuric acid to yield a blue-green color which follows Beer's law. This reaction is called:
   a. Nessler's reaction
   b. Liebermann-Burchard reaction   b
   c. Ehrlich's diazo reaction
   d. Jaffé reaction
   e. Biuret reaction

531. The Libermann-Burchard reaction is extremeley sensitive to _____ .   water

532. The three most common methods for determining total cholesterol are the Bloor method, Schoenheimer-Sperry, and Levine-Zak.   T   F   T

533. Determination of cholesterol is widely used in the diagnosis of:
   a. Anemia
   b. Diabetes mellitus
   c. Renal disease
   d. Hepatic disease   d
   e. Tularemia

534. A hypercholesteronemia usually occurs in the following condition(s):
   a. Hyperthyroidism
   b. Diabetes mellitus   b
   c. Hypothyroidism   c
   d. Obstructive jaundice   d
   e. Gout

Liver Function Tests

535. Jaundice may be caused by destruction of liver cells.   T   F   T

536. Jaundice is always due to excessive destruction of erythrocytes due to any cause.   T   F   F

537. Jaundice is always due to cholestasis preventing the outflow of bile from the liver.   T   F   F

538. Bile pigment is formed as the result of the destruction of erythrocytes within the body.   T   F   T

539. The condition known as "kernicterus" may occur in:
    a. Pernicious anemia
    b. Infectious mononucleosis
    c. Lupus erythematosus
    d. Erythroblastosis fetalis   d
    e. Banti's disease

540. In jaundice (hemolytic or cholestatic) the serum bilirubin
    content is:
    a. Increased   a
    b. Decreased
    c. Normal

541. Bilirubin is a breakdown product of _____ meta-   hemoglobin
    bolism.

542. A freshly prepared solution of sulfanilic acid and sodium
    nitrite in dilute hydrochloric acid is known as:
    a. Ehrlich's aldehyde reagent
    b. Ehrlich's diazo reagent   b
    c. Bloor's reagent
    d. Folin's reagent
    e. Exton's reagent

543. The reagent employed in quantitative serum bilirubin de-
    terminations is:
    a. Ehrlich's benzaldehyde reagent
    b. Nessler's reagent
    c. Ehrlich's diazo reagent   c
    d. Phosphomolybdic acid reagent
    e. Benzidine

544. The Malloy-Evelyn test for bilirubin is based on the diazo-
    tization of bilirubin and the measurement of the azo dye.
    T   F   T

545. Sulfanilic acid and bilirubin in the presence of nitrous acid
    undergo a diazo reaction resulting in azobilirubin. This is
    the:
    a. Jaffé reaction
    b. Nessler's reaction
    c. Liebermann-Burchard reaction
    d. Nonne-Apelt reaction
    e. Van den Bergh reaction   e

546. Normal direct reacting bilirubin is:
    a. Less than 0.4 mg.%   a
    b. Between 0.4 and 1.0 mg.%
    c. Less than the indirect bilirubin

547. Indirect reacting bilirubin—when elevated in the blood
    stream—will appear in urine.   T   F   F

548. The normal range of total serum bilirubin is:
    a. 0.1–0.4 mg.%
    b. 0.2–0.8 mg.%   b

      c. 1.5–2.5 mg.%
      d. 4–8 micrograms%
      e. 12–15 mg.%

549. "Indirect"-reacting bilirubin is water-soluble.   T   F   F

550. Direct-reacting bilirubin esterified bilirubin or bilirubin-glucuronide) is water-soluble.   T   F   T

551. Increased direct bilirubin may indicate:
      a. Hemolytic disorder
      b. Hepatic disorder   b
      c. Renal disorder
      d. Cardiovascular disorder
while a normal direct bilirubin with an increased total concentration suggests a:
      a. Hemolytic disorder   a
      b. Hepatic disorder
      c. Renal disorder
      d. Cardiovascular disorder

552. The icterus index is a rough index of the _____ content of the blood serum.   bilirubin

553. A safe maximum normal color of serum has a top icterus index value of:
      a. 1
      b. 3
      c. 5   c
      d. 10
      e. 15

554. In the icterus index test the intensity of the color of the serum is compared with a certified standard, namely a solution of:
      a. Picrate in alkali
      b. Ferric chloride
      c. Phenolphthalein
      d. $K_2Cr_2O_7$ d
      e. HgI_2

555. The bilirubinometer updates the icterus index by substituting a filter for comparison of serum color.   T   F   T

556. A liver test not based upon the ability of the liver to take up a dye and excrete it after its I.V. injection is the:
      a. Rose-Bengal test
      b. Thymol turbidity test   b
      c. Bilirubin tolerance test
      d. Bromsulfalein

557. Positive cephalin flocculation or thymol flocculation tests are indicative of:
      a. Kidney disease
      b. Thyroid disease
      c. Liver disease   c

    d. Coronary artery disease

    e. Acute pancreatitis

558. In which of the following conditions elevated thymol turbidity values would not be expected:
    a. Parenchymatous liver disease
    b. Acute pancreatitis   b
    c. Infectious hepatitis
    d. Liver cirrhosis

559. The normal range of serum cephalin-cholesterol flocculation (Hanger's test) is:
    a. 1^+ to 2^+ in 24 hours
    b. 0 to 1^+ in 48 hours   b
    c. 0 to 4^+ in 48 hours
    d. 2^+ to 4^+ in 24 hours

560. Flocculation tests such as thymol turbidity and cephalin
flocculation are related to an increase in _____ and a   globulin;
decrease in serum _____.   albumin

561. Thymol turbidity and cephalin flocculation tests are specific for liver disease.   T   F   F

562. When BSP dye is administered to a healthy individual, it
will be quickly removed from the blood by the:
    a. Kidney
    b. Liver   b
    c. Spleen
    d. Pancreas
    e. Thyroid gland

563. In the hippuric acid test the patient is given _____.   benzoic
This combines with _____ in the liver to form hippuric   acid; gly-
acid which is then excreted in the urine.   cine

564. The best known test of the detoxifying function of the
liver is the _____ test.   hippuric
                                            acid

565. In jaundice and liver cell disease, the prothrombin time
may be:
    a. Shortened
    b. Prolonged   b

566. Which of the following tests are not for liver function:
    a. Hippuric acid synthesis
    b. Response of plasma prothrombin to parenteral
       vitamin-K injection
    c. Acid phosphatase activity   c
    d. Thymol turbidity
    e. Alkaline phosphatase
    f. Colloidal gold
    g. PSP   g

Enzymes

567. What is an enzyme? | See p. 133

568. All enzymes are protein in nature. T F | T

569. Enzymatic reactions are, as a rule, not very sensitive to temperature and pH changes. T F | F

570. In the clinical laboratory enzyme activity is determined by presenting the serum with an excess of _____. This is known as a _____ order reaction. | substrate; zero

571. The following is a plot of an enzyme reaction rate:

Concentration of Starch Substrate

If the velocity of an enzyme reaction showed the relationship to the starch concentration given above, which concentration (a, b, c, or d) of starch substrate should be used to measure activity of the amylase? | d

572. Certain enzymes are produced by the cell in an inactive form. This inactive form is called _____. | zymogen

573. Trypsinogen is a zymogen. T F | T

574. Trypsinogen is converted into trypsin by an activator enzyme called _____. | enterokinase

575. Enzymes are useful:
    a. Only in digestion
    b. Only in respiration
    c. In both ingestion and digestion
    d. In both digestion and respiration
    e. Only during ingestion | d

576. All of the following are enzymes except:
    a. Sucrase
    b. Trypsin
    c. Bile
    d. Lipase
    e. Phosphatase | c

577. Which of the following substances is not an enzyme:
    a. Trypsin
    b. Lactic dehydrogenase
    c. Cholinesterase
    d. Urobilinogen
    e. Urease | d

578. Maltase, sucrase, lactase, and aminopeptidases are digestive enzymes which are secreted by:
    a. Salivary glands
    b. Pancreas
    c. Gastric mucosa
    d. Intestinal mucosa   d
    e. Küppfer's cells

579. Cholecystokinin stimulates:
    a. Liver
    b. Gallbladder   b
    c. Pancreas
    d. Duodenal mucosa
    e. Thyroid gland

580. When acid bathes the duodenal mucosa it causes the release of "secretin" and "pancreozymin." What role do
these hormones play in pancreatic physiology?   See p. 133

581. Cholinesterase hydrolyzes:
    a. Starch
    b. Fatty acids
    c. Cholesterol
    d. Acetylcholine   d
    e. Pyruvic acid

582. Trypsin digests:
    a. Starch
    b. Protein   b
    c. Sugar
    d. Fat

583: The substrate for glutamic pyruvic transaminase (SGPT)
is:
    a. Alanine and alpha-ketoglutamic acid   a
    b. Acetylcholine
    c. Aspartic and alpha-ketoglutamic acid
    d. Pyruvic acid
    e. Olive oil

584. Which of the following enzyme activities/is measured by
determining the rate of utilization of a necessary coenzyme:
    a. Amylase
    b. Glutamic oxaloacetic transaminase   b
    c. Cholinesterase
    d. Phosphatase
    e. Lipase

585. Product measured in transaminase activity determinations:
    a. Phenol
    b. Phosphorus
    c. Fatty acid
    d. ΔDPNH   d
    e. Glucose

586. The substrate for glutamic oxaloacetic transaminase
(SGOT) is:
    a. Aspartic and alpha-ketoglutamic acid   a
    b. Pyruvic acid
    c. Acetylcholine
    d. Alanine and alpha-ketoglutamic acid
    e. Olive oil

587. SGOT is specific for diagnosis of myocardial infarction.
T   F   F

588. In the colorimetric determination of SGOT and SGPT
(Reitman-Frankel), the keto acid is reacted with _____   dinitro-
_____.   phenylhy-
                                       drazine

589. While SGOT is more specific for damage to _____ muscle   heart
then SGPT, the latter shows a greater elevation in the blood
in _____ damage.   liver

590. Both SGPT and SGOT may be elevated in myocardial infarction. T   F   T

591. Coenzyme-I can be called DPN or NAD. T   F   T

592. DPN absorbs in the ultraviolet at 340 nm. while DPNH
does not. T   F   F

593. Transaminases are enzymes that have the ability to transfer an _____ group from one compound to another.   amino

594. Dehydrogenase is a:
    a. Hydrolytic enzyme
    b. Oxidative enzyme   b
    c. Transferring enzyme

595. Dehydrogenase is a hydrolytic enzyme. T   F   F

596. An enzyme which reversably oxidizes lactic acid to pyruvic acid is:
    a. SLDH   a
    b. SGOT
    c. SGPT
    d. Cholinesterase
    e. Lipase

597. The Wacker method for LDH determinations involves the
lactate to pyruvate reaction and measures the _____   increase
in U.V. absorption as DPN → DPNH.

598. Lactic dehydrogenase activity is used primarily for the
diagnosis of _____.   myocardial
                                       infarction

599. An elevated LDH (lactic dehydrogenase) persists longer
in myocardial infarction than an elevated SGOT. T   F   T

600. In certain Italian families, the ingestion of beans from the
plant *Vicia fava* is often followed by:

a. Cold hemoglobinuria
b. Allergic hemoglobinuria   b
c. Nocturnal hemoglobinuria
d. March hemoglobinuria

601. Allergic hemoglobinuria is also called:
a. Blackwater fever
b. Favism   b
c. Marchiafava-Micheli syndrome
d. Hemochromatosis
e. Bilharziasis

602. Allergic hemoglobinuria following ingestion of beans from
the plant *Vicia fava* is due to deficiency of the following
enzyme in the red blood cells:
a. SLDH
b. SGOT
c. G-6-PO$_4$ dehydrogenase   c
d. LAP

603. Glucose-6-phosphate dehydrogenase activity is determined
in:
a. Serum
b. Plasma
c. Buffy coat
d. Red blood cells   d

604. Coenzyme-II, or _____ is necessary in determining   TPN or
enzyme activity of glucose-6-phosphate dehydrogenase and   NADP
isocitric dehydrogenase.

605. In myocardial infarction the first enzyme to become elevated is:
a. CPK   a
b. LDH
c. HBD
d. SGOT

606. CPK, SGOT, HBD activities are specific for myocardial
infarction.   T   F   F

607. Multimolecular forms of an enzyme are known as ____-   iso-
_____.   enzymes

608. Alpha hydroxybutyric dehydrogenase (HBD) is an isoenzyme of:
a. CPK
b. SGOT
c. LDH   c
d. SGPT

609. The enzyme most specific for heart muscle damage is:
a. SGOT
b. CPK
c. HBD   c
d. LDH

610. The heart fraction is the (fastest, slowest) moving LDH isoenzyme fraction; the liver fraction is the (fastest, slowest) moving.

fastest

slowest

611. Isoenzymes are distinguishable from one another only by electrophoretic tests.   T   F

F

612. Increased LAP (leucine amino peptidase) values are found in patients with cancer of the:
    a. Stomach
    b. Pancreas
    c. Prostate
    d. Colon
    e. Small intestine

b

613. There is a strong correlation between the total copper content of the serum and:
    a. Ceruloplasmin levels
    b. Alkaline phosphatase
    c. Phospholipids
    d. Cholesterol
    e. Albumin values

a

614. Acid phosphatase values are usually increased in:
    a. Liver disease
    b. Prostatic cancer
    c. Hypoparathyroidism
    d. Hyperparathyroidism
    e. Myocardial infarction

b

615. The optimum pH for acid phosphatase activity to take place is:
    a. 2.8
    b. 3.5
    c. 5.0
    d. 6.5
    e. 9.5

c

616. Disodium phenylphosphate substrate is considered the most sensitive substrate for _____ phosphatase determinations. This is the Gutman and Gutman method.

acid

617. In the Gutman and Gutman method for acid phosphatase, the amount of liberated _____ is measured by its reduction of phosphomolybdic acid.

phenol

618. Acid phosphatase is a relatively stable enzyme and can therefore be stored in the refirgerator overnight.   T   F

F

619. The acid phosphatase concentration of the red cells is many times higher than the concentration in serum.   T   F

T

620. Where is acid phosphatase chiefly found?

See p. 133

621. Tartrate is known to inhibit the activity of only _____ acid phosphatase while cupric ion inhibits _____ acid phosphatase.

prostatic
erythrocyte

622. Substrates for phosphatase activity include β-glycerophosphate, α-naphthol phosphate, disodium phenyl phosphate.
T   F   T

623. In the Shinowara, Jones and Reinhart method for acid phosphatase determination it is not necessary to avoid hemolysis.   T   F   F

624. Elevated serum acid phosphatase is seen in patients with prostatic carcinoma that has metastasized.   T   F   T

625. The normal adult range of serum alkaline phosphatase values is:
    a. 0–4 King Armstrong units
    b. 4–10 King-Armstrong units   b
    c. 15-20 King-Armstrong units
    d. 25-35 King-Armstrong units
    e. 40–60 King-Armstrong units

626. The normal adult range of serum alkaline phosphatase values is:
    a. 2-4 Bodansky units   a
    b. 4–8 Bodansky units
    c. 8–12 Bodansky units
    d. 10–18 Bodansky units
    e. 20–25 Bodansky units

627. The normal adult range of serum alkaline phosphatase values is:
    a. 0–2.0 Shinowara-Jones (S-J) units
    b. 2.2–8.6 Shinowara-Jones (S-J) units   b
    c. 8.0-12.4 Shinowara-Jones (S-J) units
    d. 10–18 Shinowara-Jones (S-J) units
    e. 20–25 Shinowara-Jones (S-J) units

628. Children usually have higher serum alkaline phosphatase values than adults.   T   F   T

629. The optimum pH for alkaline phosphatase activity to take place is:
    a. 7.2
    b. 8.6   b
    c. 5.0
    d. 4.6
    e. 10.5

630. In alkaline phosphatase determinations, if liberated phosphorus is measured as a product of enzyme activity, serum inorganic phosphorus must be measured prior to the reaction and subtracted from the total.   T   F   T

631. High alkaline phosphatase activity is found mainly in:
    a. Hyperthyroidism
    b. Hyperinsulinism
    c. Bone and liver disease   c

d. Pancreatic carcinoma
e. Gout

632. Amylase and lipase values are high in:
    a. Multiple myeloma
    b. Myocardial infarction
    c. Infectious hepatitis
    d. Acute pancreatitis   d
    e. Amyloidosis

633. Amylase converts:
    a. Proteins to polypeptides
    b. Emulsified fats to fatty acids and glycerol
    c. Pepsinogen to pepsin
    d. Polysaccharides to disaccharides   d

634. Product measured in amylase activity determinations by the saccharaogenic method:
    a. Phenol
    b. Fatty acid
    c. Phosphate
    d. Glucose   d

635. Starch is the substrate for:
    a. Amylase   a
    b. Lipase
    c. Trypsin
    d. Transaminase
    e. LAP

636. Amylase is also called:
    a. Lipase
    b. Prostatic phosphatase
    c. Cholinesterase
    d. Diastase   d
    e. None of these

637. Amylase is exclusively produced by the pancreas.   T   F   F

638. Ptyalin is also called:
    a. Lipase
    b. Amylopsin
    c. Aminopeptidase
    d. Salivary amylase   d
    e. Alkaline phosphatase

639. Amylase is formed by:
    a. Pancreas   a
    b. Liver
    c. Gallbladder
    d. Thyroid
    e. None of these

640. Acid sodium chloride is employed in Somogyi iodine method for serum amylase in order to:
    a. Delay the reaction

   b. Bring about optimum conditions of pH and electro-
      lyte content   b
   c. Stop the reaction
   d. Develop the color

641. Serum enzyme activity reported in Caraway units:
     a. Lipase
     b. Amylase   b
     c. Phosphatase
     d. Cholinesterase
     e. Transaminase

642. In the amyloclastic or iodimetric method of amylase de-
     termination the amount of starch hydrolyzed is deter-
     mined using _____ as an indicator.   iodine

643. The greater the amylase activity of serum the (lesser,   lesser
     greater) the intensity of the final color of the reaction
     between the starch and the iodine.

644. The greatest source of error in amylase determinations is
     from contamination with _____ amylase, therefore   salivary
     pipets should never be blown out in any step of these de-
     terminations.

645. A blood amylase determination is an emergency procedure.
     T   F   T

646. An enzyme which converts emulsified fats to fatty acids
     and glycerol is:
     a. Amylase
     b. Aminopeptidase
     c. Lipase   c
     d. Dipeptidase
     e. Phosphatase

647. Lipase is a digestive enzyme which is exclusively produced
     by the pancreas.   T   F   F

648. Lipase will act upon *any* organic ester.   T   F   T

649. The Cherry and Crandall method of serum lipase determi-
     nation is based upon the amount of fatty acid liberated by
     this enzyme from a substrate of:
     a. Olive oil (triolein)   a
     b. Acetylcholine
     c. Starch
     d. Organic phosphate
     e. Pyruvic acid

650. In making up the substrate for lipase, acacia is added to
     olive oil to keep it emulsified and sodium benzoate acts as
     a _____.   preservative

651. Product measured in lipase activity determinations:
     a. Fatty acid   a
     b. Glucose

c. Phenol
d. Phosphorus
e. ΔDPNH

652. In acute pancreatitis lipase values remain elevated longer than amylase values.   T   F

T

ELECTROLYTES & BLOOD GASSES
Sodium, Potassium, Chloride

653. Sodium is present in the serum and extra-cellular fluid mainly.   T   F

T

654. Potassium is present in the serum but not in the red cells.   T   F

F

655. Explain why presence of hemolysis in a serum will result in inaccurate potassium determination.

See p. 199

656. There is considerably more potassium in gastric juice than in blood serum.   T   F

T

657. Sodium and potassium can only be tested for by means of a flame photometer.   T   F

F

658. The reference element used in the analysis of sodium and potassium by flame photometery is _____.

lithium

659. The potassium standard in the flame photometer contains sodium primarily because:
    a. It saves time to run sodium and potassium together
    b. Sodium enhancement of potassium must be compensated
    c. Higher dilution can be made of the patient's serum
    d. It helps make the standard more physiological

a

660. The most likely source of sodium contamination encountered in using an internal standard for the flame photometer is:
    a. Diluent in glass bottles
    b. Poor grade distilled water
    c. Poor grade lithium reagent
    d. Sample cup washed in detergent
    e. Impure propane

d

661. The cobaltinitrite method is still used for the colorimetric determination of _____ and uranyl zinc acetate method for the determination of _____.

potassium; sodium

662. Both flame and chemical determinations of Na^+ and K^+ are being replaced by ion specific electrodes.   T   F

T

663. What is the normal range of sodium and potassium levels in the serum?

See p. 133

664. Serum sodium and serum potassium levels are determined
mainly by _____ .

flame pho-
tometry

665. In the method of Schales and Schales for blood chloride
determinations, the plasma, serum, or filtrate is titrated
with standard _____ in the acid solution, using _____ as an indicator.

mercuric
nitrate;
diphenyl-
carbazone

666. In the method of Schales and Schales for blood chloride
determinations the end-point is indicated by the following
color:
    a. Light pink
    b. Pale yellow
    c. Light green
    d. Pale violet
    e. Red

d

667. In Whitehorn method for blood chloride determination
the chloride is precipitated as _____ by nitric
acid and a measured excess of standard _____
solution.

silver
chloride;
silver
nitrate

668. In Whitehorn method for blood chloride determination
the following indicator is used to estimate the end-point:
    a. Phenolphthalein
    b. Ferric ammonium sulfate (ferric alum)
    c. Methyl red
    d. PSP (phenol red)
    e. Diphenylcarbazone

b

669. The chloridometer determines serum chloride:
    a. Colorimetrically
    b. Potentiometrically
    c. Fluorometrically
    d. Calorimetrically
    e. Nephelometrically

b

670. The magnesium methods most widely used at this time
are those based on the formation of a colored complex
with the dye _____ in alkaline solution.

titan
yellow

671. Methods for determining magnesium in serum include:
    a. Titan yellow
    b. 8-hydroxyquinoline
    c. Atomic absorption spectroscopy

a
b
c

672. Low serum magnesium concentrations can result in:
    a. Coma
    b. Tetany
    c. Gout

b

673. Indicate where each of these electrolytes is found:

a. Calcium	1. Serum only	a—1
b. Sodium	2. Red cells only	b—1
c. Phosphorus	3. Both serum & cells	c—3
d. Chloride		d—3
e. Potassium		e—3
f. Magnesium		f—3

Serum Calcium, Magnesium, Phosphorus

674. The most accurate method of determining calcium is:
    a. Emission spectroscopy
    b. U.V. absorption
    c. Fluorometry
    d. Infrared spectroscopy
    e. Atomic absorption spectroscopy   e
    f. Autoanalyzer

675. In recent calcium methods using titration with chelating agents difficulty is often encountered with the following:
    a. Large amount of serum needed
    b. Need to use acid-washed glassware
    c. End-point   c

676. In Kramer-Tisdall method modified by Clark and Collip the calcium of the serum is precipitated by:
    a. Potassium oxalate
    b. Trichloroacetic acid
    c. Ferric chloride
    d. Ammonium oxalate   d
    e. Mercury bichloride

677. Oxalated or sequestrenated plasma cannot be used for a calcium test.   T   F   T

678. Explain briefly why serum which is to be used in a calcium test should be separated from the clot within 30 minutes after specimen collection.   See p. 133

679. Serum to be used for calcium determination may be kept overnight in a refrigerator.   T   F   T

680. The range of normal values for serum calcium in growing children is:
    a. Slightly higher than adult values   a
    b. Slightly lower than adult values
    c. The same as for adults

681. Calcium values are low in the following condition(s):
    a. Hypoparathyroidism   a
    b. Multiple myeloma
    c. Polycythemia vera
    d. Tetany   d
    e. Bright's disease

682. Calcium and phosphate metabolism is regulated by:
     a. Thyroid gland
     b. Parathyroid glands   b
     c. Islets of Langerhans
     d. Adrenal glands
     e. The liver

683. The normal range of total serum calcium is:
     a. 1—2 mg.%
     b. 4—8 mg.%
     c. 9.0–11.5 mg.%   c
     d. 5-15 mg.%
     e. 60–90 mg.%

684. In tetany due to decreased calcium the symptoms are
     caused by:
     a. A decrease in ionized calcium only   a
     b. A decrease in ionized and bound calcium both

685. A low total serum calcium may not result in tetany if the
     total serum protein is low.   T   F   T

686. A reciprocal relationship exists between blood calcium
     level and blood _____ level.   phosphorus

687. In the blood, inorganic phosphorus is present as:
     a. Acid phosphatase
     b. Orthophosphate   b
     c. Alkaline phosphatase
     d. Phospholipid

688. Phosphorus is usually estimated as:
     a. Alkaline phosphatase
     b. Phospholipid
     c. Organic phosphate
     d. Inorganic phosphate   d
     e. Acid phosphatase

689. The normal adult range (as inorganic phosphate) of
     phosphorus is:
     a.   0–2.0 mg.%
     b.   1.5–2.5 mg.%
     c.   3.0–4.5 mg.%   c
     d.   5.0–8.0 mg.%
     e.   12.0–15.0 mg.%

690. The method of determining phosphorus whereby a molyb-
     date solution is added to serum to form phosphomolyb-
     date and the latter is reduced by 1, 1, 4, aminonaphthol
     sulfonic acid is known as the _____ & _____ re-   Fiske &
     action.   Subbarow

691. Briefly explain why serum for a phosphorus test should
     be separated from the clot immediately after specimen
     collection.   See p. 133

692. If the BUN is increased it is quite probable that the phosphorus level will be:
     a. Increased
     b. Decreased
     c. Unaffected

a

Acid-Base Balance

693. Chiefly carbon dioxide exists in the blood as:
     a. Cholinesterase
     b. Dissolved CO_2
     c. HCO_3^-
     d. CO_2 hemoglobin combination

c

694. The carbon dioxide content method essentially measures
     _____.

HCO_3^-

695. The carbon dioxide method measures the total concentration of CO_2, physically dissolved in the blood, and the bicarbonate concentration.   T   F

T

696. Measurement of pCO_2 (partial pressure of CO_2) is replacing other CO_2 methods in biological fluids because of development of _____.

CO_2 specific electrode

697. To convert volume% CO_2 to mEq./L., one multiplies the former by the following factor:
     a. 10
     b.   4.5
     c.   0.45
     d. 45
     e.   0.1

c

698. Sixty-two volumes% of CO_2 represent:
     a. 16.2 mM./L. CO_2
     b. 23.5 mM./L. CO_2
     c. 27.6 mM./L. CO_2
     d. 31.0 mM./L. CO_2

c

699. Thirty mM./L. of CO_2 represent:
     a. 15.2 vols.% CO_2
     b. 53.4 vols.% CO_2
     c. 60.4 vols.% CO_2
     d. 67.2 vols.% CO_2

d

700. In the CO_2 combining power of plasma determination using Van Slyke and Cullen method, the CO_2 is liberated from the plasma by the production of a partial vacuum.
     T   F

T

701. Normal range of CO_2 combining power values in adults is:
     a. 24–32 mEq./L.
     b. 53–70 vol.%

a
b

    c.   0.2–0.6 Gm.%
    d.   4–8 units

702. Normal range of CO_2 combining power values in children is:
    a. 40–55 vols.%   a
    b. 53–70 vols.%
    c. 24–32 mEq./L.
    d. 18–25 mEq./L.   d

703. Serum (or plasma) CO_2 combining power values are low or high in the same clinical conditions in which serum (or plasma) bicarbonate values are low or high.   T   F   T

704. The carbonic acid to bicarbonate ratio necessary to maintain a normal (7.4) blood pH is:
    a. 2:10
    b. 1:20   b
    c. 1:12
    d. 2:5
    e. 1:10

705. Metabolic acidosis and alkalosis are less frequently encountered than respiratory acidosis or alkalosis.   T   F   F

706. A blood plasma pH lower than 6.8 or higher than 7.8 is not compatible with life.   T   F   T

707. The blood pH is always low in metabolic acidosis.   T   F   F

708. In metabolic acidosis, pCO_2 of plasma is:
    a. Increased
    b. Decreased   b
    c. Normal

709. In metabolic alkalosis, CO_2 combining power of plasma is:
    a. Increased   a
    b. Decreased
    c. Normal

710. Contact between whole blood and air has the effect of (lowering, elevating) the serum CO_2, and (lowering, elevating) the serum chloride concentration.   lowering; elevating

711. The degree of oxygen _____ is calculated by comparing the oxygen content with the oxygen capacity of whole blood.   saturation

712. In manometric determination of the oxygen content of the blood, _____ liberates oxygen from the lysed cells.   Kferricyanide

713. Oxygen saturation of arterial blood is _____ and that of venous blood is _____.   95–97% 60–85%

714. The Van Slyke manometric apparatus for CO_2 and O_2 content are being replaced by blood gas analyzers which measure PO_2, PCO_2 and pH directly by means of specific electrodes.   T   F   T

715. The concentration of carbonic acid in the blood is controlled by respiratory mechanisms.   T   F   T

716. The liver is the organ chiefly responsible for the regulation of bicarbonate in the blood.   T   F   F

717. Sodium is conserved by the excretion of _____ in the H^+ ion
renal tubules.

718. The major buffer system in the body used for lab evaluations of acid-base balance is:
    a. Bicarbonate/carbonic acid   a
    b. Disodium PO_4/monosodium PO_4
    c. Plasma protein

719. State normal values for the following:
    a. pH   7.38–7.42
    b. PO_2 35–45 mm.Hg.
    c. PCO_2 80–105 mm.
                                                                        Hg.

720. Evaluation of acid-base status of patient requires measurement of pH and PCO_2.   T   F   T

721. In plasma, the relationship between pH and the bicarbonate/carbonic acid buffer system is expressed by the Henderson-Hasselbach equation. Write out this equation.   See p. 133

722. Metabolic disturbances causing acidosis or alkalosis affect the HCO_3^- while respiratory disturbances causing acidosis or alkalosis affect the H_2CO_3.   T   F   T

723. Most conditions in which acid-base imbalance occur belong to metabolic categories.   T   F   T

724. In compensated acidosis and alkalosis the pH of the blood may be normal, but the absolute amounts of bicarbonate and carbonic acid are out of the normal range.   T   F   T

725. Membranes impermeable to CO_2 and O_2 are essential components of blood gas analyzers   T   F   F

726. In blood gas analyzers analyzed gases of known O_2 and CO_2 concentrations are used as calibration standards for the PCO_2 and PO_2 assembly.   T   F   T

727. If, when using a blood gas analyzer to measure pH of the blood, the meter needle suddenly pegged left and wouldn't respond, the likely cause would be:
    a. Fluctuating line current
    b. Coaxial cable with break in line   b
    c. Glass electrode coated with protein
    d. KCl too weak

OTHER BODY FLUIDS OF INTEREST TO CHEMISTRY
Chemical Examination of Amniotic Fluid

728. First study of importance on amniotic fluid was in regard to fetal condition in suspected _____.

Erythroblastosis fetalis (1952 Berris)

729. How early can increased hemolysis due to interaction of maternal antibody and fetal red cell antigens be detected?

About 16 weeks gestation

730. How is amniotic fluid examined for breakdown products of hemolysis?

See p. 133

731. Give three wavelengths of special importance in amniotic fluid examination for hemolytic disease.

365 nm.
450 nm.
550 nm.

732. Amniotic fluid is stable to light and need not be protected by foil wrapping the collection tubes.   T   F

F

733. How can blood in amniotic fluid be identified as maternal or fetal?

See p. 133

734. Why is it important to identify source of blood in amniotic fluid?

See p. 133

735. Describe a second substance which may obscure an amniotic fluid tracing in hemolytic disease.

See p. 133

736. What is the commonest non-amniotic fluid obtained at tap?

Maternal urine

737. How can urine be identified?

See p. 133

738. Estriol levels on amniotic fluid can show decrease associated with feto-maternal depression.   T   F

T

739. Give the creatinine values in amniotic fluid related to mature fetus.

2.0 mg./dl correlates with 37 weeks gestation

740. Name phospholipids related to fetal lung maturity which can be assayed in amniotic fluid.

lecithin and sphingomyelin

741. Describe briefly the changes in concentration which occur as the lungs mature.

See p. 134

Chemical Examination of Pleural, Peritoneal and Pericardial Fluids

742. Pleural, peritoneal and pericardial fluids are all plasma ultrafiltrates. T F	T
743. The normal function of these fluids is lubrication of surfaces. T F	T
744. How can one distinguish a traumatic tap for cerebrospinal, pleural, peritoneal or pericardial fluid from a true hemorrhagic fluid?	See p. 134
745. How may true hemothorax be identified?	See p. 134
746. Pleural effusions are often classified as "exudates" or "transudates." How are these different?	See p. 134
747. Is fibrinogen a normal part of pleural fluid?	See p. 134
748. Normally pleural fluid glucose approximates that of whole blood. T F	T
749. Name the two chemical tests most useful in examining pericardial fluid.	See p. 134
750. If the pH of peritoneal fluid is low, perforated peptic ulcer is suspected. T F	T
751. Elevated amylase in peritoneal fluid is suggestive of pancreatitis. T F	T
752. Problems in collection of peritoneal fluid make it necessary to differentiate fluid from urine. How may this be done?	See p. 134

Chemical Examination of Synovial Fluid

753. Give two means of production of synovial fluid.	See p. 134
754. Do changes in blood constituent levels affect synovial fluid very rapidly?	See p. 134
755. How much synovial fluid does one normally have?	About one ml. in each large joint
756. Name at least two reasons for aspirating synovial fluid.	See p. 134
757. Describe normal synovial fluid.	See p; 134
758. Give two practical methods for evaluating synovial fluids' viscosity.	See p. 134
759. Why are we interested in synovial fluid viscosity?	See p. 134
760. Name two crystals we are interested in identifying in synovial fluid.	See p. 134
761. What is the preferred method of examination of synovial fluid?	polarized light

762. How do the crystals differ? See p. 134

763. Give normal protein content in synovial fluid. About 2 gm./dl.

764. Is fibrinogen a normal constituent of synovial fluid? Explain briefly. See p. 134

765. What is a normal synovial fluid glucose? See p. 134

766. What one enzyme study seems to be of use in joint disease? See p. 134

Feces

767. Bile is secreted by:
    a. Liver a
    b. Gallbladder
    c. Pancreas
    d. Small intestine

768. Bile emulsifies fats in small intestine.   T   F T

769. The two pigments found in human bile are:
    a. Bilirubin and urobilin
    b. Bilirubin and biliverdin b
    c. Biliverdin and dihydrobilirubin
    d. Bilirubin and urobilinogen
    e. Melanin and carotene

770. Unchanged bile pigment is never present in the feces of normal adults.   T   F   Why? T — Action of bacterial flora

771. Urine should not be present in collection of stool for chemical or bacteriological examination.   T   F T

772. Timed stool collections for chemistry, because of varying bowel habits, should be collected for at least 72 hours. Calculations should then be based on _____ specimen dividied by _____ of days of the collection. entire number

773. To improve quantitation of stool collections, stool markers, such as chromium sesquioxide (Cr_2O_3) can be used.   T   F T

774. Stool markers are given in divided doses over the time of the collection. Determination of one day's dosage in the carrier feces gives amount of _____ corresponding to ____ day's output. stool one

775. Because of aesthetic considerations, visual inspection of feces is often avoided. Give at least three problems which could be clarified by careful stool examination. See p. 134

776. Normal fecal odor comes from two organic molecules produced by bacteria from tryptophan. They are: indole skatole

777. Presence of recognizable mucus in stool is abnormal and should be reported.   T   F

T

778. Blood present in feces originating in the upper gastro-intestinal tract imparts a dark red to black color and a tarry consistency to stool.   T   F

T

779. Stool which appears grossly bloody must still be verified by occult blood procedure.   T   F   Why?

T
See p. 135

780. Commonly applied tests for blood in feces include:
    a. Guaiac
    b. Benzidine
    c. Ortho-tolidine
    d. Ortho-toluidine
    e. Ortho-dianisidine

a
b
c

e

781. Commonly applied tests for blood in feces depend on peroxidase activity as evidence of hemoglobin content.
    T   F

T

782. Hemoglobin and myoglobin can function as peroxidases.
    T   F

T

783. The color reaction given by blood to benzidine is:
    a. Light to dark brown
    b. Purple to red
    c. Canary yellow
    d. Green to blue
    e. Black

d

784. Which of the following reagents is not used in benzidine test for occult blood:
    a. Glacial acetic acid
    b. Benzidine base
    c. Methyl alcohol
    d. Hydrogen peroxide

c

785. Which of the following bile products is colorless:
    a. Urobilin
    b. Urobilinogen
    c. Bilirubin

b

786. Normal feces do not contain any urobilinogen.   T   F

F

787. In obstructive jaundice the following is totally or partially absent from the feces (causing clay-colored specimens):
    a. Bilirubin
    b. Biliverdin
    c. Urobilinogen
    d. Carotene

c

788. Normal feces contain urobilin.   T   F

T

789. Which of the following is a test for urobilin:
    a. Ehrlich's aldehyde test
    b. Schlesinger's test

b

    c. Smith's test
    d. Fouchet's test
    e. Schmidt's test

790. In conditions with increased red blood cell destruction the amount of both urobilinogen and urobilin in feces is increased.   T   F   T

791. Bilirubin (unchanged chief bile pigment) is absent from normal feces.   T   F   T

792. Practically every stool specimen contains a small number of red blood cells on microscopic examination.   T   F   T

793. A microscopic amount of "blood" in the feces has little significance unless a meat-free diet has been observed for at least four days preceding the stool examination.   T   F   T

794. The pH range of normal feces is reasonably constant and remains close to that of the blood.   T   F   T

795. Of the weight of normal dried feces, bacteria constitute about:
    a. 1/2
    b. 1/3   b
    c. 1/5
    d. 1/10

796. In cases of malabsorption or pancreatic dystrophy a large amount of _____ can be found in the feces.   fat

797. Define steatorrhea.   See p. 135

798. Describe appearance of stools in steatorrhea.   See p. 135

799. Define malabsorption syndrome.   See p. 135

800. Is steatorrhea often a feature of malabsorption stools?   See p. 135

801. Patients with steatorrhea complicated malabsorption syndrome often are deficient in fat soluble vitamins.   T   F   T

802. The absence of trypsin from the feces of an infant suggests:
    a. Pancreatic disease   a
    b. Kidney disease
    c. Liver disease
    d. Phenylpyruvic oligophrenia
    e. Multiple sclerosis

803. Tests for reducing substances are carried out on stool to uncover what sugar intolerance?   sucrose

804. Since sucrose is not a reducing sugar, why would the presence of large amounts of reducing sugars suggest sucrose intolerance?   See p. 135

Gastric Juice

805. The presence of rennin in the gastric contents is normal.
     T   F   T

806. How is pepsin secreted?   See p. 135

807. Give four indications for performing gastric analysis.   See p. 135

808. Name the most commonly used clinical index of gastric
     secretory function.   See p. 135

809. Gastric acidity is usually low or absent in the following
     condition(s):
     a. Infectious hepatitis
     b. Gastric carcinoma   b
     c. Duodenal ulcer
     d. Pernicious anemia   d
     e. Diabetes

810. The greatest flow of juice of highest acidity of which the
     stomach is capable is obtained after administration of the
     following test meal:
     a. Ewald
     b. Boas
     c. Augmented histamine   c
     d. Alcohol

811. An abnormal constituent of gastric juice is:
     a. Hydrochloric acid
     b. Rennin
     c. Lactic acid   c
     d. Pepsin

812. The presence of a large amount of lactic acid in the gastric
     contents is always abnormal.   T   F   T

813. The presence of lactic acid in gastric contents often indi-
     cates:
     a. Gastric ulcer
     b. Duodenal ulcer
     c. Acute or chronic gastritis   c
     d. Gastric carcinoma   d
     e. Pernicious anemia

814. The presence of Boas-Oppler bacilli or sarcinae in gastric
     contents always indicates organic disease.   T   F   F

815. Presence of large numbers of Boas-Oppler bacilli and sar-
     cinae in the stomach contents is suggestive of:
     a. Duodenal ulcer
     b. Pernicious anemia
     c. Gastric carcinoma   c
     d. Gastric ulcer
     e. Typhoid fever

816. What is the classic nomenclature of gastric secretion? | See p. 135

817. These parameters were thought to depend on _____ _____ for their comparative amounts. | pH of the secretion

818. The number of ml.'s of 0.1N NaOH needed to neutralize 100 ml. of gastric juice is called _____. | degrees of acidity

819. Degrees of gastric acidity are the same as clinical units/ 100 ml. or mEq./liter.   T   F | T

820. Töpfer's reagent is:
    a. A solution of ferric chloride in distilled water
    b. A solution of dimethylaminoazobenzene in 95% alcohol | b
    c. A solution of phenolphthalein in 95% alcohol
    d. A saturated aqueous solution of ammonium sulfate
    e. A solution of phenolphthalein in absolute alcohol

821. Töpfer's reagent is used to determine (free, combined) gastric acidity whereas phenolphthalein is used to determine (free, combined) acidity. | free / combined

822. Töpfer's reagent reacts with free hydrochloric acid to produce the following color:
    a. Bright red | a
    b. Deep blue
    c. Pale blue
    d. Purple
    e. Canary yellow

823. Töpfer's end point with 0.1N NaOH is _____ for titration of free acid. Phenolphthalein end point with 0.1N NaOH is _____ for "total acid." | pH 2.8–3.5 / 8.2–10

824. New terminology for gastric secretion expressed in three measurements. | See p. 135

825. How can acid output be measure in the new way? Total acid output? | See p. 135

826. Define Anacidity the new way. | See p. 135

827. Achlorhydria and anacidity are synonyms.   T   F | T

828. A tubeless test which determines free HCl in gastric juice is the:
    a. Töpfer's
    b. Diagnex | b
    c. Levine
    d. Ewald
    e. Boas

829. Explain the principle of the Diagnex test. | See p. 135

Chemistry of Cerebro-Spinal Fluid

830. Normal spinal fluid is water clear and colorless in appearance. T   F

T

831. Normal spinal fluid may be yellow-tinged occasionally.
T   F

F

832. Xanthochromia in cerebrospinal fluid may be due to oxyhemoglobin, methemoglobin or bilirubin.   T   F

T

833. Give three conditions in which clotting may occur in cerebrospinal fluid.

See p. 135

834. Normal protein levels in cerebrospinal fluid are age dependent.   T   F

T

835. Give normal values for cerebrospinal protein for:
    a. Newborn
    b. 6–30 days
    c. 1–6 months
    d. Above 6 months
    (Method of analysis Meulemans [1960] sodium sulfate-SSA [sulfosalicylic acid] turbidometric method.)

30–200 mg./dl.
30–150 mg./dl.
30–100 mg./dl.
20–40 mg./dl.

836. Semiquantitative protein tests such as Pandy's, Zinc Sulfate, Levinson, Ross-Jones and Nonne-Aplet tests are obsolete and should be replaced by accurate total protein measurements.   T   F

T

837. Clarify further the problems encountered in spinal fluid protein testing.

See p. 135

838. Give at least two methods of testing for cerebrospinal fluid protein which are acceptable.

See p. 135

839. Name two methods of electrophoresis commonly in use for separating cerebrospinal proteins.

Cellulose acetate & Agar gel

840. Electrophoretic separation of cerebrospinal proteins is especially useful in diagnosis of multiple sclerosis.   T   F

T

841. In 50% multiple sclerosis cases the _____ globulin of the cerebral spinal fluid is increased (as determined by electrophoresis).

gamma

842. Electrophoresis is replacing other tests on cerebrospinal fluid for specific proteins such as γ-globulins.   T   F

T

843. Lange's colloidal gold test (1912) is an empirical method for evaluating cerebrospinal protein fractions. It should now be replaced by electrophoresis.   T   F

T

844. Normal glucose in CSF is approximately _____ that of blood.

2/3

845. The normal range of spinal fluid glucose (o. toluidine or hexokinase procedures) is:
    a. 20–40 mg.%
    b. 30–60 mg.%
    c. 60–80 mg.%   c
    d. 90–120 mg.%

846. Relationship of blood glucose to cerebrospinal glucose makes it wise to determine blood level when a spinal tap is to be evaluated.   T   F   T

847. In most cases of meningitis, the CSF glucose is (increased, decreased) and the CSF protein content is (increased, decreased).   decreased; increased

848. Is a reduced (under 40 mg./dl.) cerebrospinal glucose always an indication of bacterial infection?   See p. 135

849. Lymphocytes usually outnumber the segmented cells in spinal fluid in the following type of meningitis:
    a. Pneumococcal
    b. Influenzal
    c. Pyogenic
    d. Tuberculous   d
    e. Epidemic
    f. Viral   f

850. Segmented neutrophil leukocytes in spinal fluid usually outnumber the lymphocytes in the following condition:
    a. Tuberculous meningitis
    b. Pyogenic meningitis   b
    c. Epidemic meningitis
    d. Anterior poliomyelitis
    e. Latent syphilis

851. After specimen collection a spinal fluid cell count must be carried out:
    a. Within 10 minutes
    b. Within 30 minutes   b
    c. Within 1 hour
    d. Within 2 hours

852. The chloride content of spinal fluid in various diseases usually reflects the chloride content of the blood.   T   F   T

853. In advanced tuberculous meningitis one would expect the chloride content of spinal fluid to be:
    a. High
    b. Low   b
    c. Normal

854. The normal range of spinal fluid chloride (NaCl) is:
    a. 100–150 mg.%
    b. 150–250 mg.%
    c. 350–500 mg.%
    d. 700–750 mg.%   d
    e. 20–40 mg.%

855. The demonstration of elevations of glutamine in cerebro-spinal fluid strongly suggests serious liver disease.   T   F

T *LDH, GOT, CPK*

856. Name three enzymes found in cerebrospinal fluid.

See p. 135

857. Name one enzyme (isoenzyme) which may increase in bacterial meningitis. Name one which may increase in viral meningitis.

See p. 135

858. Does pCO_2 of cerebrospinal fluid affect respiration? Explain briefly.

See p. 135

859. How does CO_2 enter cerebrospinal fluid?

See p. 135

860. On what relationship does cerebrospinal pH depend?

See p. 135

861. CO_2 diffuses rapidly into cerebrospinal fluid, but what about bicarbonate?

diffuses much more slowly

862. What is patient response when cerebrospinal pH falls below 7.25?

See p. 136

HORMONE METABOLISM
Hormones

863. The hormone which is characteristically present in the blood of pregnant women and which, when its concentration in the blood reaches a certain level, also appears in the urine is:
   a. 17-ketosteroids
   b. Chorionic gonadotropin
   c. Catecholamine
   d. Aldosterone
   e. Epinephrine

b

864. Chorionic gonadotropin, the anterior pituitary-like (A.P.L.) hormone elaborated by the normal placenta, may be detected (either in serum or urine):
   a. As early as 2 days after conception
   b. As early as 5 days after conception
   c. As early as 12 days after conception
   d. As early as 3 weeks after conception
   e. As early as 3 months after conception

b

865. Which of the following fruits should be excluded from the diet, for at least two days, before collecting a urine specimen for a serotonin (5-HIAA) test:
   a. Apples
   b. Bananas
   c. Grapes
   d. Oranges
   e. Avocados

b

866. Increased serotonin is responsible for the following syndrome:
    a. Antidiuretic
    b. Acromegalic
    c. Carcinoid

c

867. A marked decrease in 5-HIAA excretion occurs in patients with argentaffinoma (malignant carcinoid of small intestine with metastasis to liver).   T   F

F

868. 5-hydroxyindolacetic acid (5-HIAA) is a metabolite of serotonin.   T   F

T

869. The color reagent used in the detection of serotonin and 5-HIAA is _____.

alpha-nitroso-β-naphthol

870. 5-hydroxytryptamine is the chemical name for _____.

serotonin

871. Serotonin causes vasoconstriction and is normally released by the _____.

platelets

872. Serotonin is rapidly oxidized to 5-HIAA as it passes through the:
    a. Liver
    b. Kidney
    c. Lung
    d. Small intestine
    e. Large intestine

c

873. Norepinephrine and epinephrine are secreted by:
    a. Thyroid
    b. Adrenals
    c. Pancreas
    d. Ovaries
    e. Spleen

b

874. Epinephrine is secreted by the cortex of the adrenal gland.   T   F

F

875. Arterenol and noradrenaline are commercial names for _____.

norepi-nephrine

876. A commercial name for epinephrine is:
    a. Insulin
    b. Secretin
    c. Orinase
    d. Adrenalin
    e. Noradrenalin

d

877. A high (3 to 100 times the normal) serum catecholamine level would be expected in:
    a. Porphyria
    b. Phenylpyruvic oligophrenia
    c. Pheochromocytoma
    d. Argentaffinoma
    e. Pernicious anemia

c

878. Catecholamine determinations are specific for pheochromocytoma.   T   F

   F

879. Alpha-methyl dopa (Aldomet) interferes with _____ _____ determinations.

   catecholamine

880. Adrenalin and noradrenalin act physiologically in (increasing, decreasing) blood pressure.

   increasing

881. In the majority of cases of pheochromocytoma the only symptom is persistent:
    a. Hypotension
    b. Hypertension
    c. Abdominal pain
    d. Flushing of face
    e. Fever

   b

882. The chief urinary metabolite of norepinephrine and epinephrine is:
    a. Metanephrine
    b. Uronephrine
    c. 17-ketosteroid
    d. Vanillylmandelic acid
    e. 5-HIAA

   d

883. Alpha-methyl dopa (Aldomet) will give a flame-positive catecholamine result but will not affect the VMA determination.   T   F

   T

884. The chief urinary metabolites of adrenocortical hormones are _____ and _____.

   17-ketosteroids;
   17-OH corticosteroids

885. Androgens are precursors of urinary steroid metabolites which have in common a ketone group in position ___.

   17

886. Metadinitrobenzene (MDB) reacts with ketosteroids in an alkaline solution to form a reddish-purple compound; this is known as the:
    a. Jaffé reaction
    b. Van den Bergh reaction
    c. Biuret reaction
    d. Liebermann-Burchard reaction
    e. Zimmerman reaction

   e

887. In women, virtually all 17-KS come from the _____; in men, 2/3 come from the _____ and the remainder from the ___.

   adrenal cortex;
   adrenal cortex;
   testes

888. The chief hormone excreted into the blood by the adrenal cortex is:
    a. Antidiuretic hormone

    b. Cortisol   b

    c. Androsterone

    d. Testosterone

    e. Estrogenic hormone

889. Cortisol and related corticosteroids are referred to as
_____ corticosteroids.   17-hydroxy

890. Cortisol is also known as:

    a. Compound F   a

    b. Hydrocortisone

    c. Corticosterone

    d. Pregnanediol

891. 17-ketosteroids, known as "urinary androgens," may be
increased only in certain gonadal tumors.   T   F   F

892. Cushing's syndrome and Addison's disease are diseases of
the:

    a. Liver

    b. Pancreas

    c. Adrenal cortex   c

    d. Ovaries

    e. Blood forming centers

893. The determination of the level of 17-hydroxycorticoster-
oids and 17-ketogenic steroids as a sensitive index of
_____ function.   adreno-
                                              cortical

894. The adrenocortical hormone responsible for water and
electrolyte balance is _____.   aldo-
                                              sterone

895. Aldosterone and desoxycorticosterone ("DOCA") are:

    a. Glycocorticoids

    b. Mineralocorticoids   b

    c. Androgenic corticoids

    d. Estrogenic corticoids

    e. None of the above

896. Structurally, steroids elaborated by the ovaries, testes, and
adrenal cortex possess in common a _____
_____ nucleus.   cyclopen-
                                                tano-perhy-
                                                drophenan-
                                              threne

897. The normal range of serum protein-bound iodine (PBI) is:

    a.   4–8 micrograms%   a

    b. 0.2–0.4 mg.%

    c. 0.1–0.4 mg.%

    d.   0–1$^+$ in 48 hours

    e. 15–25 units

898. PBI determinations are a practical and useful method for
the laboratory study of thyroid activity because they

afford a roughly quantitative measure of _____ | circulating
_____. | thyroid
                                                          | hormone

899. In hyperthyroidism the PBI:
     a. Is high | a
     b. Is low
     c. Remains unchanged

900. Briefly explain the analytical principle involved in PBI determinations. | See p. 136

901. Four different types of tests of thyroid function are:
     a._____ | serum iodine
                                        | (PBI or BEI,
                                        | T_3, T_4)
     b. _____ | BMR & cholesterol
     c. _____ | radioactive
                                        | iodine uptake
     d. _____ | TSH

902. Thyroxine and T_3 are iodine-containing amino acids and they:
     a. Circulate | a
     b. Do not circulate

903. The thyroid gland produces thyroglobulin, thyroxine, and:
     a. Insulin
     b. Adrenalin
     c. FSH
     d. T_3 | d
     e. Fibrinogen

904. About 1/3 of the iodine absorbed from the intestine into the plasma is trapped by:
     a. Spleen
     b. Liver
     c. Thyroid gland | c
     d. Adrenal glands

905. The average normal range for BMR in adults is:
     a. Plus 20 to minus 20
     b. Plus 10 to minus 10 | b
     c. Plus 19 to minus 32
     d. Plus 32 to minus 18

906. Abnormally high BMR values are found in:
     a. Hyperthyroidism | a
     b. Cretinism
     c. Myxedema
     d. Obesity
     e. Addison's disease

907. All of the following are thyroid-related diseases except:
     a. Rickets   a
     b. Myxedema
     c. Exophthalmic goiter
     d. Cretinism
     e. Addison's disease   e

908. If an unexplained high PBI is found and some type of in-
     organic contamination is suspected, a _____ T_4, com-
     test should be performed.   petitive
                                                             binding

909. The storage form of thyroid hormone is:
     a. Thyroxine
     b. Triiodothyronine
     c. Thyroglobulin   c
     d. Thyroid-albumin complex

910. The thyroid gland is stimulated by the:
     a. Adrenal cortex
     b. Pancreas
     c. Pituitary (TSH)   c
     d. Gonads
     e. Spleen

911. Triiodothyronine uptake by resin is the basis of the fol-
     lowing test for thyroid function:
     a. T_3 test   a
     b. T_4 test
     c. T_3/T_4
     d. BEI

912. A measure of total serum thyroxine iodine bound to pro-
     tein, including triiodothyronine, iodotyrosines, and or-
     ganic contamination is the:
     a. T_3
     b. T_4
     c. T_3/T_4 ratio
     d. PBI   d

913. T_4 test is a measure of thyroxine.   T   F   T

914. Marked abnormalities of T_4—iodine and PBI can be en-
     countered in eumetabolism.   T   F   T

915. Organic iodine containing medications or prior use of ra-
     diographic contrast media affect T_4 column measurements.
     T   F   T

916. The Murphy-Pattee T_4 test is more accurate than the T_4
     by column test.   T   F   T

917. What is the principle involved in the TBG (thyroxine
     binding globulin) test?   See p. 136

918. The following is not a thyroid function test:
     a. BMR

    b. TBG
    c. Murphy-Pattee
    d. LATS
    e. ACTH stimulation   e

919. *Review of clinically important hormones.* Indicate the
hormone(s) which are produced by the following:
    a. Islets of Langerhans (pancreas)   See p. 136
    b. Testis   "
    c. Ovaries   "
    d. Duodenal mucosa   "
    e. Adrenal cortex   "
    f. Adrenal medulla   "
    g. Thyroid   "
    h. Parathyroid   "
    i. Anterior pituitary   "
    j. Posterior pituitary   "

Vitamins

920. Which of the following is often called "antihemorrhagic"
vitamin:
    a. Vitamin A
    b. Vitamin C
    c. Vitamin D
    d. Vitamin K   d
    e. Cyanocobalamin (B_{12})

921. All of the following are nutritional diseases except:
    a. Scurvy
    b. Acromegaly   b
    c. Xerophthalmia
    d. Night blindness
    e. Beriberi

922. The liver stores vitamin A which it forms from:
    a. Carotene   a
    b. Bilirubin
    c. Glycogen
    d. Prothrombin
    e. Vitamin K

923. When vitamin A is treated with antimony trichloride it
develops the following color:
    a. Yellow
    b. Purple
    c. Red
    d. Blue   d
    e. White

924. The vitamin B complex does not include:
    a. Niacin
    b. Thiamin

    c. Gibberellin   c
    d. Rivoflavin
    e. Cyanocobalamin
    f. Folic acid

925. Vitamin C is the same as:
    a. Calciferol
    b. Ascorbic acid   b
    c. Naphthaquinone
    d. Tocopherol
    e. Folic acid

926. Vitamin D is fat-soluble and is present in most food.
    T   F   T

927. The best natural source of vitamin K is:
    a. Eggs
    b. Potatoes
    c. Carrots
    d. Green vegetables   d
    e. Tomatoes

928. The clinical symptoms of scurvy do not develop until af-
    ter all stored vitamin C has been depleted.   T   F   T

929. Rickets and osteomalacia are due to a deficiency of:
    a. Vitamin A
    b. Vitamin B_1
    c. Vitamin C
    d. Vitamin D   d
    e. Vitamin E

930. Match the following:
    a. Vitamin A   1. Prevents rickets   a—6
    b. Vitamin B_1 2. Prevents beriberi   b—2
    c. Vitamin B_2 3. Prevents pellagra   c—7
    d. Niacin   4. Prevents scurvy   d—3
    e. Vitamin B_{12} 5. Prevents pernicious anemia e—5
    f. Vitamin C   6. Prevents night blindness f—4
    g. Vitamin D   7. Prevents sore around mouth g—1
    h. Vitamin K   8. Plays indirect role in   h-8
                             blood clotting

931. A folic acid or vitamin B_{12} deficiency may be associated
    with the following condition:
    a. Polycythemia vera
    b. Hyperlipoproteinemia
    c. Scurvy
    d. Hemochromatosis
    e. Megaloblastic anemia   e

932. Intrinsic factor is necessary for absorption of the following
    vitamin from digestive tract:
    a. Thiamine
    b. Vitamin B_2

    c. Vitamin B_{12} c
    d. Cobalamin   d

933. The test for pernicious anemia in which the patient is given $Co^{60}B_{12}$ by mouth, a large dose of vitamin B_{12} by injection, and the recovery of the radioactive B_{12} is measured in the urine is known as the:
    a. Harrison's test
    b. Schilling test   b
    c. Parkinson's test
    d. Whipple test

934. What vitamin is used to make up coenzymes I and II:
    a. Nicotinic acid   a
    b. Pyridoxine
    c. Vitamin A
    d. Vitamin B_{12}
    e. Calciferol

935. Indicate water-soluble vitamins:
    a. A
    b. Nicotinic acid   b
    c. E
    d. Folic acid   d
    e. K
    f. D_2 and D_3

936. The fat-soluble vitamins are not appreciably excreted in the urine, therefore, with excess intake, toxic levels may accumulate in the body. T   F   T

937. The vitamin B complex and vitamin C are fat-soluble.
    T   F   F

938. Match the following:
    a. Nicotinic acid   1. Cyanocobalamin   a—4
    b. Vitamin B_{12} 2. Ascorbic acid   b—1
    c. Vitamin C   3. Riboflavin   c—2
    d. Vitamin D_2 4. PP factor   d—8
    e. Vitamin B_6 5. Pyroxidine   e—5
    f. Vitamin B_2 6. Pteroglyglutamic acid   f—3
    g. Vitamin B_1 7. Thiamine   g—7
    h. Folic acid   8. Calciferol   h—6

939. Match the following:
    a. Rickets   1. Vitamin A   a—5
    b. Osteomalacia   2. Vitamin B_1 (thiamine)   b—5
    c. Pellagra   3. Nicotinic acid   c—3
    d. Follicular keratosis   4. Vitamin C   d—1
    e. Night blindness   5. Vitamin D   e—1
    f. Scurvy, capillary   6. Vitamin K   f—4
      fragility
    g. Hypoprothrombinemia   g—6
    h. Beriberi   h—2

Iron & Iron Binding Capacity

940. The β_1 globulin to which serum iron is attached is called
_____ or _____ .

sidero-
phyllin;
transferrin

941. Serum-bound iron is important in:
   a. Vitamin synthesis
   b. Hematopoiesis
   c. Protein metabolism
   d. Glycogen storage

b

942. Serum iron is (decreased, increased) in iron-deficiency
anemia while total iron-binding capacity is (decreased, increased) in iron deficiency anemia.

decreased
increased

943. Bathophenanthroline, o-phenanthroline, and TPTZ are
color-producing reagents that react with serum _____ .

iron

944. UIBC stands for _____ .

unsaturated
iron-binding
capacity

945. A reducing agent is used in serum iron determinations to
convert the iron to the _____ state.

ferrous

ABNORMAL HEMOGLOBINS

946. The first truly "molecular" disease was _____
clarified by the work of _____ .

sickle cell
anemia;
Linus
Pauling

947. How many amino acids were substituted in the abnormal
hemoglobin?

only one

948. The structure of β-chains is controlled by ____ gene loci
and a _____ pair of homologous chromosomes.

two
single

949. The structure of α-chains is controlled by _____ gene loci.
These are located ____ each on homologous chromosomes.

four
two

950. α-chain and β-chain abnormalities are transmitted inde-
pendently.   T   F

T

951. What type of hemoglobin predominates in the newborn?
   a. Adult hemoglobin
   b. C hemoglobin
   c. Fetal hemoglobin
   d. S-hemoglobin

c

952. Give the normal concentration of fetal hemoglobin in the
adult.

1%

953. A test involving alkali denaturation of hemoglobin is a
test for:
   a. Oxyhemoglobin
   b. Carbon-monoxide hemoglobin
   c. Sulfhemoglobin
   d. Fetal hemoglobin   d
   e. Sickle cell disease hemoglobin

954. Fetal hemoglobin is (more, less) resistant to alkali dena-   more
turation than hemoglobin A.

955. Approximately how many structural variants of the hemoglobin molecule have so far been described?   250 so far

956. All of the structural variants produce pathology in the
possessor.   T   F   F

957. Abnormal hemoglobins ("S," "C," "E," etc.) result from
the substitution of at least three amino acids in the globulin chain of the hemoglobin molecule.   T   F   F

958. A derivative of hemoglobin in which the Fe^{++} is oxidized
to Fe^{+++} is _____.   methemo-
                                                                    globin

959. Factors affecting the rate of migration of protein fractions
in electrophoresis include:
   a. pH of the buffer
   b. Isoelectric point of the protein fraction in relation
      to the pH of the buffer
   c. Size of the molecule
   d. Charge of the molecule
   e. Voltage
   f. All of the above   f
   g. None of the above

960. The pH of the buffer used for protein electrophoresis is
usually ____. At this pH the various proteins migrate to   8.6
the _____ with _____ traveling the fastest.   anode;
                                                                    albumin

961. Supporting media for electrophoresis include:
   a. Paper   a
   b. Cellulose acetate   b
   c. Agar gel   c
   d. Agarose   d
   e. DEAE
   f. Acrylamide   f

962. Electrophoresis using a supporting medium such as paper,
cellulose acetate, etc., is known as _____ electrophoresis.   zone

963. In electrophoresis, if the pH of the buffer is the same as
a particular protein fraction, this protein fraction will:
   a. Migrate toward the cathode
   b. Not migrate   b

     c. Migrate toward the anode
     d. Become denatured

964. The pH at which the negative and positive charges of the
     protein are equal is known as the _____ point.   isoelectric

965. Bromphenol blue and Ponceau S are:
     a. Reagents for albumin tests
     b. Reagents for indican test
     c. Stains for fat
     d. Stains for nuclei
     e. Protein stains   e

966. When separating serum proteins by cellulose acetate, some
     of the gamma globulin migrates to the:
     a. Anode
     b. Cathode   b

967. A monoclonal peak on an electrophoretic pattern may be
     seen in _____.   multiple
                                                                   myeloma

---

QUESTIONS ON MISCELLANEOUS EXAMINATIONS

968. Which of the following hypodermic needle sizes has bore
     with widest diameter:
     a. 20 g.
     b. 19 g.   b
     c. 22 g.
     d. 21 g.

969. "Sequestrene" is synonymous with "versene."   T   F   T

970. Chloroform is difficult to pipette because its surface ten-
     sion, compared to that of an aqueous solution, is:
     a. Higher
     b. Lower   b
     c. The same

971. Alcohol + acid = _____ + water.   ester

972. The molecular and the ionic forms of a chemical indicator
     have the same color.   T   F   F

973. The weight of a fluid compared with the weight of an iden-
     tical volume of water is the:
     a. Specific gravity   a
     b. Molecular weight
     c. Absolute density
     d. Equivalent weight
     e. Absolute weight

974. The blood contains electrolytes, however the urine does
     not.   T   F   F

975. Under what form is most of the chloride excreted in the
     urine?   NaCl

976. The majority of standard solutions employed in routine
     analysis are prepared from:
        a. Primary standards
        b. Secondary standards   b

977. Mercury is an element.   T   F   T

978. When an acid is dissolved in water it produces:
        a. Hydrogen ions   a
        b. Hydroxyl ions
        c. Neither of these

979. When an alkali is dissolved in water it produces:
        a. Hydroxyl ions   a
        b. Hydrogen ions
        c. Neither of these

980. Explain meaning of term "caustic."   See p. 136

981. Mercury (or its vapors) are:
        a. Quite harmless
        b. Relatively nontoxic
        c. Exceedingly toxic   c

982. What is a catalyst? an enzyme? a coenzyme?   See p. 136

983. What is the meaning of the term "inspissation"?   See p. 136

984. Magnesium sulfate is also known as:
        a. Epsom salt   a
        b. Peptic salt
        c. Carlsbad salt
        d. Seignette's salt
        e. Baker's salt

985. When diluting an acid, water should be poured into acid
     and not acid into water.   T   F   F

986. When very small globules of a liquid are dispersed through
     another liquid in which they are insoluble one has:
        a. A chemical solution
        b. A suspension
        c. An emulsion   c
        d. A precipitate

987. Sodium hydroxide is capable of a higher degree of ioniza-
     tion than barium hydroxide.   T   F   T

988. Boric acid is capable of a higher degree of ionization than
     either sulfuric acid or hydrochloric acid.   T   F   F

989. Ionization is a property of acids and bases but not of salts.
     T   F   F

990. All of the following are carbohydrates except:
        a. Glucose
        b. Pentose

c. Carotene
d. Starch
e. Dextrin

c

991.   Most blood chemistries are run on:
a. Serum
b. Plasma
c. Cell mass
d. Whole blood

a

992.   Briefly explain the difference between "transudate"
and "exudate."

See p. 137

993.   What is "fibrin"?

See p. 137

994.   One of the medical treatments of hypertension consists in the administration of:
a. Bromide
b. Thiocyanate
c. Salicylate
d. Sulfonamides

b

995.   Which of the following tests can be used to distinguish
a transudate from an exudate:
a. Lindemann
b. Rivalta
c. Sulkowitch
d. Gerhardt
e. Töpfer

b

996.   Acute serous or serofibrinous exudates are usually of
bacterial origin.   T   F

F

997.   Charcot-Leyden crystals are frequently seen in the
sputum of:
a. Bronchial asthma
b. Lobar pneumonia
c. Pulmonary tuberculosis
d. Actinomycosis
e. Tonsillar disease

a

998.   State the normal values for the following:
a. Free acidity (fasting) of gastric juice
b. Erythrocyte sedimentation rate (indicate method)
c. Fasting blood glucose (indicate method)
d. Blood plasma chloride (as NaCl)
e. CSF glucose (indicate method)
f. Bleeding time (indicate method)
g. Urine urea
h. Blood NPN
i. Blood cholesterol
j. Red cell diameter
k. Blood serum globulin
l. Blood calcium

See p. 137
"
"
"
"
"
"
"
"
"
"
"

999.   Match the following:

a. Prostatic cancer	1. Elevated amylase & lipase	a—5
b. Metabolic acidosis (or respiratory alkalosis)	2. Elevated uric acid	b—8
c. Myocardial infarction	3. Elevated FBS	c—4
d. Gout	4. Elevated SGOT & SLDH	d—2
e. Jaundice	5. Elevated acid phosphatase	e—6
f. Diabetes mellitus	6. Elevated bilirubin	f—3
g. Ac. pancreatitis	7. Elevated PBI	g—1
h. Hyperthyroidism	8. Low CO_2 combining power	h—7

1000.   Match the following:

a. Cholesterol ester	1. Permutit powder	a—5
b. CO_2 combining power	2. Diagnex blue	b—4
c. BUN	3. Gum ghatti	c—13, 3
d. Amylase	4. Caprylic alcohol	d—7
e. Bilirubin	5. Digitonin	e—6
f. NPN	6. Diazo reagent	f—3
g. Urea N in urine	7. Starch substrate	g—1, 13, 3
h. Robert's reagent	8. Stop watch	h—10
i. Trypsin	9. ACTH	i—11
j. Bence-Jones protein	10. Epsom salt	j—12
k. Prothrombin	11. X-ray film	k—8
l. Thorn test	12. Protein electrophoresis	l—9
m. Na^+ and K^+	13. Urease	m—14
n. Tubeless gastric analysis	14. Flame photometer	n—2, 15
o. PSP test	15. Spectrophotometer	o—15

1001.   Briefly explain:

a. Edema	See p. 137
b. Eclampsia	"
c. Isoagglutinins	"
d. Cirrhosis	"
e. Jaundice	"

1002.   Briefly explain the difference between "density" and "specific gravity." See p. 137

1003.   Which blood chemistries require special caution not to hemolyze the blood? See p. 137

1004.   Briefly explain the difference between "edema" and "dehydration." See p. 137

1005.   Briefly explain the difference between "oxidation" and "reduction." See p. 137

1006.   Briefly explain the difference between "glucosuria" and "glycosuria." See p. 138

1007.   Briefly explain the difference between "nephritis" and "nephrosis." See p. 138

1008.   Briefly explain the difference between "achlorhydria" and "achylia gastrica."   See p. 138

1009.   The presence of creatinine and urea in a body fluid other than serum, indicates that the fluid is _____.   urine

1010.   Briefly explain the difference between "hypochlorhydria" and "hyperchlorhydria."   See p. 138

1011.   Briefly explain the difference between "acid" and "base."   See p. 138

1012.   Briefly explain the difference between "hypoglycemia" and "hyperglycemia."   See p. 138

1013.   Briefly explain the difference between "anion" and "cation."   See p. 138

1014.   What is "ultrafiltration"?   See p. 138

1015.   What is "ultracentrifugation"?   See p. 138

1016.   Briefly explain the difference between "normal solution" and "molar solution."   See p. 138

1017.   Briefly explain the difference between a "solution" and a "suspension."   See p. 138

1018.   Briefly explain the difference between "anabolism" and "catabolism."   See p. 138

1019.   Briefly explain the difference between "clotted blood" and "whole blood."   See p. 138

1020.   Briefly explain the difference between "I.V." and "I.M."   See p. 138

1021.   Briefly explain the difference between "ferrous" and "ferric."   See p. 138

1022.   Briefly explain the difference between "endoenzyme" and "exoenzyme."   See p. 138

1023.   Briefly explain the difference between "obstructive jaundice" and "hemolytic jaundice."   See p. 138

1024.   Katayama's test for carbon monoxide in blood makes use of the following reagent:
        a. Ammonium sulfide   a
        b. Calcium chloride
        c. P-dimethylaminobenzaldehyde
        d. Alkaline copper solution
        e. Formalin

1025.   A dye having a strong affinity for amyloid is:
        a. BSP
        b. Congo red   b
        c. PSP
        d. Rose Bengal
        e. Evans blue

1026.   Bromide is not present in the serum unless it has been administered.   T   F   F (also see p. 139)

1027. A test distinguishing between steatorrhea due to malabsorption and pancreatic steatorrhea (in which absorption is not affected) is the:
    a. Galactose tolerance test
    b. Xylose tolerance test   b
    c. Modified hippuric acid
    d. Oil Red O or Fat Red 7B test for fat

1028. In Fanconi's syndrome there is an aminoaciduria as well as increased glucose and phosphate excretion.
    T   F   T

1029. Wilson's disease is associated with an increased _____ excretion.   copper

1030. Which of the following belong to the metabolic group of diseases:
    a. Gout   a
    b. Infectious mononucleosis
    c. Diabetes mellitus   c
    d. Typhoid fever
    e. Pancreatitis

1031. In Hand-Schuller-Christian's disease, Gaucher's disease, and Tay-Sach's disease, one or more of the various kinds of _____ are deposited in the tissues or organs.   lipids

1032. What do the following standard abbreviations stand for:
    a. ACTH — BEI — PBI — HDF — EDTA — QNS — SGPT — SLDH — BJP — A/G   See p. 139
    b. BMR — AZF — CHO — CSF — SPT — PSP — BSP — FBS — NPN — BUN — 17-KS   ''
    c. GFR — OD — SBF — Cu — Cm — Cs — OR — OPD — C.E.A. — USP   ''
    d. IR — AA — TLC — GLC — RIA   ''

1033. Which of the following is not a stain for fat:
    a. Sudan III
    b. Sudan IV
    c. Scarlet R
    d. Oil Red O
    e. Fat Red 7B
    f. Hematoxylin   f
    g. Osmic acid

1034. For laboratory purposes, ml. and cc. are the same thing.
    T   F   T

1035. What is an isotonic solution? a hypotonic solution? a hypertonic solution?   See p. 139

1036. What is anuria? oliguria? polyuria?   See p. 139

1037. What term means "after a meal"?   postprandial

1038. Briefly explain the difference between "azotemia" and "uremia."   See p. 139

1039.   In a chemical analysis of a certain urinary calculus, addition of dilute HCl did not produce CO_2 bubbles. However, if a pinch of powder is heated to red hot and then treated with HCl, CO_2 bubbles form. This calculus contains the following substance:
     a. Urate
     b. Carbonate
     c. Oxalate
     d. Calcium
     e. Cystine

c

1040.   Wood's light, with which porphyrins are irradiated, is (short-wave, long-wave) ultraviolet light.

long-wave

1041.   Thymine, cystosine, and uracil, constituents of DNA and RNA, are classified as _____.

pyrimidines

1042.   When nitrogen ingested exceeds nitrogen excreted, a person is said to be in _____ nitrogen balance.

positive

1043.   The presence of large quanitities of carotene in the blood, resulting in skin pigmentation resembling jaundice, is known as:
     a. Anemia
     b. Jaundice
     c. Carotenemia
     d. Porphyria
     e. Dermathemia

c

1044.   A test, useful in the diagnosis of fibrocystic disease of the pancreas, is based upon the ability of the enzyme _____ to liquefy the gelatin layer of an X-ray film.

trypsin

1045.   A glucose tolerance test is contraindicated in a patient whose fasting blood glucose level exceeds 120 mg.%
    T   F

T

1046.   The sweat test is used in the diagnosis of:
     a. Cystic fibrosis
     b. Amyloidosis
     c. Pernicious anemia
     d. Sprue
     e. Chronic pancreatitis

a

1047.   An enzyme test, used in forensic medicine as a highly specific test for seminal fluid in cases of suspected rape, is:
     a. Cholinesterase
     b. Lipase
     c. Acid phosphatase
     d. Aminopherase
     e. Alkaline phosphatase

c

CALIFORNIA STATE LAWS

1048.   Which of the following can direct a clinical laboratory:
  a. A bioanalyst   a
  b. A physician and surgeon   b
  c. The holder of Ph.D. degree in a biological science
  d. The holder of a Master's degree in a biological
    science
  e. The holder of an MS or Ph.D. who has passed cer-
    tification tests in his specialty.   e

1049.   A registered trainee working under direct and responsible supervision of a registered technologist may legally
perform clinical laboratory procedures in a licensed
laboratory. T F   T

1050.   Provided he has not failed a previous examination for
such license, a temporary clinical laboratory technologist license may be issued to an individual who meets
state board requirements. T   F   F

1051.   To be accepted as a clinical laboratory technologist
trainee one must be a college graduate (BA, BS, or
higher). T F   F

FINAL MATH REVIEW

1052.   3.5 ml. of 0.1N NaOH were required to neutralize 10
ml. of HCl. The normality of the acid is:
  a. 0.35N
  b. 0.035N   b
  c. 0.5N
  d. 1.0N

1053.   Five ml. of 0.1N HCl were required to neutralize 15 ml.
of a certain base. The normality of the base is:
  a. 3.0N
  b. 0.33N
  c. 0.033N   c
  d. 0.003N

1054.   2.5 ml. of 1N NaOH were required to neutralize 5 ml.
of an acid. The normality of the acid is:
  a. 1.0N
  b. 0.5N   b
  c. 2.0N
  d. 0.1N

1055.   10 ml. of 1N sulfuric acid solution were required to
neutralize 12 ml. of a NaOH solution. The normality
of the NaOH solution is:
  a. 0.12N

          b. 0.08N
          c. 0.83N   c
          d. 0.24N

1056.   Fifteen ml. of 0.5N NaOH solution were required to
        neutralize 10 ml. of an acid solution. The normality of
        the acid solution is:
          a.   0.75N   a
          b.   1.50N
          c. 10.00N
          d. 15.00N

1057.   One gram contains:
          a.   10 mg.
          b.   100 mg.
          c.   500 mg.
          d. 1,000 mg.   d

1058.   One liter is the same as:
          a.   100 ml.
          b.   500 ml.
          c. 1,000 ml.   c
          d. 1,250 ml.

1059.   The lower the pH the greater the acidity.   T   F   T

1060.   The higher the pH the greater the hydrogen-ion con-
        centration.   T   F   F

1061.   The higher the pH the greater the acidity.   T   F   F

1062.   The pH system is a logarithmic system.   T   F   T

1063.   Each pH unit represents a multiple of:
          a. 12
          b. 10   b
          c.   5
          d.   2

1064.   A solution of pH 6.0 has ____ times as many hydrogen-   10
        ions as a solution of pH 7.0.

1065.   A solution of pH 5.0 has _____ times as many hydrogen-   100
        ions as a solution of pH 7.0

1066.   A solution of pH 8.0 has only _____ as many hydro-   1/10
        gen-ions as does neutral water.

1067.   How is 70% alcohol made from 95% alcohol?   See p. 139

1068.   When 0.25 ml. serum is diluted to 49.7 ml. volume the
        resulting dilution is:
          a. 1:99
          b. 1:198   b
          c. 1:250
          d. 1.497

1069.   One gram contains the following number of micrograms:
          a. 100

        b.   1,000
        c.   100,000
        d. 1,000,000   d

1070. 0.025 ml. of a 1:75 serum dilution contains the follow-
       ing volume of serum:
        a. 0.004444 ml.
        b. 0.000333 ml.   b
        c. 0.000166 ml.
        d. 0.000016 ml.

1071. One grain is equal to:
        a. 0.065 gram   a
        b. 0.005 gram
        c. 0.050 gram
        d. 0.016 gram

1072. One cm. is equal to:
        a.   1,000 microns
        b.   10,000 microns   b
        c.   100,000 microns
        d.   1,000,000 microns

1073. One kilogram is the same as:
        a. 1.0 lb.
        b. 1.2 lb.
        c. 2.2 lb.   c
        d. 3.4 lb.

1074. One fluid ounce equals:
        a. 16.22 ml.
        b. 22.26 ml.
        c. 29.57 ml.   c
        d. 32.08 ml.

1075. One large calorie equals:
        a.   10 small calories
        b.   100 small calories
        c.   1,000 small calories   c
        d.   500 small calories

1076. A ppm (part per million) is the same as:
        a. Mg./liter   a
        b. Microgram/ml.   b
        c. 100 microgram %   c

1077. One lambda (λ) is the same as:
        a. 0.001 ml.   a
        b. Microliter   b
        c. Nanoliter
        d. Millimicroliter

1078. A nanometer (nm) is the same as a _____.   millimicron
                                                                    ($m\mu$)

1079. 10^{-6} = _____.   micro
       10^{-9} = _____.   nano

10^{-12} = _____ .   pico

1080.   0°C. is the same as:
        a. 12 degrees Fahrenheit
        b. 25 degrees Fahrenheit
        c. 32 degrees Fahrenheit   c
        d. 50 degrees Fahrenheit

1081.   100°C. is the same as:
        a. 140 degrees Fahrenheit
        b. 176 degrees Fahrenheit
        c. 194 degrees Fahrenheit
        d. 212 degrees Fahrenheit   d

1082.   If 0.05 ml. of serum is diluted to 50 ml., the resulting
        dilution is:
        a. 1:50
        b. 2:50
        c. 1:100
        d. 1:1000   d

1083.   6.2 ml. of N/10 NaOH were required to neutralize 10
        ml. of an acid. The normality of the acid is:
        a. 6.200N
        b. 0.620N
        c. 0.062N   c
        d. 0.166N

1084.   3.8 ml. of NaOH solution were required to neutralize
        10 ml. of N/10 HCl. The normality of the base is:
        a. 0.380N
        b. 0.263N   b
        c. 0.038N
        d. 0.026N

1085.   ˅A 1N solution of NaOH is diluted 5:25, then rediluted
        3:100. What is the final normality? How many grams   0.006N
        of NaOH are present in 100 ml. of final dilution?   0.024 Gm.

1086.   What is the concentration of 250 ml. of physiologic
        saline in terms of percent, molarity, and normality?   .85%
                                                               0.145M
                                                               0.145N

1087.   To make 200 ml. of 70% alcohol from 95% alcohol one
        would need the following volume of 95% alcohol:
        a. 140.0 ml.
        b. 50.0 ml.
        c. 147.5 ml.   c
        d. 170.8 ml.

1088.   How much 0.1N acid is required to neutralize 15 ml. of
        0.3N base?   45 ml.

1089:   In titrating a given base into 10 ml. of 0.02N acid the
        biuret reading, at the end-point, is 9.80 ml. The nor-
        mality of the base is:

a. 0.0204N
b. 0.0980N
c. 0.9800N
d. 0.0240N

a

1090.   A serial dilution is performed using 9.0 ml. of diluent in the first tube and 2.0 ml. in each successive tube. One ml. of serum is added to the first tube, and 1 ml. of this mixture is serially diluted through the remaining tubes. The dilution in *the fifth tube* is:
    a. 1:18
    b. 1:810
    c. 1:180
    d. 1:8

b

1091.   A 5N solution is diluted 1:5, rediluted 2:15, and rediluted once more 3:25. The concentration of the resulting solution is:
    a. 0.02N
    b. 0.016N
    c. 1:50N
    d. 0.82N

b

1092.   The normality of a 0.05M sulfuric acid solution is:
    a. .1N
    b. .5N
    c. .005N
    d. .01N
    e. .025N

a

1093.   The molarity of a 5% NaCl solution is:
    a. 8.550M
    b. 85.500M
    c. 5.000M
    d. 0.855M

d

1094.   A liter of a 1N solution contains:
    a.   1 equivalent weight of solute
    b.   10 equivalent weights of solute
    c. 100 equivalent weights of solute
    d. 1,000 equivalent weights of solute

a

1095.   How would you make 150 ml. of a 1:60 dilution from 1:10 dilution?

See p. 139

1096.   How would you make 10% solution from a 95% solution?

See p. 140

1097.   One ml. contains approximately the following number of drops:
    a. 10 drops
    b. 15 drops
    c. 25 drops
    d. 32 drops

b

1098.   The normality of a 22% Na_2SO_4 solution is:
    a. 1.2N
    b. 3.1N   b
    c. 2.2N
    d. 6.2N

1099.   The molarity of a 2N H_3PO_4 solution is:
    a. 5.67M
    b. 6.67M
    c. 3.22M
    d. 0.667M   d

1100.   7.5 ml. of 1N H_2SO_4 will exactly neutralize 7.5 ml. of
1N KOH.   T   F   T

1101.   A urine specimen has a chloride concentration of 150
mEq./L. The physician desires to know the concentration of NaCl in Gm./L. (assume that the chloride is present in urine as NaCl (M.W. = 58.5).   8.78 Gm./L.

1102.   A calcium concentration is reported as 5 mEq./L. The
concentration in mg.% is:
    a.   2 mg.%
    b.   5 mg.%
    c.   8 mg.%
    d. 10 mg.%   d

1103. 10^{-3} equals:
    a. 0.1
    b. 0.01
    c. 0.001   c
    d. 0.000,1

1104;   If a solution has a hydrogen-ion concentration of 10^{-5}
the pH is:
    a.   1
    b.   5   b
    c. 10   c
    d. 15

1105.   If a solution has a pH of 5 its hydrogen-ion concentration is:
    a. 10^{-3}
    b. 10^{-5} b
    c. 10^{-10}
    d. 10^{-15}

1106.   Convert:
    a. 25°C. to °F.   77
    b. 131°F. to °C.   55

1107.   5/16 equals:
    a. 3.2
    b. 0.03125
    c. 0.16
    d. 0.3125   d

1108.   The atomic (or molecular) weight divided by the valence
        is:
        a. Gram molecular weight
        b. Milliequivalent weight
        c. Equivalent weight   c
        d. Standard weight
        e. None of the above

1109.   A milliequivalent weight is:
        a. 0.1 of an equivalent weight
        b. 0.01 of an equivalent weight
        c. 0.001 of an equivalent weight   c
        d. 0.000,1 of an equivalent weight

1110.   The molecular weight expressed in grams in also called
        the _____ .   mole
                                                                (mol)

1111.   When the valence is one the equivalent weight is the
        same as _____ .   the molecu-
                                                                lar weight

1112.   A patient's weight is 165 pounds. He therefore weighs:
        a.   82 Kgs.
        b.   75 Kgs.   b
        c.   32 Kgs.
        d. 104 Kgs.

1113.   The equivalent weight of calcium is 20. Therefore 11.5
        mg.% of calcium represent:
        a. 2.3 mEq./L.
        b. 4.5 mEq./L.
        c. 5.7 mEq./L.   c
        d. 7.3 mEq./L.

1114.   The equivalent weight of sodium is 23. Therefore 140
        mEq./L. of sodium represent:
        a.   14 mg.%
        b.   32 mg.%
        c. 280 mg.%
        d. 322 mg.%   d

1115.   Convert the following mg.% values to mEq./L.:
        a. 10 mg.% NaCl   1.7 mEq./L.
        b. 10 mg.% Ca^{++} 5.0 mEq./L.
        c. 20 mg.% K^{+} 5.1 mEq./L.

1116.   One gram of nitrogen represents the following amount
        of protein:
        a. 2.14 grams
        b. 6.25 grams   b
        c. 2.43 grams
        d. 50%

1117.   Once urea nitrogen content is known it is possible to
        determine urea values by multiplying urea nitrogen

values by:
  a. 6.25
  b. 2.43
  c. 2.14
  d. 4.17   c

1118. Which of the following factors is used in converting
       grams percent of total protein to milliequivalents per
       liter of total protein:
         a. 2.43   a
         b. 4.17
         c. 2.14
         d. 4.25

1119. Gram% Total Protein X _____ = mEq./L. Total   2.43
       Protein.

1120. BUN X _____ = Urea.   2.14

1121. A molecule of glucose has the following molecular
       weight:
         a. 180   a
         b. 120
         c. 90
         d. 60

1122. pH is the _____ logarithm (base 10) of the hy- negative
       drogen ion (H^+) concentration of a solution.

1123. A solution in which the concentration of hydrogen-ions
       equals the concentration of hydroxyl-ions is a:
         a. Neutral solution   a
         b. Acid solution
         c. Basic solution

1124. A solution which possesses a pH above 7.0 is:
         a. An acid
         b. A base   b
         c. A neutral solution

1125. A chloride concentration is reported as 300 mg.%. The
       concentration in mEq./L. is:
         a. 3.00
         b. 8.46
         c. 84.60   c
         d. 30.00

1126. Clinical Laboratories use more normal solutions than
       molar solutions.   T   F   T

1127. What elements to the following symbols stand for:
         a. As — Bi — Br — Cu — F — Au — Pb — Mg — Mn
            — Hg — Ni — Os — P — Si — Ag — Pt   See p. 140
         b. Sr — S — Th — Sn — Ti — W — U — V — Zn   "

1128: Write out the following formulas:
         a. Ammonium iodide; ammonium oxalate; amyl

alcohol; barium chloride	See p. 140
b. Benzoic acid; carbon monoxide; chloral hydrate; chloroform; ether	"
c. Ethyl acetate; hydrogen sulfide; mercuric bromide; mercury bichloride; oxalic acid	"
d. Phenol; potassium bicarbonate; potassium chlorate	"
e. Potassium chloride; potassium dichromate; potassium oxalate	"
f. Potassium ferricyanide; potassium permanganate	"
g. Sodium ferrocyanide; sucrose; urea; zinc acetate; Na thiosulfate	"

CHEMISTRY ANSWERS CONTINUED

3. Atoms of the same element containing different numbers of neutrons and therefore having different nuclear masses.

4. Naturally occurring isotope of Hydrogen. It has mass number 2. It may be found in water.

5. A property of certain isotopes which emit spontaneously from their nuclei certain radiations that can result in the formation of atoms of a different element or atoms of an isotope of the original element.

6. Radiation similar to X-rays, possessing great penetration ability, produced by radioactive material.

7. A negatively charged subatomic particle with a mass 1/1837 of a Hydrogen atom.

8. The concentric layers of electrons around the nucleus of an atom.

9. An electrovalent bond which results from a transfer of electrons.

14. The smallest unit of an element which cannot be further decomposed by ordinary chemical means.

15. Pure substances composed of two or more elements combined in definite proportions by weight.

16. The smallest particle of an element or compound that possesses all the properties of that substance. (True molecules of compounds are characteristic of non-electrolytes only.)

17. A charged particle. Atoms that enter into chemical unions to form compounds or formula units, gain or lose electrons and form negative ions (non-metals) or positive ions (metals).

19. The unit of volume employed in the metric system. It is the volume of one kilogram of water at $4°C$. One liter is also equivalent to about 1,000 cubic centimeters. One liter = 1.06 quarts.

20. They are an abbreviation for the International System of Units. This is a broad plan incorporating the metric system of units which is being advocated as a world-wide standard of measurement.

61. In emission photometry, as certain atoms and molecules are subjected to heat, they absorb energy, thus raising electrons from lower to higher energy levels. When returning to the ground state, these atoms and molecules emit the extra energy in the form of light, the wavelength of which is specific for the particular atom or molecule.

In atomic absorption spectrophotometry, the atoms in the ground state absorb energy. The energy released by these atoms in the flame is absorbed by hollow cathode tubes of the same composition as the atoms being determined.

74. It is the means to an end—to generate test results which are clinically significant and thus contribute to patient care while maintaining lowest possible cost.

76. Mechanization refers to the replacement of manual procedures by mechanical devices. Automation refers more precisely to machine systems that incorporate means for continuous monitoring and regulation.

77. A system of continuous monitoring of automated systems by the characteristics of the product and the use of this information to regulate the equipment.

78. Mere automatic reproduction of values does not deal with accuracy or specificity. Technologists must take great care in method selection and monitoring to assure appropriate patient results.

81. a. Continuous flow analysis.
     b. Discrete sample processing
     c. Centrifugal fast analysis.

82. Continuous flow is, as its name implies, a continuous pumping of samples and reagents terminating in flow through cuvettes in an interference filter photometer. Specimen in discrete analysis is handled as a separate process in its own dedicated reaction vessel.

83. a. Sample pick-up.
     b. Sample delivery.
     c. Wash out of sample probe.
     d. Protein separation: number of means available (dialysis, precipitation, etc.).
     e. Addition of reaction reagents.
     f. Incubation.
     g. Reaction detection and measurement, spectrophotometer, flame, etc.
     h. Data presentation

98. Each determination employs one (or at most two) heat-sealed plastic envelopes containing analytical reagents in separate compartments. The envelope is clear so that it can become the cuvet for photometric measurement.

102. Centrifugal force transfers reaction liquids. Chemical reactions take place and are measured in the rotating centrifuge head.

110. a. Use of continuous tubing of different diameters.
      b. Peristaltic pump meters samples and reagents through the tubes.

112. a. Provide continuous record of laboratory results.

    b. Give early warning of problems developing

    c. Permit valid judgement on accuracy of results.

    d. Facilitate comparisons between different methods of analysis.

    e. Monitor performance of equipment.

    f. Monitor technicians' skills.

114. S.D. $= \sqrt{\dfrac{\text{sum of the squared diff. between mean \& test result}}{n-1}}$

116. C.V. $= \dfrac{\text{Standard Deviation}}{\text{Mean}} \times 100$

118. Avoids unconscious bias technicians may develop to control pools or commercial sera. Sharp change in direction of slope warns of problems.

119. a. Careful study of chart can often suggest lead to problem solving.

    b. Increasing variability, even within approved deviation, can warn of problems developing.

    c. Sudden out of range deviation should lead to repeat analyses under careful supervision.

120. a. Normal level.

    b. Region just above normal level. (Can be commercial or appropriate pool.)

121. a. Carry out at least 20 determinations for each parameter to be assayed. Preliminary set up for quality control chart.

    b. Assay each working day with 40 values. Set up mean, standard deviation, variability on chart.

128. a. Use sulfuric acid and potassium dichromate cleaning solution (chromic acid is active agent).

    b. Rinse with tap water at least four times.

    c. Rinse with distilled water three times.

129. a. Rinse with dilute nitric acid. *Do not use chromic acid.* Any trace of chromium or any other heavy metal will inactivate enzymes.

    b. Wash with detergent.

    c. Complete with adequate distilled water rinses.

130. The glass ware drys without water spots.

131. Has lowest coefficient of friction of any solid.

132. Light weight, inexpensive (one use disposable), can be molded into precision shapes, as for autoanalyzer cups.

133. In small measurements glass adsorbs unpredictably, thus introducing significant error.

134. In red biohazard bags to be autoclaved and incinerated.

143. a. Nutritional status.

    b. State of metabolic processes.

    c. Ability of kidney to handle selectively materials presented to it.

147. a. Man is a diurnal creature, thus he does not excrete all metabolite equally day and night.

148. A specimen appropriate for most qualitative diagnostic studies which has the great advantages of freshness and availability any time.

149. At the hour set for beginning, patient empties bladder and discards. From that time to the same time next day every drop of urine passed is collected. At the concluding time bladder is again emptied and this is added.

171. pH, protein, glucose, ketone, blood, bilirubin (urobilinogen and nitrites included sometimes too!).

172. Fast, neat, reliable. Ease makes sure the tests are done.

189. This may be earliest sign of intercapillary glomerulosclerosis (Kimmelsteil-Wilson syndrome).

190. **True albuminuria (true proteinuria)** is the presence, in qualitatively detectable amount, of blood protein in the urine due to (abnormally) increased permeability of the glomerular membrane. **False albuminuria** is the presence, due to other causes such as pus or epithelial cells, of qualitatively detectable protein in the urine.

196. No. Any time carbohydrate intake is low—as in nausea, anorexia, or severe dieting—ketones will appear in urine as a sign of nutritional state.

238. Epithelial cells, pus cells, erythrocytes, casts, bacteria, animal parasites, spermatozoa.

239. Amorphous urates, uric acid crystals, calcium oxalate crystals, fat droplets, sodium urate crystals, tyrosine needles, leucine spheres, cystine.

240. Amorphous phosphates, calcium carbonate crystals, triple phosphate crystals, calcium phosphate crystals, ammonium biurate crystals.

270. The abnormal increase in the secretion of urine.

287. **Porphyrin:** Any of a group of iron-free (or magnesium-free) pyrrole derivatives which occur universally in protoplasm and form the basis of the respiratory pigments of animals and plants.
Porphyria: A disease (also known as "hematoporphyria") characterized by abnormal porphyrin metabolism. In this condition abnormal quantities of porphyrin (coproporphyrin and uroporphyrin) are present in the tissues and excreted in the urine. There also occurs pigmentation of the face and bones, skin photosensitivity, vomiting, and intestinal disturbances. Two porphyrins (coproporphyrin types I and III and uroporphyrin types I and III) are important from the clinical laboratory standpoint.

317. BUN is affected by the production as well as the excretion of urea, whereas the clearance is an index of its excretion *only*.

320. Creatinine production is not directly affected by diet. It is a waste product with little reabsorption. Results are easier to interpret than urea clearance.

326. Red cells may be removed by centrifugation. When hemolysis is present add 1 ml. 10% sodium tungstate and 1 ml. 2/3 N sulfuric acid. Let stand until pink color of blood has disappeared, then filter.

336. Inulin Conc. in Urine $\times$ urine volume = inulin conc. in plasma $\times$ G.F.R.

$$\text{G.F.R.} = \frac{\text{Inulin conc. in urine} \times \text{urine volume}}{\text{Inulin conc. in plasma}}$$

337. Bladder is usually catheterized/and rinsed well at end of each clearance.

375. Na fluoride (also see p. 60). Denatures most enzymes including red cell and bacterial.

422. a. Protein-free filtrate + buffer solution + urease (incubation of this mixture results in decomposition of urea with liberation of NH_4 and formation of ammonium carbonate).
    b. Nitrogen content of ammonium compound is then determined colorimetrically (as yellow dimercuric ammonium iodide) after Nessler's reaction.

436. Most methods based on reducing properties of uric acid. Thioneine in red cells will contribute to the reduction. Protein-free filtrates have small quantities of interfering substances.

453. Copper is added as a catalyst to accelerate the conversion of nitrogen (contained in a blood protein-free filtrate) to ammonia.

454. Digestion of nitrogenous products (present in protein-free filtrate) with sulfuric acid and heat to form ammonia compound. The nitrogen in the ammonia compound is determined colorimetrically after reaction with Nessler's reagent (or by aeration or distillation and titration with acid).

476. Albumin and globulins (alpha-1, alpha-2, beta and gamma).

567. A highly thermolabile and highly specific protein synthesized by living cells and which catalyzes reactions that are possible thermodynamically.

580. **Secretin** (a polypeptide with a molecular weight of about 5,000) causes the secretion of a very alkaline pancreatic juice poor in enzymes. **Pancreozymin** causes the secretion of pancreatic juice rich in enzymes.

620. Erythrocytes and prostate gland.

655. Because of the high potassium content of red cells.

663. Na: 138–146 mEq./l.   K: 3.8–5.0 mEq./l.

678. Calcium diffuses into the cells when the blood is allowed to stand.

691. As soon as blood is removed from the vessels, enzymes in the cells begin to split free phosphoric acid from organic phosphates. These changes affect not only cell composition but serum phosphate content as well.

721. $pH = pK + \log \dfrac{[HCO_3^-]}{[H_2CO_3]}$

730. Absorbance of the fluid is recorded continuously on spectrophotometer between 350 and 700 nm. The resulting curve can tell whether bilirubin is present and how much.

733. By antiglobulin technique, typing and identification of fetal hemoglobin.

734. a. If fetal blood loss from an already anemic fetus.
    b. Maternal blood may make curve harder to interpret.

735. Discharge of meconium into fluid. This is important as a fetal distress signal.

737. Tracing is similar to normal amniotic fluid but much steeper slope. Urea nitrogen should approach 300 mg./dl., amniotic fluid 30 mg./dl.

741. At first the two are secreted in similar concentrations into amniotic fluid. At about 36 weeks the lungs mature and begin to secrete much more lecithin than sphingomyelin.

744. In traumatic tap the blood typically is non-uniform and tends to clear with continued aspiration.

745. Capillary hematocrit and hematocrit done on fluid should be similar.

746. **Exudates** have protein above 3 gm./dl.
     Transudates have protein below 3 gm./dl.

747. No. So fluid should be observed for clotting. Presence suggests inflammation or neoplasm.

749. a. **Protein.** to determine transudate or exudate status.
     b. **Glucose.** Low level bacterial pericarditis as well as rheumatoid disease and malignancy.

752. Simultaneous measurements of creatinine and urea nitrogen on blood and peritoneal fluid. High levels of these parameters in the fluid with normal BUN and creatinine in blood fluid is urine.

753. a. Dialysis of plasma across synovial membranes.
     b. Active secretion—β cells probably.

754. No. They require 4–8 hours because equilibrium is so slowly achieved.

756. a. Arthritis of unknown etiology.
     b. Suspected infection—to get culture material as well as chemistry.
     c. With large effusions—to relieve pain and improve mobility.

757. Crystal clear and colorless to pale yellow.

758. a. As normal fluid drips from syringe a tenacious thread forms at least 5 cm. in length.
     b. Mucin "clot" test of ropes. Add 1 ml. of fluid to 20 ml. of 5% (x. to v.) acetic acid. Grade clot from firm (normal) to poor (flaky).

759. Decreased viscosity is related to decreased hyaluronic acid. Decrease reflects poor lubrication of joints.

760. Monosodium urate (MSU) and calcium pyrophosphate dihydrate (CPPD).

762. a. **Urate crystals.** Often in phagocytes, they appear bipefringent and needle-like.
     b. **CPPD crystals.** Will be bipefringent and rhomboid.

764. Fibrinogen normally is absent. With inflammatory joint disease synovial fluid approaches plasma in composition.

765. Normally about 10 mg. less than blood level.

766. LDH activity may occur with rheumatoid arthritis, septic arthritis, Reiter's syndrome or gout.

775. a. Obstructive liver disease (clay-colored stool).
     b. Diarrhea.
     c. Dysentery.
     d. Malabsorption.
     e. G.I. tract bleeding.
     f. Parasitic infestation.

779. red colored dietary substances such as beets, or medications can fool one.

797. Pathological increase in stool fat content.

798. Generally fluid, semifluid or soft and pasty and bulky. They are pale in color and foul-smelling.

799. Impaired digestion or assimilation of foodstuffs by small bowel.

800. Yes. Since commonest form of malabsorption results from pancreatic disease.

804. Bacterial activity on sucrose in lower bowel will release glucose and fructose too low in bowel for absorption.

806. It is secreted by the chief or peptic cells as the zymogen, pepsinogen. This must be activated by gastric acid. Optimal pH: 1.6–2.4.

807. a. Determine whether or not patient can secrete gastric acid.
   b. To measure amount of acid produced by patient.
   c. To reveal hypersecretory state (Zollinger-Ellison syndrome).
   d. To determine completeness of vagotomy (insulin test).

808. HCl production. It has ease of measurement and good correlation with disease states.

816. Free acid, combined acid, total acid.

824. a. Volume of specimen in milliliters.
   b. Titratable acidity in milliequivalents per liter. Titrate suitable aliquot
   c. 0.1N NaOH to neutrality—pH 7.0 or 7.4. Use good pH meter for end point.
   c. Measure pH of specimen using good pH meter.

825. Multiply the specimen's volume in milliters by the titratable acid and divide by 1000. Total acid output will be given for a gastric analysis by adding the individual sample values.

826. Failure of gastric pH to fall below 6.0 or 7.0 in the augmented histamine test.

829. The patient swallows a resin containing azure-A. If free HCl is present in the stomach the hydrogen ions replace some of the indicator dye. The latter is absorbed and appears in the urine.

833. a. Traumatic tap.
   b. Markedly elevated protein.
   c. Moderately elevated protein in tuberculous meningitis.

837. Different tests are not comparable. Globulin gives greatest turbidity with trichloracetic acid, albumin with sulfosalicylic acid.

838. a. Meuleman's sodium sulfate sulfosalicylic acid (1960).
   b. Folin-Ciocalteu modifications (Watson, 1964).
   c. Modified Biuret (Burgi, et al., 1967).

848. No. Aside from bacterial infection, hypoglycemia is commonest cause although meningeal carcinomatosis or leukemic infiltration may have this effect.

856. Lactic dehydrogenase (LBH), aspartate transferase (AT), Glutamic oxalacetic transaminase (GOT), creatine phosphokinase (CPK).

857. Slow migrating LDH 4-5 may increase in bacterial meningitis. Fast migrating LDH 1-2 may increase in viral meningitis (Beatty and Oppenheimer, 1968).

858. Yes. Increase increases respiration; decrease slows respiration.

859. It diffuses rapidly and easily across blood-CSF barrier. pCO_2 levels closely follow arterial pCO_2.

860. Almost entirely on ratio $\dfrac{HCO_3^-}{pCO_2}$

862. Confusion, delirium and even coma (attempt to treat respiratory acidosis with intravenous HCO_3 may precipitate).

900. Protein precipitation is followed by ashing (thus converting organic iodine to iodide). Iodide catalyzes the reduction of yellow ceric ion by arsenite and the rate of decolorization is proportional to the amount of iodine present.

917. Serum is saturated with I^{131}-labeled thyroxine and subjected to reverse-flow paper electrophoresis. Radioscanning of the paper strip permits identification and quantitation of TBG in terms of its thyroxine binding capacity.

919. **Islets of Langerhans (pancreas):** Insulin
Testis: Testosterone
Ovaries: Estrogen, progesterone
Duodenal mucosa: (a) Secretin and pancreozymin (b) Cholecystokinin (c) Enterogastrone
Adrenal cortex: (a) Glucocorticoids (such as cortisone and hydro-cortisone) (b) Mineralocorticoids (c) Sex hormones (androgens, estrogens, progesterone)
Thyroid: Thyroxin
Parathyroid: Parathormone
Pituitary:
  A. Anterior pituitary:
    (a) Thyrotropic hormone
    (b) Adrenotropic hormone
    (c) Somatotropic hormone
    (d) Gonadotropic hormone (FSH, LH, LTH)
  B. Posterior pituitary:
    (a) Antidiuretic hormone
    (b) Oxytocin

980. Said of a substance (other than an acid) which is corrosive to organic matter.

982. **Catalyst:** A substance that promotes a reaction without itself being consumed.
Enzyme: An organic catalyst produced by living cells. All enzymes are protein in nature and specific for the type of reactions which they catalyze.
Coenzyme: A nonprotein substance the presence of which is required for enzyme activity to take place. Certain vitamins serve as raw materials from which coenzymes are produced.

983. Inspissation means concentration of a liquid by evaporation.

992. **Transudate:** Fluid accumulated in a serous cavity as a result of non-inflammatory process.
Exudate: Fluid accumulated in a body cavity as a result of inflammatory process.

993. **Fibrin** is the fibrous (i.e., net-like) protein formed by the interaction of thrombin (a ferment-like substance) and fibrinogen (one of the plasma proteins). Fibrin enmeshes the red cells to form blood clot.

998. a. Free acidity of gastric juice, 5–20 degrees
b. Erythrocyte sedimentation rate (Wintrobe-Landsberg or Westergren), 0–9 mm./hr. (men and 0–20 mm./hr. (women)
c. Fasting blood glucose, 80–120 mg.% (Folin-Wu) or 70–90 mg.% (true sugar technique)
d. Blood plasma chloride as NaCl, 570–620 mg.% (98–106 mEq./l.)
e. CSF glucose, 60–90 mg.% (Folin-Wu)
f. Bleeding time, 1–6 minutes (Duke)
g. Urine urea: urea N = 10–15 Gm./24 hrs., urea N X 2.14 = urea
h. Blood NPN, 25–35 mg.%
i. Blood cholesterol, 150–250 mg.% (total)
j. Red cell diameter, 7.5 microns (average)
k. Blood serum globulin, 1.5–3.4 Gm.% (total globulin)
l. Blood calcium, 9–11 mg.% (4.5–5.5 mEq./l.)

1001. **Edema:** Excessive accumulation of fluid in tissue spaces.
Eclampsia: A convulsive or epileptiform seizure.
Isoagglutinin (isohemagglutinin): An agglutin which acts upon red cells of members of the same species.
Cirrhosis: A chronic liver disease characterized by progressive parenchymal cell destruction and accompanied by parenchymal regeneration and connective tissue proliferation.
Jaundice: Yellowness of the skin and mucous membranes due to the presence of excessive amounts of bilirubin (unchanged chief bile pigment) in the blood.

1002. **Density (Absolute Density):** The ratio of the mass of a substance to its volume.
Specific Gravity: The measured mass of a substance compared with that of an equal volume of standard (for liquids and solids, distilled water at a specified temperature is usually the standard).

1003. CO_2 combining power, icterus index, quantitative bilirubin determinations, liver function tests. As a rule hemolysis should always be avoided.

1004. **Edema:** Excessive accumulation of fluid in tissue spaces.
Dehydration: *Removal of water from a tissue or from the body; also the condition which results from undue loss of water.

1005. **Oxidation:**
(a) The combination of oxygen with another element to form an oxide.
(b) The gain of positive charges (or the loss of negative charges) on an atom.
Reduction:
(a) Subtraction of oxygen.
(b) Addition of hydrogen

(c) The gain of negative charges (or the loss of positive charges) on an atom.

1006. Glucosuria: The presence of glucose in the urine.
Glycosuria: The presence of *any* sugar in the urine.

1007. Nephritis: Inflammation (glomerulonephritis, pyelonephritis, etc.) of the kidney.
Nephrosis: Any degenerative condition of the kidney not accompanied by signs of inflammation.

1008. Achlorhydria: The absence of hydrochloric acid from gastric secretions.
Achylia gastrica: The absence of, or the marked decrease in, the secretion of gastric juice.

1010. Hypochlorhydria: A condition in which there is a diminished amount of hydrochloric acid in the gastric juice.
Hyperchlorhydria: A condition in which there is an increased amount of hydrochloric acid in the gastric juice.

1011. Acid: Substance having hydrogen, replaceable by metals, to form salts and capable of dissociating in aqueous solution to give hydrogen ions.
Base: Substance which reacts with an acid to produce a salt and water.

1012. Hypoglycemia: A substantial decrease in the glucose content of the blood. The clinical symptoms of hypoglycemia appear when the glucose content of the blood falls below 60 mg.%.
Hyperglycemia: A substantial increase in the glucose content of the blood.

1013. Anion: An ion carrying a negative charge.
Cation: An electropositive ion.

1014. A method of filtration under pressure through filters with minute pores and employed in separating colloids from their dispersion mediums.

1015. A method for the study of lipoproteins, viruses, etc., using a centrifuge with an exceedingly high speed of rotation.

1016. Normal Solution: A solution that contains one gram-equivalent weight of reagent per liter of solution.
Molar solution: A solution that contains one gram-molecular weight of reagent per liter of solution.

1017. A solution is a fluid consisting of the mixture of two or more substances which are *molecularly dispersed* through one another in a homogeneous manner. A suspension is the dispersion of a finely powdered solid through a fluid in which it is not soluble.

1018. Anabolism: Constructive metabolism. The conversion, by living cells, of simple substances into more complex compounds.
Catabolism: Destructive metabolism. The conversion, by living cells, of complex compounds to simpler ones.

1019. Clotted blood: Blood clot (fibrin + cells) and serum. This serum will separate from the clot on standing or by centrifugation.
Whole blood is drawn blood which has been prevented from clotting by the addition of an anticoagulant. Whole blood consists of free blood cells plus plasma.

1020. Intravenous; intramuscular.

1021. **Ferrous:** Containing divalent iron (i.e., containing iron in its lower valence).
Ferric: Containing trivalent iron (i.e., containing iron in its higher valence).

1022. **Endoenzyme:** An intracellular enzyme. It normally remains within the cell and does not diffuse out into the surrounding medium.
Exoenzyme: An enzyme which acts outside of the cell that produces it.

1023. **Obstructive jaundice:** Jaundice resulting from impediment to the flow of bile from the liver to the duodenum.
Hemolytic jaundice: Jaundice resulting from excessive hemolysis which is due to increased red cell fragility.

1026. Without bromide medication there is, according to Wikoff and associates, a normal range of bromine in the serum of from 0.33 to 1.73 mg.%.

1032. ACTH, adrenocorticotropic hormone; BEI, butanol-extractable iodine; PBI, protein-bound iodine; HDF, high dry field; EDTA, ethylene diamine tetracetic acid; QNS, quantity not sufficient; SGPT, serum glutamic pyruvic transaminase; SLDH or LDH, serum lactic dehydrogenase; BJP, Bence-Jones protein; A/G, albumin-globulin ratio; BMR, basal metabolic rate; AZF, Aschheim-Zondek modified by Friedman; CHO, carbohydrate; CSF, cerebrospinal (spinal) fluid; SPT, slightest possible trace; PSP, phenolsulphonphthalein; BSP, bromsulfalein; FBS, fasting blood sugar; NPN, total nonprotein nitrogen; BUN, blood urea nitrogen; 17-KS, 17-ketosteroids; GFR, glomerular filtration rate; OD, optical density; SBF, said to be fasting; C_u, urea clearance; C_m, maximal urea clearance; C_s, standard urea clearance; OR, operating room; OPD, out-patient department; C.E.A., cholinesterase activity; USP, United States Pharmacopoeia; I.R., infrared; A.A., atomic absorption; TLC, thin-layer chromatography; GLC, gas-liquid chromatography; RIA, radioimmunoassay.

1035. **Isotonic solution:** A solution whose osmotic pressure *equals* that of normal saline (or some other standard).
Hypotonic solution: A solution whose osmotic pressure *is below* that of normal saline (or some other standard).
Hypertonic solution: A solution whose osmotic pressure *is above* that of normal saline (or some other standard).

1036. **Anuria:** The complete absence of urinary secretion.
Oliguria: Abnormal decrease in the secretion of urine.
Polyuria: Abnormal increase in the secretion of urine.

1038. **Azotemia:** The accumulation, as a result of renal insufficiency, of urinary nitrogenous substances, especially urea, in the blood.
Uremia: The clinical condition resulting from the presence of azotemia.

1067. Place 70 ml. of 95% alcohol in graduated cylinder. Add water to the 95 ml. mark and mix.

1095. Twenty-five ml. of 1:10 dilution diluted to a total of 150 ml. gives a 1:60 dilution.

1096.   Take 10 ml. of 95% and dilute to a total volume of 95 ml.

1127.   As, arsenic; Bi, bismuth; Br, bromine; Cu, copper; F, fluorine; Au, gold; Pb, lead; Mg, magnesium; Mn, manganese; Hg, mercury; Ni, nickel; Os, osmium; P, phosphorus; Si, silicon; Ag, silver; Pt, platinum; Sr, strontium,; S, sulphur; Th, thorium; Sn, tin; Ti, titanium; U, uranium; V, vanadium; Zn, zinc.

1128:   a. Ammonium iodide, NH_4I; ammonium oxalate, $(NH_4)_2C_2O_4.H_2O$; amyl alcohol, $C_5H_{11}OH$; barium chloride, $BaCl_2$

   b. Benzoic acid, $C_7H_6O_2$; carbon monoxide, CO; chloral hydrate, $CCl_3CH(OH)_3$; chloroform, $CHCl_3$; ether, $(C_2H_5)_2O$

   c. Ethyl acetate, $CH_3COO\ C_2H_5$; hydrogen sulfide, H_2S; mercury bromide, $HgBr_2$; mercury bichloride, $HgCl_2$; oxalic acid, $H_2C_2O_4.\ 2H_2O$

   d. Phenol, C_6H_5OH; potassium bicarbonate, $KHCO_3$; potassium chlorate, $KClO_3$

   e. Potassium chloride, KCl; potassium dichromate, $K_2Cr_2O_7$; potassium oxalate, $K_2C_2O_4$

   f. Potassium ferricyanide, $K_3Fe(CN)_6$; potassium permanganate, $KMnO_4$

   g. Sodium ferrocyanide, $Na_4Fe(CN)_6$; sucrose, $C_{12}H_{22}O_{11}$; urea, $(NH_2)_2CO$: zinc acetate, $Zn(C_2H_3O_2)_2$; sodium thiosulfate, $Na_2S_2O_3.\ 5H_2O$

Section II

HEMATOLOGY

HEMATOLOGY EXAMINATION

Edited by Stanley L. Schrier, M.D., Head Hematology Division, Stanford University

INTRODUCTORY QUESTIONS

1. Briefly indicate chief role(s) played by each of the following peripheral blood components:
   a. Red cells See p. 188
   b. Platelets "
   c. Eosinophils "
   d. Neutrophils "
   e. Monocytes "
   f. Lymphocytes "
   g. Basophils "

2. Plasma differs from serum in that it contains:
   a. Albumin
   b. Globulin
   c. Active Factor VIII   c
   d. Cholesterol

3. Which of the following proteins is not present in the serum:
   a. Albumin
   b. Alpha globulin
   c. Fibrinogen   c
   d. Gamma globulin

4. Normal serum contains platelets.　T　F   F

5. The only consistently reliable means of differentiating between human and animal blood is the:
   a. Guaiac test
   b. Benzidine test
   c. Teichmann's test
   d. Precipitin test   d

6. Teichmann's test (hemin crystals) is reliable only when positive.　T　F   T

7. Normal blood is bacteriologically sterile.　T　F   T

8. The 0.85% solution of sodium chloride is known as:
   a. Zenker's fluid
   b. Bouin's fluid
   c. Wright's buffer
   d. Normal saline   d

9. To remove fresh blood from a lab coat you would:
   a. Apply a 10% solution of sodium carbonate
   b. Apply methyl alcohol
   c. Apply a 3% hydrogen peroxide solution then rinse thoroughly with water   c
   d. Apply a solvent such as benzene or chloroform

143

10. Which of the following achromatic objectives would be an oil immersion objective:
    a. N.A. 0.65
    b. N.A. 0.12
    c. N.A. 1.25   c
    d. N.A. 0.30

11. What do the following standard abbreviations stand for:
    a. ACTH — MCHC — MCV — EDTA — L.E. — I.M.   See p. 188
    b. CBC — RBC — r.b.c. — WBC — w.b.c. — Hb — MCH   ,,

12. Which of the following tests would not be included in a routine CBC:
    a. Differential leukocyte count
    b. Total erythrocyte count
    c. Reticulocyte count   c
    d. Total leukocyte count

13. Match the following:
    1. Reticulocyte count   a. No blood prepara-   1—e
    2. Sedimentation rate   tion required   2—f
    3. PCV (hematocrit reading)   3—f
    4. Heinz body preparation   b. Suspension of pa-   4—e or f
    5. Differential white cell count   tient's cells or of   5—e
    6. Prothrombin time   cells from the cord   6—d
    7. Capillary resistance test   c. Diluted blood from   7—a
    8. Direct Coombs   patient   8—b
    9. Eosinophil count   d. Patient's plasma   9—c
    10. Direct platelet count   e. Smear of patient's   10—c
    11. Partial thromboplastin time   blood   11—d
    12. Malarial parasites   f. Patient's whole   12—e
    13. Bone marrow studies   blood   13—i
    14. Hemoglobin determinations   g. Patient's serum   14—c or f
    15. Rh titer   h. No blood prepara-   15—g
    16. Indirect Coombs   tion (or wet films)   16—g
    17. Clotting time   i. Bone marrow   17—a or f
    18. RBC   smears   18—c
    19. WBC   19—c
    20. Sickle cells   20—h
    21. Bleeding time   21—a
    22. Clot retraction   22—a or f
    23. Heterophil antibody test   23—g

14. A blood pressure cuff is needed to carry out the following test(s):
    a. Ivy's bleeding test   a
    b. Duke's bleeding test
    c. Capillary fragility   c
    d. Lee & White

15. The so-called "direct method" of thrombocyte enumeration requires a:
    a. Dilution of blood in a red pipette using a special
       (such as Rees-Ecker) fluid   a

    b. Blood smear
    c. Both a & b
    d. Neither a nor b

16. Accurate platelet counts can be obtained on capillary blood.
    T   F   F

17. The "L.E. cell phenomenon" may be detected in bone
marrow smears as well as in smears from venous blood.
    T   F   T

18. An alternate test for the disease systemic lupus erythematosis is to see if there are antinuclear antibodies in the patient's serum.   T   F   T

19. Blood smears prepared from whole blood which has stood for a few hours are just as satisfactory for differential counting as blood smears prepared from fresh blood, provided the specimen was kept in the refrigerator and that it was thoroughly mixed just before the smears were made.   T   F   F

20. The tourniquet should not be released until after the needle is out of the vein.   T   F   F

21. Which of the following tests always require blood drawn from a vein:
    a. Wintrobe-Landsberg ESR   a
    b. Lee & White   b
    c. Ivy bleeding time
    d. Westergren ESR   d

22. Which of the following tests does not call for dilution of blood in a special diluting pipette:
    a. Total erythrocyte count
    b. Total leukocyte count
    c. Sedimentation rate   c
    d. Circulating eosinophil count

23. Which of the following tests does not require the preparation of a blood smear:
    a. Reticulocyte count
    b. Stippled cells
    c. Sedimentation rate   c
    d. Thrombin time

24. Plasma volume can only be determined by using a dye (such as Evans blue) which forms a bond with plasma protein.   T   F   F (also See p. 188)

25. A 21 gage needle has a bore with a wider diameter than either a 19 or a 20 gage needle.   T   F   F

26. Which of the following solutions may be employed as diluting fluids for a red cell count:
    a. Hayem's solution   a
    b. 3% acetic acid

   c. Gower's solution   c
   d. Toison's fluid   d

27. 1% HCl may be used as red cell diluting fluid.   T   F   F

28. List various ingredients employed in making up the follow-
     ing solutions:
         a. Hayem's solution   See p. 188
         b. Gower's solution   „
         c. Rees-Ecker solution   „

29. Türk's diluting fluid for WBC is made up of 1% glacial
     acetic acid and a tinge of:
         a. Eosin
         b. Basic fuschsin
         c. Gentian violet   c
         d. Wright's stain

30. Which of the following substances is not employed as a
     blood anticoagulant:
         a. EDTA
         b. Sodium oxalate
         c. Heparin
         d. Thromboplastin   d
         e. Sodium citrate

31. The anticoagulant (0.5 ml. per each 4.5 ml. blood) required
     for the prothrombin time test is:
         a. Heparin
         b. Ammonium and potassium oxalate mixture
         c. Defibrinated serum
         d. EDTA
         e. 3.8% sodium citrate   e

32. The first polychrome stain was discovered by:
         a. Ehrlich
         b. Romanowsky
         c. Wright   b
         d. Giemsa
         e. Gram

33. Methylene blue is:
         a. An acid stain
         b. A basic stain   b
         c. A neutral stain

34. Eosin is:
         a. An acid stain
         b. A basic stain   a
         c. A neutral stain

35. Wright's stain contains eosin and:
         a. Basic fuchsin
         b. Gentian violet
         c. Brilliant cresyl blue
         d. Methylene blue   d

36. Indicate pH range of buffer solution employed in connection with Wright's stain:
    a. 5.6–6.0
    b. 6.0–6.4
    c. 6.4–6.8
    d. 6.8–7.2

    c

37. Briefly describe how cells will stain in a blood smear with Wright's stain when the pH of the buffer is:
    a. Too acid
    b. Too alkaline

    See p. 189
    "

38. How will the smear look if water finds its way into the Wright's stain?

    See p. 189

39. Indicate a practical method for adjusting the pH of the buffer for the Wright's stain when the former is either too acid or too alkaline.

    See p. 189

40. When Wright's stain is used, preliminary fixation of smear is not required.   T   F

    F

41. Which of the following blood stains is not used for differential leukocyte counts:
    a. Wright's stain
    b. Brilliant cresyl blue
    c. Giemsa stain
    d. May-Grünwald

    b

42. Which of the following blood stains is used to demonstrate reticulocytes:
    a. Giemsa
    b. Wright
    c. Brilliant cresyl blue
    d. May-Grünwald

    c

43. 1% brilliant cresyl blue is the only stain that can be used for reticulocyte staining.   T   F

    F (also
    See p. 189)

44. Reticulocytes can be stained after the cells are fixed.   T   F

    F

45. Heinz bodies can be seen on Wright stained blood smears.   T   F

    F

46. Heinz bodies can be seen on wet preparations stained with methyl violet.   T   F

    T

47. How can eosinophils be demonstrated in the sputum?

    See p. 189

48. The cells of the granulocytic series, except the myeloblast, are peroxidase-positive.   T   F

    T

49. Wright's stain is the only stain that can be employed for differential leukocyte counting.   T   F

    F

50. Wright's stain is an excellent stain for bone marrow smears.   T   F

    T

51. Bone marrow smears usually require a longer staining time
     than smears of peripheral blood.   T   F   T

52. To remove a Romanowsky-type stain from a lab coat you
     would:
     a. Apply a solvent such as chloroform or benzene
     b. Apply methyl alcohol   b
     c. Apply a 5% aqueous solution of hydrochloric acid
        and then rinse in water.
     d. Apply a 3% solution of hydrogen peroxide then rinse
        thoroughly with water.

NORMAL VALUES

53. The diameter of a normal erythrocyte measures approx-
     imately:
     a.   3.0 microns
     b.   4.5 microns
     c.   7.5 microns   c
     d. 10.0 microns

54. Normoblasts are frequently found in normal peripheral
     adult blood.   T   F   F

55. The normal volume of the blood in males is approximately:
     a. 2 liters
     b. 5 liters   b
     c. 7 liters
     d. 9 liters

56. Normal values for total blood volume are usually expressed
     as ml. of blood/kilogram of body weight.   T   F   T

57. For every 500 red cells a normal adult person has approx-
     imately the following number of white cells:
     a.   1 white cell   a
     b.   3 white cells
     c. 10 white cells
     d.   6 white cells

58. For every white cell there is approximately the following
     number of platelets:
     a.   9 platelets
     b.   30 platelets   b
     c.   500 platelets
     d. 1,000 platelets
     e. 2,500 platelets

59. For every 500 red cells a normal adult person has approxi-
     mately the following number of platelets:
     a.   12 platelets
     b.   30 platelets   b
     c. 100 platelets
     d.   75 platelets

60. One hundred ml. of normal adult male blood contains
    approximately the following amount of plasma:
    a. 20–30%
    b. 30–40%
    c. 51–55%   c
    d. 65–69%

61. The normal range of prothrombin concentration is:
    a. 20–30%
    b. 30–40%
    c. 40–60%
    d. 60% or more   d

62. The normal range of bleeding time using Duke's method
    (ear lobe puncture) is:
    a. 4–6 minutes   a
    b. 3–7 minutes
    c. 4–8 minutes
    d. 5–10 minutes

63. The average platelet has a diameter of:
    a. 0.5–1.0 micron
    b. 1.0–1.5 microns
    c. 2.0–4.0 microns   c
    d. 5.0–7.0 microns

64. A monocyte measures approximately:
    a. 7.5 microns
    b. 15.0 microns
    c. 20.0 microns   c
    d. 32.0 microns

65. A segmented granulocyte measures approximately:
    a. 7.5 microns
    b. 10.0 microns
    c. 15.0 microns   c
    d. 20.0 microns

66. In a normal differential white cell count you would expect
    to find the following percentage of lymphocytes:
    a. 0%
    b. 2–6%
    c. 20–35%   c
    d. 55–75%

67. The normal number of neutrophils per cu. mm. is:
    a. 1,000–2,000
    b. 1,500–2,500
    c. 2,000–6,000   c
    d. 5,000–10,000

68. A patient is considered to be neutropenic if his neutrophil
    count is below:
    a. 2500 cu. mm.
    b. 3500 cu. mm.
    c. 1800 cu mm.   c

69. In a normal differential white cell count you would expect to find the following percentage of segmented neutrophils:
    a. 10–20%
    b. 20–40%
    c. 40–60%   c
    d. 60–80%

70. In a normal differential white cell count you would expect to find the following percentage of band ("stab") cells:
    a. 0%
    b. 2–6%   b
    c. 20–35%
    d. 55–75%

71. In a normal differential white cell count you would expect to find the following percentage of eosinophils:
    a. 1–3%   a
    b. 3–6%
    c. 6–8%
    d. 8–12%

72. In a normal differential white cell count you would expect to find the following percentage of basophils:
    a. 0–1%   a
    b. 2–6%
    c. 8–12%
    d. 10–16%

73. In a normal differential white cell count you would expect to find the following percentage of monocytes:
    a. 10–15%
    b. 20–30%
    c. 2–8%   c
    d. 8–12%

74. In a normal differential white cell count you would expect to find the following percentage of myelocytes:
    a. 0%   a
    b. 2%
    c. 3%
    d. 5%

75. The normal range of total white cell count (WBC) is:
    a. 5,000–8,000/cu. mm.
    b. 8,000–10,000/cu. mm.
    c. 5,000–10,000/cu. mm.   c
    d. 8,000–12,000/cu. mm.

76. The normal range of circulating eosinophils is:
    a. 0–10 per cu. mm.
    b. 15–30 per cu mm.
    c. 50–300 per cu. mm.   c
    d. 1500–2000 per cu. mm.

77. The normal platelet count using Rees-Ecker diluting fluid is:
    a. 50,000–150,000 per cu. mm.
    b. 100,000–200,000 per cu. mm.
    c. 250,000–350,000 per cu. mm.   c
    d. 350,000–500,000 per cu. mm.

78. Normal platelet count values usually vary with the method.
    T   F   T

79. Platelet counts are the same in infants and adults.   T   F   T

80. Retraction of a normal clot begins in:
    a. 1–2 hours   a
    b. 20–24 hours
    c. 6–12 hours
    d. 12–18 hours

81. Retraction of a normal clot is complete within:
    a. 30 minutes
    b. 1 hour
    c. 2–4 hours   c
    d. 36–48 hours

82. The normal range of coagulation time for venous blood
    (Lee & White three-tube test) is:
    a. 1–6 minutes
    b. Less than 4 minutes
    c. 5–10 minutes   c
    d. 12–18 minutes

83. The normal range of prothrombin time is:
    a. 1–3 seconds
    b. 4–8 seconds
    c. 10–12 seconds   c
    d. 19–24 seconds

84. The normal adult female values for the ESR using Wintrobe-
    Landsberg or Westergren method is:
    a. 0–9 mm./hr.
    b. 0–10 mm./hr.
    c. 0–20 mm./hr.
    d. 40–48 mm./hr.

85. The normal adult male values for the ESR using Wintrobe-
    Landsberg or Westergren method is:
    a. 0–9 mm./hr.   a
    b. 5–15 mm./hr.
    c. 10–20 mm./hr.
    d. 15–25 mm./hr.

86. If the RBC is 5,000,000/mm.^{3} and the reticulocyte count
    is 1%, the absolute reticulocyte count is:
    a. 3,000/mm.^{3}
    b. 50,000/mm.^{3} b
    c. 500,000/mm.^{3}

      d.   10,000/mm.^{2}

87.   The most accurate way to enumerate platelets is to identify
the platelets by using phase microscopy.   T   F   T

88.   The normal number of grams of hemoglobin in an adult
male is:
      a.   10 plus or minus 2 grams%
      b.   12 plus or minus 2 grams%
      c.   13 plus or minus 2 grams%
      d.   15 plus or minus 2 grams%   d

89.   Hemolysis of normal erythrocytes in hypotonic salt solution begins at the following sodium chloride concentration:
      a.   .48%
      b.   .44%   b
      c.   .40%
      d.   .34%

90.   Hemolysis of normal erythrocytes in hypotonic salt solution is complete at the following sodium chloride concentration:
      a.   .48%
      b.   .44%
      c.   .40%
      d.   .34%   d

91.   The normal range of MCHC is:
      a.   28–32 micromicrograms
      b.   33–35%   b
      c.   80–94 cu microns
      d.   1.7–2.5 microns

92.   The presence of reticulocytes in peripheral blood is abnormal.   T   F   F

93.   With a normal rate of red cell production in adults the following percentage of circulating r.b.c. are reticulocytes:
      a.   0–9.5%
      b.   0.5–1.5%   b
      c.   1.5–2.0%
      d.   2.0–4.0%

94.   The normal adult female values for the red cell count
(RBC) are:
      a.   3.5–4.5 millions/cu. mm.
      b.   5.0–6.0 millions/cu. mm.
      c.   4.3–5.5 millions/cu. mm.   c
      d.   4.5–6.0 millions/cu. mm.

95.   The normal range of erythrocyte count (RBC) in adult
males is:
      a.   4.5–6.0 millions/cu. mm.   a
      b.   5.5–6.5 millions/cu. mm.
      c.   4.0–5.0 millions/cu. mm.
      d.   3.8–5.4 millions/cu. mm.

96. The normal range of PCV in adult males is:
    a. 33–38%
    b. 42% plus or minus two
    c. .44 to .34%
    d. 47% plus or minus two   d

97. The normal range of MCH is:
    a. 80–94 cu. microns
    b. 1.7–2.5 microns
    c. 33–38%
    d. 28–32 micromicrograms   d

98. The normal range of MCV is:
    a. 28–32 micromicrograms
    b. 80–94 cu. microns   b
    c. 33–38%

99. The normal number of grams of hemoglobin in an adult
    female is:
    a. 10 plus or minus 2 grams%
    b. 12 plus or minus 2 grams%
    c. 14 plus or minus 2 grams%   c
    d. 16 plus or minus 2 grams%

100. Normal sedimentation rate values do not change with the
     method.   T   F   F

101. With a normal rate of red cell production in a newborn in-
     fant the following percentage of circulating r.b.c. are reti-
     culocytes:
     a. 0.5–1.0%
     b. 1.0–2.0%
     c. 4.0–5.5%
     d. 2.0–6.0%   d

102. In a normal bone marrow smear you would expect to find
     the following number of reticulocytes:
     a. 0–1.0%
     b. 1–5.0%   b
     c. 0–0.3%
     d. 15–35.0%

103. In a normal bone marrow smear you would expect to find
     the following number of lymphocytes:
     a. 0–5.0%
     b. 0–2.0%
     c. 4–16.0%   c
     d. 1–8.0%

104. In a normal bone marrow smear you would expect to find
     the following number of plasma cells:
     a. 0–1.0%   a
     b. 0–5.0%
     c. 5–25.0%
     d. 0–8.0%

105. In a normal bone marrow smear you would expect to find
     the following number of normoblasts:
     a. 0–5.0%
     b. 1–2.0%
     c. 2–3.5%
     d. 10–20%   d

106. In a normal bone marrow smear you would expect to find
     the following number of myeloblasts:
     a. 0–2.0%   a
     b. 5–20.0%
     c. 0–0.5%
     d. 0–2.0%

107. In a normal bone marrow smear you would expect to find
     the following number of neutrophilic myelocytes:
     a. 0–5.0%
     b. 1–8.0%
     c. 5–20.0%   c
     d. 0–2.0%

108. In a normal bone marrow smear you would expect to find
     the following number of neutrophilic metamyelocytes:
     a. 0–1.0%
     b. 5–10.0%   b
     c. 0–0.3%
     d. 0–4.0%

109. In a normal bone marrow smear you would expect to find
     the following number of neutrophilic band (stab) cells:
     a. 0–2.0%
     b. 0–3.0%
     c. 0–5.0%
     d. 15–35%   d

110. In a normal bone marrow smear you would expect to find
     the following number of segmented neutrophils:
     a. 0–4.0%
     b. 0–5.0%
     c. 0–7.0%
     d. 7–30.0%   d

111. The normal myeloid-erythroid ratio in the adult ranges
     from _____ or _____ to _____.   2 or 3 to 1

HEMOCYTOMETRY

112. Write out general formula for counting chamber calcula-
     tions.   See p. 189

113. The total ruled area of the counting chamber covers:
     a. 1 sq. mm.
     b. 9 sw. mm.   b

c. 10 sq. mm.
d. 12 sq. mm.

114. The counting chamber has the following depth:
    a. 0.05 mm.
    b. 0.10 mm.   b
    c. 0.20 mm.
    d. 0.25 mm.

115. The counting chamber has a depth of 1/10 mm. and a total ruled area which measures 3 mm. on each side. Therefore, the counting area of a chamber has a ruled area of 9 sq. mm., a depth of 0.1 mm. and a volume of:
    a. 0.9 cu. mm.   a
    b. 1.0 cu. mm.
    c. 0.5 cu. mm.
    d. 1.5 cu. mm.

116. Each of the smallest squares of the hemocytometer grating measures:
    a. 1/25 sq. mm.
    b. 1/4 sq. mm.
    c. 1/40 sq. mm.
    d. 1/400 sq. mm.   d

117. Distinguish between "original Neubauer" ruling and "improved Neubauer" ruling.   See p. 189

118. Distinguish between RBC pipette and WBC pipette.   See p. 189

119. The dilution range of a red cell pipette is:
    a. 1:10–1:100
    b. 1:20–1:200
    c. 1:50–1:500
    d. 1:100–1:1,000   d

120. The dilution range of a white cell pipette is:
    a. 1:10–1:100   a
    b. 1:20–1:200
    c. 1:50–1:500
    d. 1:100–1:1,000

121. In routine RBC the red cells are counted under high power in the following number of smallest squares:
    a. 16
    b. 64
    c. 80   c
    d. 120

122. An RBC should be replated whenever the greatest variation between "R" squares exceeds:
    a. 5 cells
    b. 10 cells
    c. 15 cells
    d. 20 cells   d

123. For routine RBC the blood is diluted 1:200 and, in order to report r.b.c./cu. mm., the number of these cells counted in 80 of the smallest squares may be directly multiplied by:
    a.   10
    b.   20
    c.   50
    d. 10,000   d

124. In routine WBC the white cells are counted under low power in the following number of sq. mm.:
    a. 1
    b. 2
    c. 4   c
    d. 9

125. A WBC should be replated whenever the greatest variation between "W" squares exceeds:
    a.   6 cells
    b.   12 cells   b
    c.   8 cells
    d.   4 cells

126. For routine WBC the blood is diluted 1:20 and, in order to report w.b.c. per cu. mm., the number of these cells counted within 4 sq. mm. may be directly multiplied by:
    a.   10
    b.   20
    c.   50   c
    d. 10,000

127. The presence of a small clot in the dilution will not, as a rule, render a count inaccurate.   T   F   F

128. Four major causes of error in doing chamber counts are:
    a. _____   See p. 189
    b. _____   "
    c. _____   "
    d. _____   "

129. The volume correction factor is obtained by multiplying the particular area factor by 10 (depth factor). Thus the volume correction factor for an ordinary red cell count would be:
    a.   2.5
    b.   10.0
    c.   20.0
    d.   50.0   d

130. White cells are counted in the four large corner squares of the counting chamber. Each one of these squares covers the following area:
    a.   9 sq. mm.
    b.   4 sq. mm.
    c.   1 sq. mm.   c
    d.   10 sq. mm.

131. The volume correction factor for an ordinary white cell count is:
    a. 2.5   a
    b. 4.0
    c. 5.0
    d. 10.0

132. The dilution correction factor for ordinary white cell counts (WBC) is:
    a. 200
    b. 10
    c. 100
    d. 20   d

133. The dilution correction factor for routine platelet count is:
    a. 50
    b. 100   b
    c. 200
    d. 500

134. The dilution correction factor for ordinary red cell counts (RBC) is:
    a. 20
    b. 50
    c. 100
    d. 200   d

135. Which of the following blood dilutions is employed for routine RBC:
    a. 1:20
    b. 1:50
    c. 1:100
    d. 1:200   d

136. Which of the following blood dilutions is employed for routine WBC:
    a. 1:10
    b. 1:20   b
    c. 1:50
    d. 1:200

137. When you draw blood to the 1.0 mark of an RBC pipette and platelet diluting fluid to the 101 mark you have the following blood dilution:
    a. 1:50
    b. 1:100   b
    c. 1:200
    d. 1:500

138. When you draw blood to the 1.0 mark of a WBC pipette and white cell diluting fluid to the 11.0 mark you have the following blood dilution:
    a. 1:10   a
    b. 1:20
    c. 1:50

d. 1:100

139. When you draw blood to the 0.5 mark of a WBC pipette and
white cell diluting fluid to the 11.0 mark, you have the following blood dilution:
    a. a:10
    b. 1:20   b
    c. 1:50
    d. a:100

140. When you draw blood to the 1.0 mark of an RBC pipette
and red cell diluting fluid to the 101 mark you have the
following blood dilution:
    a. 1:50
    b. 1:100   b
    c. 1:200
    d. 1:500

141. When you draw blood to the 0.5 mark of an RBC pipette
and red cell diluting fluid to the 101 mark you have the following blood dilution:
    a. 1:50
    b. 1:100
    c. 1:200   c
    d. 1:500

142. Explain the principle of photoelectric methods as they
apply to red blood cell enumeration. See p. 189

143. Explain the principle of the electronic (Coulter) blood
cell counter. See p. 189

144. The Coulter counter may also be used for WBC.   T   F | T

HEMOGLOBIN

145. Hemoglobin is a:
    a. Nucleoprotein
    b. Glycoprotein
    c. Lipoprotein
    d. Chromoprotein   d
    e. None of these

146. Name at least three (3) factors which, apart from disease,
may have an effect on hemoglobin concentration.   Age, altitude,
sex.

147. When changing from a low to a high altitude, hemoglobin
will show a:
    a. Physiologic increase   a
    b. Physiologic decrease
    c. Physiologic stability

148. Hemoglobin is a conjugated (heme plus globin) protein.
Heme contains iron in the ferrous state and can unite with

oxygen to form:
   a. Reduced hemoglobin
   b. Oxyhemoglobin
   c. Methemoglobin
   d. Carbon monoxide hemoglobin

b

149. Distinguish between "oxyhemoglobin" and "reduced hemo-globin."

See p. 189

150. Adult A hemoglobin is composed of 2 pairs of polypeptide chains called _____ and _____.

alpha (α) & beta (β)

151. Small amounts of fetal hemoglobin are normally present into adult life.   T   F

T

152. Fetal hemoglobin is composed of 2 pairs of polypeptide chains, _____ and _____.

alpha (α) & gamma (γ)

153. Hemoglobin synthesis occurs in:
   a. Liver
   b. Bone marrow
   c. Lungs
   d. Heart

b

154. Hemoglobin is synthesized in which of the following cells:
   a. Myeloblasts
   b. Normoblasts
   c. Monocytes
   d. Reticulocytes

b

d

155. Bilirubin, hemosiderin, and hematin are pigments derived from _____.

hemoglobin

156. Most of the hemoglobin degraded each day appears in the stool in the form of _____.

fecal uro-bilinogen

157. When the iron in hemoglobin is oxidized to the ferric form, the new compound is called _____ and it (can/cannot) carry oxygen.

methemo-globin; cannot

158. Slight variations in the isoelectric points of some of the various human hemoglobins provide the basis for recognition by _____.

electro-phoresis

159. It is actually better to report a hemoglobin test in percent than in grams.   T   F

F

160. Which of the following hemoglobin estimation methods is least reliable:
   a. Sahli
   b. Tallqvist
   c. Dare
   d. Newcomer

b

161. Which of the following hemoglobin estimation methods is
     based upon the acid hematin principle:
     a. Sheard-Sanford
     b. Osgood-Haskin   b
     c. Dare
     d. Tallqvist

162. Which of the following hemoglobin estimation methods is
     not based upon the acid hematin principle:
     a. Sahli
     b. Sheard-Sanford   b
     c. Newcomer
     d. Haden-Hauser

163. Acid hematin has the following color:
     a. Pink
     b. Purple
     c. Blue
     d. Brown   d

164. Drabkin's solution contains:
     a. Calcium chloride
     b. Cyanide   b
     c. Magnesium sulfate
     d. Sulfosalicylic acid

165. The most accurate method for measuring hemoglobin in
     clinical use is the _____.   cyanomethemo-
                                                          globin method

166. The copper sulfate method of hemoglobin determination
     is so accurate it can be relied upon for standardization of   ▼
     hemoglobinometers.   T   F   F

167. Iron content of hemoglobin (method of Wong). Hemo-
     globin contains 0.335% iron (some report 0.339%, others
     0.340%). Therefore, to obtain grams% hemoglobin, the
     amount of iron in milligrams% should be divided by:
     a.   0.335
     b.   3.35   b
     c.   33.5
     d.   335.0

168. The estimation (Van Slyke apparatus) of hemoglobin from
     amount of oxygen it will absorb is a measure of the non-
     functional hemoglobin (i.e., sulfhemoglobin, methemo-
     globin, etc.) as well as of the function (active) hemoglobin.
     T   F   F (only active
                                                       Hb measured)

169. To convert oxygen capacity to grams of hemoglobin per
     100 ml. of blood you would multiply oxygen capacity by:
     a. 1.315
     b. 0.746   b
     c. 0.625
     d. 0.116

170. One gram of hemoglobin can carry:
     a. 4 ml. of oxygen
     b. 1.3 ml. of oxygen   b
     c. 95% oxygen

171. A patient with a hemoglobin content of 14.5 grams% and
     an RBC of 5.0 million will have the following MCH value:
     a. 10 micromicrograms
     b. 7.25 micromicrograms
     c. 29 micromicrograms   c
     d. 72.5 micromicrograms

172. Old red blood cells are trapped in the cells of the _____   RE System:
     _____.   reticuloendo-
                                                                        thelial system

173. There the iron is removed from the hemoglobin and re-
     turned to the peripheral blood where it circulates bound
     to _____.   transferrin

174. Which of the following indices expresses a relationship
     between the hemoglobin content and the erythrocyte count:
     count;
     a. MCV
     b. MCH   b
     c. MCHC

175. Hemoglobin in plasma is usually bound by haptoglobin.
     T   F   T

176. The haptoglobin-binding capacity for hemoglobin is in the
     order of _____ hemoglobin   100 mg.%

RED BLOOD CELLS

177. In adults, the formation of red blood cells takes place in
     the:
     a. Heart
     b. Liver
     c. Pancreas
     d. Bone marrow   d
     e. Lymph nodes

178. The L.E. factor is present in the red cells.   T   F   F

179. Normal erythrocytes are:
     a. Neutrophilic
     b. Acidophilic   b
     c. Basophilic

180. Heinz bodies represent denatured globin from hemoglobin.
     T   F   T

181. The basic mechanisms that result in formation of a target
     cell are:

a. _____   increased
surface area
b. _____   decreased
cell Hgb. con-
tent

182. A nucleated cell resembling a lymphocyte but which has
denser nuclear chromatin and an orange-pink tinted cytoplasm would probably be a:
    a. Normoblast   a
    b. Monocyte
    c. Basophil
    d. Plasmacyte

183. Normoblasts are nucleated erythrocytes.   T   F   T

184. Reticulocyte counts are used as an index of red cell production.   T   F   T

185. Reticulocytes can often be detected in Wright's stained
smears provided examination is carried out under dimmed
light.   T   F   F

186. Reticulocytes may appear larger and polychromatophilic
on Wright stained smears.   T   F   T

187. Reticulocytes may look like adult erythrocytes in Wright
stained blood smears.   T   F   T

188. What causes Cabot rings? What are Cabot rings made of?   See p. 190

189. Any abnormal changes in the erythrocytes need not be
noted in a CBC report.   T   F   F

190. Which of the following structures is not classified as an
erythrocyte inclusion:
    a. Cabot rings
    b. Auer's rods   b
    c. Heinz bodies
    d. Howell-Jolly bodies

191. Howell-Jolly bodies are:
    a. Remnants of nuclear material shaped like dots   a
    b. Remnants of nuclear material shaped like a ring
    c. Either a or b
    d. Neither a nor b

192. An abnormally thin erythrocyte ("leptocyte") presenting
a bull's eye appearance in the stained smear is a:
    a. Sickle cell
    b. Target cell   b
    c. Burr cell
    d. Crenalated cell

193. The term schistocyte is used to describe a variation in red
blood cell stage. Synonyms include:
    a. Helmet cells   a
    b. Microangiopathic red cells   b

    c. Target cells
    d. Hypochroma

194. Mention at least six different tests involving the erythrocytes. See p. 190

195. Echinocytes are also called:
    a. Burr cells   a
    b. Spiculated red blood cells   b
    c. Prickle red blood cells   c
    d. Target cells

196. A test to determine maximum capacity of erythrocytes to withstand hypotonic stress is the:
    a. Osmotic fragility test   a
    b. Mechanical fragility test
    c. Thorn test
    d. Rumpel-Leede test

197. When fresh blood is mixed with 0.85% salt solution the erythrocytes will:
    a. Shrink
    b. Swell
    c. Either a or b
    d. Neither a nor b   d

198. In relation to body fluids, the salt solution employed in the osmotic fragility test of erythrocytes may be said to be:
    a. Isotonic
    b. Hypotonic   b
    c. Hypertonic

199. Which of the following cells is most resistant to hemolysis by hypotonic salt solution:
    a. Normal erythrocyte
    b. Spherocyte
    c. Thin cell or leptocyte ("target" cell)   c
    d. Sickle cell

200. Stomatocytes are:
    a. Red cells with holes
    b. Red cells with spurs and progectiles
    c. Red cells with cup shapes having lost half of their biconcavity   c

201. The PCV can be accurately determined only by means of a hematocrit tube.   T   F   T

202. Explain how the PCV is determined in the Coulter Models. See p. 190

203. Distinguish between "hematocrit" and "microhematocrit." See p. 190

204. Distinguish between "sedimentation rate" and "sedimentation index. See p. 190

205. Which of the following is not a method of sedimentation rate determination:

a. Wintrobe-Landsberg
b. Lee & White   b
c. Cutler
d. Westergren
e. Linzenmeier

206. The primary factors measured by sedimentation rate deter-
     minations are:
     a. Plasma albumin content
     b. Fibrinogen-globulin concentration   b
     c. Rouleaux formation   c
     d. Blood specific gravity

207. The longer the column of blood the faster the ESR.   T   F   T

208. Prolonged standing (over 3 hours) will:
     a. Decrease the ESR   a
     b. Increase the ESR
     c. Have no effect on the ESR

209. An increase in temperature will:
     a. Decrease the ESR
     b. Increase the ESR   b
     c. Have no effect on the ESR

210. Tilting the tube will:
     a. Decrease the ESR
     b. Increase the ESR   b
     c. Have no effect on the ESR

211. Whole blood dilution by aqueous substances will:
     a. Markedly decrease the ESR   a
     b. Markedly increase the ESR
     c. Neither a nor b

212. Using a test tube of smaller (below 2.5 mm.) diameter will:
     a. Decrease the ESR   a
     b; Increase the ESR
     c. Neither a nor b

213. The percent dilution of the blood in Cutler's method is:
     a.   0
     b.   0.4
     c. 10   c
     d. 20

214. The percent dilution of the blood in Westergren method is:
     a.   0   a
     b.   0.4
     c. 10
     d. 20

215. The percent dilution of the blood in Wintrobe method is:
     a.   0   a
     b.   0.4
     c. 10
     d. 20

216. A Cutler tube is graduated between:
    a. 0–18 mm.
    b. 0–50 mm.   b
    c. 0–100 mm.
    d. 0–200 mm.

217. A Westergren tube is graduated between:
    a. 0–18 mm.
    b. 0–50 mm.
    c. 0–100 mm.
    d. 0–200 mm.   d

218. A Wintrobe tube is graduated between:
    a. 0–18 mm.
    b. 0–50 mm.
    c. 0–100 mm.   c
    d. 0–200 mm.

219. The height of the blood column in a Cutler tube is:
    a. 10 mm.
    b. 50 mm.   b
    c. 100 mm.
    d. 200 mm.

220. The height of the blood column in a Westergren tube is:
    a. 10 mm.
    b. 50 mm.
    c. 100 mm.
    d. 200 mm.   d

221. The height of the blood column in a Wintrobe tube is:
    a. 10 mm.
    b. 50 mm.
    c. 100 mm.   c
    d. 200 mm.

222. The internal diameter of a Cutler tube is:
    a. 1.0 mm.
    b. 2.5 mm.
    c. 4.0 mm.
    d. 5.0 mm.   d

223. The internal diameter of a Westergren tube is:
    a. 1.0 mm.
    b. 2.5 mm.   b
    c. 4.0 mm.
    d. 5.0 mm.

224. The internal diameter of a Wintrobe tube is:
    a. 1.0 mm.
    b. 2.5 mm.   b
    c. 4.0 mm.
    d. 5.0 mm.

225. A Cutler tube has the following length:
    a. 65 mm.

    b. 300 mm.
    c. 70 mm.   c
    d. 120 mm.

226. A Westergren tube has the following length:
    a. 65 mm.
    b. 300 mm.   b
    c. 70 mm.
    d. 120 mm.

227. A Wintrobe tube has the following length:
    a. 65 mm.
    b. 300 mm.
    c. 70 mm.
    d. 120 mm.   d

WHITE BLOOD CELLS

228. Lymphoblasts are peroxidase-positive.   T   F   F

229. Lymphocytes are peroxidase-positive.   T   F   F

230. Basophils are peroxidase-negative.   T   F   F

231. Monocytes can pass through blood vessel walls and become fixed to tissues.   T   F   T

232. Monocytes are granulocytes.   T   F   F

233. Eosinophils are granulocytes.   T   F   T

234. Acute stress or electric shock may cause the white blood cell count to:
    a. Increase   a
    b. Decrease
    c. Stay the same

235. The white blood cell count is normally higher in the afternoon than in the morning.   T   F   T

236. The most immature cell in the plasmacytic series is the:
    a. Plasmacyte
    b. Plasmablast   b
    c. Lymphoblast
    d. Megakaryoblast

237. The most immature cell in the granulocytic series is the:
    a. Monocyte
    b. Myelocyte
    c. Myeloblast   c
    d. Monoblast

238. All granulocytes contain the enzyme:
    a. Lipase
    b. Phosphatase
    c. Ptyalin
    d. Peroxidase   d

239. The phagocytes in the liver sinusoids are called:
    a. Plasma cells
    b. Downey cells
    c. Türk cells
    d. Küppfer's cells   d

240. All leukocytes are capable of phagocytosis.   T   F   F

241. Neutrophils may show toxic changes under certain conditions.   T   F   T

242. Write out a Schilling hemogram.   See p. 190

243. Monocytes (like neutrophilic leukocytes) are actively phagocytic.   T   F   T

244. Plasma cells can usually be seen in peripheral blood smears.   T   F   F

245. Lymphocytes possess phagocytic properties.   T   F   F

246. The formation of lymphocytes takes place in the bone marrow exclusively.   T   F   F

247. Which of the following cells is largest and possesses a "sprawling" nucleus:
    a. Small lymphocyte
    b. Large lymphocyte
    c. Neutrophilic segmented cell
    d. Monocyte   d

248. Lymphocytes derived from the thymus:
    a. produce antibodies
    b. are involved in cell mediated immune responses like tuberculin hypersensitivity
    c. can undergo phagocytosis   b

249. Which of the following cells is characterized by a number of bluish-black coarse cytoplasmic granules:
    a. Monocyte
    b. Neutrophil
    c. Eosinophil
    d. Basophil   d

250. Which of the following cells is characterized by numerous large brilliant red cytoplasmic granules:
    a. Monocyte
    b. Neutrophil
    c. Eosinophil
    d. Basophil   c

251. Lymphocytes derived from the bone marrow:
    a. Can produce antibodies   a
    b. Are involved in cell mediated immunity
    c. Become phagocytes

252. The segmented cell is the most immature cell of the granulocytic series.   T   F   F

253. The segmented cell precedes the band cell.   T   F   F

254. Which of the following cells of the granulocytic series is characterized by nuclear lobes connected by filaments:
     a. Myelocyte
     b. Metamyelocyte
     c. Band cell
     d. Segmented cell   d

255. The normal adult neutrophil has ____ lobes   3

256. There are at least two functional classes of lymphocytes. They are called:
     a. T cells   a
     b. R cells
     c. B cells   c
     d. Y cells

257. Antibody producing lymphocytes can, under stimulation, undergo differentiation into:
     a. Plasma cells   a
     b. Monocytes
     c. Monoblasts

258. Eosinophils generally have ____ lobes   2

259. Neutrophils and monocytes can ingest red blood cells coated with specific antibodies.   T   F   T

260. Monocytes are derived from cells that normally grow in the bone marrow.   T   F   T

261. The monoblast is derived from the same precursor cell that gives rise to the myeloblast.   T   F   T

262. Mention at least four tests involving the leukocytes.   See p. 190

263. What role to reticuloendothelial cells play?   See p. 190

264. The blood cell that is the precursor cell for fixed tissue macrophages is the _____.   monocyte

PLATELETS

265. The immediate precursor of the thrombocyte is:
     a. Promegakaryocyte
     b. Megakaryocyte   b
     c. Megakaryoblast

266. Platelet size and shape are quite constant.   T   F   F

267. Platelets can release:
     a. Serotonin   a
     b. Epinephrine   b
     c. Norepinephrine
     d. Cholesterol

268. Platelets also can release:
     a. Fibrinogen   a
     b. ADP (adenosine diphosphate)   b
     c. Calcium   c
     d. Thrombin

269. List the various methods for determining platelet counts.   See p. 190

270. Which of the following methods of platelet enumeration are
     indirect methods:
     a. Fonio   a
     b. Rees-Ecker
     c. Tocantin
     d. Olef   d

271. On a well stained blood smear of a normal person there
     should be how many platelets in each oil immersion
     (900X) field:
     a. 8–12   a
     b. 2–4
     c. 4–6
     d. 6–8

BLEEDING AND COAGULATION

272. The role of the platelet in coagulation is:
     a. To provide the initial hemostatic plug at a vessel's
        break
     b. To contribute platelet lipid required for coagulation
        in the intrinsic system
     c. To control clot retraction
     d. All of the above   d

273. Ivy's bleeding time is a measure of _____
     _____.   ability of
                                                      platelets to
                                                      form a hemo-
                                                      static plug

274. There are two pathways in coagulation. These are called:
     a. The inferior system
     b. The extrinsic system   b
     c. The intrinsic system   c
     d. The superior system

275. In the intrinsic system all the coagulant factors are found
     in circulating blood.   T   F   T

276. In the extrinsic system all the coagulant factors are found
     in circulating blood.   T   F   F

277. Thromboplastin for the extrinsic system is present in tissue
     extracts.   T   F   T

278. Thromboplastin complexes with Factor ____ in blood   VII
     before it can be fully active.

279. In the extrinsic system, thromboplastin reacts with Factor VII to stimulate the activation of Factor ___ ;   X

280. In the intrinsic system Factor X is activated by a complex of _____ , _____ , _____ , and _____   Factor IX, Factor VIII, Ca^{++}, platelet phospholipid _____ .

281. Factor X, in the presence of Factor ____ , _____ , and _____ phospholipid, can catalyze the conversion of prothrombin (II) into _____ .   V, Ca^{++}, platelet thrombin

282. Blood also contains factors that antagonize coagulation.
T   F   T

283. When blood clots the fibrinogen of the plasma becomes converted to:
    a. Thromboplastin
    b. Thrombin
    c. Fibrin   c
    d. Prothrombin

284. A test which determines the rate of fibrin formation under a standardized set of conditions is the:
    a. Bleeding time
    b. Partial thromboplastin time   b
    c. Clot retraction time
    d. Thorn test

285. The actions of thrombin are:
    a. To convert fibrinogen to fibrin   a
    b. To activate plasminogen to plasmin   b
    c. To activate Factor XIII   c
    d. Aggregate and fuse platelets   d

286. The activity of the plasminogen-plasmin system can be assayed in the:
    a. Whole blood clot lysis time   a
    b. The euglobulin clot lysis time   b
    c. The P & P time
    d. Quick prothrombin time

287. The plasminogen-plasmin system is concerned with lysing clots in the circulation.   T   F   T

288. Plasmin is a proteolytic enzyme that can lyse fibrinogen and fibrin.   T   F   T

289. Fibrin split products may be detected in the serum by using tests based on the following two general principles:
    a. _____   See p. 191
    b. _____   ,,

290. The longer the prothrombin time the greater the prothrombin concentration.   T   F   F

291. When the prothrombin time is increased the prothrombin

concentration is:
   a. Increased
   b. Decreased   b
   c. Neither a nor b

292. Which of the following tests is not related to blood coagu-
     lation:
   a. Platelet count
   b. Coagulation time
   c. Erythrocyte fragility   c
   d. Prothrombin time

293. Venous blood methods have a shorter clotting time than
     capillary blood methods.   T   F   F

294. The procoagulant factors: prothrombin, Factor IX, Factor
     X, Factor VII, and fibrinogen are made in the:
   a. Pancreas
   b. Liver   b
   c. Bone marrow
   d. Ovary

295. The bleeding time is only abnormally prolonged in the case
     of thrombocytopenia.   T   F   F

296. Prothrombin production is governed by the availability of
     the following vitamin:
   a. A
   b. B_{12}
   c. C
   d. K   d

297. Vitamin K is required for the adequate provision of the fol-
     lowing procoagulant factors:
   a. Factor VII   a
   b. Factor VIII
   c. Factor II   c
   d. Factor IX   d
   e. Factor X   e

TECHNICAL TERMS

298. Chemical substances liberated from infected tissues attract
     circulating neutrophils. This phenomenon is known as:
   a. Chemotaxis   a
   b. Phagocytosis
   c. Leukopoiesis
   d. Diapedesis

299. A condition of unknown cause is said to be:
   a. Symptomatic
   b. Chronic
   c. Psychosomatic
   d. Idiopathic   d

300. The suffix "–osis" at the end of a word means:
    a. Separation from
    b. Without
    c. Increase in   c
    d. Decrease in

301. The prefix "aniso–" means:
    a. The same
    b. Without
    c. New
    d. Unequal   d

302. Incomplete or defective development of tissue is called:
    a. Anemia
    b. Aplasia   b
    c. Microcytosis
    d. Mononucleosis

303. Reduction, below physiologic levels, of oxygen in body
     tissues is called:
    a. Anemia
    b. Anopsia
    c. Anorexia
    d. Anoxia   d

304. A substance which, when added to a solution, is responsible
     for increased resistance to changes in hydrogen-ion concen-
     tration when either acid or alkali is added is called:
    a. An electrolyte
    b. A buffer   b
    c. An indicator
    d. A primary standard

305. The combination of hemoglobin and carbon dioxide is
     called:
    a. Oxyhemoglobin
    b. Sulfhemoglobin
    c. Carboxyhemoglobin   c
    d. Methemoglobin

306. The word "leukopenia" refers to a:
    a. Low total white cell count   a
    b. High total white cell count
    c. Normal white cell count

307. The term "neutropenia" refers to a:
    a. Low total white cell count
    b. Low neutrophil count   b
    c. Elevated lymphocyte count

308. A high total white cell count is called:
    a. Erythrocytosis
    b. Leukocytosis   b
    c. Leukopenia
    d. "Shift to the left"

309. White blood cell formation is also called:
    a. Erythropoiesis
    b. Leukemia
    c. Leukopoiesis   c
    d. Leukocytosis

310. The term "pleocytosis" refers to:
    a. A variation in shape of red cells
    b. An increase in the number of CSF lymphocytes   b
    c. Erythrocyte basophilia
    d. A condition characterized by the presence of oval-
       shaped erythrocytes

311. When the total number of red cells in the blood becomes
    excessive the condition is known as:
    a. Leukemia
    b. Polycythemia   b
    c. Anemia
    d. Erythroblastosis
    e. Erythremia   e

312. Variation in hemoglobin content of erythrocytes is called:
    a. Orthochromia
    b. Hyperchromia
    c. Anisochromia   c
    d. Hypochromia

313. The presence of red cells in the urine is called:
    a. Hemoglobinemia
    b. Hematuria   b
    c. Hemoglobinuria
    d. Erythremia

314. The presence of hemoglobin in the plasma is called:
    a. Hemoglobinuria
    b. Hemoglobinemia   b
    c. Occult blood
    d. Hematuria

315. The presence of free hemoglobin in the urine is called:
    a. Hemoglobinemia
    b. Occult blood
    c. Hemoglobinuria   c
    d. Hematuria

316. When the hemoglobin content of cells is decreased the cen-
    tral pale area of erythrocytes becomes larger and paler. This
    condition is known as:
    a. Hypochromia   a
    b. Hyperchromia
    c. Anisochromia
    d. Normochromia

317. Sickle cells are also called:
    a. Ovalocytes

b. Target cells
c. Burr cells
d. Drepanocytes   d

318. Basophilic stippling is also known as:
    a. Polychromatophilia
    b. Poikilocytosis
    c. Hemochromatosis
    d. Punctate basophilia   d

319. The presence of basophilic stippling means that:
    a. There is too much methylene blue in the Wright's
       stain
    b. There is aggregation of residual ribosomal RNA in the
       affected red cells   b
    c. There is lead in the Wright's stain

320. When basophilic stippling is seen it must be in:
    a. Old red blood cells
    b. Young red blood cells   b
    c. All ages of red blood cells

321. "Schizocytes" are:
    a. Larger than normal erythrocytes
    b. Fragments of erythrocytes   b
    c. Smaller than normal erythrocytes
    d. Normal size erythrocytes

322. The splitting up of a nucleus is known as:
    a. Mononucleosis
    b. Karyorrhexis   b
    c. Anisocytosis
    d. Polychromatophilia

323. A term opposed to "anemia" is:
    a. Erythrocytosis   a
    b. Leukemia
    c. Leukemoid
    d. Leukocytosis

324. A small red cell is a:
    a. Metarubricyte
    b. Macrocyte
    c. Microcyte   c
    d. Reticulocyte

325. A large red cell is a:
    a. Poikilocyte
    b. Normocyte
    c. Macrocyte   c
    d. Microcyte

326. The abnormal variation in shape among r.b.c. is called:
    a. Anisocytosis
    b. Poikilocytosis   b

    c. Polychromatophilia
    d. Spehrocytosis

327. The abnormal variation in size among r.b.c. is called:
    a. Anisocytosis   a
    b. Poikilocytosis
    c. Polychromatophilia
    d. Spherocytosis

328. Polychromatophilia is also called:
    a. Poikilocytosis
    b. Polychromasia   b
    c. Erythroblastosis
    d. Neutrophilia

329. "Juveniles" are technically known as:
    a. Myelocytes
    b. Metamyelocytes   b
    c. Band cells
    d. Segmented cells

330. Explain the difference(s) between "anemia" and "erythremia." See p. 191

331. Explain the difference between "leukocytosis" and "leukemia." See p. 191

332. Explain the difference between "leukocytosis" and "leukopenia." See p. 191

333. Explain the difference between "leukemia and "leukemoid reaction." See p. 191

334. Explain the difference between "polycythemia vera" and "pseudopolycythemia." See p. 191

335. Explain the difference between "anisocytosis" and "poikilocytosis." See p. 191

336. Explain the difference between "polychromatophilia" ("polychromasia") and "basophilic stippling" ("punctate basophilia"). See p. 191

337. Explain the difference between "macrocyte" and "microcyte." See p. 191

338. Explain the difference between "acidophilic structures" and "basophilic structures." See p. 191

339. Explain the difference between "rouleaux formation" (a form of pseudoagglutination) and "true agglutination." See p. 191

340. In the presence of extensive polychromatophilia the reticulocyte count will be:
    a. Normal
    b. Increased   b
    c. Decreased
    d. None of the above

341. If the haptoglobin-combining capacity of the plasma for hemoglobin is exceeded, free hemoglobin appears in the urine. This condition is called _____ .

hemoglo-binuria

ABNORMAL HEMATOLOGY

342. Which of the following animal parasites cannot be present in a blood smear:
    a. Plasmodium
    b. Microfilaria
    c. Trypanosoma
    d. Schistosoma

d

Red Cells

343. Pernicious anemia is caused by a deficiency of:
    a. Vitamin K
    b. Vitamin B_{12}
    c. Vitamin C
    d. Vitamin A

b

344. Another vitamin deficiency that is similar to pernicious anemia in that it presents with anemia, macrocytic r.b.c., and megaloblasts in the marrow is:
    a. Folic acid deficiency
    b. Vitamin D deficiency
    c. Vitamin B deficiency
    d. Vitamin K deficiency

a

345. In anemia due to vitamin B_{12} deficiency or folic acid deficiency the reticulocyte count is high.   T   F

F

346. Hypochromia is seen in:
    a. Iron deficiency anemia
    b. Thallasemia
    c. The anemia of chronic disease
    d. All of the above

d

347. Heinz bodies occur in r.b.c. in which of the following conditions:
    a. Drug-induced hemolysis
    b. Hemolysis associated with the unstable hemoglobins
    c. Hemolysis associated with hereditary deficiency of glucose-6-phosphate dehydrogenase
    d. PNH

a
b

c

348. The osmotic fragility test is increased in _____ _____ and in the _____ .

hereditary spherocytosis; autoimmune hemolytic anemias

349. A high MCV would be expected in an untreated PA case.
     T   F   T

350. A low PCV indicates anemia.   T   F   T

351. Both RBC and PCV are increased in:
     a. Anemia
     b. Leukemia
     c. Polycythemia vera   c
     d. Dehydration   d

352. Basophilic stippling of erythrocytes occurs characteristi-
     cally in the following:
     a. Infectious mononucleosis
     b. Lead poisoning   b
     c. Erythroblastosis fetalis
     d. Viral hepatitis

353. Lead poisoning is the only condition in which the erythro-
     cytes are likely to show basophilic stippling (punctate baso-
     philia).   T   F   F

354. Lead poisoning cannot be diagnosed unless basophilic stip-
     pling of erythrocytes can be demonstrated.   T   F   F

355. A macrocytosis characteristically occurs in:
     a. Sickle cell anemia
     b. Erythroblastosis fetalis
     c. Lead poisoning
     d. Pernicious anemia   d

356. In severe or acute anemia very large polychromatophilic
     RBC appear in the blood.   T   F   T

357. These large RBC are called:
     a. Shift macrocytes   a
     b. Leptocytes
     c. Drepanocytes
     d. Spherocytes

358. They probably represent the occurrence of skipped divi-
     sions in the marrow normoblasts in order to deliver RBC
     to the blood more quickly.   T   F   T

359. Target cells are found in some of the hereditary hemoglo-
     binopathies.   T   F   T

360. The hemoglobinopathies one associates with target cells
     include:
     a. Hemoglobin C disease   a
     b. Hemoglobin SC disease   b
     c. Thalassemia   c
     d. Hemoglobin G

361. The autohemolysis test is used for detecting:
     a. Hereditary spherocytosis   a
     b. Hereditary metabolic disorders of RBC   b
     c. Pernicious anemia

d. Sickle cell anemia

362. In a case of obstructive jaundice you would expect the erythrocyte fragility to be:
    a. Increased
    b. Decreased
    c. Normal

    b

363. In a case of hereditary spherocytosis you would expect the erythrocyte fragility to be:
    a. Increased
    b. Decreased
    c. Normal

    a

364. In cases of sickle cell anemia the red cells become sickle-shaped when:
    a. Oxygen is added to the cells
    b. Oxygen is removed from the cells
    c. Cell fragility is increased
    d. Cell fragility is decreased.

    b

365. Therefore only deoxy sickle hemoglobin can undergo the sickling process.   T   F

    T

366. When sickle cell erythrocytes have been deoxygenated and have undergone sickling, restoration of oxygen to the system causes most of the erythrocytes to resume a normal shape.   T   F

    T

367. Those sickle cell erythrocytes that retain their sickle shape even after oxygen is restored and the cells contain only oxy sickle hemoglobin are called _____.

    irreversibly sickled cells

368. An elevated sedimentation rate is generally associated with:
    a. Metabolic disease
    b. Diseases of inflammation
    c. Collagen disease
    d. Diseases of nutrition
    e. Allergic diseases

    b
    c

369. The sedimentation rate is usually increased in the following condition(s):
    a. Pregnancy
    b. Infectious mononucleosis
    c. Rheumatic fever
    d. Cancer
    e. Pernicious anemia.

    a
    b
    c
    d

370. The situations wherein reduced r.b.c. contents lead to target cell formation include:
    a. Thalassemia
    b. Iron deficiency anemia
    c. Some forms of hemoglobinopathy (C disease)
    d. Pernicious anemia

    a
    b
    c

371. The situations wherein increased surface area leads to the formation of target cells occurs in:
    a. Obstructive jaundice
    b. Renal failure
    c. Hereditary spherocytosis
    d. Shock

a

372. Spur cells are r.b.c. with long projections. They are seen associated with hemolytic states in:
    a. Overwhelming hepatic failure
    b. Pneumonia
    c. Infectious mononucleosis
    d. Acquired autoimmune hemolytic anemia

a

373. Schizocytes or burr cells are characteristically seen in:
    a. Microangiopathic hemolytic anemia
    b. Hereditary spherocytosis
    c. Disseminated intravascular coagulation
    d. Sickle cell anemia
    e. Hemolysis associated with prosthetic heart valves

a

c

e

374. Stomatocytes are cup-shaped r.b.c. that have a slit appearance on Wright-stained smears. They are seen in:
    a. Hemolysis with alcoholic cirrhosis
    b. Hemolysis in certain hereditary conditions
    c. In thalassemia
    d. In iron deficiency anemia

a
b

375. A normal sedimentation rate excludes serious disease.
    T   F

F

376. Sickle cell disease is a hereditary disease which affects blacks predominantly.   T   F

T

377. Sickle cell trait and sickle cell anemia are one and the same condition.   T   F

F

378. In the seventh month of pregnancy a woman may have a PCV of 38 and still have a normal or even slightly increased total red cell mass.   T   F

T

379. An important factor in plasma that determines the ESR is:
    a. Fibrin
    b. Fibrinogen
    c. Prothrombin

b

380. It is possible to have an elevated sedimentation rate with a normal plasma protein level.   T   F

T

381. The difference between polycythemia vera and erythremia is that polycythemia vera is due to primary marrow disease and is associated with increases in:
    a. _____
    b. _____
    On the other hand, erythremia is secondary to some other condition, namely:
    a. _____

WBC
platelet count

See p. 192

b. _____

c. _____

See p. 192
"

Hemoglobin

382. In anemias and leukemias and other diseases that affect the bone marrow you would expect hemoglobin values to b.:
    a. Decreased
    b. Increased
    c. Normal

a

383. In a case of classical sickle cell anemia about 90% of the hemoglobin would be S or sickle hemoglobin.   T   F

T

384. The remaining hemoglobin is usually:
    a. Hemoglobin A
    b. Hemoglobin A_2
    c. Fetal hemoglobin

c

385. All of the hemoglobin found in sickle cell trait ("sicklemia") is of the "S" variety.   T   F

F

386. In sickle trait what per cent of the hemoglobin is sickle hemoglobin:
    a. 45%
    b. 10%
    c. 85%

a

387. The hemoglobin concentration of blood may be increased in:
    a. Anemia
    b. Polycythemia vera
    c. Dehydration
    d. Erythremia secondary to cardiac or pulmonary disease

b
c

d

388. The total body hemoglobin is increased in:
    a. Anemia
    b. Polycythemia vera
    c. Leukemia
    d. Dehydration
    e. Erythremia secondary to severe pulmonary disease or congenital heart disease

b

e

389. Polycythemic blood is more viscous.   T   F

T

390. The hemoglobin content of the blood is decreased in:
    a. Erythremia
    b. Polycythemia vera
    c. Dehydration
    d. Anemia

d

391. The presence of an abnormal hemoglobin is responsible for sickle cell formation.   T   F

T

392. "S" hemoglobin may be separated from other hemoglobins by _____ and by _____.   electrophoresis;
differential
solubility

White Cells

393. A white blood cell differential count which contains in-creased numbers of stab forms and myelocytes is said to:
    a. Be shifted to the right
    b. Be normal
    c. Be shifted to the left   c

394. A white blood count of 3,500 where there are 15% PMN and 85% lymphocytes indicates that the patient has:
    a. Balanced leucopemia
    b. Absolute lymphocytosis
    c. Neutropenia
    d. All of the above   c

395. The L.E. cell factor is a component of:
    a. Serum albumin
    b. Serum alpha globulin
    c. Serum beta globulin
    d. Serum gamma globulin   d

396. Distinguish between "L.E." cells and "tart cells."   See p. 192

397. In whooping cough peripheral blood smears show a high lymphocyte count.   T   F   T

398. Acute infectious lymphocytosis affects:
    a. Children
    b. Adults   a

399. Acute infectious lymphocytosis and infectious mononucle-osis are one and the same condition.   T   F   F

400. In infectious mononucleosis the total white cell count (WBC) is:
    a. Low
    b. Normal
    c. Mildly elevated
    d. Very high   c

401. The characterized finding on the peripheral smear in in-fectious mononucleosis is:
    a. An eosinophilic leucocytosis
    b. A distinct increase in atypical lymphocytes
    c. Decreased number of basophils   b

402. Atypical lymphocytes are really lymphocytes that have been transformed by contact with viruses or antigens.
    T   F   T

403. In suspected infectious mononucleosis a helpful test is:
    a. Heterophile test   a
    b. Monospot   b

404. When the body is invaded by pyogenic bacteria there occurs
    a dramatic increase in the number of:
    a. Circulating eosinophils
    b. Circulating neutrophils   b
    c. Small lymphocytes
    d. Large lymphocytes
    e. Monocytes

405. The white blood cell count is usually high in viral infec-
    tions.   T   F   F

406. In the presence of inflammation or infection the neutro-
    phils may show:
    a. Toxic granulation   a
    b. Döhle bodies   b
    c. Auer rods

407. The percent number of neutrophils is increased in:
    a. Appendicitis   a
    b. Tuberculosis
    c. Pneumonia   c
    d. Infectious mononucleosis

408. The percent number of eosinophils is increased in:
    a. Brucellosis
    b. Asthma   b
    c. Hay fever   c
    d. Parasitic infections   d

409. The circulating monocyte is the precursor of the fixed tis-
    sue macrophages.   T   F   T

410. The total white cell count is always high in leukemia.
    T   F   F

411. Which of the following cell types is usually increased in
    asthma, hay fever, and certain parasitic diseases:
    a. Segmented neutrophil
    b. Segmented eosinophil   b
    c. Basophil
    d. Monocyte

412. A patient with a white blood count of 3,500 and a differ-
    ential count of 65% PMN, 5% monocytes, and 30% lym-
    phocytes has:
    a. Balanced leucopenia   a
    b. A left shift
    c. Neutropenia
    d. Lymphocytosis

413. In typhus, brucellosis, tuberculosis, and monocytic leu-
    kemia you would expect the monocytes to be:

a. Increased   a
b. Decreased
c. Normal in number

414. In mumps and whooping cough you would expect the lymphocytes to be:
    a. Increased   a
    b. Decreased
    c. Normal in number

415. Cells of the granulocyte series have primary granules that appear at the promyelocyte stage.   T   F   T

416. At what stage in development of the granulocyte line do the specific or secondary granules appear:
    a. Myeloblast
    b. Promyelocyte
    c. Myelocyte   c

417. Toxic granulation represents persistence of the primary granules of the neutrophils.   T   F   T

418. In appendicitis, meningitis, and pneumonia, you would expect the total white cell count to be:
    a. Increased   a
    b. Decreased
    c. Normal

419. In these conditions the differential count would be:
    a. Left shifted   a
    b. Right shifted
    c. Normal

420. The percent number of monocytes is increased in:
    a. Whooping cough
    b. Tuberculosis   b
    c. Typhus fever   c
    d. Hay fever

421. In typhoid fever, influenza, measles, brucellosis, and neutropenia you would expect the total white cell count to be:
    a. Increased
    b. Decreased   b
    c. Normal

422. A real increase in the absolute numbers of small mature lymphocytes occurs in:
    a. Systemic lupus
    b. Chronic lymphocyte leukemia   b
    c. Hodgkins disease

423. Atypical lymphocytes are seen in the following condition:
    a. Infectious mononucleosis
    b. Toxoplasmosis
    c. Cytomegalovirus infection
    d. Infectious hepatitis

e. All of the above   e

424. In some forms of lymphosarcoma abnormal lymphocytes
and lymphoblasts can be seen in the peripheral blood smear.
T   F   T

425. The lymphocyte count may be low in Hodgkin's disease.
T   F   T

426. In Vitamin B_{12} deficiency and folic acid deficiency a useful clue to the diagnosis is the presence of hypersegmented
PMN (more than 4 lobes) in the peripheral smear.   T   F   T

427. Match the following:
a. Leukocytes (high	1. Typhoid fever		b
total white cell	2. Meningitis		a
count)	3. Brucellosis		b
b. Leukopenia (low	4. Pneumonia		a
total white cell	5. Influenza		b
count)	6. Appendicitis		a
	7. Measles		b
	8. Neutropenia		b
	9. Leukemia		a (or b)
	10. Diphtheria		a

Platelets

428. List various causes of low platelet counts.   See p. 192

429. In Vitamin B_{12} deficiency the platelet count and WBC
count may be decreased.   T   F   T

430. In aplastic anemia you would expect the platelet count to
be:
a. High
b. Low   b
c. Normal

431. A low capillary resistance may be expected in:
a. Thrombocytopenic purpura   a
b. Scurvy   b
c. Hemophilia
d. Pernicious anemia

Bleeding & Coagulation

432. If a platelet count is below 50,000/cu. mm. you would expect the bleeding time to be:
a. Decreased
b. Increased   b
c. Either a or b
d. Neither a nor b

433. If a platelet count is low you would expect the clot retrac-

tion time to be:
   a. Decreased
   b. Increased   b
   c. either a or b
   d. Neither a nor b

434. Abnormal platelet function may modify normal values for
     the following except:
        a. Capillary fragility
        b. Prothrombin time   b
        c. Clot retraction
        d. Bleeding time

435. A patient taking aspirin may have a prolonged bleeding
     time even though the platelet count is normal.   T   F   T

436. Aspirin modifies platelets so that their ability to adhere to
     wound surfaces and release their granular contents is im-
     paired.   T   F   T

437. Hemorrhagic disease of newborn is often due to hypopro-
     thrombinemia. This condition may be prevented by giv-
     ing expectant mothers adequate doses of:
        a. Vitamin A
        b. Vitamin C
        c. Vitamin D
        d. Vitamin K   d

438. In hemophilia you would expect the platelet count to be:
        a. Decreased
        b. Increased
        c. Neither a nor b   c

439. In hemophilia the bleeding time is:
        a. Normal   a
        b. Prolonged
        c. Short

440. Bleeding may occur when the plasma concentration of pro-
     thrombin drops below:
        a. 50% of normal
        b. 40% of normal
        c. 20% of normal   c

441. Vitamin K absorption cannot take place in the absence of:
        a. Bile   a
        b. Carotene
        c. Prothrombin
        d. Insulin

442. Vitamin K absorption is also impaired in disease of the:
        a. Small intestine   a
        b. Lungs
        c. Spleen
        d. Bone marrow

443. All of the following apply to vitamin C except:
    a. It prevents scurvy
    b. It is used in the formation of prothrombin   b
    c. It is used in the formation of capillary walls
    d. Citrus and other fruits are excellent source

444. If the bleeding time is abnormal in a patient who is thought
    to have hemophilia, he may:
    a. Be taking aspirin   a
    b. Have von Willebrand's disease and not hemophilia   b
    c. Have uremia   c
    d. Have nothing else wrong since the bleeding time is
       always abnormal in hemophilia

445. Presence of any amount of the following in the circulating
    blood is abnormal:
    a. Fibrinogen
    b. Fibrin   b
    c. Neutral fat
    d. Cholesterol

446. During anticoagulant therapy the prothrombin and proconvertin time is:
    a. Increased   a
    b. Decreased
    c. Neither a nor b   ▼

447. After dicumarol or warfarin administration the prothrombin time:
    a. Increases   a
    b. Decreases
    c. Remains unchanged

448. Warfarin administration reduces the following procoagulant factors:
    a. IX   a
    b. II   b
    c. V
    d. VII   d
    e. X   e

449. In classical hemophilia the PTT is increased as a result of:
    a. Vitamin K deficiency
    b. Inadequate synthesis of prothrombin
    c. Deficiency of active Factor VIII   c
    d. A low platelet count

450. A fibrinogen deficiency may bring about extensive hemorrhage.   T   F   T

451. Tests particularly useful in detecting intravascular coagulation include:
    a. Platelet count   a
    b. Lee & White clotting time
    c. Measurement of plasma fibrinogen   c

    d. Thrombin time   d

    e. Search for products of fibrin metabolism in serum   e

452. The best test for making the diagnosis of hemophilia is the clotting time.   T   F   F

453. In a suspected case of hemophilia you would first do a
_____ and, if it were abnormal you would then proceed to assays of the following Factors: partial thromboplastin time

    a. _____   VIII

    b. _____   IX

    c. _____   XI

454. In hemophilia the partial thromboplastin time is prolonged but the bleeding time, the clot retraction time, the platelet count, and the capillary fragility remain normal.   T   F   T

455. In classical hemophilia the prothrombin time is prolonged.
T   F   F

456. The prothrombin time tests:

    a. Factor II   a

    b. Factor V   b

    c. Factor VII   c

    d. Factor X   d

    e. Factor I   e

457. In the presence of normal numbers of platelets the Ivy bleeding time may be prolonged in the following condition(s):

    a. Severe liver disease

    b. Uremia

    c. Hereditary platelet functional disorders

    d. Acquired platelet functional disorders

    e. Circulating macroglobulins

    f. All of the above   f

458. In disseminated intravascular coagulation fibrin monomers and fibrin degradation products appear in the serum.   T   F   T

459. In disseminated intravascular coagulation the following coagulation components are frequently depleted:

    a. Platelets

    b. Factor I

    c. Factor VIII

    d. Factor II

    e. Factor V

    f. All of the above   f

460. In the condition of intravascular coagulation both the _____ system and the _____ system are activated.   coagulation; fibrinolytic

461. During anticoagulant therapy the prothrombin time is usually kept between:

a. 5 and 15 seconds
b. 10 and 20 seconds
c. 20 and 30 seconds   c

462. When the P&P time is used to monitor anticoagulant therapy it is usually kept between _____ and _____.   15% & 20%

Bone Marrow

463. In the following list of diseases indicate:
1. Those conditions which can only be diagnosed with
   certainty by aspiration of bone marrow.   c, e, f, g, h
2. Those conditions in which bone marrow studies are
   helpful in confirming diagnosis.   a, b, d, i, j

a. Pernicious anemia   g. Multiple myeloma
b. Leishmaniasis   h. Aleukemic leukemia
c. Aplastic anemia   i. Granulocytopenia
d. Felty's syndrome   j. "Idiopathic" thrombo-
e. Leukemias   cytopenia
f. Familial splenic ane-
   mia (Gaucher's dis.)

464. In Vitamin B_{12} deficiency the bone marrow shows megalo-
blastic erythroid hyperplasia.   T   F   T

HEMATOLOGY ANSWERS CONTINUED

1.   **Red Cells:** Carry oxygen to the tissues.
     Platelets: Blood coagulation and hemostasis
     Eosinophils: Destroy antigen-antibody complexes
     Neutrophils: Phagocytosis of bacteria
     Monocytes: Phagocytosis inside and outside blood vessels
     Lymphocytes: At least two sorts. B lymphocytes secrete antibodies. T
     lymphocytes are involved in cell mediated immunity. Also infilter areas of
     chronic inflammation.
     Basophils: Release the histamine in their granules in the presence of anti-
     gen and antibody of IgE class. Function in immediate hypersensitivity.

11. a. Adrenocorticotropic hormone; mean corpuscular hemoglobin concen-
        tration; mean corpuscular volume; ethylene-diamine tetracetic acid;
        lupus erythematosus; infectious mononucleosis (also intramuscularly).
     b. Complete blood count; total red cell count; red blood cell(s); total
        white cell count; white blood cell(s); hemoglobin; mean corpuscular
        hemoglobin.

24. Other methods for measuring plasma volume include:
     a. Radioiodine or technicium labeled serum albumin
     b. Cr^{51} tagged r.b.c. with correction made for plasmacrit

28. **Hayem's solution (for RBC):** Add 2.5 grams mercuric chloride, 25 grams
     sodium sulfate, 5 grams sodium chloride; to 1,000 ml. distilled water.

Gower's solution (for RBC): Add 12.5 grams sodium sulfate and 33.3 ml. glacial acetic acid to 200 ml. distilled water.

Rees-Ecker solution (for platelet count): 3.8 grams sodium citrate; 0.2 ml. neutral 40% solution of formaldehyde; 0.05 gram brilliant cresyl blue; water to make 100 ml.

37. a. *If the pH is too acid,* the smear will appear pink with the nuclei stained light blue, the red cells orange-red, and the eosinophilic granules bright orange.

    b. *If the pH is too alkaline,* the smear will appear too blue, with the nuclei stained deep blue, the red cells blue or greenish, and the eosinophilic granules gray.

38. There will appear to be refractile crystals in the red blood cells.

39. Weak hydrochloric acid or acetic acid can be added to lower the pH, and potassium or sodium carbonate to raise the pH. The best solution is to use phosphate buffers as diluting fluid.

    The pH of the buffer can be tested with hematoxylin, an acid solution producing a lavender-pink color when the pH is 6.6 to 6.8, or a reddish-purple when it is excessively alkaline. However, it is best to test the buffer with a standard laboratory pH meter.

43. Other reticulocyte stains include:
    a. Janus green
    b. Nile blue sulfate
    c. New methylene blue

47. By fixing and staining a smear with Wright's stain, then observing under oil immersion.

112. Any cells/cu.mm. = Count X (depth factor) X area factor that applies X dilution factor (if any)

117. For convenience in counting the Neubauer type of ruling has been improved by grouping the small squares in blocks of 16 (in the older form of center ruling each fifth square was subdivided down the middle both horizontally and vertically).

118. **RBC pipette:** This pipette has a rather large bulb and is etched with marks at 0.5, 1.0, and 101.0

    WBC pipette: This pipette has a smaller bulb and is etched with marks at 0.5, 1.0, and 11.0

128. a. Failure to draw blood *exactly* to the 0.5 mark
     b. Inadequate shaking
     c. Failure to discard the first few drops
     d. Overfilling (or underfilling) the chamber

142. Photoelectric methods depend on principle of light scattering, comparison in colorimeter. Errors due to difference in size of cells.

143. Cells suspended in electrically conducting medium which flows through small aperture. The relatively non-conducting cells cause voltage to drop, recording the cell. Accuracy (average count 50,000 cells). Error: 2%.

149. Hemoglobin is a conjugated (heme + globin) protein. Heme contains iron in the ferrous state and can unite with oxygen to form *oxyhemoglobin.*

Without this loosely bound oxygen it is "reduced hemoglobin."

188. Nuclear remnants; chromatin (i.e., basophilic) structures.

194. 1. Hematocrit reading (PCV)
2. ESR
3. Osmotic fragility test
4. Reticulocyte count
5. RBC
6. Basophilic stippling
7. Sickle cells

202. The Model S determines hemoglobin concentration, red blood count and also determines the size of the red blood cells. Using this information, the machine adds in a factor for plasma trapping and then calculates the PCV.

203. Microhematocrit: A method of packed cell volume (PCV) determination which uses capillary (instead of Wintrobe) tubes. Either capillary or venous blood may be used in this method as only a few drops of blood are sufficient to carry out test.

204. Sedimentation rate (ESR): The rate (somewhat more rapid in women than in men) at which the red cells settle out of whole (i.e., citrated, heparinized, etc.) blood. This rate is usually measured in mm. per hour.
Sedimentation index: The logarithm of the number of mm. of erythrocyte sedimentation rate would have occurred in 100 minutes at the maximum sedimentation rate observed at 10 minute intervals during a 2–2½ hour period.

242. V. Schilling (German hematologist, born 1883) arranged the white cells according to age, including all leukocytes. A normal Schilling hemogram may be represented as follows:

Total White Count	5,000–10,000
Myeloblasts and promyelocytes	0%
Myelocytes	0%
Metamyelocytes (juveniles)	0%
Band (stab) cell neutrophils	1–6%
Segmented neutrophils	40–60%
Lymphocytes	20–35%
Eosinophils	1–3%
Basophils	0–1%
Monocytes	2–8%

262. 1. WBC
2. Differential counts
3. Circulating eosinophil counts
4. L.E. cells
5. Peroxidase reaction

263. They ingest colloidal material foreign particles and destroy old white and red blood cells.

269. 1. Indirect method

2. Direct method (Rees-Ecker, Brecher-Cronkhite)
3. Electronically (Coulter counter)
4. Optically (automated)

289. a. Search for material reacting with antifibrinogen antibody in serum.
b. Add materials like ethanol or protamine to serum to allow fibrin monomers to precipitate out.

330. **Anemia:** A deficiency in the quantity of blood caused by a lowered hemoglobin content, or by a substantial decrease, below the lower normal limit, in the number of erythrocytes.
Erythremia: A substantial increase, above the upper normal limit, in the number of erythrocytes.

331. **Leukocytosis:** An increase in the total white blood cell count.
Leukemia: A disease of the blood-forming organs resulting in a permanent, progressive increase in total white cells that infiltrate organs, the bone marrow in particular.

332. **Leukocytosis:** See the preceding answer.
Leukopenia: A decrease in total white cell count.

333. **Leukemia:** See answer No. 331 above.
Leukemoid: A blood picture resembling leukemia in that the WBC may be quite high and there may be some immaturity of the circulating w.b.c. however organ infiltration does not occur.

334. **Polycythema vera:** An unusual disease characterized by an elevated PCV and RBC, an increased total red blood cell mass as measured by the Cr^{51} technique, increased erythropoiesis and, usually, increased granulopoiesis and thrombopoiesis
Pseudopolycythemia: Characterized by an increased PCV and RBC but the total red blood cell mass is normal. Therefore the increase in PCV is due to plasma volume constriction of usually unknown cause. WBC and platelet count are normal.

335. **Anisocytosis:** Abnormal variation in *size* among r.b.c.
Poikilocytosis: Abnormal variation in *shape* among r.b.c.

336. **Polychromatophilia (polychromasia):** Diffused basophilia (blue gray staining of r.b.c. in fixed blood smears).
Basophilic stippling (punctate basophilia): Young erythrocytes under toxic conditions show dark staining of punctate bodies by routine stain.
Note: Both circumstances reflect residual ribosomal material remaining from the nucleated erythroid precursors.

337. **Macrocyte:** A large red blood cell. MCV greater than 96.
Microcyte: A small red blood cell. MCV less than 75.

338. **Acidophilic structures:** Structures within a cell or tissue which have a marked affinity for eosin (stains red) or other acid dyes.
Basophilic structures: Structures within a cell or tissue which have a marked affinity for methylene blue and other basic dyes.

339. **Rouleaux formation:** A form of pseudoagglutination resulting from the tendency of the red cells to form rolls similar to piles of coins. Rouleaux formation results from physical phenomena whereas *true agglutination*

(i.e., actual clumping of the cells) results from a serological (antigen-antibody) reaction.

381. a. Hypoxia (low oxygen content or tension) because of pulmonary disease.
     b. Hypoxia because of cardiac disease.
     c. The presence of erythropoietin-secreting tumors.

396. The L.E. cell factor (a component of serum gamma globulin) reacts with nuclei (depolymerizes desoxyribonucleic acid) and this amorphous material is phagocytized by leukocytes. The L.E. cells' nuclear material is homogeneous, without chromatin structure, as opposed to still visible chromatin of "tart" cells which are ingested nuclei.

428. 1. Absence of megakaryocytes in marrow (aplastic anemia or leukemic infiltration).
     2. Rapid removal (idiopathic thrombocytopenic purpura).
     3. Sequestration in spleen (hypersplenism).
     4. Rapid removal (as in artificial heart valves or in consumption coagulopathy).

Section III MICROBIOLOGY

THE NEW MICROBIOLOGY SECTION

In response to current trends, a formal separate section dealing with clinical microbiology has been formed for the first time within the existing subject matter of this book.

Microbiology includes the fields of Bacteriology, Mycology, Parasitology, Virology, Serology, and similar related work (California Clinical Laboratory Technology, Laboratory Services, California Department of Health).

This new Microbiology section is composed of three subsections as follows:

> I – Parasitology
>
> II – Bacteriology & Allied Fields
>
> III – Serology & Immunology

Subsequent editions of this book will reflect a more specific treatment of Microbiology matter than is possible at this early stage in the formation of this new section.

—The Publisher

Section III MICROBIOLOGY
Subsection I: PARASITOLOGY

1.

CLINICAL PARASITOLOGY EXAMINATION

Edited by Derek Wakelin, Ph.D., The University of Glasgow

GENERAL QUESTIONS

1.	List the important classes of the Protozoa.	Sarcodina, Mastigophora, Ciliata, Sporozoa
2.	Presence of animal parasites within the body is always accompanied by blood eosinophilia. T F	F
3.	Infection with worm parasites is frequently accompanied by eosinophilia. T F	T
4.	Protozoa are found in the alimentary canal only in the small and large intestines. T F	F
5.	A polymorphonuclear leukocyte may be distinguished from the intestinal protozoa by its: a. Cytoplasmic inclusions b. Size c. Nuclear structure d. Lack of motility e. Absence of flagella	c
6.	Explain difference(s) between "infection" and "infestation."	See p. 230
7.	Explain difference(s) between "parasitism" and "commensalism."	See p. 230
8.	Explain difference(s) between "egg" and "ovum."	See p. 230
9.	Define "definitive host" and "intermediate host."	See p. 230
10.	Define "embryo" and "larva."	See p. 230
11.	Define "trophozoite" and "cyst."	See p. 230
12.	Match the following common and scientific names: a. Tapeworms 1. *Nematoda* b. Flatworms 2. *Digenea* c. Roundworms 3. *Cestoda* d. Flukes 4. *Platyhelminthes*	a—3 b—4 c—1 d—2
13.	List major methods of transmission of parasites to man.	See p. 231
14.	Why is it necessary to study and know the morphology, habitat, and staining characteristics of the protozoa of man which are not parasitic in nature?	See p. 231
15.	Which of the following phyla contain important parasites of man: a. Protozoa b. Annelida	a

197

	c. Platyhelminthes	c
	d. Aschelminthes	d
	e. Acanthocephala	

16. The flukes and tapeworms parasitic in man belong to the phylum:
    a. Protozoa
    b. Aschelminthes
    c. Arthropoda
    d. Platyhelminthes   d
    e. Annelida

17. All of the following are parasitic worms except:
    a. Filaria
    b. Ringworm   b
    c. Pinworm
    d. Blood fluke
    e. Guinea worm

18. Which of the following are practical methods of parasite control:
    a. Drug treatment   a
    b. Immunization
    c. Sanitation   c
    d. Insecticide spraying   d
    e. Meat inspection   e

19. "Swimmers' itch" is caused by:
    a. Migrating nematode larvae
    b. Ringworm
    c. Penetrating nematode larvae
    d. Penetrating schistosome larvae   d
    e. None of these

20. Hypersensitivity during parasitic infections is often associated with elevated reaginic antibody (IgE) levels.   T F   T

21. What is meant by "larva migrans"?   See p. 231

22. Man can acquire protozoal or worm infections from contact with pet:
    a. Cats   a
    b. Birds
    c. Dogs   c
    d. Fish
    e. Rodents

23. Name three common ectoparasites of Man.   Flea, louse, scabies mite

---

LABORATORY PROCEDURES

24. What is "Blastocystis hominis"?   See p. 231

25. The identity of a parasitic organism may usually be ascertained more reliably by serological tests than by any other means.   T F   F

26. In which of the following may biopsy material be valuable in diagnosis:
    a. Onchocerciasis (skin snip)   a
    b. Ascariasis
    c. Trichuriasis
    d. Trichinosis   d
    e. None of these

27. What is "xenodiagnosis"? Name one disease in which it is used.   See p. 231

28. What do the abbreviations "LPF," "HDF," "L.E.S.," and "NNN" stand for?   See p. 231

29. Name at least five methods for the examination of fecal samples.   See p. 231

30. Three concentration methods for intestinal parasites in the feces are:
    1. _____   See p. 231
    2. _____   "
    3. _____   "

31. Zinc sulfate flotation/technique destroys the motile trophozoites, but not the cysts, of protozoa.   T   F   T

32. The specific gravity of the 33% zinc sulfate solution used . for the flotation of protozoan cysts and certain worm eggs should be:
    a. 1.018
    b. 1.080
    c. 1.081
    d. 1.180   d

33. Lugol's iodine is suitable for the staining of cysts in wet preparations of fecal material.   T   F.   T

34. Gram's iodine is suitable for the staining of cysts in wet preparations of fecal material.   T   F   T

35. Trophic amoebae and flagellates are killed by iodine staining.   T   F   T

36. The protozoa that most consistently grow in cultures are:
    a. *Trichomonas vaginalis*   a
    b. *Entamoeba histolytica*   b
    c. *Chilomastix mesnili*
    d. *Dientamoeba fragilis*
    e. *Entamoeba gingivalis*

37. A suitable medium for the cultivation of *Entamoeba histolytica* and other amoebae is:
    a. McLeod's
    b. Egg yolk agar
    c. Milk agar
    d. Locke-egg serum   d
    e. Nutrient agar

38. Schaudinn's fixative is composed of alcohol and:
    a. Ether
    b. Mercuric chloride   b
    c. Potassium dichromate
    d. Formalin
    e. Acetic acid   e

39. A method for the permanent staining of intestinal para-
    sites in fecal material is:
    a. Buffered Giemsa stain
    b. Iron-hematoxylin stain   b
    c. Carbol-fuchsin stain
    d. Albert's stain
    e. Masson stain

40. Cellophane anal swabs are employed for collection of the
    following eggs from the perianal region for examination:
    a. Whipworm eggs
    b. Pinworm eggs   b
    c. Hookworm eggs
    d. Ascaris eggs
    e. Tapeworm eggs

41. Cysts and other parasite stages are always evenly distrib-
    uted in the formed stool.   T   F   F

42. A single stool examination, if negative, is sufficient to
    rule out intestinal parasite infection.   T   F F

43. The loose stool, obtained by means of a saline cathartic,
    is more likely to contain the trophic forms of protozoa.
    T   F   T

44. Which of the following helminth eggs may be found in
    urine?
    a. *Paragonimus westermani*
    b. *Schistosoma mansoni*
    c. *Schistosoma hematobium*   c
    d. *Necator americanus*
    e. *Taenia saginata*

45. Which of the following parasites is not seen in blood
    smears?
    a. *Trypanosoma*
    b. *Loa loa*
    c. *Plasmodium*
    d. *Schistosoma mansoni*   d
    e. *Wuchereria bancrofti*

46. The stain usually preferred for microfilariae in blood
    staining is:
    a. Wright's stain
    b. Hematoxylin-eosin   b
    c. May-Grünwald
    d. Giemsa
    e. Leishman's stain

47. Examination of the C.S.F. is valuable in the diagnosis of:
    a. Hydatid disease
    b. Schistosomiasis
    c. Malaria
    d. Taeniasis
    e. African trypanosomiasis   e

48. Serological tests are valuable in the diagnosis of:
    a. Schistosomiasis   a
    b. Clonorchiasis
    c. Trichinosis   c
    d. Trichuriasis
    e. Toxoplasmosis   e

49. What do the abbreviations "CF," "ID," "IFA," and
    "IHA" stand for?   See p. 231

50. For what infections have the following serological tests
    been used as diagnostic aids?
    a. Craig complement-fixation test   *Entamoeba
                                                  histolytica*
    b. Moan haemagglutination test   *Entamoeba
                                                  histolytica*
    c. Casoni intradermal test   hydatid cyst

51. Intradermal injection of a suitable antigen is a useful aid
    to diagnosis in:
    a. Infection with *Schistosoma mansoni*
    b. Visceral larva migrans
    c. Infection with *Trichinella spiralis*
    d. Hydatid disease
    e. All of these   e

52. Name two diseases of protozoal origin in which raised   Kala-azar &
    serum immunoglobulin levels are useful in aiding diag-   Afr. Trypano-
    nosis.   somiasis

53. Briefly explain the formol-gel test. In the diagnosis of
    which disease is it usually employed?   See p. 231

54. Serological diagnosis of certain parasitic infections can be
    made from blood samples dried onto absorbent paper.
    T   F   T

55. Name five immunological tests which have been utilized
    in the diagnosis of parasitic infections.   See p. 231

56. What test can be used to demonstrate raised levels of   radial immuno-
    specific immunoglobulin classes.   diffusion

57. What is the basis of the indirect fluorescent antibody test
    (IFA) used in diagnosis of parasitic disease?   See p. 231

58. In what situations are immunodiagnostic tests of particu-
    lar value?   See p. 231

AMOEBAE

(Although *Dientamoeba fragilis* is no longer recognized as a
member of the amoebae, but is considered a member of the
Mastigophora, it is included here for convenience.)

59. Binuclearity characterizes the following intestinal proto-
    zoa:
    a. *Iodamoeba bütschlii*
    b. *Dientamoeba fragilis*   b
    c. *Trichomonas hominis*
    d. *Giardia lamblia*   d
    e. *Entamoeba coli*

60. *Dientamoeba fragilis* may cause diarrhea, abdominal pain,
    and discomfort.   T   F   T

61. Average diameter of active *Dientamoeba fragilis*:
    a. 9–18 microns
    b. 3–6 microns
    c. 15–25 microns
    d. 7–12 microns   d
    e. 20–40 microns

62. The nucleus has a central karyosome in:
    a. *Entamoeba coli*
    b. *Endolimax nana*
    c. *Iodamoeba bütschlii*   c
    d. *Entamoeba histolytica*   d
    e. *Entamoeba gingivalis*   e

63. Which of the following amoebae has a cyst with only one
    nucleus when fully mature:
    a. *Entamoeba gingivalis*
    b. *Iodamoeba bütschlii*   b
    c. *Entamoeba coli*
    d. *Entamoeba histolytica*
    e. *Endolimax nana*

64. Which of the following intestinal amoebae may give rise
    to pathogenic symptoms?
    a. *Iodamoeba bütschlii*
    b. *Entamoeba coli*
    c. *Entamoeba hartmanni*
    d. *Endolimax nana*
    e. *Entamoeba histolytica*   e

65. When the microscropic examination of a fresh watery stool
    reveals a rapidly moving amoeba with ingested red blood
    cells the amoeba is likely to be:
    a. *Entamoeba coli*
    b. *Endolimax nana*
    c. *Iodamoeba bütschlii*
    d. *Entamoeba histolytica*   d
    e. *Entamoeba hartmanni*

66. Which of the following amoebae are known in the trophic stage only:
    a. *Entamoeba gingivalis*   a
    b. *Endolimax nana*
    c. *Entamoeba histolytica*
    d. *Iodamoeba bütschlii*
    e. *Entamoeba coli*

67. In identifying trophic amoebae nuclear characteristics are the most important feature.   T   F   T

68. The intestinal amoebae are:
    a. *Endolimax nana*   a
    b. *Iodamoeba bütschlii*   b
    c. *Entamoeba gingivalis*
    d. *Entamoeba histolytica*   d
    e. *Entamoeba coli*   e

69. The only pathogenic amoebae in man are those which live in the digestive tract.   T   F   F

70. Which of the following amoebae do not encyst?
    a. *Endolimax nana*
    b. *Iodamoeba bütschlii*
    c. *Entamoeba coli*
    d. *Entamoeba gingivalis*   d
    e. *Entamoeba hartmanni*

71. The presence or absence of glycogen in an amoebic cyst can be detected only after staining with iodine.   T   F   T

72. Glycogen is present only in the immature cysts of:
    a. *Entamoeba gingivalis*
    b. *Entamoeba coli*   b
    c. *Endolimax nana*   c
    d. *Iodamoeba bütschlii*
    e. *Entamoeba histolytica*

73. Which of the following amoebae are characterized by a cyst with four nuclei?
    a. *Entamoeba coli*
    b. *Endolimax nana*   b
    c. *Iodamoeba bütschlii*
    d. *Entamoeba histolytica*   d
    e. *Entamoeba hartmanni*   e

74. An amoeba, sometimes found in the mouth in conditions of pyorrhea is:
    a. *Entamoeba histolytica*
    b. *Entamoeba coli*
    c. *Entamoeba gingivalis*   c
    d. *Endolimax nana*
    e. *Iodamoeba bütschlii*

75. The structure of nuclei in the cysts is identical to the structure of nuclei in the trophic amoebae of the same species.
    T   F   T

76. For the study of the nuclear structure of amoebae, properly fixed iron-hematoxylin stained or trichrome stained material is always necessary.   T   F   T

77. The trophozoite of all human intestinal amoebae may occasionally be parasitized by a microorganism which appears as a spherical mass of granules which stain with iron-hematoxylin.   T   F   T

78. How can one easily distinguish between "macrophages" and "amoebae"?   See p. 232

79. Briefly summarize the differences between "amoebic dysentery" and "bacillary dysentery."   See p. 232

80. In bowel discharges, bacillary dysentery produces a much more abundant cellular exudate than amoebic dysentery.
T   F   T

81. Eoseinophils in large numbers may be seen in the stool of acute bacillary dysentery.   T   F   F

82. Charcot-Leyden crystals are a frequent finding in the stool of acute amoebic dysentery.   T   F   T

83. Charcot-Leyden crystals are not characteristic of any particular type of infection.   T   F   T

84. The presence of 4-nucleate *Entamoeba* cysts in a stool specimen always indicates a potential danger to health.
T   F   F (also see p. 232)

85. What is the difference between the "minuta" form of *Entamoeba histolytica* and *Entamoeba hartmanni*.   See p. 232

86. Acute amoebic dysentery can be diagnosed by the presence of 4-nucleate *Entamoeba* cysts in stool specimens.   T   F   F

87. Average diameter of active *Entamoeba histolytica* from a case of amoebic dysentery:
    a. 5–12 microns
    b. 15–25 microns
    c. 9–14 microns
    d. 3–6 microns
    e. 20–40 microns   e

88. Infection with *Entamoeba histolytica* occurs as a result of:
    a. Ingestion of contaminated food   a
    b. Bite by an infected blood-sucking fly
    c. Contamination of a skin wound
    d. Ingestion of contaminated water   d
    e. Contact with infected animals   e (possibly)

89. Natural infections with *Entamoeba histolytica* occur in:
    a. Monkeys   a
    b. Cattle
    c. Rats   c

     d. Birds
     e. None of these

90. Diagnosis of extra-intestinal infection with *Entamoeba histolytica* may be aided by serological tests.   T   F   T

91. List four immunological tests which can be used to diagnose infection with *Entamoeba histolytica*.   See p. 232

92. Invasion of the intestinal wall by *Entamoeba histolytica* is sometimes followed by secondary infection of extra-intestinal sites. These commonly include:
     a. Brain   a
     b. Bone
     c. Muscle
     d. Liver   d
     e. Lungs   e

93. When a cyst of *Entamoeba histolytica* is swallowed excystation occurs in the intestine and subsequent division produces:
     a. 4 amoebae
     b. 16 amoebae
     c. 8 amoebae   c
     d. 32 amoebae

94. Infection with *Entamoeba histolytica* leads to amoebic dysentery:
     a. Always
     b. Rarely
     c. Never
     d. In a relatively small proportion of cases   d

95. The amoebae which cause amoebic dysentery are transmitted only by patients suffering from the disease.   T   F   F

96. Mature cysts of *Entamoeba histolytica* are characterized by the following number of nuclei:
     a. 2 nuclei
     b. 4 nuclei   b
     c. 6 nuclei
     d. 8 nuclei

97. Average diameter of active *Entamoeba histolytica* from an asymptomatic patient:
     a. 5–12 microns
     b. 15–25 microns   b
     c. 9–14 microns
     d. 3–6 microns
     e. 20–40 microns

98. The young (binucleate) cyst of *Entamoeba histolytica* usually contains a large glycogen vacuole which displaces the nuclei to the periphery.   T   F   T

99. The nucleus of *Entamoeba histolytica* is easily seen in the fresh unstained specimen.   T   F   F

100. Trophozoites of *Entamoeba histolytica* live in the:
    a. Small intestine
    b. Stomach
    c. Large intestine   c

101. The presence of red cells within an amoeba rules out
    Entamoeba coli.   T   F   F

102. Cysts of *Entamoeba histolytica* and *Entamoeba coli* always
    contain 4 and 8 nuclei respectively.   T   F   F

103. Glycogen and chromatoid bodies are usually present in:
    a. Mature cysts of *Entamoeba coli* or of *Entamoeba
       histolytica*
    b. Young cysts of *Entamoeba coli* or of *Entamoeba
       histolytica*   b

104. In the precystic stage, *Entamoeba histolytica* may be quite
    similar to *Entamoeba coli*.   T   F   T

105. Cysts of *Entamoeba histolytica* and cysts of *Entamoeba
    coli* are always spherical in shape.   T   F   T

106. The layer of peripheral chromatin in the nucleus of *Enta-
    moeba histolytica* is finer than the layer of peripheral
    chromatin in the nucleus of *Entamoeba coli*.   T   F   T

107. The karyosome of *Entamoeba histolytica* is somewhat
    smaller in size than the karyosome of *Entamoeba coli*.
    T   F   T

108. Rapidity of movement is one of the most dependable char-
    acteristics in distinguishing *Entamoeba histolytica* from
    Entamoeba coli.   T   F   F

109. Briefly summarize the differences between *Entamoeba
    coli* and *Entamoeba histolytica*.   See p. 232

110. Mature cysts of *Entamoeba coli* are characterized by the
    following number of nuclei:
    a. 2 nuclei
    b. 4 nuclei
    c. 6 nuclei
    d. 8 nuclei   d

111. Average diameter of active *Entamoeba coli:*
    a. 5–12 microns
    b. 15–25 microns   b
    c. 9–14 microns
    d. 3–6 microns
    e. 20–40 microns

112. In the cytoplasm of *Entamoeba coli* there is often a con-
    spicuous clear area around nucleus.   T   F   T

113. The movement of *Entamoeba coli* may be defined as:
    a. Rapid
    b. Sluggish   b
    c. Flowing

114. The outstanding characteristic of *Iodamoeba bütschlii* trophozoite is its:
    a. Size
    b. Type of movement
    c. Large karyosome surrounded by granules   c
    d. Food vacuoles
    e. Cytoplasmic inclusions

115. Average diameter of active *Iodamoeba bütschlii:*
    a. 5-12 microns
    b. 15-25 microns
    c. 9-14 microns   c
    d. 3-6 microns
    e. 20-40 microns

116. The outstanding characteristics of *Iodamoeba bütschlii* cysts are their:
    a. Variable (6-16 microns) size
    b. Frequent irregularity in shape   b
    c. Glycogen mass   c
    d. Number of nuclei
    e. Nuclear structure   e

117. The trophozoite of *Endolimax nana* is sluggish in activity, showing resemblance in this respect to *Entamoeba coli.*
    T   F   T

118. Average diameter of active *Endolimax nana:*
    a. 7-12 microns
    b. 15-25 microns
    c. 5-12 microns   c
    d. 9-14 microns
    e. 20-40 microns

119. The outstanding characteristic of *Endolimax nana* is its:
    a. Size
    b. Sluggish motility
    c. Very large chromatic mass or karyosome   c
    d. Nonpathogenic nature
    e. Granular cytoplasm

120. Free-living amoebae are capable of establishing themselves in the tissues of man and causing severe disease.
    T   F   T

121. What is "amoebic meningoencephalitis"?   See p. 232

122. Amoebic meningoencephalitis is a disease associated with infection by:
    a. *Entamoeba*
    b. *Naegleria*   b
    c. *Dientamoeba*
    d. *Hartmanella*   d
    e. *Acanthamoeba*   e

INTESTINAL FLAGELLATES

123. The riblike structure within the cytostome (cell "mouth") at the base of the undulating membrane of trichomonad flagellates is called:
    a. Axoneme
    b. Cytopharynx
    c. Axostyle
    d. Costa   d
    e. Parabasal body

124. Which of the following flagellates are transmitted by ingestion of resistant cysts:
    a. *Trichomonas hominis*
    b. *Chilomastix mesnili*   b
    c. *Giardia lamblia*   c
    d. *Trichomonas vaginalis*
    e. *Trichomonas tenax*

125. Which of the following protozoa is known only in the trophic stage:
    a. *Giardia*
    b. *Trichomonas*   b
    c. *Chilomastix*
    d. *Balantidium*
    e. *Retortamonas*

126. In cases of intestinal flagellate infections the chances of finding trophozoites in the stool are better after saline catharsis.   T   F   T

127. A lemon-shaped protozoan cyst with a large nucleus containing a large karyosome near the nuclear membrane would be:
    a. *Balantidium coli*
    b. *Giardia lamblia*
    c. *Trichomonas hominis*
    d. *Chilomastix mesnili*   d
    e. *Trichomonas tenax*

128. An intestinal flagellate whose posterior portion has a twisted appearance and which possesses three flagella, cytostome, nucleus, intracytoplasmic flagellum, and two blepharoplastic fibrils which surround the cytostome would be:
    a. *Chilomastix mesnili*   a
    b. *Balantidium coli*
    c. *Trichomonas hominis*
    d. *Giardia lamblia*
    e. *Trichomonas tenax*

129. An intestinal flagellate possessing a large sucking disk, two nuclei, two axostyles, eight flagella, and two parabasal bodies would be:
    a. *Chilomastix mesnili*

    b. *Giardia lamblia*   b

    c. *Trichomonas hominis*

    d. *Trichomonas vaginalis*

    e. *Trichomonas tenax*

130. 'An oval-shaped protozoan cyst with four nuclei and remnants of fibrils and other organelles of the trophic stage would be:
    a. *Chilomastix mesnili*
    b. *Balantidium coli*
    c. *Trichomonas hominis*
    d. *Giardia lamblia*   d
    e. *Trichomonas vaginalis*

131. Which of the following motile trophozoites may occur in urine:
    a. *Trichomonas tenax*
    b. *Trichomonas vaginalis*   b
    c. *Giardia lamblia*
    d. *Chilomastix mesnili*
    c. *Trichomonas hominis*

132. *Giardia lamblia* may cause enteritis and interfere with intestinal absorption.   T   F   T

133. *Giardia lamblia* is never pathogenic.   T   F   F

134. *Trichomonas* has the following number of anterior flagella:
    a. 2 anterior flagella
    b. 3 anterior flagella
    c. 4 anterior flagella   c
    d. 5 anterior flagella

135. The locomotive structures of *Trichomonas* are:
    a. Flagella   a
    b. Cilia
    c. Undulating membrane   c
    d. Pseudopods
    e. Unknown

136. Which of the following trichomonad flagellates inhabits the human mouth:
    a. *Trichomonas hominis*
    b. *Trichomonas tenax*   b
    c. *Trichomonas vaginalis*

137. *Trichomonas vaginalis* may occur in the urine of men as well as of women.   T   F   T

138. How is *Trichomonas vaginalis* transmitted? See p. 232

139. In what form is *Trichomonas hominis* transmitted? See p. 232

140. The motile form of *Tricercomonas hominis (Enteromonas hominis)* is a very active flagellate 4–10 microns in length, which swims jerkily by rapid movements of its:

a. Single anteriorly directed flagellum
b. Two anteriorly directed flagella
c. Three anteriorly directed flagella   c
d. Four anteriorly directed flagella

141. *Retortamonas intestinalis,* an ovoid or pyriform flagellate usually 4–10 microns in length, usually moves very actively by means of:
    a. 1 flagellum
    b. 2 flagella   b
    c. 4 flagella
    d. 8 flagella
    e. Many flagella

142. *Chilomastix mesnili* cysts of two nuclei are common.
    T   F   F

BLOOD FLAGELLATES

143. In which of the following does division of the trypanosome (trypomastigote) form occur in the peripheral blood?
    a. *Trypanosoma gambiense*   a
    b. *Trypanosoma cruzi*
    c. *Trypanosoma rhodesiense*   c

144. In man, *Leishmania* is exclusively an intracellular parasite.   T   F   T

145. Reservoir hosts are known for all species of *Leishmania.*
    T   F   T

146. Leishmanial infection may be diagnosed by:
    a. Thick blood film
    b. Serological methods   b
    c. Stool examination
    d. CSF examination
    e. Tissue biopsy   e

147. Briefly describe morphological characteristics of intracellular *Leishmania* forms.   See p. 232

148. "Kala-azar" is transmitted by:
    a. House fly
    b. Mosquito
    c. Tsetse fly
    d. Sand fly   d
    e. Flea

149. "Oriental sore" is transmitted by:
    a. House fly
    b. Mosquito
    c. Sand fly   c
    d. Tsetse fly
    e. Flea

150. Match the following:
    a. *Leishmania donovani*   1. Muco-cutaneous   a—2
                                   leishmaniasis
    b. *Leishmania tropica*   2. Kala-azar   b—3
    c. *Leishmania brasiliensis* 3. Oriental sore   c—1

151. Give four immunological tests which may be used to diag-   gel diffusion;
     nose leishmanial infection.   ID; IFA; IHA

152. Serological diagnosis of leishmania infection may be com-
     plicated by cross reaction with *Trypanosoma cruzi*.   T F   T

153. African trypanosomiasis is transmitted by:
     a. Mosquito
     b. Sandfly
     c. Flea
     d. Triatoma bug
     e. Tsetse fly   e

154. In African trypanosomiasis the level of serum IgM is
     greatly increased.   T   F   T

155. To make a laboratory diagnosis of sleeping sickness during
     the "sleeping" stage you would examine the following ma-
     terial:
     a. Blood
     b. Urine
     c. Feces
     d. CSF   d
     e. Skin biopsy

156. To make a laboratory diagnosis of sleeping sickness during
     the febrile stage you would examine the following material:
     a. Blood   a
     b. Urine
     c. Feces
     d. CSF
     e. Skin biopsy

157. Give three serological tests which could be used to con-
     firm diagnosis of trypanosome infection in the absence of
     detectable parasites.   CF; IFA;
                                                                 raised IgM
                                                                   level

158. In the life cycle of *Trypanosoma gambiense*, the Tsetse
     fly is the:
     a. Intermediate host
     b. Final host
     c. Vector host   c (also see
                                                                 p. 233)

159. Match the following:
     a. Chagas' disease   1. *T. Brucei*   a—3
     b. E. African sleeping   2. *T. gambiense*   b—2
        sickness   3. *T. cruzi*

c. W. African sleeping   4. *T. rhodesiense*   c—4
    sickness   5. *T. equiperdum*

160. Which species of *Trypanosoma* is characteristically "C"
     shaped when examined in a stained blood film?
     a. *brucei*
     b. *rhodesiense*
     c. *equiperdum*
     d. *cruzi*   d
     e. *gambiense*

161. Following initial parasitaemia after infection with *Trypa-*
     nosoma cruzi the trypanosome (trypomastigote) form of
     the parasite disappears from the peripheral blood.   T   F   T

162. The intracellular amastigote forms of *Trypanosoma cruzi*
     may be found in:
     a. Red blood cells
     b. Muscle fibers   b
     c. Reticulo-endothelial cells   c
     d. White blood cells
     e. Epidermal cells

163. What is "Romaña's sign"? With what infection is it asso-
     ciated?   See p. 233

164. The vector host of *Trypanosoma cruzi* is:
     a. Tsetse fly
     b. Mosquito
     c. Kissing bug (*Triatoma*)   c
     d. Sand fly
     e. Horse fly

165. How is xenodiagnosis of Chagas' disease performed?   See p. 231
                                                                     (ques. 27)

166. *Trypanosoma cruzi* is the only parasite which has amasti-
     gote forms in its life cycle.   T   F   F

167. In cases of Chagas' disease the blood examination for
     Trypanosoma cruzi is usually negative except when taken
     at time of febrile attacks.   T   F   T

168. What is the difference between "Chagas' disease" and
     "Chagas' syndrome"?   See p. 233

SPOROZOA – TOXOPLASMA

169. Which of the following sporozoa are known to infect man:
     a. *Plasmodium*   a
     b. *Eimeria*
     c. *Babesia*   c (v. rarely)
     d. *Isospora*   d
     e. *Toxoplasma*   e

170. *Toxoplasma* is most closely related to:
    a. *Giardia lamblia*
    b. *Isospora hominis*   b
    c. *Trypanosoma cruzi*
    d. *Plasmodium falciparum*
    e. *Leishmania donovani*

171. Infection with *Toxoplasma gondii* may be acquired congenitally.   T   F   T

172. In the life cycle of *Toxoplasma gondii* the final host is:
    a. Man
    b. Mouse
    c. Rat
    d. Flea
    e. Cat   e

173. Toxoplasmosis may be diagnosed by means of:
    a. Casoni's test
    b. Stool examination
    c. Thin blood film
    d. Sabin Feldman dye test   d
    e. Culture of blood specimen

174. Name four serological tests used for diagnosis of *Toxoplasma* infection.   dye test;
                                                              CF; IFA,
                                                              IHA

175. *Toxoplasma gondii* may be transmitted to man by contact with:
    a. Dogs
    b. Rodents
    c. Birds
    d. Cats   d
    e. Cattle

SPOROZOA – MALARIA

176. Malaria is only found in tropical countries.   T   F   F

177. Malaria is transmitted only by species of *Anopheles* mosquito.   T   F   T

178. The *Anopheles* mosquito is the:
    a. Definitive host of malarial parasites   a
    b. Intermediate host of malarial parasites
    c. Reservoir host of malarial parasites

179. Only female *Anopheles* mosquitoes are blood feeders and thus capable of transmitting malaria.   T   F   T

180. The spindle-shaped forms of malarial parasites injected into man by the *Anopheles* mosquito are called:
    a. Schizonts
    b. Segmenters

c. Sporozoites
d. Trophozoites
e. Merozoites

c

181. In malaria, the sexual (sporogenous) cycle takes place in:
a. Man
b. Mosquito

b

182. Man is the intermediate host of the malaria parasite.
T   F

T

183. The female sex-cell of malarial parasites is the:
a. Trophozoite
b. Microgametocyte
c. Band form
d. Macrogametocyte
e. Schizont

d

189. A malarial parasite undergoing asexual multiplication and characterized by dividing masses of chromatin is called:
a. Sporozoite
b. Schizont
c. Ring stage
d. Segmenter
e. Gametocyte

b

185. The early stage of malarial parasites in the red cells is called:
a. Sporozoite
b. Schizont
c. Segmenter
d. Ring stage
e. Merozoite

d

186. The male malarial parasite is called:
a. Schizont
b. Microgametocyte
c. Sporozoite
d. Macrogametocyte
e. Trophozoite

b

187. What is the difference between "sporogony" and "schizogony"?

See p. 233

188. What is the best time to collect a peripheral blood specimen for examination for malarial parasites?

See p. 233

189. The thin film is especially valuable in detecting latent malaria.   T   F

F

190. What is the value of a thick blood film in examination for malaria? What are the major differences between thick and thin films?

See p; 233

191. No clinical diagnosis of malaria can be confirmed without the finding of some stage of the plasmodia, or their pigments, in the blood.   T   F

T

192. The malarial parasites are less abundant in the blood during the latter stages of febrile paroxisms.   T   F   **T**

193. The sporozoites injected into man by an infected mosquito:
     a. Invade red cells directly
     b. Are taken up by white cells
     c. Divide in the blood plasma
     d. Enter cells of the liver   **d**
     e. Become flagellated

194. The pigment seen in malarial parasites in blood films is:
     a. An artifact produced by staining
     b. A food store for the parasite
     c. Digested by the parasite during growth
     d. A waste product of digestion by the parasite   **d**
     e. Derived from hemoglobin   **e**

195. Relapses in malarial infections are caused by:
     a. Further mosquito bites
     b. Delayed development of red cell schizonts
     c. Differentiation of gametocytes into trophozoites
     d. Reinvasion of the blood from infected liver cells   **d**
     e. None of these

196. Oval presegmenters may be seen in infections with:
     a. *Plasmodium malariae*
     b. *Plasmodium vivax*
     c. *Plasmodium falciparum*
     d. *Plasmodium ovale*   **d**

197. Which of the following species are known to cause relapses of malarial infection:
     a. *Plasmodium ovale*
     b. *Plasmodium vivax*   **b**
     c. *Plasmodium malariae*   **c**
     d. *Plasmodium falciparum*

198. Which of the following species cause a form of tertian malaria in man:
     a. *Plasmodium falciparum*   **a**
     b. *Plasmodium ovale*   **b**
     c. *Plasmodium malariae*
     d. *Plasmodium vivax*   **d**

199. Which of the following causes "quartan malaria":
     a. *Plasmodium ovale*
     b. *Plasmodium malariae*   **b**
     c. *Plasmodium falciparum*
     d. *Plasmodium vivax*

200. What is the approximate length of the asexual cycle in:
     a. Tertian malaria   **48 hours**
     b. Quartan malaria   **72 hours**

201. Which is the commonest species of *Plasmodium* in man?   ***P. vivax***

202. After one infection with malaria, man is immune to further infection.   T   F

F

203. Which of the following malarial parasites has the *longest* sexual cycle?
    a. *Plasmodium malariae*
    b. *Plasmodium vivax*
    c. *Plasmodium falciparum*
    d. *Plasmodium ovale*

a

204. Which of the following malarial parasites have the *shortest* (7–10 days) sexual cycle:
    a. *Plasmodium malariae*
    b. *Plasmodium vivax*
    c. *Plasmodium falciparum*
    d. *Plasmodium ovale*

b
c

205. Schüffner's dots (abundant pink-staining granules) are often seen within red cells infected by:
    a. *Plasmodium malariae*
    b. *Plasmodium vivax*
    c. *Plasmodium falciparum*
    d. *Plasmodium ovale*

b

d

206. Mature schizonts containing 6–12 merozoites in "rosette" may be seen in infections with:
    a. *Plasmodium malariae*
    b. *Plasmodium vivax*
    c. *Plasmodium falciparum*
    d. *Plasmodium ovale*

a

207. Mature schizonts containing 12–24 merozoites may be seen in the peripheral blood in infections with:
    a. *Plasmodium malariae*
    b. *Plasmodium vivax*
    c. *Plasmodium falciparum*
    d. *Plasmodium ovale*

b

208. Fringed or oval red cells are most likely to be seen in infections with:
    a. *Plasmodium malariae*
    b. *Plasmodium vivax*
    c. *Plasmodium falciparum*
    d. *Plasmodium ovale*

d

209. Which of these malarial parasites enlarge the red cells?
    a. *Plasmodium malariae*
    b. *Plasmodium vivax*
    c. *Plasmodium falciparum*
    d. *Plasmodium ovale*

b

d

210. Not all the stages of the parasite occur in peripheral blood in infections with:
    a. *Plasmodium malariae*
    b. *Plasmodium vivax*

c. *Plasmodium falciparum*   c
d. *Plasmodium ovale*

211. Large irregular rings within the red cells may be found in infections with:
    a. *Plasmodium malariae*
    b. *Plasmodium vivax*   b
    c. *Plasmodium falciparum*
    d. *Plasmodium ovale*

212. Presence of more than one malarial parasite within a single red cell is impossible.   T   F   F

213. Multiple infection of the same red cell occurs frequently in infections with:
    a. *Plasmodium malariae*
    b. *Plasmodium vivax*
    c. *Plasmodium falciparum*   c
    d. *Plasmodium ovale*

214. Multiple infection of the same red cell rarely occurs in infections with:
    a. *Plasmodium malariae*
    b. *Plasmodium vivax*   b
    c. *Plasmodium falciparum*
    d. *Plasmodium ovale*

215. Crescent-shaped gametocytes are characteristic of:
    a. *Plasmodium malariae*
    b. *Plasmodium vivax*
    c. *Plasmodium falciparum*   c
    d. *Plasmodium ovale*

216. Maurer's dots are irregular, red-stained bodies that appear after Romanowsky staining in human erythrocytes infected by:
    a. *Plasmodium vivax*
    b. *Plasmodium malariae*
    c. *Plasmodium falciparum*   c
    d. *Plasmodium ovale*

217. Which species of *Plasmodium* causes the most serious form of malaria in man?   *P. falciparum*

218. Which of the following statements are true of *Plasmodium falciparum*:
    a. "Applique" forms are usually seen   a
    b. Infection produces enlarged red cells
    c. All asexual stages occur in peripheral blood
    d. Double chromatin dots are often seen   d
    e. Infection produces fringed red cells

219. Red cells infected with *Plasmodium falciparum* become "sticky" and may block capillaries in vital organs.   T   F   T

220. A highly fatal disease associated with *Plasmodium falciparum* infections in which hemoglobin is lost rapidly

through the urine is:
    a. Oroya fever
    b. Dengue fever
    c. Chagas' disease
    d. Blackwater fever   d
    e. Yellow fever

221. Malarial hemoglobinuria is another name for blackwater fever. T F   T

222. Which of the following is true of *Plasmodium malariae:*
    a. Infected red cells show Schüffner's dots
    b. Trophozoite may appear as a band in the red cell   b
    c. Gametocytes are crescentic/
    d. Infected red cells are enlarged
    e. Pigment is abundant, very dark, and coarsely granular   e

223. What serological tests can be used in diagnosis of malarial infection?   CF; IFA; IHA

224. In what clinical situations is serological diagnosis of malarial infection useful. See p. 233

CILIATES – BALANTIDIUM

225. Diagnosis of *Balantidium coli* infection is by:
    a. Complement-fixation test
    b. Stool examination   b
    c. Intradermal test
    d. Tissue biopsy
    e. Thick blood film

226. *Balantidium coli* is transmitted by:
    a. An infected intermediate host
    b. A blood-sucking insect
    c. Ingestion of living trophozoites
    d. Ingestion of cysts   d
    e. A parasitic nematode

227. What are the distinctive nuclear features of *Balantidium coli*? See p. 233

228. *Balantidium coli* may cause liver abscess in man. T F   F

229. *Balantidium coli* has the following number of nuclei:
    a. 1 nucleus
    b. 2 nuclei   b
    c. 3 nuclei
    d. 4 nuclei
    e. Many nuclei

230. Which of the following animals acts as a reservoir of infection of *Balantidium coli*?
    a. Cattle
    b. Pigs   b

    c. Sheep
    d. Dogs
    e. Rats

231. *Balantidium coli* trophozoites are so large they can be seen
    with the low-power objective.   T   F   T

232. Human infection by *Balantidium coli* occurs:
    a. Commonly
    b. Rarely   b
    c. Never
    d. Occasionally

233. Which of the following statements apply to *Balantidium
    coli?*
    a. It is non-pathogenic in pigs   a
    b. It is non-pathogenic in man
    c. It may invade the intestinal mucosa in man   c
    d. It is transmitted by an intermediate host
    e. It is a member of the *Sporozoa*

FLUKES

234. Eggs of Trematodes may occur in:
    a. Urine   a
    b. Feces   b
    c. Sputum   c
    d. Spinal fluid
    e. Thin blood films

235. Match the following:
    a. Human lung fluke   1. *Clonorchis sinensis*   a—3
    b. Chinese liver fluke   2. *Schistosoma haematobium* b—1
    c. Large intestinal fluke   3. *Paragonimus westermani*   c—5
    d. Vesicle fluke   4. *Schistosoma japonicum*   d—2
    e. Oriental blood fluke   5. *Fasciolopsis buski*   e—4

236. In which of the following flukes is there an extensive mi-
    gration of larvae around the body?
    a. *Schistosoma mansoni*   a
    b. *Fasciolopsis buski*
    c. *Clonorchis sinensis*
    d. *Schistosoma haematobium*   d
    e. *Paragonimus westermani*

237. The sheep liver fluke *(Fasciola hepatica)* occurs in man:
    a. Commonly
    b. Rarely
    c. Occasionally   c

238. Ingestion of contaminated vegetation is the mode of in-
    fection in:
    a. *Paragonimus westermani*
    b. *Clonorchis sinensis*

    c. *Fasciola hepatica*   c
    d. *Fasciolopsis buski*   d
    e. *Schistosoma japonicum*

239. Which of the following flukes is acquired by ingestion of infected fish?
    a. *Fasciolopsis buski*
    b. *Clonorchis sinensis*   b
    c. *Schistosoma mansoni*
    d. *Paragonimus westermani*
    e. None of these

240. All flukes require snails as intermediate hosts.   T   F   T

241. The largest fluke found in man is:
    a. *Paragonimus westermani*
    b. *Clonorchis sinensis*
    c. *Fasciolopsis buski*   c
    d. *Schistosoma haematobium*
    e. *Schistosoma mansoni*

242. Eggs of *Clonorchis sinensis* may occur in duodenal contents.   T   F   T

243. Eggs of *Fasciolopsis buski* are similar to those of:
    a. *Paragonimus westermani*
    b. *Clonorchis sinensis*
    c. *Fasciola hepatica*   c
    d. *Schistosoma japonicum*
    e. *Opisthorchis felineus*

244. Which of the following eggs has no operculum (lid):
    a. *Fasciola hepatica*
    b. *Fasciolopsis buski*
    c. *Clonorchis sinensis*
    d. *Paragonimus westermani*
    e. *Schistosoma mansoni*   e

245. An inoperculated egg with a terminal spine seen in urine or feces indicates infection with:
    a. *Schistosoma japonicum*
    b. *Clonorchis sinensis*
    c. *Paragonimus westermani*
    d. *Schistosoma haematobium*   d
    e. *Fasciolopsis buski*

246. Which of the following fluke eggs is small, embryonated, operculated, and is shaped like an old-fashioned electric bulb?
    a. *Fasciolopsis buski*
    b. *Clonorchis sinensis*   b
    c. *Paragonimus westermani*
    d. *Schistosoma haematobium*
    e. *Fasciola hepatica*

247. The most important flukes, from the medical standpoint,
     are the:
     a. Intestinal flukes
     b. Liver flukes
     c. Blood flukes   c
     d. Lung flukes

248. Infection with *Paragonimus westermani* is acquired by:
     a. Ingestion of infected vegetation
     b. Ingestion of infected crustacea   b
     c. Direct penetration of cercariae
     d. Ingestion of infected fish
     e. None of these.

249. The egg of *Paragonimus westermani* may be found in:
     a. Urine
     b. Feces   b
     c. Vaginal exudate
     d. Sputum   d
     e. Blood

250. Which of the following can at present only be diagnosed
     reliably by finding eggs of the parasite:
     a. *Fasciola hepatica*
     b. *Paragonimus westermani*
     c. *Clonorchis sinensis*
     d. *Fasciolopsis buski*   d
     e. *Schistosoma mansoni*

251. Intradermal injection of antigen can be usefully used in
     the diagnosis of:
     a. *Clonorchis sinensis*   a
     b. *Fasciolopsis buski*
     c. *Schistosoma mansoni*   c
     d. *Paragonimus westermani*
     e. *Fasciola hepatica*   e

Infection with schistosomes can be acquired by:
     a. Ingesting contaminated vegetation
     b. Drinking contaminated water   b
     c. Ingesting infected fish
     d. Bathing in contaminated water   d
     e. Ingesting infected eggs

253. The finding of few schistosome eggs in a stool specimen
     indicates an early stage of infection:
     a. Yes
     b. No
     c. Not necessarily   c

254. What is the most obvious difference between the egg of
     Schistosoma mansoni and *Schistosoma japonicum* as seen
     in stool examination?   See p. 233

255. Eggs of *Schistosoma japonicum* may be found in:
     a. Urine

b. Feces   b
c. Sputum
d. Spinal fluid
.e. Blood

256. Eggs of *Schistosoma mansoni* may be found in:
a. Urine
b. Feces   b
c. Sputum
d. Spinal fluid
e. Blood

257. Eggs of *Schistosoma haematobium* may be found in:
a. Urine   a
b. Feces   b
c. Sputum
d. Spinal fluid
e. Blood

258. Hematuria is frequent in cases of vesicular schistosomiasis.
T   F   T

259. How many species of *Schistosoma* infect man?   See p. 233

260: Which species of schistosome is the only one likely to
infect people who have never lived outside the Americas?   *S. mansoni*

261. Which species of schistosome is the only one likely to infect people who have lived in the Far East?   *S. japonicum*

262. What immunological tests can be used to aid diagnosis of
schistosomiasis when eggs cannot be found.   CF; ID;
                                                            IFA
263. Acute infections with schistosomes are associated with
hypersensitivity reactions and raised levels of IgE.   T   F   T

TAPEWORMS

264. Unless the scolex of a tapeworm is removed from the intestine an adult worm may regrow.   T   F   T

265. Adult tapeworms are only found in the small intestine of
man.   T   F   T

266. Autoinfection is possible in the case of infection with:
a. *Taenia solium*
b. *Hymenolepis nana*   b
c. *Diphyllobothrium latum*
d. *Dipylidium caninum*
e. None of these

267. Diagnosis by means of stool examination is possible in the
case of:
a. *Taenia saginata*   a
b. *Sparganosis*
c. Hydatid cyst

d. *Hymenolepis nana*   d
e. *Diphyllobothrium latum*   e

268. The ingestion by man of tapeworm eggs may result in the
development of larval stages in:
   a. Muscles   a
   b. C.N.S.   b
   c. Blood
   d. Liver   d
   e. Bone   e

269. Which of the following tapeworm infections may man
acquire from dogs:
   a. Hydatid cyst   a
   b. *Hymenolepis nana*
   c. *Taenia saginata*
   d. *Dipylidium caninum*   d
   e. *Coenuriasis*   e

270. Which of the following tapeworm larval stages can occur
in man:
   a. Coenurus   a
   b. Hydatid cyst   b
   c. Cysticercus   c
   d. Cysticercoid   d
   e. Procercoid

271. Match the following common and scientific names of tapeworms:
   a. Pork tapeworm   1. *Diphyllobothrium latum*   a—3
   b. Fish tapeworm   2. *Hymenolepis nana*   b—1
   c. Beef tapeworm   3. *Taenia solium*   c—4
   d. Dwarf tapeworm   4. *Taenia saginata*   d—2

272. A tapeworm having small, pumpkin-seed segments with
one genital pore on each margin is:
   a. *Dipylidium caninum*   a
   b. *Taenia saginata*
   c. *Echinococcus granulosus*
   d. *Hymenolepis nana*
   e. *Taenia solium*

273. Which of the following tapeworm eggs is operculate:
   a. *Taenia solium*
   b. *Taenia saginata*
   c. *Diphyllobothrium latum*   c
   d. *Hymenolepis nana*
   e. *Dipylidium caninum*

274. Which of the following tapeworms has centrally-located,
rosette-shaped uterus:
   a. *Diphyllobothrium latum*   a
   b. *Dipylidium caninum*
   c. *Hymenolepis nana*

d. *Taenia saginata*
e. *Echinococcus granulosus*

275. Which of the following tapeworms has an almond-shaped scolex ("head") with two lateral grooves and no hooks?
    a. *Diphyllobothrium latum*   a
    b. *Dipylidium caninum*
    c. *Taenia solium*
    d. *Hymenolepis nana*
    e. *Taenia saginata*

276. "Sparganosis" is due to infection of man by the plerocercoid larvae of:
    a. *Echinococcus granulosus*
    b. *Diphyllobothrium latum*   b
    c. *Taenia saginata*
    d. *Hymenolepis nana*
    e. *Dipylidium caninum*

277. An egg which is practically spherical in shape, has two membranes, two hair-like processes (polar filaments) and three pairs of hooks belongs to:
    a. *Taenia saginata*
    b. *Dipylidium caninum*
    c. *Hymenolepis nana*   c
    d. *Diphyllobothrium latum*
    e. *Echinococcus granulosus*

278. Infections with *Taenia solium* or *Taenia saginata* usually involve relatively few worms.   T   F   T

279. Briefly differentiate between *Taenia saginata* and *Taenia solium*.   See p. 233

280. The larval stage in *Taenia saginata* and *Taenia solium* is known as the:
    a. Procercoid
    b. Cysticercoid
    c. Plerocercoid
    d. Cysticercus   d
    e. Coenurus

281. *Taenia saginata* infections are acquired in the following manner:
    a. By ingestion of mature eggs with food
    b. By penetration of cercaria larvae through skin
    c. By ingestion of infected beef   c
    d. By ingestion of infected pork
    e. By ingestion of cysts with food contaminated by flies

282. What is "cysticercosis" and how is it acquired?   See p. 233

283. *Dipylidium caninum* infection is acquired by accidental ingestion of:
    a. A gravid segment
    b. Food contaminated with eggs

    c. Infected meat
    d. Infected fleas   d
    e. None of these

284. The length in meters of the adult *Diphyllobothrium latum* is:
    a. 1–2 meters
    b. 2–4 meters
    c. 4–8 meters
    d. 8–12 meters   d

285. The scolex or "head" of *Diphyllobothrium latum* (fish tapeworm) is provided with:
    a. 4 sucking cups
    b. 2 sucking cups
    c. 2 lateral grooves   c
    d. 2 sucking cups and 2 grooves

286. In cases of diphyllobothriasis, segments of fish tapeworm may be found in the stool.   T   F   T

287. The larval stage of *Diphyllobothrium latum* which occurs in infected fish is known as the:
    a. Procercoid
    b. Cysticercoid
    c. Plerocercoid   c
    d. Cysticercus
    e. Coenurus

288. What is hydatid disease? Define hydatid cyst.   See p. 233

289. What is the Casoni test?   See p. 234

290. What serological tests can be used to diagnose infection with hydatid cyst?   CF; IFA; IHA

291. Is *E. granulosus* the only *Echinococcus* to infect Man?   No, also *E. multilocularis*

NEMATODES

292. Arrange the following species in order of *increasing size* of the adult worm:
    a. *Trichuris trichiura*   1—d
    b. *Enterobius vermicularis*   2—b
    c. *Ascaris lumbricoides*   3—e
    d. *Trichinella spiralis*   4—a
    e. *Ancylostoma duodenale*   5—c

293. Which of the following enter the body of man by direct penetration of a larval stage?
    a. *Necator americanus*   a
    b. *Ascaris lumbricoides*
    c. *Trichinella spiralis*

d. *Strongyloides stercoralis*   d
e. *Ancylostoma duodenale*   e

294. Which of the following show a larval migration in the body
     of man?
     a. *Trichuris trichiura*
     b. *Trichinella spiralis*   b
     c. *Toxocara canis*   c
     d. *Enterobius vermicularis*
     e. *Ascaris lumbricoides*   e

295. In which of the following is man infected by ingestion of
     fully embryonated eggs?
     a. *Trichuris trichiura*   a
     b. *Trichinella spiralis*
     c. *Ancylostoma duodenale*
     d. *Onchocerca volvulus*
     e. *Ascaris lumbrocoides*   e

296. Which of the following are transmitted to man by inter-
     mediate hosts?
     a. *Trichinella spiralis*
     b. *Dracunculus medinensis*   b
     c. *Wuchereria bancrofti*   c
     d. *Enterobius vermicularis*
     e. *Strongyloides stercoralis*

297. Which of the following species is not a round worm?
     a. *Trichuris trichiura*
     b. *Schistosoma mansoni*   b
     c. *Trichinella spiralis*
     d. *Enterobius vermicularis*
     e. *Paragonimus westermani*   e

298. Which of the following does not ordinarily produce eggs
     in feces?
     a. *Trichuris trichiura*
     b. *Ancylostoma duodenale*
     c. *Ascaris lumbricoides*
     d. *Strongyloides stercoralis*   d
     e. *Necator americanus*

299. Which of the following species neither lays eggs nor de-
     posits its larvae in the intestinal canal?
     a. *Wuchereria bancrofti*   a
     b. *Trichuris trichiura*
     c. *Trichinella spiralis*
     d. *Enterobius vermicularis*
     e. *Ascaris lumbricoides*

300. Which of the following eggs is football-shaped and has a
     typical plug at each pole?
     a. *Necator americanus*
     b. *Ascaris lumbricoides*
     c. *Enterobius vermicularis*
     d. *Trichuris trichiura*   d

301. Which of the following eggs is characteristically flattened
on one side.
   a. *Trichuris trichiura*
   b. *Ascaris lumbricoides*
   c. *Necator americanus*
   d. *Enterobius vermicularis*   d
   e. *Strongyloides stercoralis*

302. The "pinworm" or "seatworm" is scientifically known as:
   a. *Enterobius vermicularis*   a
   b. *Trichuris trichiura*
   c. *Ascaris lumbricoides*
   d. *Strongyloides stercoralis*
   e. *Necator americanus*

303. Pinworm eggs are infective when laid by the female worm.
   T   F   T

304. Eggs are a frequent finding in the stool of patients with
pinworm infection.   T   F   F

305. Heavy infections with *Ascaris lumbricoides* may give rise
to:
   a. Intestinal bleeding
   b. Secondary anemia   b
   c. Allergic symptoms   c
   d. Paralysis
   e. Intestinal blockage   e

306. In order to reach the small intestine the larvae of *Ascaris
lumbricoides* migrate through and may damage:
   a. Liver   a
   b. Subcutaneous tissue
   c. Muscle
   d. Lungs   d
   e. Intestinal wall   e

307. The adult giant intestinal round worm *(Ascaris lumbricoides)* may appear in the stool or exit through mouth
or nose.   T   F   T

308. The larva of *Ascaris lumbricoides* may be found in the
sputum.   T   F   T

309. Eosinophilia may be present in cases of *Ascaris lumbricoides* infection.   T   F   T

310. Indicate method(s) of diagnosis of *Trichinella spiralis* infection:
   a. Muscle biopsy   a
   b. Thick blood film
   c. Stool examination
   d. Intradermal skin test   d
   e. Agglutination test   e

311. Trichinosis is acquired by eating _____,   infected pork,
_____.   not well cooked

312. What is an early sign of acute infection with *Trichinella spiralis?*

periorbital edema

313. Ordinary curing of pork is sufficient to kill the larvae of *Trichinella spiralis.*   T   F

F

314. Which of the following may act as sources of infection of *Trichinella spiralis* in the domestic pig?
    a. Man
    b. Rats
    c. Contaminated vegetation
    d. Pork meat scraps
    e. Contaminated water

b

d

315. *Trichinella spiralis* larvae may be found in:
    a. Blood
    b. Feces
    c. CSF
    d. Deltoid muscle
    e. Urine

a

c
d

316. The larva of *Strongyloides* may be found in fresh feces.
    T   F

T

317. Which of the following is the infective larva of *Strongyloides stercoralis?*
    a. Rhabditiform larva
    b. Filariform larva

b

318. Compared to the buccal cavity of the hookworm larve, the buccal cavity of the *Strongyloides* larva:
    a. Is much shorter
    b. Is much longer
    c. It has approximately the same length

a

319. The larva of hookworm may be found in fresh feces.
    T   F

F

320. Which of the following are hookworm species?
    a. *Strongyloides stercoralis*
    b. *Ancylostoma duodenale*
    c. *Necator americanus*
    d. *Trichuris trichiura*
    e. *Ascaris lumbricoides*

b

c

321. Briefly summarize the differences between larvae and adults of Old World and New World hookworms.

See p. 234

322. What are the differences between the larvae of hookworms and *Strongyloides stercoralis?*

See p. 234

323. Infection with *Ancylostoma duodenale* is always associated with anemia.   T   F

F

324. What is a "microfilaria"?

See p. 234

325. Larvae of *Wuchereria bancrofti* are sometimes found in milky urine.   T   F   T

326. Chyluria occurs frequently in cases of Bancroft's filariasis. T   F   T

327. Bancroft's filaria infection is acquired through:
    a. Bite of infected mosquito   a
    b. Contaminated food or water
    c. Penetration of skin by larva
    d. Bite of infected sand fly

328. The microfilariae of *Wuchereria bancrofti* are usually most abundant in peripheral blood smears taken from:
    a. 10:00 P.M. to 2:00 A.M.   a
    b. 8:00 A.M. to 2:00 P.M.
    c. 2:00 P.M. to 8:00 P.M.

329. The microfilariae of *Wuchereria bancrofti* are characterized by:
    a. Diurnal periodicity
    b. Nocturnal periodicity   b
    c. Possession of sheath   c
    d. Lack of sheath
    e. Lack of nuclei in tip of tail   e

330. The microfilariae of *Loa loa* are characterized by:
    a. Diurnal periodicity   a
    b. Nocturnal periodicity
    c. Lack of periodicity
    d. Possession of sheath   d
    e. Lack of sheath

331. *Loa loa* is the:
    a. Guinea worm
    b. Eye worm   b
    c. Convoluted filaria
    d. Bancroft's filaria
    e. None of these

332. *Acanthocheilonema perstans* microfilariae are periodic and sheathed.   T   F   F

333. *Dracunuculus medinensis* is the:
    a. Eye worm
    b. Guinea worm   b
    c. Pinworm
    d. Bancroft's filaria
    e. Whipworm

334. Which of the following is true of *Dracunuculus medinensis*?
    a. Intermediate host a mosquito
    b. Intermediate host a crustacean   b
    c. Causes elephantiasis
    d. Causes skin ulcers   d
    e. May be 120 cm. long   e

335. Visceral larva migrans is caused by infection with:
    a. *Wuchereria bancrofti*
    b. *Trichuris trichiura*
    c. *Mansonella ozzardi*
    d. *Toxocara canis*   d
    e. *Enterobius vermicularis*

336. Visceral larva migrans is a nematode infection of man acquired by the accidental ingestion of eggs of a nematode from:
    a. Cattle
    b. Rats
    c. Pigs
    d. Dogs   d
    e. Man

337. Immunologically-based tests can be used to diagnose infection with:
    a. *Toxocara canis*   a
    b. *Enterobius vermicularis*
    c. *Wuchereria bancrofti*   c
    d. *Trichuris trichiura*
    e. *Trichinella spiralis*   e

338. Larval nematodes present in marine fish used as food can occasionally infect man.   T   F   T

CLINICAL PARASITOLOGY ANSWERS CONTINUED

6. **Infestation:** The presence of animal parasites UPON the human body.
   Infection: The presence of animal parasites INSIDE the human body.

7. **Parasitism:** A state of symbiosis in which the association is more or less detrimental to one of the organisms (so-called the host) involved. A parasite may injure its host in a variety of ways. Thus it may: (a) Rob him of food, (b) Destroy his tissues, (c) Inoculate him with poisons, (d) Infect him with other parasites, (e) Reduce his resistance, and (f) Cause him psychological disturbances.
   Commensalism: A state of symbiosis in which only one of the two organisms involved is benefited but neither is injured.

8. **Egg:** The female germ cell.
   Ovum: The female germ cell *while still within the uterus.*

9. **Definitive Host:** The host in which the sexual multiplication of a parasite takes place.
   Intermediate Host: The host in which only the asexual stages of a parasite occur.

10. **Embryo:** The early or developing stage of any organism. The embryo of *Taenia saginata* is called "hexacanth embryo."
    Larva: The early and usually active feeding stage of an animal after the embryo. Not resembling the adult.

11. **Trophozoite:** The active, vegetative stage of a protozoan parasite.

Cyst: The nonmotile, latent stage (surrounded by a wall) of certain protozoa.

13. Parasites may invade man through:
   a. Skin. Direct penetration by the parasite or inoculation by transmitting vectors.
   b. Digestive System. Ingestion of contaminated food, water.
   c. Reproductive System. Transmission during sexual activity.

14. To ensure accuracy in identification and prevent unnecessary medical treatment.

21. Larva migrans describes infection with larval stages of worm parasites (usually nematodes) which do not mature, but wander through the body, often with pathological consequences. Visceral larva migrans denotes larvae wandering in deep organs; cutaneous larva migrans denotes larvae migrating in superficial tissues.

24. *Blastocystis hominis* is a yeast or yeast-like organism, 5–15 microns in diameter. It superficially resembles a protozoan cyst. The nuclear structure of the various protozoan cysts provides the best differential criterion.

27. Xenodiagnosis: Use of the natural vector host to determine the presence of infection where other diagnostic methods are inappropriate. In the case of *Trypanosoma cruzi* the vector (Triatoma) is allowed to take a blood meal from the suspected patient and, after an interval, the gut of the bug is examined for developing stages of the parasite.

28. LPF, low power field; HDF, high dry field; L.E.S., Locke's egg-serum medium for *Entamoeba histolytica;* NNN, Novy, MacNeal and Nicolle medium for Leishmania, trypanosomes.

29. 1. Direct observation of fresh material
    2. Iodine staining (with or without eosin)
    3. Permanent preparation (iron-hematoxylin or trichrome staining)
    4. Centrifugal concentration
    5. Concentration by flotation

30. 1. Zinc sulfate flotation
    2. Formalin-ether sedimentation
    3. Special cultures

49. CF, complement fixation test; ID, intradermal antigen test; IFA, indirect fluorescent antibody test; IHA, indirect haemagglutination test.

53. **Formol-gel Test.** A drop of formalin is added to a serum sample. An opalescent gel is obtained if the serum globulin content is high. Used in diagnosis of Kala-azar but not specific to this.

55. Complement-fixation test; Gel-diffusion test; Agglutination test; Intradermal test; Indirect fluorescent antibody test.

57. A test serum is reacted with a preparation of parasite antigen, the preparation washed and treated with a fluorescein labelled, anti-globulin reagent. In positive cases the reagent combines with antibody complexed with the test antigen and can be visualized by fluorescence microscopy.

58. (a) In early stages of infection, (b) when parasite occurs only in low numbers, (c) when parasite occurs only in deep tissues.

78. **Macrophages** are large mononuclear, wandering phagocytic cells which originate in the tissues. They may be distinguished from amoebae on the basis of nuclear structure.

79. **Amoebic dysentery:** *Entamoeba histolytica* present in stool. Few pus cells and macrophages. Eosinophils and Charcot-Leyden crystals are often present. Large number of motile bacilli occur.
    Bacillary dysentery: *Entamoeba histolytica* is absent. Numerous pus cells and macrophages are present in the stool. Eosinophils few if any. Charcot-Leyden crystals do not occur in uncomplicated bacillary dysentery. Very few bacilli present.

84. Apart from rare 4-nucleate *Entamoeba coli* cysts there is a species, *Entamoeba hartmanni*, which, although similar to *Entamoeba histolytica*, is never pathogenic. The cysts of *E. hartmanni* are smaller (7–8 microns diameter) than those of *E. histolytica* (11–12 microns).

85. The "minuta" form of *Entamoeba histolytica* is the harmless form of the species which lives in the intestinal lumen without invading the intestinal wall. These forms may change into the "magna" forms which do invade and cause disease. *Entamoeba hartmanni*, though similar, is never pathogenic. It is the "minuta" forms of *E. histolytica* which produce the cysts by which the amoeba is transmitted.

91. CF; gel diffusion; IFA; IHA. See also page 231, answer to question 49.

109. **Entamoeba coli:** Nucleus with large, eccentric karyosome. Organism moves sluggishly. Red cells rarely present in cytoplasm. Cyst usually larger than 15 microns, with 8 nuclei (may vary) and splinter-shaped chromatoid bodies.
    Entamoeba histolytica: Nucleus with small, central karyosome. Organism has directional motility. Red cells usually present when amoeba is from dysenteric patient. Cyst usually smaller than 15 microns, with 4 nuclei (may vary) and blunt-ended chromatoid bodies.

121. **Amoebic meningoencephalitis:** A severe and often fatal infection associated with invasion of the central nervous system by trophic amoebae of the genera *Acanthamoeba*, *Hartmanella*, and *Naegleria*. These are free-living soil and water amoebae which can invade the tissues of man, gaining entry through the nasal mucosa.

138. *Trichomonas vaginalis* is transmitted venereally or by contact of infected material with vaginal mucous membrane.

139. *T. hominis* is transmitted as a rounded-up resistant trophozoite, not a cyst.

147. The intracellular forms (amastigotes) of Leishmania are ovoidal or spheroidal in form, 2–4 microns in longer diameter, and may occur in large number within a cell. The nucleus of the parasite often lies against the membrane of its cytosome. The rod-shaped kinetoplast often lies with its long axis directed toward the nucleus. The more usual direction of the kinetoplast, which occurs in the flagellate form and in some of the L.D. bodies, is tangential to the nucleus. In some instances there is visible an axoneme, extending to the margin of the parasite from the blepharoplast, which is close to the kinetoplast. The L.D. bodies multiply, usually by simple binary fission, in the nonflagellate form. Occasionally, owing to delayed plasmotomy, several nuclei and kinetoplasts may occur in the cytosome. The

infection spreads in the vertebrate host evidently, when parasites released by fragmentation of infected macrophages are ingested by other phagocytic cells.

158. In the life cycle of *Trypanosoma gambiense* the Tsetse fly is the vector host (no sexual stages in cycle).

163. **Romaña's sign** is a unilateral swelling of the eyelids following penetration of *Trypanosoma cruzi* stages through the mucous membranes after deposition in the feces of the vector host. An early diagnostic sign for Chagas' disease.

168. **Chagas' disease:** The condition caused directly by infection with *Trypanosoma cruzi* and associated with the presence of the parasite.
Chagas' syndrome: A chronic degeneration in structure and function of e.g. heart and intestine which develops long after acute infection has disappeared.

187. **Sporogony:** The sexual development and multiplication of malarial parasites. Sporogony takes place in the mosquito (definitive host).
Schizogony: The asexual development and multiplication of malarial parasites. Schizogony takes place in man (intermediate host).

188. The best time to collect a specimen of peripheral blood for examination for malarial parasites is the period just before or at the beginning of a paroxysm.

190. Thick films allow detection of infection when density of parasites is low. Apart from thickness of film, the thick film is not fixed prior to staining to allow the blood to lake, thus removing hemoglobin from the cells.

224. (a) To confirm the cause of recent febrile illness, especially after chemotherapy; (b) to confirm the cause of secondary pathological changes; (c) to trace donors of infected blood used in transfusion.

227. The two nuclei of *Balantidium coli* are unequal in size. The larger macronucleus is involved in asexual reproduction only; sexual reproduction is the function of the micronucleus.

254. Eggs of *Schistosoma mansoni* have a well-developed lateral spine; those of *S. japonicum* a *minute* lateral spine.

259. Four: *S. haematobium, S. intercalatum, S. japonicum, S. mansoni.*

279. **Taenia saginata:** Beef tapeworm. Adult reaches 4–8 meters. Scolex with 4 suckers, no hooks. Gravid segment has uterus with 15–30 lateral branches.
Taenia solium: Pork tapeworm. Adult reaches 2–4 meters. Scolex with 4 suckers and 2 rows of hooks. Gravid segment has uterus with 5–10 lateral branches.

282. **Cysticercosis:** Human infection with the larval stages (cysticerci) of *Taenia solium*. Acquired by ingestion of infective eggs.

288. **Hydatid disease** is the most serious human tapeworm infection. The symptoms are caused by the pressure exerted by growing cysts on internal organs and the allergic reactions which follow cyst rupture. The hydatid cyst is the larval stage of *Echinococcus granulosus* and is a hollow, fluid-filled sphere, from the wall of which many scoleces of potential worms are budded off.

289. An early (1911) intradermal test for hydatid cyst using cyst fluid as an antigen. The test is of relatively low specificity and is improved by the use of purified antigens.

321. **Old World hookworm** *(Ancylostoma duodenale):* Infective larva has unequal esophageal spears. Adult has two paris of teeth, large bursa with three-pronged dorsal ray; head does not curve as sharply as that of *Necator americanus.*
    New World hookworm *(Necator americanus):* Infective larva has equal esophageal spears. Adult has one pair of cutting plates and no teeth, small bursa with two-pronged dorsal ray; head turned opposite to general body curve.

322. **Hookworm:** Rhabditiform has long and narrow buccal cavity, snake-like motion. Filariform (infective larval stage) has elongated esophagus, Tail without notch in caudal extremity.
    Strongyloides: Rhabditiform has short buccal cavity of small diameter, purposeless motion. Filariform (infective larval stage) has an esophagus similar to that of hookworm but longer. Tail with notch in caudal extremity.

324. **Microfilaria:** So-called the prelarval stage of a filaria. Microfilariae occur in the blood of man or in the tissues of various vectors.

2.

COLLEGE MEDICAL PARASITOLOGY TEST
Edited by Derek Wakelin, Ph.D., The University of Glasgow

1. List methods of transmission of infection. See p. 282

2. Walking barefoot on infected soil may result in:
   - a. Hookworm infection a
   - b. Amoebic dysentery
   - c. Ascaris infection
   - d. Trichinosis
   - e. Sparganosis

3. Protozoan organisms which are able to live and often to multiply in moist fecal matter outside the body are said to be:
   - a. Parasitic
   - b. Saprophytic
   - c. Coprophilic c
   - d. Symbiotic

4. Bosman bodies (these have doubtless been mistaken for forms of protozoa, to some of which they show some similarity) usually contain:
   - a. One nucleus
   - b. Two nuclei b
   - c. Three nuclei
   - d. Four nuclei

5. Indicate the meaning of the following abbreviations:
a. CNS	e. PVA
b. CSF	f. LES
c. RES	g. NNN
d. LD	h. CPLM

   See p. 282

6. Mention the three important types of symbiotic relationship. parasitism, commensalism, mutualism

7. What is the effect of a parasite on its host? See p. 282

8. Name two ways in which a parasite may indirectly be harmful to the host. See p. 282

9. Why is it necessary to study and know the morphology, habitat, and staining characteristics of the protozoa of man which are not parasitic in nature? See p. 282

10. A state of symbiosis in which the association may be beneficial to one of the two organisms without effect on the other is:
    - a. Amensalism
    - b. Mutualism

c. Parasitism
d. Commensalism   d
e. Synnecrosis

11. A state of symbiosis in which the association may be beneficial to both organisms is:
    a. Parasitism
    b. Commensalism
    c. Mutualism   c
    d. Synnecrosis
    e. Amensalism

12. An organism which is usually parasitic upon another but still capable of independent existence is a:
    a. Facultative parasite   a
    b. Obligatory parasite
    c. Incidental parasite
    d. None of these

13. Amoebae move by means of:
    a. Pseudopodia   a
    b. Flagella
    c. Cilia
    d. None of the above

14. How does a cyst differ from a trophozoite?   See p. 282

15. List changes that occur in passage from trophozoite to cyst.   See.p. 282

16. The process of emerging from the encysted state is:
    a. Encystation
    b. Encystment
    c. Excystation   c
    d. Gametogenesis

17. List cystic forms and those which do not have cysts.   See p. 283

18. A polymorphonuclear leukocyte may be distinguished from the intestinal protozoa by its nuclear structure.
    a. Yes   a
    b. No

19. The Amoeba which causes dysentery belongs to class:
    a. Mastigophora
    b. Sarcodina   b
    c. Sporozoa
    d. Ciliata

20. What two protozoa may be found in the human mouth?   See p. 283

21. The granule to which a flagellum is connected is the:
    a. Axoneme
    b. Axostyle
    c. Kinetosome   c
    d. Centrodesmus

22. Briefly explain meaning of terms "cytosome" and "cyto-
    stome."

    See p. 283

23. Sporozoa are always parasitic.
    a. Yes
    b. No

    a

24. *Trichomonas vaginalis* is a member of the following group:
    a. Sarcodina
    b. Mastigophora
    c. Ciliata
    d. Sporozoa
    e. None of the above

    b

25. Identify and, if you believe no definite identification pos-
    sible, explain:
    a. Amoeba in the mouth
    b. Cyst, cytostome, cyst elevated away from contents
       of wall
    c. Two flagella, no undulating membrane, fibrils, one
       nucleus in trophozoite
    d. Flagellate, 4 plus 1 plus 1 flagella
    e. Eight nuclei, chromatin beads, endosome

    E. gingivalis

    C. mesnili
    *Embadomonas**
    intestinalis
    T. hominis
    E. coli

26. A large sucking disk, 2 nuclei, 2 axostyles, 8 flagella, and
    2 parabasal bodies are characteristic of:
    a. *Giardia lamblia*
    b. *Trichomonas vaginalis*
    c. *Chilomastix mesnili*
    d. *Isospora hominis*
    e. None of these

    a

27. *Acanthocephala* are:
    a. Tapeworms
    b. Flukes
    c. Thorny-headed worms
    d. Roundworms
    e. Earthworms

    c

28. Two phyla that include worms are:
    a. Protozoa and Platyhelminthes
    b. Annelida and Arthropoda
    c. Platyhelminthes and Aschelminthes

    c

29. Platyhelminthes are commonly called:
    a. Roundworms
    b. Earthworms
    c. Flatworms
    d. Leeches

    c

30. A nematode is a segmented roundworm.
    a. Yes
    b. No

    b

---

*Retortamonas

31. Nematodes possess complete alimentary tracts.
     a. Yes   a
     b. No

32. The flukes and tapeworms parasitic in man belong to
     phylum:
     a. Playthelminthes   a
     b. Nemathelminthes
     c. Protozoa
     d. Annelida
     e. None of these

33. All of the following are parasitic worms except:
     a. Filaria
     b. Ringworm   b
     c. Lung fluke
     d. Leech
     e. Hookworm

34. Indicate parasite(s) which may cause human liver infection:
     a. *Schistosoma mansoni*
     b. *Enterobius vermicularis*
     c. *Fasciola hepatica*   c
     d. *Entamoeba histolytica*   d
     e. *Strongyloides stercoralis*

35. Indicate parasites with stages present in stools:
     a. *Wuchereria bancrofti*
     b. *Entamoeba histolytica*   b
     c. *Schistosoma mansoni*   c
     d. *Enterobius vermicularis*
     e. *Taenia saginata*   e

36. Indicate parasites with stages which may invade central
     nervous system or eyes:
     a. *Schistosoma haematobium*
     b. *Toxocara canis*   b
     c. *Onchocerca volvulus*   c
     d. *Trypanosoma gambiense*   d
     e. *Loa loa*   e
     f. *Leishmania tropica*

37. Indicate parasites with stages present in peripheral blood:
     a. *Schistosoma haematobium*
     b. *Wuchereria bancrofti*   b
     c. *Trypanosoma gambiense*   c
     d. *Entamoeba histolytica*
     e. *Plasmodium falciparum*   e
     f. *Leishmania donovani*
     g. *Onchocerca volvulus*

38. Indicate parasite(s) which is (are) hermaphroditic:
     a. *Ascaris lumbricoides*
     b. *Trichinella spiralis*
     c. *Clonorchis sinensis*   c

    d. *Schistosoma haematobium*
    e. *Fasciolopsis buski*   e

39. Indicate the parasite(s) which, in the adult stage, is (are) microscopic in size:
    a. *Diphyllobothrium latum*
    b. *Echinococcus granulosus*
    c. *Hymenolepis diminuta*
    d. *Trichinella spiralis*   d
    e. *Strongyloides stercoralis*

40. Indicate the parasite(s) which is (are) chiefly (or exclusively) extracellular:
    a. *Trypanosoma gambiense*   a (also see
    b. *Trypanosoma cruzi*   p. 283)
    c. *Plasmodium ovale*
    d. *Leishmania donovani*

41. Parasitic protozoa occur in the class:
    a. Sarcodina
    b. Sporozoa
    c. Mastigophora
    d. Ciliata
    e. All of these   e

42. Indicate parasite(s) which require(s) no intermediate host:
    a. *Echinococcus granulosus*
    b. *Enterobius vermicularis*   b
    c. *Hymenolepis nana*   c
    d. *Trichuris trichiura*   d
    e. *Wuchereria bancrofti*

43. Larva enters body through skin:
    a. Hookworm   a
    b. Tapeworm
    c. Pinworm
    d. *Strongyloides*   d
    e. None of these

44. *Paragonimus westermani, Clonorchis sinensis*, and *Fasciolopsis buski* are:
    a. Tapeworms
    b. Roundworms
    c. Flukes   c
    d. None of these

45. Parasitic arthropods which infest man belong to:
    a. Insecta   a
    b. Scorpionida
    c. Acarina   c
    d. Crustacea

46. Two insects which live on man and suck blood are: Fleas, lice

47. Blood sucking flies which may transmit pathogens are:

         a. Bot flies
         b. Sand flies   b
         c. Mosquitoes   c
         d. House flies
         e. Tsetse flies   e
48. Ticks and mites are:
         a. Class Insecta
         b. Class Arachnida   b
         c. Order Acarina   c
         d. Order Diptera
         e. Phylum Arthropoda   e
49. The soft-bodied ticks belong to the:
         a. Ixodidae
         b. Argasidae   b

AMOEBAE

The following statements apply to the amoebae listed
below. Place the appropriate letter(s) in the space before
the question.

         Entamoeba histolytica   a
         Entamoeba coli   b
         Endolimax nana   c
         Dientamoeba fragilis   d
         Iodamoeba bütschlii   e

50. _____ Karyosome may be surrounded by perikaryosomal
         granules.   e

51. _____ Karyosome usually diffuse, large, eccentric.   b

52. _____ Karysome usually compact, central.   a

53. _____ Karysome extremely large.   e

54. _____ Karysome typically granular, composed of 4–6
         granules.   d

55. _____ Shape of karyosome extremely variable.   c

56. _____ Nuclear membrane usually composed of a series of
         fine regular granules, but occasionally plaques may
         occur.   b

57. _____ Large granules occur on linin network.   b

58. _____ Halo effect may occur behind nucleus.   b

59. _____ Two nuclei common in trophozoite.   d

60. _____ One nucleus common in cyst.   e

61. _____ Has no cyst.   d

62. *Entamoeba histolytica* occurs in every part of the world.
         a. Yes   a
         b. No

63. Only the trophic form of *Entamoeba histolytica* is tissue invading.
    a. Yes
    b. No

    a

64. *Entamoeba histolytica* primarily parasitizes the:
    a. Liver
    b. Colon
    c. Rectum
    d. Lung
    e. Small intestine

    b

65. The vegetative stage of *Entamoeba histolytica* is characterized by aimless movement and slow formation of pseudopodia.
    a. Yes
    b. No

    b

66. Active trophozoites of *Entamoeba histolytica* typically show "directional" motility.
    a. Yes
    b. No

    a

67. There exists, in *Entamoeba histolytica*, a lack of differentiation between ectoplasm and endoplasm.
    a. Yes
    b. No

    b

68. The nucleus, in the trophozoite of *Entamoeba histolytica*, is usually visible.
    a. Yes
    b. No

    b

69. Trophozoites of *Dientamoeba fragilis* usually contain two nuclei.
    a. Yes
    b. No

    a

70. *Dientamoeba fragilis* usually forms irregular shaped cysts.
    a. Yes
    b. No

    b

71. Bacterial inclusions are often found in *Dientamoeba fragilis* trophozoites.
    a. Yes
    b. No

    a

72. *Dientamoeba fragilis* can be studied with facility in iodine-stained preparations.
    a. Yes
    b. No

    b

73. According to recent research, *Dientamoeba fragilis* may be mildly pathogenic.
    a. Yes
    b. No

    a

74. *Dientamoeba fragilis* is parasitic in very few individuals in
     the U.S.
     a. Yes
     b. No   a

75. The pseudopodia of *Dientamoeba fragilis* are usually clear,
     like those of *Entamoeba histolytica.*
     a. Yes
     b. No   a

76. *Dientamoeba fragilis* may ingest r.b.c.
     a. Yes
     b. No   b

77. *Dientamoeba* produces a cyst.
     a. Yes
     b. No   b

78. The cyst form of *Iodamoeba bütschlii* often contains large
     glycogen vacuole.
     a. Yes
     b. No   a

79. The trophozoite of *Iodamoeba bütschlii* has a karyosome
     which may appear to be very similar to that of *Endolimax
     nana.*
     a. Yes
     b. No   a

80. The cyst form of *Iodamoeba bütschlii* rarely has more than
     one nucleus.
     a. Yes
     b. No   a

81. The trophozoite of *Iodamoeba bütschlii* ingests bacteria.
     a. Yes
     b. No   a

82. Metachromatic substances are frequently found in the cyst
     form of *Iodamoeba bütschlii.*
     a. Yes
     b. No   a

83. A large vacuole is characteristic of *Iodamoeba bütschlii*
     only.
     a. Yes
     b. No   b

84. The chromatoidal bars of *Iodamoeba bütschlii* often appear
     as vacuoles.
     a. Yes
     b. No   b

85.

Differential Criteria, Entamoeba		
	E. histolytica	*E. coli*
Nuclear structure		
Karyosome		See p. 283
Membrane		" 283
Linin network		" 283
Nuclei (characteristic number)		
Cyst		" 283
Trophozoite		" 283
Chromatoidal bodies		" 283
What does animal ingest?		" 283
Type and progression of movement		" 283

MASTIGOPHORA

86. *Retortamonas intestinalis* and *Embadomonas intestinalis* are one and the same organism.
    a. Yes
    b. No   a

The following hints apply to the flagellates listed below. Place the appropriate letter(s) in the space before the question.

> *Giardia lamblia*   a
> *Chilomastix mesnili*   b
> *Trichomonas vaginalis*   c
> *Trichomonas hominis*   d
> *Trichomonas tenax*   e

87. _____ Inhabits small intestine.   a

88. _____ Inhabits mouth.   e

89. _____ Inhabits vagina.   c

90. _____ Inhabits urethra of male.   c

91. _____ Inhabits large intestine (probably).   b

92. _____ May be transmitted by fecal contamination.   d

93. _____ May be transmitted by oral contact.   e

94. _____ May be transmitted by sexual contact.   c

95. _____ Undulating membrane full length of parasite.   d

96. _____ Undulating membrane 1/3 to 1/2 of length of parasite.   c

97. _____ Definitely non-pathogenic.   b

98. _____ Lemon-shaped cyst.   b

99. _____ Fibrils present in cyst.   a & b

100. _____ Cytostome present.   b

101. _____ Resembles an old man with glasses.   a

102. Briefly explain how *Giardia lamblia* infection is acquired.   See p. 283

103. *Giardia lamblia* has been known to cause a tremendous
amount of biliary tract and abdominal pain intermittently.
    a. Yes
    b. No   a

104. *Giardia lamblia* contains fibrils and parabasal-like bodies.
    a. Yes
    b. No   a

105. *Giardia lamblia* has a very fine and centrally located
costa.
    a. Yes
    b. No   b

106. The trophozoite of *Giardia lamblia* contains a cytostome.
    a. Yes
    b. No   b

107. *Giardia lamblia* is able to encyst outside the body, therefore both trophozoites and cysts are frequently found in
the same specimen.
    a. Yes
    b. No   a

108. *Giardia lamblia* cyst is uninucleated.
    a. Yes
    b. No   b

109. *Giardia lamblia* cysts are round to oval in shape.
    a. Yes
    b. No   a

110. *Trichomonas hominis* is found in the urethra of man.
    a. Yes
    b. No   b

111. The undulating membrane of *Trichomonas hominis* ex-
tends from the anterior to extreme posterior end.
    a. Yes
    b. No   a

112. What parasite or parasites have "costa"? Explain.   See p. 283

113. *Trichomonas tenax* is found only in diseased gums.
    a. Yes
    b. No   b

114. Briefly explain how *Trichomonas vaginalis* infection is
acquired.   See p. 283

115. As a rule, *Trichomonas vaginalis* is pathogenic
    a. Yes
    b. No   b

116. *Trichomonas vaginalis* may be found in the male urethra.
    a. Yes   a
    b. No

117. What morphological characteristics help to show that the three trichomonads of man are not one and the same species. See p. 283

118. A flagellate that invades the cells of the heart, other organs, and voluntary muscle is:
    a. *Trypanosoma gambiense*
    b. *Trypanosoma rhodesiense*
    c. *Trypanosoma cruzi*   c
    d. *Leishmania tropica*

119. *Trypanosoma cruzi* is the only flagellate which has amastigote forms in its life cycle.
    a. Yes
    b. No   b

120. In practically every organ of the human body, *Trypanosoma cruzi* multiplies under the following form:
    a. Amastigote   a
    b. Trypomastigote
    c. Epimastigote
    d. Promastigote

121. Infections by *Trypanosoma cruzi* (Chagas' disease) usually involve:
    a. R.E.S.
    b. Cardiac muscle
    c. C.N.S.
    d. All of the above   d
    e. None of the above

122. The multiplication of *Trypanosoma cruzi* takes place in the blood.
    a. Yes
    b. No   b

123. The reduviid bugs which transmit *Trypanosoma cruzi* bite at daytime as a rule.
    a. Yes
    b. No   b

124. Unilateral swelling of eyelids (characteristic of Chagas' disease) is:
    a. Romaña's sign   a
    b. Weber's sign
    c. Wernicke's sign
    d. Winterbottom's sign

125. The genus *Trypanosoma* has _____, _____,
     _____, and _____ stages in its life cycle.   See p. 283

126. The female tsetse fly can infect man with trypanosome
     however the male tsetse fly cannot.
     a. Yes
     b. No   b

127. In trypanosomiasis, the spinal fluid cell count:
     a. Is increased   a
     b. Remains normal

128. The human disease produced by *Trypanosoma rhodesiense*
     usually follows a more rapid course than that produced by
     Trypanosoma gambiense.
     a. Yes   a
     b. No

129. The human disease produced by *Trypanosoma rhodesiense*
     is more likely to be fatal than that produced by *Trypano-
     soma gambiense.*
     a. Yes   a
     b. No

130. All tsetse flies belong to the following genus:
     a. *Phlebotomus*
     b. *Glossina*   b
     c. *Sarcophaga*
     d. *Cordylobia*

The following statements refer to certain species of *Trypanosoma.* Place the appropriate letter(s) in the space before
the question.
             Trypanosoma cruzi   a
             T. rhodesiense and *T. gambiense*   b
             If it does not apply   c

131. _____ Transmitted by *Triatoma.*   a

132. _____ Transmitted by tsetse fly.   b

133. _____ Transmitted by bite of *Triatoma.*   c

134. _____ Transmitted by fecal contamination   a

135. _____ African.   b

136. _____ Western hemisphere.   a

137. _____ Enlarged kinetoplast   a

138. _____ "C" shaped   a

139. _____ Winterbottom's sign.   b

140. _____ Romaña's sign.   a

141. _____ Amastigote forms present.   a

142. _____ Xenodiagnosis.   a

143. _____ Spinal tap.   b

144. All *Leishmanias* are forms of *Trypanosoma*.
    a. Yes
    b. No   b

145. *Leishmanias* are transmitted by the bite of the Glossina fly.
    a. Yes
    b. No   b

146. Vectors of *Leishmania* species are always sandflies.
    a. Yes   a
    b. No

147. *Leishmanias* are transmitted by the bite of a _____   *Phlebotomus*
    fly.

148. The genus *Leishmania* has only _____ and _____   amastigote
    _____ stages in its life cycle.   promastigote

149. The promastigote forms of the genus *Leishmania* are iden-
    tical in structure with members of the genus:
    a. *Crithidia*
    b. *Leptomonas*   b
    c. *Trypanosoma*
    d. None of these

150. *Leishmania tropica* morphological lesions are _____
    _____.   See p. 283

151. Secondary lesions due to *Leishmania brasiliensis* destroy
    the _____
    _____ of the human host.   See p. 283

CILIATA – BALANTIDIUM COLI

152. An increase in free hydrochloric acid in the stomach makes
    one more susceptible to infection by *Balantidium coli*.
    a. Yes
    b. No   b

153. Human infection by *Balantidium coli* occurs:
    a. Commonly
    b. Rarely   b
    c. Never
    d. Occasionally.

154. A reservoir of *Balantidium coli* infection is the pig.
    a. Yes   a
    b. No

155. The cyst form of *Balantidium coli* is always found in in-
    fection in man but trophozoites are rarely seen.
    a. Yes
    b. No   b

156. *Balantidium coli* is sometimes said to have cyst forms in
    liver abscesses.

a. Yes
b. No   b

157. *Balantidium coli* occurs only in the large intestine of humans.
    a. Yes
    b. No   b

158. *Balantidium coli*, like *Entamoeba histolytica*, may produce secondary sites of infection.
    a. Yes
    b. No   b

159. *Balantidium coli* may invade the large intestinal wall of humans.
    a. Yes   a
    b. No

160. In *Balantidium coli*, the trophic nucleus (i.e., the nucleus required for vegetative but not for sexual reproduction) is the:
    a. Macronucleus   a
    b. Micronucleus

161. The purpose of the cytopyge in *Balantidium coli* is to evacuate indigested food materials.
    a. Yes   a
    b. No

SPOROZOA OF THE BLOOD AND TISSUES — MALARIAS

162. Malaria is transmitted by mosquitoes of the genus *Anopheles*.
    a. Yes   a
    b. No

163. *Anopheles* may breed in stagnant water.
    a. Yes   a
    b. No

164. Female *Anopheles* mosquitoes can transmit malaria to man but male *Anopheles* mosquitoes cannot.
    a. Yes   a
    b. No

165. The most effective method of preventing malaria is:
    a. Mosquito control   a
    b. Immunization
    c. Chemotherapy
    d. Improved hygiene

166. The four species of the human *Plasmodium* are transmitted by mosquitoes of the genus *Anopheles* only.
    a. Yes   a
    b. No

167. In blackwater fever the characteristic feature is:
    a. Intravascular hemolysis   a
    b. Loss of appetite
    c. Liver enlargement
    d. Insomnia
    e. Spleen enlargement

168. Most of the parasites a mosquito ingests from an infected
    human degenerate.
    a. Yes   a
    b. No

169. The malarial parasite stage infective to man is:
    a. Schizont
    b. Gametocyte
    c. Sporozoite   c
    d. Trophozoite
    e. Merozoite

170. Match the following:
    a. Salivary glands of female   1. May contain   a—1
       Anopheles mosquito   sporozoites
    b. Stomach of female   2. May contain   b—2
       Anopheles mosquito   oöcysts

171. Sporozoites from mosquitoes enter the red cells of the
    human body directly.
    a. Yes
    b. No   b

172. Cryptozoites in the hidden tissues divide by multiple
    fission.
    a. Yes   a
    b. No

173. The body of *Plasmodium* consists of cytoplasm, nucleus,
    and certain cytoplasmic inclusions. Early in growth a
    large _____ often develops in the cytoplasm, so that   vacuole
    the living protoplasm (the nucleus too is forced to a peri-
    pheral position) is restricted to the peripheral layer that
    appears in section as a ring.

174. The ring stage is the mature schizont.
    a. Yes
    b. No   b

175. The ring stage grows to maturity in the red blood cell.
    a. Yes   a
    b. No

176. The oökinete is found in the human.
    a. Yes
    b. No   b

177. The oöcyst is found in the mosquito.
    a. Yes   a
    b. No

178. Merozoites from different species are easily differentiated.
    a. Yes
    b. No   b

179. The production of male and female gametocytes occurs only in *Plasmodium falciparum*.
    a. Yes
    b. No   b

180. Enlarged r.b.c. are usually seen in *Plasmodium vivax* infection.
    a. Yes   a
    b. No

181. *Plasmodium vivax* is characterized by large chromatin dots.
    a. Yes   a
    b. No

182. Schüffner's dots are found in *Plasmodium malariae*.
    a. Yes
    b. No   b

183. The red granules which appear after Romanowsky staining in erythrocytes of man infected with *Plasmodium vivax* or *Plasmodium ovale* are:
    a. Sporozoites
    b. Schüffner's dots   b
    c. Segmenters
    d. Microgametocytes

184. Schüffner's dots are more frequent and abundant in erythrocytes with *Plasmodium ovale* than in those with *Plasmodium vivax*.
    a. Yes   a
    b. No

185. Schizogony can be observed in the peripheral blood of an individual harboring *Plasmodium falciparum*:
    a. Yes
    b. No   b

186. More than one malarial parasite may infect the same r.b.c.
    a. Yes   a
    b. No

187. The length of the asexual cycle in *Plasmodium vivax* is 48 hours.
    a. Yes   a
    b. No

188. Multiple infection of red blood cells occurs more frequently in *Plasmodium vivax* than in *Plasmodium falciparum* infections.
    a. Yes
    b. No   b

189. A large distinctly ameboid trophozoite in a stippled enlarged r.b.c. is characteristic of *Plasmodium vivax.*
    a. Yes   a
    b. No

190. Microgametes and macrogametes unite to form zygotes in the mosquito.
    a. Yes   a
    b. No

191. Part of the sexual cycle of *Plasmodium* occurs in the mosquito.
    a. Yes   a
    b. No

192. Merozoites can infect a red cell becoming the ring stage.
    a. Yes   a
    b. No

193. Gametocytes may be seen in the blood of an individual harboring *Plasmodium falciparum.*
    a. Yes   a
    b. No

194. Pigmented "band" forms are indicative of *Plasmodium malariae.*
    a. Yes   a
    b. No

195. A crescent-shaped gametocyte is characteristic of *Plasmodium vivax.*
    a. Yes
    b. No   b

196. Malaria is transmitted by the bite of the *Phlebotomus* fly.
    a. Yes
    b. No   b

197. A red cell parasitized by *Plasmodium vivax* is usually larger than normal.
    a. Yes   a
    b. No

198. Seventy-two hours is the length of the asexual cycle in *Plasmodium malariae.*
    a. Yes   a
    b. No

199. All stages of the developing parasite of *Plasmodium falciparum* may be found in the peripheral blood.
    a. Yes
    b. No   b

200. Alternatively maturing forms of *Plasmodia* may on occasion give atypical fever charts.
    a. Yes   a
    b. No

201. The macrogametocyte will form the female gamete.
    a. Yes   a
    b. No

202. The entire growth from small trophozoite to mature schiz-
    ont requires *(Plasmodium vivax)* 72 hours.
    a. Yes
    b. No   b

203. Some stages of *Plasmodia* may be found in the liver.
    a. Yes   a
    b. No

204. Briefly, give the life cycle of the malarial parasites in:
    a. Mosquito   See p. 283
    b. Man   ,,

Plasmodium vivax

205. Period between attacks:
    a. 48 hours   a
    b. 72 hours
    c. 24 hours

206: Size of red blood cell:
    a. Increases   a
    b. Decreases
    c. Remains the same

207. Gametocytes:
    a. Round   a
    b. Crescent-shaped
    c. Band form

208. Identifying characteristics:
    a. Band form
    b. Crescent-shaped gametocytes
    c. Oval r.b.c.
    d. Schüffner's dots   d

209. Typical number of merozoites:
    a.   6–12
    b.   8–36
    c. 12–24   c

210. Trophozoite is very:
    a. Active   a
    b. Sluggish

211. Multiple infection of same blood cell:
    a. Does not occur
    b. Occurs rarely   b
    c. It is quite common

Plasmodium malariae

212. Period between attacks:
    a. 48 hours
    b. 72 hours   b
    c. 24 hours

213. Size of red blood cells:
    a. Increases
    b. Decreases
    c. Remains the same   c

214. Gametocytes:
    a. Round   a
    b. Crescent-shaped
    c. Band form

215. Identifying characteristics:
    a. Band form   a
    b. Crescent-shaped gametocytes
    c. Oval r.b.c.
    d. Schüffner's dots

216. Typical number of merozoites:
    a. 6-12   a
    b. 8-36
    c. 12-24

217. Trophozoite is very:
    a. Active
    b. Sluggish   b

218. Multiple infection of same blood cell:
    a. Does not occur
    b. Occurs rarely   b
    c. Common

Plasmodium falciparum

219. Period between attacks:
    a. 48 hours   a
    b. 72 hours
    c. 24 hours

220. Size of red blood cell:
    a. Increases   a
    b. Decreases
    c. Remains the same

221. Gametocytes:
    a. Round
    b. Crescent-shaped   b
    c. Band form

222. Identifying characteristics:
    a. Band form

      b. Crescent-shaped gametocytes   b
      c. Oval r.b.c.
      d. Schüffner's dots

223. Typical number of merozoites:
      a. 6–12
      b. 8–36   b
      c. 12–24

224. Trophozoite is very:
      a. Active
      b. Sluggish   b

225. Multiple infection of same blood cell:
      a. Does not occur
      b. Occurs rarely
      c. Very common   c

Plasmodium ovale

226. Period between attacks:
      a. 48 hours   a
      b. 72 hours
      c. 24 hours

227. Size of red blood cell:
      a. Increases   a
      b. Decreases
      c. Remains the same

228. Gametocytes:
      a. Round   a
      b. Crescent-shaped
      c. Band form

229. Identifying characteristics:
      a. Band form
      b. Crescent-shaped gametocytes
      c. Oval r.b.c.
      d. Schüffner's dots   d

230. Typical number of merozoites:
      a. 6–12   a
      b. 8–36
      c. 12–24

231. Trophozoite is very:
      a. Active
      b. Sluggish   b

232. Multiple infection of same blood cell:
      a. Does not occur
      b. Occurs rarely   b
      c. Common

Life Cycle, Plasmodium

233. Cryptozoites occur in:
    a. Stomach wall of the mosquito
    b. Liver of man   b
    c. Salivary gland of mosquito
    d. Blood of man

234. Sporozoites occur in:
    a. Salivary gland of mosquito   a
    b. Intestine of man
    c. Red blood cells of man

235. Ring stage occurs in:
    a. Red blood cell of mosquito
    b. Red blood cell of man   b
    c. Brain of man

236. Sporozoites transform into:
    a. Oöcysts
    b. Cryptozoites
    c. Merozoites
    d. Schizonts   d (in liver)
    e. None of these

237. Cryptozoites transform into:
    a. Oöcysts
    b. Cryptozoites
    c. Merozoites
    d. Schizonts   d (in liver
    e. None of these   or r.b.c.)

238. Gametocytes remaining within the human blood stream
    are transformed into:
    a. Oöcysts
    b. Cryptozoites
    c. Merozoites
    d. Schizonts
    e. None of these   e (also see
                    p. 284)

The following characteristics apply to the malarial parasites listed below. Place the appropriate letter(s) in the space before the question.

Plasmodium vivax	a
P. malariae	b
P. falciparum	c
P. ovale	d

239. _____ Band forms.   b

240. _____ Schüffner's dots.   a & d

241. _____ Enlarged r.b.c.   a & d

242. _____ Frequent double dots.   c

243.	_____ 6–12 (8–10) merozoites.	b
244.	_____ Red blood cells become "sticky."	c
245.	_____ Not all asexual stages found in peripheral blood.	c
246.	_____ Most dangerous.	c

PLATYHELMINTHES – DIGENEA

247. Flukes are pear-shaped in contrast to the long ribbon-like structure of tapeworms.
    a. Yes   a
    b. No

248. The greater portion of the larval life of human flukes is spent as parasites of:
    a. Snails   a
    b. Cats
    c. Mosquitoes
    d. Fresh-water fish
    e. None of these.

249. Briefly, what is a "miracidium"? a "cercaria"? a "metacercaria"? See p. 284

250. All flukes have operculate eggs:
    a. Yes
    b. No   b

251. Which of the following flukes are common in man?
    a. *Fasciolopsis buski*   a
    b. *Fasciola hepatica*
    c. *Clonorchis sinensis*   c
    d. *Opistorchis felineus*
    e. *Heterophyes heterophyes*   e
    f. *Metagonimus yokogawai*   f
    g. *Paragonimus westermani*   g
    h. *Schistosoma mansoni*   h
    i. *Watsonius watsoni*
    j. *Troglotrema salminicola*
    k. *Dicrocoelium dentriticum*
    l. *Echinostoma ilocanum*

252. From a medical standpoint the most important flukes are the:
    a. Liver flukes
    b. Lung fluke
    c. Intestinal flukes
    d. Blood flukes   d

253. The three species of human blood flukes have as intermediate host:
    a. A Cyclops
    b. An aquatic snail   b

    c. An insect
    d. None of these

254. Match the following:

a. *Paragonimus westermani*	1. Human liver fluke	a—4
b. *Clonorchis sinensis*	2. Human intestinal fluke	b—1
c. *Fasciolopsis buski*	3. Human blood fluke	c—2
d. *Schistosoma haematobium*	4. Human lung fluke	d—3

255. Source of human fluke infection. Match the following:

a. *Fasciolopsis buski*	1. Direct penetration skin by fork-tailed cercaria	a—2
b. *Schistosoma haematobium*	2. Cercaria encysted on vegetation	b—1
c. *Paragonimus westermani*	3. Cercaria encysted in fresh-water fish	c—4
d. *Clonorchis sinensis*	4. Cercaria encysted in fresh-water crustacea	d—3

256. An important parasite of sheep is:
    a. *Fasciola hepatica*   a
    b. *Schistosoma japonicum*
    c. *Schistosoma mansoni*

257. The largest fluke found in man is:
    a. *Fasciolopsis buski*   a
    b. *Opistorchis felineus*
    c. *Heterophyes heterophyes*
    d. *Paragonimus westermani*
    e. *Schistosoma mansoni*

258. Flukes are always hermaphroditic.
    a. Yes
    b. No   b

259. All flukes require snails as intermediate hosts.
    a. Yes   a
    b. No

260. Briefly outline most important differences between the blood flukes and the other human flukes. See p. 284

261. Eggs of schistosomes lack an operculum:
    a. Yes   a
    b. No

262. Lung fluke:
    a. *Fasciola hepatica*
    b. *Fasciolopsis buski*
    c. *Paragonimus westermani*   c
    d. *Clonorchis sinensis*

263. Egg appears in sputum:
    a. *Fasciola hepatica*

      b. *Clonorchis sinensis*
      c. *Paragonimus westermani*   c
      d. *Fasciolopsis buski*

264. The egg resembles an old-fashioned electric bulb:
      a. *Fasciola hepatica*
      b. *Clonorchis sinensis*   b
      c. *Paragonimus westermani*
      d. *Fasciolopsis buski*

265. *Schistosoma haematobium* may damage the tissues of the bladder, causing considerable loss of blood.
      a. Yes   a
      b. No

266. *Schistosoma haematobium* is most prevalent in:
      a. India
      b. Mexico
      c. Brasil
      d. North Africa   d
      e. Cuba

The following statements apply to the *Schistosomas* listed below. Place the appropriate letter(s) in the space before the question.

          Schistosoma japonicum   a
          Schistosoma mansoni   b
          Schistosoma haematobium   c

267. _____ Egg has very small spine.   a

268. _____ Egg has large terminal spine.   c

269. _____ Egg has large lateral spine.   b

270. _____ Adults are usually found in venules of bladder.   c

271. _____ Adults are in venules of intestine.   a & b

272. _____ Bloody urine is typical of illness.   c

PLATYHELMINTHES – CESTODA

273. Match the following:

a. Scolex with suckers	1. *Taenia solium*	a—1,2,4,5
	2. *Taenia saginata*	
b. Scolex with hooks	3. *Diphyllobothrium latum*	b—1,4,5
	4. *Hymenolepis nana*	
c. Scolex with bothria	5. *Dipylidium caninum*	c—3

274. A "bothrium" (plural "bothria") is:
      a. A groovelike organ of attachment   a
      b. An onchosphere or hexacanth embryo
      c. A gravid proglottid
      d. A type of tapeworm larva
      e. None of these

275. The part of an adult tapeworm which contains the organs of
attachment is the:
   a. Immature proglottid
   b. Mature proglottid
   c. Scolex   c
   d. Gravid proglottid

276. A type of tapeworm larva with a large bladder producing
daughter cysts, brood capsules and numerous scolices is:
   a. Cysticercoid
   b. Coenurus
   c. Plerocercoid
   d. Cysticercus
   e. Hydatid cyst   e

277. What is "cysticercosis"? How is it acquired?   See p. 284

278. Pumpkin-seed shaped proglottids are characteristic of:
   a. *Taenia solium*
   b. *Dipylidium caninum*   b
   c. *Hymenolepis nana*
   d. *Diphyllobothrium latum*

279. *Taenia saginata* and *T. solium* stage infective to man:
   a. Cysticercus   a
   b. Strobila
   c. Embryonated egg
   d. None of these.

280. The scolex of *Taenia solium* is more likely to perforate the
intestinal wall, and initiate a peritonitis, than is the scolex
of *Taenia saginata*.
   a. Yes   a
   b. No

281. Eggs, when voided, are immediately infective:
   a. *Diphyllobothrium latum*
   b. *Hymenolepis nana*   b
   c. *Taenia solium*
   d. *Taenia saginata*

Diphyllobothrium latum

282. Usual location of parasite in man: :
   a. Intestine   a (adult)
   b. Blood
   c. Heart muscle
   d. Perianal surface
   e. Hidden tissues   e (sparganum)

283. Intermediate host for parasite:
   a. Cattle
   b. Cyclops   b (procercoid)
   c. Dog
   d. Fish   d (plerocercoid)
   e. Pig

284. Stage infective to man:
    a. Cysticercoid
    b. Plerocercoid   b
    c. Procercoid
    d. Hydatid cyst
    e. Cysticercus

285. Larval migration through blood and lymphatic systems of man.
    a. Yes
    b. No   b

286. Size of adult:
    a. Microscopic
    b. Visible to naked eye but less than 15 cm.
    c. Longer than 15 cm.   c

287. Autoinfection:
    a. Yes
    b. No   b

288. Bothria present:
    a. Yes   a
    b. No

289. Gravid proglottid:
    a. Broader than long   a
    b. Longer than broad

290. Hooklets in scolex of parasite:
    a. Yes
    b. No   b

291. Genital pore:
    a. Marginal
    b. Central   b

292. Uterine branches:
    a. More than 14–15
    b. Less than 14–15   b

293. Mode of infection by parasite (how acquired):
    a. Ingestion   a (plerocercoid
    b. Penetration

294. Egg hatches outside body of host:
    a. Yes   a
    b. No

295. Human infection with the larval stage of *Diphyllobothrium* results in the condition known as:
    a. Cysticercosis
    b. Cenurosis
    c. Hydatid disease
    d. Sparganosis   d

Taenia solium

296. Usual location in man:
    a. Intestine   a (adult)
    b. Blood
    c. Muscle   c (larva)
    d. Perianal surface
    e. Bile ducts

297. Intermediate host:
    a. Cattle
    b. Sheep
    c. Hog   c
    d. Flea
    e. Dog

298. Stage infective to man:
    a. Cysticercoid
    b. Plerocercoid
    c. Egg   c (to give cysticercus)

    d. Hydatid cyst
    e. Cysticercus   e (to give adult)

299. Size of adult parasite in man:
    a. Microscopic
    b. Visible to naked eye but less than 15 cm.
    c. Longer than 15 cm.   c

300. Autoinfection:
    a. Yes   a (cysti-
    b. No   cercosis)

301. Bothria present:
    a. Yes
    b. No   b

302. Gravid proglottid:
    a. Broader than long
    b. Longer than broad   b

303. Hooklets present on scolex of parasite:
    a. Yes   a
    b. No

304. Genital pore:
    a. Marginal   a
    b. Central

305. Number of uterine branches in the mature proglottid:
    a. More than 14–15
    b. Less than 14–15   b

306. Method of infection:
    a. Ingestion   a (egg or
    b. Penetration   cysticercus)

307. Size of larval parasite:
     a. Microscopic
     b. Visible to naked eye but less than 15 cm.   b
     c. Longer than 15 cm.

308. Larval stages can develop in man:
     a. Yes   a
     b. No

309. The usual larval host of *Taenia solium* is:
     a. Dog
     b. Pig   b
     c. Cat
     d. Cattle

Taenia saginata

310. Usual location in man:
     a. Intestine   a (adult)
     b. Blood
     c. Heart muscle
     d. Perianal surface
     e. Bile ducts

311. Intermediate host:
     a. Cattle   a
     b. Sheep
     c. Pig
     d. Flea
     e. Dog

312. Stage infective to man:
     a. Cysticercoid
     b. Plerocercoid
     c. Procercoid
     d. Hydatid cyst
     e. Cysticercus   e

313. Size of adult parasite in man:
     a. Microscopic
     b. Visible to naked eye but less than 15 cm.
     c. Longer than 15 cm.   c

314. Autoinfection:
     a. Yes
     b. No   b

315. Bothria present:
     a. Yes
     b. No   b

316. Gravid proglottid:
     a. Broader than long
     b. Longer than broad   b

317. Hooklets present on scolex of parasite:
    a. Yes
    b. No   b

318. Genital pore:
    a. Marginal   a
    b. Central

319. Number of uterine branches in the mature proglottid:
    a. More than 14-15   a
    b. Less than 14-15

320. Method of infection:
    a. Ingestion   a (egg)
    b. Penetration

321. Polar filaments are found in the ova:
    a. Yes
    b. No   b

322. Larval stages can develop in man:
    a. Yes   a
    b. No   b

Echinococcus granulosus

323. Usual location in man:
    a. Intestine
    b. Liver   b (hydatid cyst)

    c. Heart muscle
    d. internal organs   d (hydatid cyst)

    e. Bile ducts

324. Intermediate host:
    a. Cattle   a
    b. Sheep   b
    c. Pig
    d. Flea
    e. Dog

325. Stage infective to man:
    a. Cysticercoid
    b. Plerocercoid
    c. Procercoid
    d. Cysticercus
    e. Egg   e

326. Size of adult parasite:
    a. Microscopic
    b. Visible to naked eye but less than 15 cm.   b
    c. Longer than 15 cm.

327. Autoinfection:
    a. Yes
    b. No   b

328. Bothria present:
     a. Yes
     b. No   b

329. Gravid proglottid:
     a. Broader than long
     b. Longer than broad   b

330. Hooklets present on scolex of parasite:
     a. Yes   a
     b. No

331. Genital pore:
     a. Marginal   a
     b. Central

332. Number of uterine branches in the mature proglottid:
     a. More than 14–15   a
     b. Less than 14–15

333. Method of infection:
     a. Ingestion   a (egg)
     b. Penetration

334. The adult *Echinococcus granulosus* is found in man:
     a. Commonly
     b. Never   b
     c. Rarely
     d. Occasionally

335. Size of larval parasite:
     a. Microscopic
     b. Visible to naked eye but less than 15 cm.   b (can grow
                                                        indefinitely)
     c. Longer than 15 cm.   c

336. How is hydatid disease acquired?   See p. 284

337. *Echinococcus granulosus* is common in sheep-raising
     countries.
     a. Yes   a
     b. No

Hymenolepis nana

338. Usual location in man:
     a. Intestine   a (adult)
     b. Blood
     c. Heart muscle
     d. Perianal surface
     e. Hidden tissues

339. Intermediate host of parasite:
     a. Cattle
     b. Sheep
     c. Pig
     d. Dog

    e. Flea

    f. None of these   f (also see
p. 284)

340. Stage infective to man:
    a. Cysticercoid   a
    b. Plerocercoid
    c. Procercoid
    d. Hydatid cyst
    e. Cysticercus
    f. Fully embryonated egg   f

341. Larval migration through blood and lymphatic systems of
man:
    a. Yes
    b. No   b

342. Size of adult parasite:
    a. Microscopic
    b. Visible to naked eye but less than 15 cm.   b
    c. Longer than 15 cm.

343. Autoinfection.
    a. Yes   a
    b. No

344. Rostellum:
    a. Armed   a
    b. Unarmed

345. Bothria present:
    a. Yes
    b. No   b

346. Mode of infection:
    a. Ingestion   a
    b. Penetration

347. *Hymenolepis nana* is the dwarf tapeworm found in man:
    a. Yes   a
    b. No

348. Egg thin shelled with conspicuous polar filaments:
    a. Yes   a
    b. No

Hymenolepis diminuta

349. Usual location in man:
    a. Intestine   a (adult)
    b. Blood
    c. Heart muscle
    d. Perianal surface
    e. Hidden tissues

350. Intermediate host of parasite:
    a. Cattle

b. Sheep
c. Pig
d. Dog
e. Flour bettle   e

351. Stage infective to man:
    a. Cysticercoid   a
    b. Plerocercoid
    c. Procercoid
    d. Hydatid cyst
    e. Cysticercus
    f. Egg

352. Larval migration through blood and lymphatic systems of
    man:
    a. Yes
    b. No   b

353. Size of adult parasite:
    a. Microscopic
    b. Visible to naked eye but less than 15 cm.   b
    c. Longer than 15 cm.

354. Autoinfection:
    a. Yes
    b. No   b

355. Rostellum:
    a. Armed
    b. Unarmed   b

356. Bothria present:
    a. Yes
    b. No   b

357. Mode of infection:
    a. Ingestion   a
    b. Penetration

358. *Hymenolepis diminuta* is the dwarf tapeworm found in
    man:
    a. Yes
    b. No   b

359. *Hymenolepis diminuta* is common in rats but it only occa-
    sionally infects man.
    a. Yes   a
    b. No

360. Egg thin shelled with conspicuous polar filaments:
    a. Yes
    b. No   b

Dipylidium caninum

361. Usual location in man:
    a. Intestine   a

    b. Blood
    c. Heart muscle
    d. Perianal surface
    e. Bile ducts

362. Intermediate host for parasite:
    a. Cattle
    b. Horse
    c. Flea   c
    d. Pig
    e. Fly

363. Size of adult:
    a. Microscopic
    b. Visible to naked eye but less than 15 cm. long
    c. More than 15 cm. long   c

364. Autoinfection:
    a. Yes
    b. No   b

365. Stage infective to man:
    a. Cysticercoid   a
    b. Plerocercoid
    c. Procercoid
    d. Cysticercus
    e. Hydatid cyst

366. Bothria present:
    a. Yes
    b. No   b

367. Gravid proglottid:
    a. Broader than long
    b. Longer than broad   b

368. Rostellum:
    a. Armed   a
    b. Unarmed

369. Mode of infection:
    a. Ingestion   a
    b. Penetration

370. Many eggs of *D. caninum* in the stools of man may be encapsulated in a single membrane:
    a. Yes   a
    b. No

371. *Dipylidium caninum* is common among cats and dogs but it only occasionally infects man.
    a. Yes   a
    b. No

NEMATODA

372. *Ancylostoma braziliense* is:
    a. A hookworm   a
    b. The pinworm
    c. The whipworm
    d. A tapeworm
    e. None of these

373. In its life history and relation to man, *Strongyloides stercoralis* somewhat resembles:
    a. The hookworms   a
    b. The whipworms
    c. The pinworm
    d. The tapeworms
    e. *Ascaris lumbricoides*

374. Most of the injury produced by either new world or old world adult hookworms is due to:
    a. Toxins secreted by worms
    b. Allergic reaction to worms
    c. Loss of blood in the intestine   c
    d. Digestive disturbances
    e. None of these reasons

375. A pathogenic roundworm causing a serious disease with ocular complications (these often result in blindness) in Africa, Southern Mexico, and Guatemala:
    a. *Dipetalonema perstans*
    b. *Loa loa*
    c. *Onchocerca volvulus*   c
    d. *Mansonella ozzardi*
    e. None of these

376. Match the following:
    a. *Onchocerca volvulus*   1. Transmitted by midges   a—2
    b. Hookworm—*Strongy-*   2. Transmitted by black   b—8
       loides   fly
    c. *Wuchereria bancrofti*   3. Transmitted by mango   c—4
                                   fly
    d. *Trichinella spiralis*   4. Transmitted by mosquitos   d—7
    e. *Loa loa*   5. Infection acquired   e—3
                                   through fecal contamina-
                                   tion.
    f. *Ascaris*—Whipworm—   6. Infection acquired   f—5
       Pinworm   by drinking water
                                   containing the infected
                                   Cyclops
    g. *Dipetalonema perstans* 7. Infection acquired by eat-   g—1
       —*Mansonella ozzardi*   ing infected pork, insuf-
                                   ficently cooked
    h. *Dracunculus medinen-*   8. Filariform larvae in in-   h—6
       sis   fected soil

377. Infection often associated with eosinophilia:
    a. Yes   a
    b. No

Trichuris trichiura

378. Adults are usually found in:
    a. Intestine   a
    b. Blood
    c. Striated muscle
    d. Perianal surface
    e. Sputum

379. Stage infective to man:
    a. Rhabditiform larva from stool
    b. Filariform larva from stool
    c. Fully embryonated eggs from soil   c
    d. In mosquito
    e. Encysted larva in muscle

380. Intermediate host
    a. Yes
    b. No   b (also see
                                                 p. 284)

381. Adult migration through blood and/or lymphatic systems
of man:
    a. Yes
    b. No   b

382. Size of adult:
    a. Microscopic
    b. Clearly visible to naked eye but less than 15 cm.   b
    c. Longer than 15 cm.

383. Larval migration through blood and lymphatic systems of
man.
    a. Yes
    b. No   b

384. Location of larvae:
    a. Lung
    b. Blood
    c. Muscle
    d. Intestine   d
    e. All of these

385. Size of larva:
    a. Microscopic   a
    b. Visible to naked eye but less than 15 cm.
    c. Longer than 15 cm.

386. Autoinfection:
    a. Yes
    b. No   b

387. Method of infection:
     a. Ingestion
     b. Penetration
     c. Vector

a (egg)

388. How does the whipworm *(Trichuris trichiura)* attach itself to the host?

See p. 284

389. Infection associated with eosinophilia:
     a. Yes
     b. No

b

390. Technique that applies:
     a. Scotch tape swab
     b. Zinc sulfate or other concentration method
     c. Blood smear
     d. Biopsy
     e. Serological test

b

Trichinella spiralis

391. Adults are usually found in:
     a. Intestine
     b. Blood
     c. Striated muscle
     d. Perianal surface
     e. Sputum

a

392. Stage infective to man:
     a. Rhabditiform larva from stool
     b. Filariform larva from stool
     c. In mosquito
     d. Encysted larva in muscle
     e. In fly

d

393. Intermediate host:
     a. Yes
     b. No

b (also see p. 284)

394. Adult migration through blood and/or lymphatic systems of man:
     a. Yes
     b. No

a
b

395. Size of adult:
     a. Microscopic
     b. Clearly visible to naked eye but less than 15 cm.
     c. Longer than 15 cm.

a

396. Larval migration through blood and lymphatic system of man:
     a. Yes
     b. No

a

397. Location of larvae:
    a. Lung
    b. Blood
    c. Muscle   c
    d. Intestine
    e. All of these

398. Size of larva:
    a. Microscopic   a
    b. Visible to naked eye but less than 15 cm.
    c. Longer than 15 cm.

399. Autoinfection:
    a. Yes
    b. No   b

400. Method of infection:
    a. Ingestion   a (larvae)
    b. Penetration
    c. Vector

401. Infection associated with eosinophilia:
    a. Yes   a
    b. No

402. Technique that applies:
    a. Scotch tape swab
    b. Zinc sulfate concentration
    c. Biopsy   c
    d. Blood smear
    e. Serological test   e

Hookworms

403. Usual location of adult:
    a. Intestine   a
    b. Blood
    c. Muscle
    d. Lung
    e. All of these

404. Intermediate host:
    a. Yes
    b. No   b

405. Stage infective to man:
    a. Rhabditiform larva from stool
    b. Filariform larva from stool   b
    c. In mosquito
    d. Encysted larva
    e. In fly

406. Method of infection:
    a. Ingestion
    b. Penetration through skin   b
    c. Both a and b

      d. Neither a nor b
      e. Vector

407. Migration through blood and lymphatic systems of man
     by the larvae:
      a. Yes   a
      b. No

408. Size of adult:
      a. Microscopic
      b. Visible to naked eye but less than 15 cm.   b
      c. Longer than 15 cm..

409. Technique that applies:
      a. Scotch tape swab
      b. Zinc sulfate or other methods of concentration   b
      c. Biopsy
      d. Thick blood film
      e. Fecal smears   e

410. Autoinfection:
      a. Yes
      b. No   b

Strongyloides stercoralis

411. Usual location of adult:
      a. Intestine   a
      b. Blood
      c. Muscle
      d. Lung
      e. All of these

412. Intermediate host:
      a. Yes
      b. No   b

413. Stage infective to man:
      a. Rhabditiform larva from stool
      b. Filariform larva   b
      c. In mosquito
      d. Encysted larva in muscle
      e. In fly

414. Migration of larva through blood and lymphatic systems
     of man:
      a. Yes   a
      b. No

415. Size of adult:
      a. Microscopic
      b. Visible to naked eye but less than 15 cm.   b
      c. Longer than 15 cm.

416. Technique that applies:
      a. Scotch tape swab

        b. Zinc sulfate or other methods of concentration   b
        c. Thick blood film
        d. Thin blood film
        e. Fecal smear   e

417. Autoinfection:
        a. Yes   a (under some
        b. No   conditions—
                                                                   see p. 284)

418. Usual method of infection:
        a. Ingestion
        b. Penetration through skin   b
        c. Vector

Ascaris lumbrocoides

419. Usual location of adult:
        a. Intestine   a
        b. Blood
        c. Muscle
        d. Lung
        e. All of these

420. Intermediate host:
        a. Yes
        b. No   b

421. Stage infective to man:
        a. Embryonated egg   a
        b. Rhabditiform larva from stool
        c. Filariform larva from stool
        d. Encysted larva in muscle
        e. In mosquito

422. Larval migration through blood and lymphatic systems of
     man:
        a. Yes   a
        b. No

423. Size of adult:
        a. Microscopic
        b. Less than 15 cm.
        c. More than 15 cm.   c (20–40
                                                                   cm.)

424. Common name:
        a. Whipworm
        b. Large roundworm of man   b
        c. Pinworm
        d. Guinea worm
        e. Creeping eruption

425. Preferred technique for demonstration:
        a. Scotch tape swab
        b. Zinc sulfate or other method of concentration   b

c. Thick blood film
d. Thin blood film
e. Biopsy

426. Method of infection:
    a. Ingestion
    b. Penetration through skin   a (egg)
    c. Vector

427. Pathogenicity:
    a. Yes   a
    b. No

428. Infection associated with eosinophilia:
    a. Yes   a (especially
    b. No   in larval stages)

Enterobius vermicularis

429. Usual location of adult:
    a. Intestine   a
    b. Blood
    c. Muscle
    d. Lung
    e. All of these

430. Intermediate host:
    a. Yes
    b. No   b

431. Stage infective to man:
    a. Rhabditiform larva from stool
    b. Filariform larva from stool
    c. In mosquito
    d. Embryonated egg   d
    e. Encysted larva in muscle

432. Size of adult:
    a. Microscopic
    b. Visible to naked eye but less than 15 cm.   b
    c. Longer than 15 cm.

433. Common name:
    a. Whipworm
    b. Large roundworm of man
    c. Pinworm   c
    d. Guinea worm
    e. Creeping eruption

434. Preferred technique for demonstration:
    a. Scotch tape swab   a
    b. Zinc sulfate or other methods of concentration
    c. Iodine-saline smear
    d. Blood smear
    e. Biopsy

435. Autoinfection:
    a. Yes   a
    b. No

436. Method of infection:
    a. Ingestion   a (egg)
    b. Penetration through skin
    c. Vector

437. When laid, pinworm eggs are infective and require no intermediate host:
    a. Yes   a
    b. No

Wuchereria bancrofti

438. Usual location of adult:
    a. Intestine
    b. Lymphatic nodes   b
    c. Muscle
    d. Lung
    e. All of these

439. Interemediate host:
    a. Yes   a (mosquito)
    b. No

440. Stage infective to man:
    a. Rhabditiform larva from stool
    b. Filariform larva from stool
    c. In mosquito   c
    d. Encysted larva in muscle
    e. In fly

441. Larval migration through blood and lymphatic systems of man:
    a. Yes   a
    b. No

442. Size of adult:
    a. Microscopic
    b. Visible to naked eye but less than 15 cm.   b
    c. Longer than 15 cm.

443. Autoinfection:
    a. Yes
    b. No   b

444. Preferred technique for demonstration:
    a. Scotch tape swab
    b. Zinc sulfate or other methods of concentration
    c. Iodine-saline smear
    d. Blood smear   d
    e. All of these

445. Method of infection:
     a. Ingestion
     b. Direct penetration of skin by larva
     c. Vector   c (mosquito)

Dracunculus medinensis

446. Usual location of adult:
     a. Subcutaneous tissue   a
     b. Blood
     c. Lung
     d. Intestine
     e. All of these

447. Intermediate host:
     a. Yes   a (cyclops)
     b. No

448. Stage infective to man:
     a. Rhabditiform larva from stool
     b. Filariform larva from stool
     c. In waterflea   c
     d. In mosquito
     e. In fly

449. Size of adult:
     a. Microscopic
     b. Visible to naked eye but less than 15 cm.
     c. Longer than 15 cm.   c (50–80
                                                            cm.)

450. Common name:
     a. Whipworm
     b. Large roundworm of man
     c. Pinworm
     d. Guinea worm   d
     e. Creeping eruption

451. Technique that applies:
     a. Biopsy
     b. Douching of ulcer   b
     c. Scotch tape swab
     d. Iodine-saline smear   d
     e. Zinc sulfate or other methods of concentration

452. Autoinfection:
     a. Yes
     b. No   b

453. Method of infection:
     a. Ingestion   a (cyclops)
     b. Penetration through skin
     c. Vector

Onchocerca volvulus

454. Usual location of adult:
    a. Intestine
    b. Blood
    c. Subcutaneous tissue   c
    d. Lung
    e. All of these

455. Intermediate host:
    a. Yes   a (simulium)
    b. No

456. Stage infective to man:
    a. Rhabditiform larva from stool
    b. Filariform larva in stool
    c. Embryo
    d. In mosquito
    e. Infective larva in blackfly   e

457. Migration through blood and lymphatic systems of man:
    a. Yes   a
    b. No

458. Size of adult:
    a. Microscopic
    b. Visible to naked eye but less than 15 cm.
    c. More than 15 cm.   c

459. Technique that applies:
    a. Scotch tape swab
    b. Thick blood film
    c. Thin blood film
    d. Iodine-saline smear
    e. Biopsy   e (skin
    f. Nodule aspiration   snip)

460. Autoinfection:
    a. Yes
    b. No   b

461. Method of infection:
    a. Ingestion
    b. Penetration through skin
    c. Vector   c (simulium)

Differential Criteria, Strongyloides—hookworm

462. Fill out:

Organism	Rhabditiform Buccal Cavity	Filariform Esophagus	Tail
Strongyloides			
Hookworm			

See p. 285

Toxocara canis

463. Usual location of parasite in man:
    a. Intestine
    b. Blood
    c. Internal organs   c
    d. CNS   d
    e. All of these

464. Intermediate host:
    a. Yes   ▼
    b. No   b

465. Stage infective to man:
    a. Rhabditiform larva from stool
    b. Embryonated egg   b
    c. Encysted larva in muscle
    d. In vector
    e. Filariform larva from stool

466. Migration through tissues of man:
    a. Yes   a
    b. No

467. Size of parasite in man:
    a. Microscopic   a
    b. Visible to naked eye but less than 15 cm.
    c. More than 15 cm.

468. Technique that applies:
    a. Biopsy
    b. Thin blood film
    c. Iodine-saline smear
    d. Serological test   d
    e. Zinc sulfate concentration

469. Autoinfection:
    a. Yes
    b. No   b

470. Method of infection:
    a. Ingestion   a (of egg)
    b. Penetration through skin
    c. Vector

471. Association with eosinophilia:
    a. Yes   a
    b. No

472. Name of disease in man: Visceral
                                             larva migrans

473. Source of infection to man:
    a. Dog   a
    b. Pig
    c. Cyclops
    d. *Anopheles*
    e. None of these

PARASITOLOGY LABORATORY PROCEDURES

474. Three methods of preparing a stool for examination are:
    a. _____   See p. 285
    b. _____   "
    c. _____   "

475. All parasites in cystic form have deep staining heavy
    walls.
    a. Yes
    b. No   b

476. Why can a stain fail to show any parasite and yet the stool
    be positive?   See p. 285

477. List three phenomena that make a stool not suited for
    examination.   See p. 285

478. Study of many details of protozoan structure is possible
    only with the aid of the oil immersion lens.
    a. Yes   a
    b. No

479. Only the plane side of the mirror should be used with the
    substage condenser.
    a. Yes   a
    b. No

480. Trophic amoebae and flagellates can be detected most
    easily when they are motile.
    a. Yes   a
    b. No

481. In a loose stool (generally obtained by using a purgative),
    cysts are almost as likely to occur as in a formed stool.
    a. Yes   a
    b. No

482. The examination of a single loose stool only is as useful
    as the examination of a series of six formed stools.
    a. Yes   a (also see
    b. No   p. 285)

483. In cases of suspected intestinal amebiasis, to obtain diag-
    nostic evidence of infection with *Entamoeba histolytica*
    when routine examination of the stools have been consis-
    tently negative, a purged specimen is usually examined.
    Briefly indicate:
    a. A suitable purgative agent for the purpose   See p. 285
    b. What portion or portions of the specimen are to be
       examined.   See p. 285

484. In fresh stool specimens cysts may best be observed by
    adding a small amount of _____ to the prepar-   iodine
    ation.   stain

485. Lugol's iodine is a satisfactory stain for the iodine stain-
    ing of parasites.

a. Yes   a
b. No

486. Iodine staining is useful for the examination of trophic
amoebae and motile flagellates.
a. Yes
b. No   b (also see
                                                               p. 285)

487. As far as the intestinal protozoa are concerned, concentration methods are good for the cysts only.
a. Yes   a
b. No

488. The technique of sedimentation (primarily useful for the
concentration of protozoan cysts and helminth eggs) utilizes a liquid suspending medium heavier than the parasite
objects themselves.
a. Yes
b. No   b

489. Briefly outline zinc sulfate centrifugal flotation technique.   See p. 285

490. Inoculation into a suitable culture medium may be effective in diagnosis of *Trichomonas tenax* infection.
a. Yes   a
b. No

491. All human intestinal amoebae, flagellates, and ciliate have
been cultivated in vitro except:
a. *Giardia*   a
b. *Chilomastix*
c. *Dientamoeba fragilis*
d. *Iodamoeba bütschlii*
e. *Entamoeba histolytica*

492. What human parasites may be identified in fresh, unstained blood preparations?   See p. 285

493. Briefly outline the two-slide method of making thin blood
film ("smear").   See p. 286

494. The thick film is useful for rapid identification of malaria.
a. Yes   a
b. No

495. Before a thick film for malaria is stained the red cells must
be rendered almost invisible by laking the blood.
a. Yes   a
b. No

496. Dry blood films prepared with Romanowski stains (such
as Wright or Giemsa) may, unless properly protected, fade
in time.
a. Yes   a
b. No

497. Concentration methods may be used to detect malarial parasites in the blood.
    a. Yes
    b. No   b

498. Briefly explain how the formol-gel test is carried out. What condition is it used for? Exactly what is responsible for positive reactions?   See p. 286

499. For the early diagnosis of Kala-azar, a serological test using proper antigen is usually more reliable than sternal punctures.
    a. Yes   a
    b. No

500. CSF examinations are of value in the diagnosis of:
    a. Strongyloidiasis
    b Trichuriasis
    c. Hydatid disease
    d. African trypanosomiasis   d
    e. All of these
    f. None of these

501. Casoni's intradermal reaction may be used in diagnosis of:
    a. Hydatid cyst   a
    b. Sparganosis
    c. Trichinosis
    d. *Hymenolepis nana* infection

502. Diagnosis of hydatid cyst is best accomplished by:
    a. Serological methods   a
    b. Palpation
    c. X-ray
    d. Puncture of cyst so contents can be studied
    e. Demonstration of eosinophilia in the blood

503. Parasitic females and rhabditiform larvae of *Strongyloides stercoralis* will be seen in the:
    a. Feces   a
    b. Blood
    c. CSF
    d. Subcutaneous tissues
    e. None of these

504. Briefly explain why urine, or water, must not contaminate stool specimens for parasitological examination.   See p. 286

505. In Chagas' disease, when is "xenodiagnosis" indicated? How is it carried out?   See p. 286

506. Which parasite, or parasites, may be recovered from the urine?   See p. 286

507. There is a simple, satisfactory culture method for the "in vitro" cultivation of the malarial parasites.
    a. Yes
    b. No   b

508. Boeck and Drbohlav's L.E.S. medium is employed for the cultivation of blood and tissue flagellates.
    a. Yes
    b. No   b

509. *Toxoplasma gondii* can be cultivated "in vitro."
    a. Yes
    b. No   b

510. Serological tests are of value in diagnosis of:
    a. Hookworm infection
    b. Trichinosis   b
    c. Pinworm infection
    d. Toxoplasmosis   d
    e. *Taenia* infection

511. Intradermal tests can be used in diagnosis of infections with:
    a. *Schistosoma mansoni*   a
    b. *Trypanosoma rhodesiense*
    c. *Fasciola hepatica*   c
    d. *Trichinella spiralis*
    e. *Toxocara canis*   e

COLLEGE MEDICAL PARASITOLOGY ANSWERS CONTINUED

1. A parasite may invade man through his:
    a. Skin (direct penetration by the parasite per se or through transmitting vectors)
    b. Respiratory tract (contaminated air)
    c. Digestive system (contaminated food, milk, water)
    d. Reproductive organs during sexual activity or otherwise

5. a. Central nervous system; b. Cerebrospinal fluid; c. Reticuloendothelial system; d. Leishman-Donovan bodies; e. Polyvinyl alcohol (fixative); f. Locke-egg serum medium (for *Entamoeba histolytica*); g. Nicolle's modification of Novy-MacNeal medium for *Leishmania donovani*); h. Cysteine-peptone-liver-maltose medium (for *Trichomonas vaginalis*).

7-8. A parasite may injure its host in a variety of ways. Thus it may:
    a. Rob him of food
    b. Destroy his tissues
    c. Inoculate him with poisons
    d. Infect him with other parasites
    e. Reduce his resistance
    f. Cause him psychological disturbances

9. To ensure accuracy in identification.

14. Cysts are nonfeeding, nonmotile stages. They are surrounded by a protective wall.

15. The precystic stages *(E. hystolytica)* are smaller than the vegetative stages, lack food vacuoles but may possess glycogen vacuoles and chromatoidal bodies.

17. No cyst: *D. fragilis, Trichomonas.*

20. *Entamoeba gingivalis* and *Trichomonas tenax.*

22. **Cytosome:** The cytoplasmic body, excluding the nucleus.
    Cytostome: The differentiated region of the cytosome through which food is ingested. This may or may not be a definite opening.

40. a (Note: *Trypanosoma cruzi* is found in the blood only in the early stages of the disease.)

85. **Karyosome:** *E. histolytica:* small, central, usually compact. *E. coli:* large, diffuse, eccentric (usually).
    Membrane: *E. histolytica:* single layer of fine granules, occasionally plaques may occur. *E. coli:* usually composed of irregular patches of chromatin.
    Linin network: *E. histolytica:* without granules. *E. coli:* with granules.
    Number of nuclei (cyst): *E. histolytica:* 1-4, rarely 8. *E. coli:* 1-32, usually 8.
    Number of nuclei (trophozoite); *E. histolytica:* one. *E. coli:* one.
    Chromatoidal bodies: *E. histolytica:* with blunt ends. *E. coli:* with pointed ends, usually splinter-shaped.
    What does animal ingest? *E. histolytica:* r.b.c. may be present. *E. coli:* bacteria, epithelial cells, protozoa, starch, rarely r.b.c.
    Type and progression of movement: *E. histolytica:* progressive by finger-like pseudopodia in fresh warm stools. *E. coli:* Rarely progressive, sluggish with blunt pseudopodia slowly extruded and frequently withdrawn.

102. Through fecally contaminated water or by ingestion of cyst-containing food.

112. Three species in the genus *Trichomonas (T. tenax, T. hominis* and *T. vaginalis)* are of interest in human parasitology. They are morphologically characterized by flagella, an undulating membrane, a costa, an axostyle, and an anterior nucleus of normal oval shape.

114. a. Coitus
     b. Contamined towels
     c. Douche equipment
     d. Examination instruments

117. By means of special methods morphological differences can be detected which clearly differentiate the three human species. Normally, the identity of a *Trichomonas* will be indicated by the source of material: *T. tenax,* mouth; *T. hominis,* intestine; *T. vaginalis,* uro-genital tract.

125. The genus *Trypanosoma* has amastigote, promastigote, epimastigote and trypomastigote stages in its life cycle.

150. Ulcers of the skin which leave disfiguring scars on healing.

151. Tissues of muco-cutaneous junctions (nose, mouth, etc.).

204. In the life history of *Plasmodium,* as in all the Sporozoa of the group to which the genus belongs, there are three stages which each initiate a growth period. One of these results from multiple fission—it is the merozoite. A second is the zygote, which results from union of two gametes. The third is the sporozoite. The complete life history, therefore, is divisible into three periods. One period of development leads to the production of

merozoites, and this whole period may be termed merogenesis. It may repeat itself indefinitely. A second period leads to the production of gametes, and is gametogenesis. At the end of the third period sporozoites are produced; this period is that of sporogenesis. The organism in the period of merogenesis is customarily known as the schizont; when it is a young schizont it has one nucleus, and when it is a mature schizont it has many nuclei. The term segmenter is used for the parasite just preceding multiple fission in the red blood cell; it segments into a group of merozoites. The organisms in the period of gametogenesis are the gametocytes; these occur in red blood cells, but the final stage of gamete formation does not take place until the blood is exposed to air and cooled, which may occur on a slide or in the alimentary tract of the blood-sucking insect. Young schizonts and young gametocytes usually cannot be distinguished from one another, and may be referred to together as trophozoites. The zygote, to which in this instance the special term oökinete is applied, develops in the body of a suitable kind of mosquito into an oöcyst consisting of a growing body of cytoplasm which becomes increasingly more multinucleate. By the process of sporulation, numerous sporozoites are formed; and these develop further only after entry into a cell of the vertebrate host.

238. e. (They disintegrate unless taken up by the mosquito.)

249. **Miracidium:** First larval stage (ciliated, multicellular) of a fluke.
Cercaria: Late larval stage of a fluke.
Metacercaria: An encysted cercaria.

260. In the blood flukes:
a. The sexes are separate
b. No rediae occur in the larval stage
c. Cercariae are fork-tailed and can enter body through skin
d. Because of "c," no encysted metacercaria occurs

277. a. Human infection with the larval form ("Cysticercus cellulosae") of *Taenia solium*
b. Through the ingestion of *T. solium* eggs

336. Human infections result from the accidental ingestion of the eggs from the feces of infected dogs.

339. f (Note: No intermediate host is required as the worm can complete cycle in one host, but an intermediate host can also be used.)

380. f (Note: Man is the only proven host although the whipworms of pig and certain monkeys are morphologically similar.)

388. Whipworms feed, and attach themselves to the host, by thrusting their thin anterior end into the lining of the cecum or colon of the host and injecting into this a digestive fluid which converts the tissues around the mouth into a liquid which the worm sucks up.

393. Two hosts are required to complete the life cycle, but each host has the development of both larval and adult forms and thus strictly neither is an intermediate host.

417. b (Note: Under certain conditions, the rhabditiform larvae while still in the intestine change into infective, filariform larvae. The latter penetrate the intestinal wall causing "superinfection" ["hyperinfective cycle"].)

462. **Strongyloides:** Rhabditiform with buccal cavity short and of small diameter. Filariform with esophagus similar to hookworm but longer. Tail with notch in caudal extremity.

   Hookworm: Rhabditiform with long and narrow buccal cavity. Filariform with elongated esophagus. Tail without notch in caudal extremity.

474. a. Wet films (saline, iodine)
   b. Stained films
   c. Concentrations (sedimentation, flotation)

476. Few organisms may be present. Concentration methods may be indicated.

477. Stools should not be collected from patients who have recently received barium, bismuth, or oil purgatives.

482. a (Note: Examination of a single loose stool only has been found to reveal about ¾ of infections, a proportion roughly the same as that obtained from six formed stools. In addition to this advantage, the examination is more representative of all the protozoan species that may be present in the intestine [Svenson, 1935; Andrews, 1934].)

483. a. Sodium sulfate (Glauber salts) and phospho-soda are superior to magnesium sulfate (Epsom salts) for obtaining motile, undamaged trophozoites.
   b. The material to be examined is the mucus and tissue detritus in the liquid portion. Examination must be made while specimen is still warm.

486. b (It actually kills them.)

489. The flotation solution is prepared by adding 33 grams of zinc sulfate (granular U.S.P.) to 100 ml. distilled water. It is used for concentration of protozoan cysts and eggs of helminths, and it does not necessarily kill the cysts, as do certain other methods. It is used as follows:
   a. The fecal specimen (about the size of a pea) is broken up in ten times its volume of water.
   b. The mixture is strained through a layer of cheesecloth in a funnel into a centrifuge tube.
   c. The suspension is centrifuged for about one minute, and the supernatant fluid poured off from the sediment.
   d. Water or salt solution is added, the sediment shaken up, and the suspension centrifuged as before. This process is repeated until the fluid is clear.
   e. After the last washing and centrifuging the supernatant fluid is poured off and zinc sulfate solution added. The mixture is shaken up, the tube filled with zinc sulfate solution to within a half inch of the rim, and the suspension centrifuged for about a minute.
   f. Cysts and helminth eggs may be concentrated at the surface of the solution. A suitable amount for examination is removed with a platinum loop and placed on a slide; or zinc sulfate solution is carefully added with a pipette to the solution in the tube until the surface rises slightly above the brim of the tube, and the surface film is then removed by applying a coverglass.
   g. For examination, a drop of iodine stain may be added.

492. Trypanosomas, microfilariae, malaria (the latter usually only when the pigment of the parasites is abundant).

493. A small drop of blood is placed on a slide in the center of the surface about an inch from one end. This drop may be taken up directly from the patient by touching the slide to the blood exuding from the puncture; or the drop may be taken from a collection of blood. The second slide is used as a spreader. Its edge is placed on the slide, free of the blood drop and toward the middle of the slide. The angle between the spreader slide and the film slide should be about 30 degrees; this angle encloses the blood drop. The spreader slide is drawn back until it touches the drop of blood, which will spread along its edge; and is then rapidly pushed toward the more distant end of the film slide. This movement drags the blood behind the edge of the spreader slide, giving a blood film whose thickness varies with the speed at which the slide was pushed.

498. a. A drop of commercial formalin is added to 1 ml. clean serum
   b. An opalescent gel (clot) is obtained in Kala-azar
   c. An increase in serum globulin content

504. a. Urine kills protozoa rather rapidly
   b. The admixture of water speeds up the growth of nonpathogenic forms and renders examination more difficult (water may even destroy the motile trophozoites)

505. a. When it is impossible to demonstrate the trypanosomas in the blood
   b. Laboratory-reared Triatomid bugs are fed upon patient's blood. Ten to 30 days later the intestinal contents of the bugs are examined for the presence of flagellates. These may then be inoculated into mice for further confirmation.

506. a. *Trichomonas vaginalis*
   b. *Schistosoma haematobium* eggs
   c. Bancroft's microfilariae (when chyluria is present)
   d. *Entamoeba histolytica* (rare)
   e. *Strongyloides* larvae (rare)

3.

MEDICAL ENTOMOLOGY TEST

Edited by Derek Wakelin, Ph.D., The University of Glasgow

1. Match the following:

1. Fleas	a. Order Hemiptera	1—f
2. Spiders	b. Order Diptera	2—c
3. Scorpions	c. Class Arachnida	3—c
4. Soft ticks	d. Family Ixodidae	4—c & g
5. Bugs (true bugs)	e. Order Anoplura	5—a
6. Sandflies	f. Order Siphonaptera	6—b
7. Hard ticks	g. Family Argasidae	7—c & d
8. Mosquitoes	h. Order Chilopoda	8—b
9. Centipedes		9—h
10. Midges		10—b
11. Lice		11—e
12. Flies		12—b

2. Match the following:

1. *Anopheles* mosquito	a. Bancroft's filariasis	1—b & a
2. *Culex* mosquito	b. Malaria	2—a
3. *Aëdes* mosquito	c. Bubonic plague	3—a
4. *Pediculus humanus* (louse)	d. Chagas' disease	4—f & g
	e. Dipylidiasis	
5. Dog flea	f. Epidemic typhus	5—e
6. Rat flea	g. Trench fever	6—c
7. Kissing bug (assassin bug)		7—d

3. Match the following:

1. *Aëdes* mosquito	a. African trypanosomiasis	1—g & i
2. *Chrysops* sp.	b. Amebic & bacillary	2—d
3. House fly	dysenteries	3—b
4. *Phlebotomus* sand fly	c. Onchocerciasis	4—j
5. Tsetse fly	d. Loaiasis	5—a
6. Blackfly *(Simulium* sp.)	e. Tularemia & anthrax	
	f. Cutaneous myasis in man	6—e
7. Horse bot fly	g. Yellow fever	7—f
8. Gnat *(Culicoides* sp.)	h. Acanthocheilonema &	8—h
9. *Tabanus* sp.	Mansonella infections	9—c
	i. Dengue fever	
	j. Leishmaniasis	

4. What two domestic animals are the commonest sources of fleas which can temporarily infest man? — dog; cat

5. The human flea is:
   a. *Phthirus pubis*
   b. *Sarcoptes scabei*
   c. *Pediculus humanus*
   d. *Pulex irritans* — d
   e. *Cteno-cephalides felis*

287

6. What one feature readily distinguishes the human flea from those of dog or cat origin? — absence of ctenidia (combs)

7. What is scabies? — See below

8. How is a conclusive diagnosis of scabies obtained? — See below

9. The head louse is easily distinguished from the body louse. T F — F

10. The eggs of the head louse can be found attached to hairs of infected people.   T   F — T

11. The body louse is transmitted by contact with soiled clothes or bedding.   T   F — T

12. The crab louse is found:
    a. On hair on the head
    b. In hair follicles
    c. In the superficial layers of the skin
    d. On coarse body hair — d

13. The follicle mite is:
    a. *Pediculus humanus*
    b. *Cimex lectularius*
    c. *Sarcoptes scabei*
    d. *Demodex folliculorum*
    e. *Pulex irritans* — d

14. Match the following:
    1. *Ctenocephalides felis*   a. Crab louse — 1—f
    2. *Pulex irritans*   b. Rat flea — 2—e
    3. *Xenopsylla cheopsis*   c. Body louse — 3—b
    4. *Pediculus humanus*   d. Bed bug — 4—c
    5. *Cimex lectularius*   e. Human flea — 5—d
    6. *Phthirus pubis*   f. Cat flea — 6—a

15. What is myiasis? — See below

16. What are the major groups of venomous arthropods? — See below

MEDICAL ENTOMOLOGY TEST ANSWERS CONTINUED

7. A skin condition caused by infection with *Sarcoptes scabei,* a mite which burrows into the skin and produces intense irritation and edema, often followed by secondary infection.

8. By microscopic examination of scrapings from infected areas of skin.

15. Infestation by maggots, larval stages of certain flies such as *Sarcophaga.*

16. Scorpions, spiders, centipedes.

Section III MICROBIOLOGY

Subsection II: BACTERIOLOGY & ALLIED FIELDS

BACTERIOLOGY & ALLIED FIELD EXAMINATION

Edited by Lois H. Lindberg, Ph.D., Prof. of Microbiology, San Jose State University

GENERAL BACTERIOLOGY

1. Differentiate between pH, pK, and Eh. See p. 379

2. Differentiate between thermoduric bacteria and thermophilic bacteria. See p. 379

3. How can the following structures in bacteria be identified and what is their function? See p. 379
    a. Cell Wall
    b. Cytoplasmic membrane
    c. Ribosomes
    d. Fimbriae or pili

4. Why do you, or do you not, believe that bacteria possess mitochondrial systems? See p. 379

5. One word answers. In the column at right, fill in the word which the phrase at left best describes:
    a. Unicellular, true fungi . . . .   Phyco-mycetes
    b. Chlorophyllous thallophytes . . . .   Algae
    c. Multicellular, true fungi . . . .   Basidio-mycetes
    d. Threadlike strand of mold . . . .   hyphae
    e. Plant body of mold . . . .   mycelium
    f. Round bacteria . . . .   cocci
    g. Filterable, obligate parasites . . . .   viruses
    h. Study of all microorganisms . . . .   micro-biology
    i. Molds without sexual reproductions . . . . .   Fungi imperfecti
    j. Grow well at low temperatures . . . . . .   psychrophiles
    k. Chemical which kills bacteria . . . .   chemo-therapeutic agent
    l. Maintains pH in media . . . .   buffer
    m. Most commonly used to solidify media . . . .   agar
    n. Live only on living tissue . . . .   viruses

6. An organism which grows on a blood agar plate incubated in a candle jar as well as on a duplicate blood agar plate incubated under strict anaerobic conditions, but will not grow on a triplicate blood agar plate incubated aerobically should be called:

   a. A strict anaerobe
   b. Microphilic   b
   c. Capnophilic
   d. A facultative anaerobe

7. Place the corresponding number before the term in column 2 which links it MOST LIKELY with the term in
   column 1:

   Column 1   **Column 2**

   1. Sucrose   Virulence
   2. Virus   Obligate parasite   2
   3. Plasmolysis   Tiny colony   10
   4. Acid formation   Hypertonic solution
   5. Starch   Prismatic effect   7
   6. Word ending in "-ase"   Carbon dioxide
   7. Spherical aberration   Hypotonic solution   3
   8. Photosynthesis   Buffer action
   9. Acid-fast   Carbohydrate decompo-
                                      sition   4
   10. Punctate   Wax content   9
   11. Used in vinegar pro-   Enzyme   6
       duction.   Polysaccharide   5
   12. Causes boils   Chlorophyll   8
   13. Causes tuberculosis   Inability to focus the
   14. Causes bacillary   whole field
       dysentery   Disaccharide   1
   15. Urease producer   *Bacillus*   20
   16. Coliform   *Clostridium*   17
   17. Anaerobic   *Proteus*   15
   18. Fixes nitrogen   *Enterobacter*   16
   19. Causes diphtheria   *Acetobacter*   11
   20. Aerobic sporeformers   *Azotobacter*   18
                                    Entamoeba
                                    Salmonella
                                    Shigella   14
                                    Staphylococcus   12
                                    Vibrio
                                    Mycobacterium   13
                                    Corynebacterium   19

8. What structures of the bacterial cell are likely to contain
   significant amounts of:
   a. Teichoic acid   cell wall
   b. DNA   nuclear appa-
                                                          ratus
   c. Diaminopinelic acid   cell wall
   d. Muramic acid   "   "
   e. Dipicolinate   spore
   f. RNA   cytoplasm

9. How does selenite broth act as an enrichment medium? See p. 379

10. What is meant by the term "fixing the smear," and what occurs during the process? See p. 379

11. What advantages has the negative stain over the simple stain? See p. 379

12. What diagnostic significance are metachromatic granules? See p. 379

13. What is the difference, if any, between dextrose and glucose; sucrose and saccharose; bacteria and bacterium? None; none; Singular or plural

14. Which one of the following includes all the types of bacteria that grow in nutrient broth overlaid with sterile vaspar?
    a. Obligate anaerobes only
    b. Obligate aerobes and anaerobes
    c. Anaerobic and facultative bacteria   c
    d. Obligate aerobes only
    e. Mesophiles only

15. Bacterial action on proteins in litmus milk changes the color to:
    a. Red
    b. Blue
    c. Colorless   c
    d. Pink

16. Bacterial cells of one species which do vary in their size and arrangement are said to be:
    a. Amorphic
    b. Metamorphic
    c. Monomorphic
    d. Pleomorphic   d
    e. Polymorphic

17. Which of the following substrates may be decomposed by lipase?
    a. Butter   a
    b. Starch
    c. Casein
    d. Gelatin
    e. Lactose

18. Which of the following is not a product of microbial synthesis when produced in a glucose broth culture?
    a. Pigments
    b. Toxins
    c. Lactic acid   c
    d. Antibiotics
    e. Cell wall material

19. Which of the following is not true about the standard plate count?
    a. Counts all viable organisms
    b. Accurate for samples with low bacterial counts   b

      c. Samples with high populations can be diluted before plating

      d. Colonies can be accurately counted

20. Which of the following enzymes is not named on the basis of function?
      a. Deaminase
      b. Oxidase
      c. Amylase   c
      d. Decarboxylase
      e. Transaminase

21. To detect gelatin liquefaction using Frazier's gelatin agar:
      a. Incubate gelatin tubes at 45°C.
      b. Flood the plates with iodine solution
      c. Flood the plates with saturated ammonium sulfate after incubation   c
      d. Observe for a change in the indicator from red to blue

22. Which is the better buffer, KH_2PO_4 or K_2HPO_4? Explain   Neither
See p. 379

23. If we know that an organism ferments lactose, then as far as glucose is concerned, it is safe to say that:
      a. It probably will be fermented
      b. It definitely will be fermented   b
      c. It definitely will not be fermented
      d. It probably will not be fermented

24. The ingredients in Loeffler's medium are:
      a. Whole blood, coagulated egg, and dextrose
      b. Lactose broth, agar, egg yolk, and citrate
      c. Coagulated plasma, dextrose broth, and citrate
      d. Coagulated serum, lactose broth, and citrate
      e. Coagulated serum, dextrose broth, and citrate   e

25. Gram stained smears to determine morphology and staining characteristics should be made from:
      a. Any age culture on any medium
      b. Single colony pickings made from any medium
      c. Young, actively growing organisms grown on a nonselective medium   c
      d. Old cultures on rich medium

26. Biochemical studies should be performed using:
      a. Suspensions of several similar colonies in broth
      b. Any type of culture of any age
      c. Any culture so long as Gram-stained smear does not show organisms having different morphology or staining characteristics
      d. Young, actively growing cultures made from single colony pickings   d

27. Bacteria are measured in units called _____, which are
    _____ of a millimeter or approximately _____
    of an inch.

    microns
    0.001 mm.
    1/24,000

28, Name, *in order,* the four ingredients of the Gram stain:
    a. _____
    b. _____
    c. _____
    d. _____

    crystal violet
    iodine
    95% alcohol
    safranin

29. Petri dishes, after inoculation, are inverted during the incu-
    bation period because _____.

    See p. 379

30. The substance used to solidify media in bacteriology is
    called _____. It melts at _____°C. and solidifies at _____°C.
    The optimal temperature for pouring the Petri dish is
    _____°C.

    agar; 100°C.
    45°C.
    50°C.

31. Two methods which may be used to determine motility are
    _____ and _____.

    hanging drop;
    motility test
    medium

32. Lactic acid is a product of anaerobic respiration.   T   F

    T

33. Organisms which can utilize organic materials as a source
    of energy are called:
    a. Heterotrophic
    b. Holozoic
    c. Autotrophic
    d. Saprophytic

    c

34. The most readily available source of energy for all cells is:
    a. Protein
    b. Fat
    c. Carbohydrate

    c

35. A synonym for "fat-splitting enzyme" is:
    a. Catalase
    b. Amylase
    c. Diastase
    d. Lipase

    d

36. Most bacteria prefer to grow at a pH near _____.

    neutrality

37. The reason that anaerobes cannot exist aerobically is that
    under these conditions they form _____ and do not
    produce the enzyme _____.

    peroxides
    peroxidase

38. In aerobic respiration, _____ is
    utilized as the hydrogen acceptor.

    inorg. element
    such as N, S, O.

39. Synonym for fermentation: _____.

    anaerobic
    respiration

40. Each of the following is a degradation product of either
    fermentation or putrefaction reactions; for each, indicate
    the substrate from which it evolved or a substrate from
    which it could evolve:

a. Disaccharide . . . .   oligo-
                                           saccharide
b. Acetyl methyl carbinol . . . .   glucose →
                                           pyruvic acid
c. Hydrogen sulfide . . . .   NaHSO₄
                                           (−SH con-
                                           taining sub-
                                           stances
d. Amoonia . . . .   proteins
e. Indole . . . .   tryptophane
                                           or tryptone
f. Lactic acid . . . .   glucose →
                                           pyruvic acid

41. The only bacteria able to show the Pasteur effect are
    _____.   facultative
                                             anaerobes

42. Opposite the genera listed below, write the number of its
    position in the following simplified key:
    a. Rod-shaped
       1. Not acid-fast
          (a) Produce spores
              (1) Aerobic   1
              (2) Anaerobic   2
          (b) Do not produce spores
              (1) Give AG from lactose
                  a. Indole and MR positive . . 3
                  b. Indole and MR negative . . 4
              (2) Do not ferment lactose
                  a. Produce urease 5
                  b. Do not produce urease . . 6
       2. Acid-fast   7
    b. Coccus-shaped
       1. Gram-positive
          (a) Grow in chains   8
          (b) Do not grow in chains
              (1) Grow in regular packets . . .   9
              (2) Grow in irregular packets . . 10
       2. Gram-negative 11

    a. *Streptococcus*   _____   8
    b. *Staphylococcus*   _____   10
    c. *Salmonella*   _____   6
    d. *Bacillus*   _____   1
    e. *Neisseria*   _____   11
    f. *Escherichia*   _____   4
    g. *Mycobacterium*   _____   7
    h *Clostridium*   _____   2
    i. *Proteus*   _____   5
    j. *Sarcina*   _____   9
    k. *Enterobacter*   _____   3

43. If you wanted to perform the indole test, went to the media storeroom, requested a tube of tryptone broth, and was told that they had no tryptone broth, but did have some tryptone-glucose broth, would this be acceptable or not acceptable to you? Explain your answer.   See p. 379

44. In the methylene blue reduction test, could you substitute phenol red dye for the reductase test? Why or why not?   See p. 379
How is the time of declorization related to the bacterial density?   See p. 379

45. Exudates differ from transudates in that they:
    a. Usually have a (higher; lower) specific gravity   higher
    b. Contain (more; fewer) cells   more
    c. (May; may not) contain bacteria   may
    d. Have a (high; low) protein content   high

46. The oil immersion objective has the longest working distance.   T   F   F

47. *Salmonella typhi* as well as other organisms which are entirely surrounded by flagella are said to be:
    a. Atrichous
    b. Lophotrichous
    c. Amphitrichous
    d. Peritrichous   d

48. Monotrichous bacteria have:
    a. A single polar flagellum   a
    b. A tuft of flagella at one of the cell poles
    c. A tuft of flagella at each pole
    d. Flagella distributed over entire cell

49. Thermoduric bacteria are bacteria which:
    a. Are cold-loving
    b. Are heat-loving
    c. Grow best at a moderate temperature
    d. Are capable of withstanding high temperatures   d

50. What is meant by "negative staining" of cells?   See p. 379

51. Thioglycollate medium will support the growth of aerobes as well as many anaerobes.   T   F   T

52. Chloral hydrate is put in plating media to prevent _____
_____.   The spread of *Proteus*

53. What enzyme may be added to culture media in order to counteract penicillin?   penicilinase

54. What is added to media to counteract the action of sulfonamides?   PABA. (Also See p. 379)

55. If only one kind of microorganism is obtained in a culture, it is called a _____ culture.

pure

56. To remove crystal violet, or similar stains, from a lab coat you would apply:
    a. Methyl alcohol
    b. A 10% sodium carbonate solution
    c. A 5% aqueous solution of HCl and then rinse in water
    d. Acid-alcohol and then hypochlorite solution followed by water

d

57. The Gram staining procedure begins with the application of an acid dye.   T   F

F

58. Which of the following organisms is Gram-positive:
    a. *Neisseria*
    b. *Staphylococcus*
    c. *Branhella*
    d. *Actinobacillus*
    e. *Veillonella*

b

59. Sodium desoxycholate inhibits the growth of:
    a. Gram-positive organisms
    b. Gram-negative organisms

a

60. Both facultative anaerobes and anaerobes will grow in thioglycollate medium.   T   F

T

61. Aerobic and anaerobic bacteria will grow in thioglycollate medium.   T   F

T

62. Pasteurization of milk is usually carried out at:
    a. 54°C. for 40 minutes
    b. 63°C. for 30 minutes
    c. 70°C. for 70 minutes
    d. 82°C. for 90 minutes

b

63. Explain difference(s) between "fermentation" and "putrefaction."

See p. 379

64. Explain difference(s) between "cocci" and "bacilli."

See p. 380

65. Red blood cells are Gram-negative.   T   F

T

66. Explain difference(s) between "disinfection" and "sterilization."

See p. 380

67. Explain difference(s) between "disinfection" and "asepsis."

See p. 380

68. Explain difference(s) between "thermolabile" and "thermostable."

See p. 380

69. Explain difference(s) between "aerobic" organisms and "microaerophilic" organisms.

See p. 380

70. Explain difference(s) between "S" colonies and "R" colonies.

See p. 380

71. Explain difference(s) between "bacteriostatic" and "bactericidal."

See p. 380

72. Explain difference(s) between "in vivo" and "in vitro." See p. 380

73. Explain difference(s) between "bright-field" microscopy and "dark-field" microscopy. See p. 380

74. Explain difference(s) between "serum" (antibacterial serum) and "vaccine." See p. 380

75. Explain difference(s) between bacterial "antagonism" and bacterial "synergism." See p. 381

76. Explain difference(s) between "active immunity" and "passive immunity." See p. 381

77. Explain difference(s) between "DNA" and "RNA." See p. 381

78. Explain difference(s) between "aerobic" organisms and "anaerobic" organisms. See p. 381

GENERAL MEDICAL BACTERIOLOGY

79. What single specific growth requirements are necessary for the cultivation of:
    - a. *Francisella tularensis*
    - b. *Brucella abortus*
    - c. *Clostridium perfringens*

    cystine
    10% CO_2
    anaerobic conditions

80. Examine the list of organisms below:

    A. *Brucella*
    B. *Y. pestis*
    C. *F. tularensis*
    D. *B. pertussis*
    E. *H. influenzae*
    F. Koch-Weeks bacillus
    G. *Pseudomonas*

    After each of the statements below, indicate by capital letter A through G which of the organisms are particularly related to the statements. Any number of the possibilities A through G exist or none of the organisms listed fits the statement.

    - a. Frequent cause of meningitis ____ — E
    - b. May be found in raw milk ____ — A
    - c. Often present as a secondary invader ____ — E, G
    - d. Cause of whooping cough ____ — D
    - e. Spread from animal host to man by arthropod vector ____ — B
    - f. Grows well on ordinary medium ____ — G
    - g. Eye infection occurs frequently ____ — F
    - h. Produces soluble pigments ____ — G
    - i. Animals usually become infected during pregnancy ____ — A
    - j. May show bipolar staining ____ — B
    - k. Often easily spread from man to man by droplets ____ — B, D, E
    - l. Causative agent of undulant fever in man ____ — A
    - m. Causative agent of plague in man ____ — B

o. Main reservoir of infection found in wild rabbits ____   C
p. Found in material aspirated from buboes ____   B

81. Cite Koch's postulates.   See p. 381

82. _____ and _____ are the carbo-   Glucose 1%
hydrates present in Russell's Dougle Sugar. State the con-   & lactose 10%
tration of each carbohydrate and very briefly discuss the
purpose of using these concentrations, i.e., the principle of
the reaction.   See p. 382

83. Resistance to disease is the result of a dynamic balance of
host defense factors and parasite attack factors. Categor-
ize the defense factors listed below with an "N" if non-
specific or with an "S" is specific.
   a. Intact skin ____   N
   b. Antibodies ____   S
   c. Physiological condition ____   N
   d. Adequate nutrition ____   N
   e. Body fluids and secretions ____   N
   f. Tetanus antitoxin ____   S

84. Matching. Opposite the phrase at left, put the letter of the
genus at right best described:
   ____ 1. Used in vinegar production   a. *Bacillus*   e
   ____ 2. Causes boils   b. *Clostridium*   j
   ____ 3. Causes tuberculosis   c. *Proteus*   l
   ____ 4. Causes bacillary dysentery   d. *Enterobacter*   i
   ____ 5. Protozoan   e. *Acetobacter*   g
   ____ 6. Aerobic sporeformers   f. *Azotobacter*   a
   ____ 7. Urease producer   g. *Entamoeba*   c
   ____ 8. Coliform   h. *Salmonella*   d
   ____ 9. Causes diphtheria   i. *Shigella*   m
   ____10. Causes typhoid   j. *Staphylococcus*   h
   ____11. Anaerobic   k. *Vibrio*   b
   ____12. Fixes nitrogen   l. *Mycobacterium*   f
   ____13. Causes cholera   m. *Corynebacterium*   k

85. What general kinds of media would you use for the isolation
of a bacterium from the following sources:
   a. Aseptically collected urine   See p. 381
   b. Blood   "
   c. Material from a superficial wound   "
   d. Fecal specimen   "
   e. Spinal fluid   "

86. How are the following diseases spread in a population:
   a. Epidemic cerebrospinal meningitis   droplets
   b. Plague   flea bite or
      droplets
   c. Cholera   ingesting
      contaminated
      water
   d. Anthrax   handling
      contaminated
      hides

87. Name five genera of bacteria of which one or more species produce exotoxins.

Staphylococcus
Streptococcus
Clostridium
Shigella
Vibrio

88. What are the two major reasons for employing blood agar for the cultivation of certain pathogenic species?

See p. 382

89. Most bacteria of interest in medical bacteriology are:
    a. Facultative anaerobic or strictly anaerobic
    b. Strict aerobes or strict anaerobes
    c. Strict anaerobes
    d. Strict aerobes

a

90. A virulent culture of a human pathogen would:
    a. Be a rough variant
    b. Be a mesophile
    c. Form an exotoxin
    d. Be motile

b

91. R type bacteria are best for making vaccines since they are less virulent.   T   F

F

92. Pathogenic organisms are always invasive.   T   F

F

93. Toxins, lysins, and capsular material are all examples of:
    a. An antigen
    b. An antibody
    c. Virulence factors
    d. Non-virulence factors

c

94. The successful parasite:
    a. Is usually beneficial to the host
    b. Doesn't harm the host
    c. Needs a means of transmission to a new host after it kills its original host
    d. Is maladjusted

b

95. The dynamics of infection are based on a very delicate host-parasite equilibrium. Which of the following do not relate to the parasite's "attack factors"?
    a. Immunity
    b. Ability to produce toxins
    c. Invasiveness
    d. Number of organisms

a

96. Mention at least six diseases in which the carrier state is of particular interest.

See p. 382

97. What is the best way to culture for organisms in blood:
    a. Aerobically
    b. Anaerobically
    c. Both a and b

c

98. The prevention of access by microorganisms to any materials is known as:

    a. Disinfection
    b. Sterilization
    c. Asepsis   c
    d. Fumigation

99. The prevention of disease is called:
    a. Asepsis
    b. Prophylaxis   b
    c. Therapeutics
    d. Immunology

100. A person who, without exhibiting symptoms of a communicable disease, harbors and disseminates a disease-producing microorganism is called a _____.   carrier

101. Diseases which are epidemic over a large territory are said to be:
    a. Pandemic   a
    b. Endemic
    c. Epidemic
    d. Sporadic

102. All bacterial diseases are infectious.   T   F   T

103. All infectious diseases are contagious.   T   F   F

104. What is "pyelitis"?   See p. 382

105. Inflammation of the oral mucosa is also called:
    a. Orchitis
    b. Stomatitis   b
    c. Pharyngitis
    d. Phallitis

106. Blood cultures may be indicated for:
    a. *Clostridium tetani*
    b. *Corynebacterium diphtheriae*
    c. *Shigella dysenteriae*
    d. *Mycobacterium tuberculosis*
    e. All of these
    f. None of these   f

107. All inflammations are bacterial in etiology.   T   F   F

108. Boas-Oppler bacilli are usually present in the gastric contents of patients with gastric or duodenal ulcer.   T   F   F

109. In the following list indicate those organisms which are Gram-negative:

a. *Salmonella*	j. *B. anthracis*	a
b. *Escherichia*	k. *Streptococcus*	b
c. *Corynebacterium*	l *Neisseria*	l
d. *Pasteurella*	m. *Enterobacter*	d, m
e. *Klebsiella*	n. *Actinomyces*	e
f. *Mycobacterium*	o. *Shigella*	o
g. *Spirillum*	p. *Pseudomonas*	g, p
h. *Treponema*	q. *B. subtilis*	h
i. *Vibrio cholerae*		i

110. In the bloodstream, a few organisms have the same clinical significance as a large number.   T   F   T

111. A single negative blood culture is sufficient to rule out septicemia.   T   F   F

112. Blood cultures should be taken prior to antibiotic treatment.   T   F   T

113. Mention at least six conditions in which a positive blood culture may be obtained.   See p. 382

114. A "urinary antiseptic" which liberates formaldehyde in acid urine is:
    a. Acetanilid
    b. Chloral hydrate
    c. Methenamine   c
    d. Antipyrine

115. The broth above the settled cells is always uniformly turbid when a blood culture is positive.   T   F   F

116. Materials from wounds, ulcers, abscesses, body fluids, surgical swabs, abdominal cavity, ear, mastoid, and sinus, and compound fractures are best cultured·
    a. Aerobically
    b. Anaerobically
    c. Both a and b   c

117. A blood culture may be regarded as sterile if there is no evidence of growth at 72 hours of incubation.   T   F   F

118. Distinguish between "bacteremia" and "septicemia."   See p. 382

119. Distinguish between "pyelitis" and "pyelonephritis."   See p. 382

120. Distinguish between "boil" and "abscess."   See p. 382

121. Distinguish between "furuncle" and "carbuncle."   See p. 382

122. Milk-curding is caused by:
    a. Rennin   a
    b. Lipase
    c. Maltase
    d. Trypsin

123. What is commonest source of food poisoning?   poorly canned food

124. Distinguish between "ptomaine poisoning" and "food poisoning."   See p. 382

125. Agar pour plates are of questionable value in blood culture work.   T   F   T

126. Most bacterial cultures are incubated from:
    a.   1–12 hours
    b. 12–24 hours
    c. 12–48 hours   c
    d. 24–72 hours

127. The fluid obtained from a patient suffering from dropsy is
called:
    a. Ascitic fluid   a
    b. Hydatid fluid
    c. Exudate
    d. Colostrum

128. Distinguish between "somatic" and "capsular" antigen. See p. 383

129. Distinguish between "somatic" and "flagellar" antigen. See p. 383

130. Pleural, pericardial, and abdominal transudates normally
contain organisms.   T   F   F

131. Distinguish between "myelitis" and "encephalitis." See p. 383

GENERAL MEDIA AND STERILIZATION

132. Which type of sterilization would you use for the following:
    1. Empty Erlenmeyer flask   dry heat
    2. Container of pipettes   "   "
    3. Pair of rubber gloves   autoclave or
                                  ethylene oxid
                                  gas
    4. Beaker of corks   autoclave
    5. Contaminated needles and syringes   boiling
    6. Can of green beans   autoclave
    7. Dead, infected mouse   incineration
    8. Discarded culture tubes   autoclave

133. What would happen to a carbohydrate such as lactose if it
were subjected to autoclave sterilization for a prolonged
period, i.e., greater than the recommended time and temperature for carbohydrates? Could this medium be used
for fermentation reactions? Explain.   See p. 383

134. Class of substances added to media to promote anaero-
biosis: _____ _____.   reducing
                                      agents

135. Is nutrient agar a synthetic or non-synthetic medium?
Explain.   See p. 383

136. The perecentage of NaCl in a medium influences its pH.
T   F   F

137. Insert the number serving the following function (in the
space provided for each) from the list of ingredients:
    ____ a. energy source   1. Lactose   1, 2
    ____ b. nitrogen source   2. Peptose   2, 4
    ____ c. integrity of the cell 3. Water   5, 3
    ____ d. growth factors   4. Plasma   4
                            5. Sodium chloride

138. When a medium is greenish-blue with bromthymol blue, it
indicates that it is isotonic.   T   F   F

139. In order for ultraviolet light to be effective, it must be relatively (far, near) to the surface to be affected.

near

140. Matching. On the left are listed substances that could be present in culture media. Opposite each ingredient, put the letter or letters of the function(s) it serves.

     ____ 1. KH_2PO_4 a. Solidification

     ____ 2. Beef extract   b. Source of carbon

     ____ 3. Peptone   c. Redox indicator

     ____ 4. Glucose   d. pH indicator

     ____ 5. Phenol red   e. Vitamins and minerals

     ____ 6. Agar   f. Source of nitrogen

     ____ 7. TTC   g. Buffer

     ____ 8. Citrate

     ____ 9. $NH_4H_2PO_4$

1—g
2—e
3—f
4—b
5—d
6—a
7—c
8—b
9—g

141. Certain sugars (such as lactose) which decompose even with fractional sterilization methods should be sterilized by _____.

filtration

142. Certain media (e.g., sugar, gelatin, potato) are injured by excessive heat and should be sterilized by _____.

Tyndalli-
zation

143. Some sugars decompose in the autoclave.   T   F

T

144. To kill spores, moist heat (15–30 minutes exposure) must be employed for:
     a. Two successive days
     b. Three successive days
     c. Neither of these

b

145. The above method is called _____ or _____

sterilization or _____.

intermittent
or fractional
Tyndallization

146. Exposure for 15–20 minutes to moist heat (100°C.) is sufficient to kill all vegetative forms of bacteria.   T   F

T

147. Exposure for 15–20 minutes to moist heat (100°C.) is sufficient to kill the spores.   T   F

F

148. Sugars, serum, and tissue extracts should be sterilized by:
     a. Heat without pressure
     b. Special chemicals
     c. Filtration
     d. None of these

c

149. Oversterilization of media should be avoided in order to prevent:
     a. Blowing of cotton plugs
     b. Evaporation of media
     c. Decomposition of ingredients in the media

c

150. A steam pressure of 15 lbs. with only 2/3 of the air discharged will reach a temperature of 250°F.   T   F

F

151. What temperature is usually used to sterilize media in an autoclave?

See p. 383

152. Sporulating bacteria are most resistant to destruction by heat and moisture.   T   F

T

153. Cold sterilization by chemicals will be effective if the instrument to be sterilized is immersed for a minimum of:
     a. 1 hour
     b. 2 hours
     c. 3 hours
     d. 5 hours

c

154. Boiling at 212°F. (the highest temperature of boiling water) will destroy only nonspore-forming bacteria.   T   F

T

155. The bactericidal activity of light is maximal at the following wavelength:
     a. 2536 Angstrom units
     b. 3256 Angstrom units
     c. 5326 Angstrom units
     d. 6532 Angstrom units

a

156. Indicate a suitable method to sterilize mineral oil.

See p. 383

157. The efficiency of a disinfectant is determined by testing its ability to kill a test organism and by comparing it with that of _____ under similar conditions.

phenol

158. Distinguish between "plain blood agar" and "chocolate agar."

See p. 383

159. Agar is derived from a certain kind of _____ which, when dissolved in water and heated to a sufficiently high degree will, upon cooling, form a thick jelly.

seaweed

160. Sodium azide is used in media to prevent the growth of _____ and _____.

Proteus and other Gram-negative organisms

161. Sodium bicarbonate is added to media to _____.

buffer it.

162. Glassware is sterilized by heating in a hot air sterilizer at 150°C. for:
     a. 5–10 minutes
     b. 10–20 minutes
     c. 30–60 minutes

c

163. Name and describe four ways that media can be sterilized.

See p. 383

ANTIBIOTICS

164. *Briefly* outline an experiment which would determine whether a disinfectant is bacteriostatic or bactericidal.

See p. 383

165. Plate sensitivity tests usually are not made:
    a. On pure cultures of organisms isolated from blood cultures
    b. Directly on wound drainage
    c. Directly from urine specimens
    d. Directly from throat swabbings   d
    e. On pure cultures of organisms isolated from urine specimens

166. *Quantitative* estimation of antibiotic sensitivity of an organism may be most *accurately* obtained by:
    a. Determining the size of the zone of inhibition around the routine antibiotic sensi-disc
    b. Testing growth of the organism in medium containing serial dilutions of the antibiotic
    c. Using sensi-discs containing three concentrations of each antibiotic

167. Penicillin will inhibit the growth of most Gram-positive organisms.   T   F   T

168. Ten ml. stock solution of Terramycin contain 500 micrograms. Dilute so that 1 ml. contains 0.5 micrograms.   See p. 383

169. Methenamine mandelate (Mandelamine) is employed in the management of:
    a. Subacute bacterial endocarditis
    b. Urinary tract infections   b
    c. Meningitis
    d. Whooping cough

170. The results of an antimicrobial susceptibility test carried out on a plate directly inoculated with the clinical specimen is more reliable than the results of a susceptibility test carried out on a plate inoculated with a pure culture obtained from the original material.   T   F   F

171. Distinguish between "antibiotic" and "chemotherapeutic agent."   See p. 383

172. An antibiotic used in the treatment of typhus and Rocky Mountain spotted fever is:
    a. Terramycin
    b. Chloromycetin   b
    c. Aureomycin
    d. Penicillin

173. Gantrisin, Mandelamine, and Furadantin are:
    a. Antibiotics
    b. Chemotherapeutic agents   b
    c. Neither a nor b

174. Sulfisoxazole is also known as:
    a. Gantrisin   a
    b. Mandelamine
    c. Furadantin
    d. None of these

175. Polymyxin has no effect on Proteus but it is the drug of choice in the treatment of infections due to *Pseudomonas aeruginosa.*   T   F   T

176. Most strains of gonococci are highly susceptible to penicillin.   T   F   T

177. Mycobacterium tuberculosis may be susceptible to:
     a. Streptomycin
     b. Isonicotinic acid hydrazide (INH)
     c. Para-aminosalicylic acid (PAS)
     d. All of these
     e. None of these

178. A drug which, while having little effect on other microorganisms, is highly effective against mycobacteria (tubercle bacilli in particular) is:
     a. Isoniazid   a
     b. Novobiocin
     c. Bacitracin
     d. Polymyxin B

THE MICROCOCCUS SECTION

179. The characteristic which best distinguishes staphylococci from streptococci is:
     a. Staphylococci are catalase-positive and streptococci are catalase-negative   a
     b. Streptococci occur in chains while staphylococci do not
     c. Staphylococci produce acid from glucose while streptococci do not
     d. Streptococci produce pinpoint colonies and staphylococci produce larger colonies.

180. Members of the genus *Micrococcus* either do not produce acid from glucose or:
     a. Produce acid only in the presence of oxygen   a
     b. Produce acid either in the presence or absence of oxygen
     c. Produce both acid and gas
     d. Produce acid only in the absence of oxygen

181. Name four soluble toxic factors produced by *Staphylococcus aureus.*   See p. 384

182. How can the coagulase and fibrinolytic activities of *Staphylococcus* be demonstrated?   See p. 384

183. Gram-positive spheres in grape-like clusters, aerobic and facultatively anaerobic, catalase positive, ferments glucose, coagulase positive:_____.   *Staph. aureus*

184. The catalase test is useful in quickly differentiating staph from what other genus of Gram-positive cocci?

   Streptococcus and *Strep. pneumoniae*

   This test should not be performed on media containing _____. Why?

   red blood cells (also see p. 384)

185. The most valid criterion for determining potential pathogeniety of staphylococcus is:
   a. Production of gold pigments
   b. Fermentation of mannitol
   c. Coagulase activity
   d. Hemolytic activity

   c

186. Phage typing of *Staph. aureus* is most valuable in:
   a. Preliminary diagnosis of *Staph.* spp. infections
   b. Guiding therapy of *Staph* spp. infections
   c. Classification of *Micrococcus* spp.
   d. Epidemiologic studies of outbreaks of *Staph aureus* infections.

   d

187. Strains of *Staph. aureus* never vary in ability to produce which of the following?
   a. Pigmentation
   b. Gelatinase
   c. Enterotoxin
   d. Hemolysins
   e. Coagulase

   e

188. A reliable test for distinguishing *Staph. aureus* from *Staph. epidermidis* is the:
   a. Catalase test
   b. O/F glucose test
   c. Coagulase test
   d. Clumping factor test

   c

189. *Staphylococcus* spp., which are etiologic agents of food poisoning:
   a. Are easily differentiated, morphologically, from other members of the genus *Staphylococcus*
   b. Produce a characteristic enterotoxin
   c. Are members of the enterococci group
   d. Produce a characteristic erythrogenic toxin

   b

190. What bacteriologic conditions would have to be obtained to permit the formation of botulism toxin in food? of toxin from staphylococci?

   See p. 384

191. The plasma of choice for the coagulase test is _____ _____. State reasons why.

   rabbit plasma
   See p. 384

192. Classical hot-cold lysis can be produced by:
    a. Some strains of beta hemolytic streptococci
    b. Some staphylococci cultured on sheep blood agar
    c. All staphylococci when cultured on sheep blood agar
    d. Staphylococci which produce delta toxin only   d
    e. Some staphylococci when cultured on human blood agar

193. What is the most striking difference noted between colonies of staphylococci and streptococci on blood agar?   See p. 384

194. A Gram-stained smear from an aerobic blood agar plate growth shows Gram-positive cocci grouped in tetrads and encapsulated. The organism is:
    a. *Streptococcus pneumoniae*
    b. A staphylococcus
    c. A streptococcus
    d. *Micrococcus tetragena*   d

195. Pathogenicity of staphylococci is best confirmed by:
    a. Mannitol fermentation
    b. Hemolysis and pigment production
    c. Ability to liquefy gelatin
    d. Coagulase production   d

196. A Gram-stained smear from an aerobic blood agar plate growth shows Gram-positive cocci grouped in packets of eight or more cells. The organism is probably:
    a. *Micrococcus tetragena*
    b. *Neisseria meningitidis*
    c. *Micrococcus luteus*   c
    d. *Streptococcus pneumoniae*

197 *Micrococcus tetragena* is Gram-negative.   T   F   F

198. The genus *Sarcina* is Gram-negative.   T   F   F

199. Carbuncles are caused by _____.   *Staph. aureus*

200. Name two bacteria which produce hyaluronidase.   *Staph. aureus* & group A β-hem. streptococci

201. What is the coagulase test employed for?   See p. 384

202. *Staphylococcus aureus* and *Staph. epidermidis* may cause:
    a. Suppurative processes   a
    b. Rat-bite fever
    c. Dysentery
    d. Whooping cough

203. Pigment production by staphylococci is best demonstrated by culturing on:
    a. Blood agar plates
    b. Löeffler's serum slants   b

c. Nutrient agar slants
d. TSI agar slants

THE STREPTOCOCCUS

204. The spreading factor produced by certain microorganisms is called:
    a. Fibrinolysis
    b. Coagulase
    c. Hyaluronidase   c
    d. Hyaluronic acid

205. Schultz-Charlton phenomenon refers to:
    a. Detection of streptococci antitoxin as an indication of immunity to strep throat
    b. A skin test for tularemia
    c. Demonstration of passive immunity
    d. Local blanching reaction in scarlet fever following antitoxin injection   d

206. Name the genus and species associated with the following diseases:
    a. Scarlet fever   See p. 384
    b. Septic sore throat   "
    c. Puerperal sepsis   "
    d. Rheumatic fever   "
    e. Subacute bacterial endocarditis   "

207: Growth in 6.5% salt broth and the fermentation of mannitol are tests for:
    a. Enterococci   a
    b. Alpha streptococci
    c. Microaerophilic streptococci
    d. Pneumococci

208. The factor in the streptococcus most closely related to virulence is called the:
    a. C carbohydrate
    b. D substance
    c. M protein   c
    d. P substance
    e. T protein

209. The classical hemolytic patterns produced by streptococci:
    a. Are influenced by the type of medium used for culture   a
    b. Are always constant within a given strain
    c. Are always constant within a given species
    d. Are entirely dependent on the intrinsic physiology of the organism
    e. Occur only when the organisms are grown on sheep blood agar.

210. Bacteria of the genus *Streptococcus* are divided into sero-
     groups on the basis of group specific:
     a. Lipoproteins
     b. Carbohydrates   b
     c. Proteins
     d. Phospholipids
     e. Polysaccharide-protein-phospholipid complex

211. Type of hemolytic pattern produced by most common
     Streptococcus in the mouth: _____.   alpha

212. The enzyme hyaluronidase of streptococci is:
     a. Non-antigenic
     b. Not present in tissue
     c. One of the Duran-Reynals "spreading factors"   c
     d. Of little significance

213. Lancefield's serological grouping of the streptococci is
     based on:
     a. M protein, a nucleoprotein
     b. C carbohydrate, a polysaccharide hapten   b
     c. O substance, a lipopolysaccharide
     d. Fluorescent antibody technique

214. Does hemolysis always indicate the presence of strepto-
     cocci? Explain.   See p. 384

215. What kinds of serologic classifications are employed for
     the streptococci?   See p. 384

216. In preparing blood agar plates for determining hemolytic
     patterns of streptococci:
     a. What animal species blood is recommended and why?   See p. 385
     b. What concentration of blood is recommended and
        why?   ,,
     c. What two substances found in human blood bank
        blood make it unsatisfactory for use in hemolytic
        pattern studies?   ,,

217. A streptococcus which grows from 10–45°C., in the pres-
     ence of 6.5% NaCl, and on EMB is classified as a member
     of the _____ group.   entero-
                                                                  coccus

218. What organism(s) most frequently responsible for subacute
     bacterial endocarditis, and under what conditions does this
     disease occur?   See p. 385

219. Streptococci responsible for the majority of human infec-
     tions are:
     a. Members of Lancefield group A
     b. Beta-hemolytic
     c. Usually senitive to bacitracin
     d. All of these   d
     e. None of these

220. What reaction is available to distinguish between *Streptococcus salivarius* and *Streptococcus pneumoniae*?   See p. 385

221. Fill in the appropriate organism(s) from the numbered list:

   1. *Staph. aureus*
   2. *Staph. epidermidis*
   3. *Strep. fecalis*
   4. *Strep. lactis*
   5. *Micrococcus luteus*

Catalase	Pigment	Coagulase	(grows at) 45°C.	10°C.	
—	—	—	+	+	3
+	+	+	—	—	1
—	—	—	—	—	4
+	—	—	±	±	2
+	+	—	—	—	5

222. Distinguish between "streptococci" and "staphylococci."   See p. 385

223. Microaerophilic streptococci may be alpha, beta, or gamma in type.   T   F   T

224. The alpha streptococci which are included in the enterococcus group are:
   a. *Strep. fecalis*   a
   b. *Strep. zymogenes*
   c. *Strep. durans*
   d. *Strep. liquefaciens*   d

225. According to their hemolytic properties, enterococci may be alpha, beta, or gamma in type.   T   F   T

226. All enterococci, from the serological standpoint, belong to the following Lancefield group:
   a. A
   b. B
   c. C
   d. D   d

227. All enterococci are proteolytic (i.e., they liquefy gelatin) with the exception of the following:
   a. *Strep. liquefaciens*
   b. *Strep. fecalis*   b
   c. *Strep. zymogenes*
   d. *Strep. durans*

228. Anaerobic streptococci may be alpha, beta, or gamma in type.   T   F   T

229. Enterococci, such as *Streptococcus fecalis,* are streptococcal strains isolated from:
   a. Respiratory tract
   b. Intestine   b
   c. Blood   c
   d. None of these

230. Streptococcal strains which produce no change on blood agar belong to the following type:
    a. Alpha
    b. Beta
    c. Gamma   c

231. Streptococcal strains whose colonies on defibrinated sheep blood agar are surrounded by a zone of clear, cell-free hemolysis belong to the following type:
    a. Alpha
    b. Beta   b
    c. Gamma

232. Alpha streptococci are bile-soluble.   T   F   F

233. Lancefield divided the various beta hemolytic streptococci into a number of groups on the basis of:
    a. Morphology
    b. Cultural behavior
    c. Physiological characteristics
    d. Sero-type specific C-carbohydrate   d
    e. All of these
    f. None of these

234. The pathogenic form most frequently isolated from throat cultures is:
    a. *Corynebacterium diphtheriae*
    b. Group A beta hemolytic streptococci   b
    c. *Bordetella pertussis*
    d. *Neisseria meningitidis*

235. According to Smith and Brown's classification, a streptococcus with fully hemolyzed and clear colorless zones around its colonies would belong to the following group:
    a. Alpha
    b. Beta   b
    c. Gamma

236. On defibrinated sheep blood agar plates, gamma type streptococcal colonies are surrounded by an area of:
    a. Total hemolysis
    b. Greenish coloration of medium
    c. No hemolysis   c

237. Mention at least eight organisms that may be isolated from a healthy throat.   See p. 385

238. Mention at least six organisms that may be isolated from an *infected* throat.   See p. 385

239. An acute inflammation of the skin or mucous membranes without suppuration and due to several strains of beta hemolytic streptococci is called:
    a. Erysipelas   a
    b. Furuncle
    c. Carbuncle
    d. Cellulitis

240. Subacute bacterial endocarditis (S.B.E.) is most frequently caused by:
    a. Staphylococci
    b. Green streptococci (alpha hemolytic)   b
    c. *Candida albicans*
    d. A virus

241. Most cases of hemolytic streptococcal infections in man are due to infection with Lancefield serogroups:
    a. A   a
    b. B
    c. C
    d. G

242. The beta hemolytic streptococci implicated in the etiology of glomerulonephritis and rheumatic fever belong to the following Lancefield sero-groups:
    a. A   a
    b. D
    c. G
    d. H

243. A skin test used to determine sensitivity to the erythro-genetic toxin of certain group A streptococci is called:
    a. Dick test   a
    b. Schick test
    c. Mallein test
    d. Vollmer's test

244. What is the Shick test? the Dick test? the Neufeld test?   See p. 385

245. An acute spreading inflammation of the skin and subcutaneous tissues due to infection of the lymph spaces of the corium and underlying parts by a hemolytic (Lancefield's group A) streptococcus is called:
    a. Scarlet fever
    b. Erysipelas   b
    c. Typhus fever
    d. Measles

246. Distinguish between "alpha streptococci" and "beta streptococci."   See p. 385

247. Distinguish between "alpha streptococci" and "gamma streptococci."   See p. 385

248. Group A beta streptococci are never found in urine cultures.   T   F   F

249. In the routine laboratory, aerobic gamma streptococci are more frequently encountered than either alpha or beta streptococci.   T   F   F

THE PNEUMOCOCCUS

250. Pneumococci are differentiated from other alpha hemolytic streptococci on the basis of:
    a. Carbohydrate fermentation reactions
    b. Gram stain reaction
    c. Size of colony
    d. Type of hemolysis
    e. Bile solubility

e

251. Give genus and species names of two Gram-positive and two Gram-negative organisms causing spinal meningitis.

See p. 385

252. Name a practical test which differentiates pneumococcus from the other alpha hemolytic streptococci.

See p. 385

253. What is the main basis for the virulence of the pneumococcus?

See p. 386

254. Name a microscopic and a macroscopic laboratory test for the identification of the type of a pneumococcus.

See p. 386

255. Give a reason for the fact that labor pneumonia caused by Type III S. pneumoniae results in higher mortality than that caused by other types.

See p. 386

256. *Streptococcus pneumoniae* is:
    a. A highly pathogenic organism, always clinically significant when isolated from the throat
    b. An organism of relatively low pathogenicity which occurs as a normal inhabitant of the upper respiratory tract of about half the population
    c. Usually considered clinically significant when isolated from bloody or "rusty" sputum
    d. Bile-insoluble

c

257. What is meant by "R" and "S" forms of bacterial colonies and what relation do they have to capsule formation?

See p. 386

258. Capsules are one of the factors controlling virulence because they:
    a. Cause lysis of red cells
    b. Protect the bacterium from phagocytes
    c. Make the organism mucoid
    d. Speed up invasiveness

b

259. On 10% defibrinated sheep blood agar plate:
    a. A small, circular, transparent, glistening colony, often surrounded by a greenish zone of hemolysis, with a depressed center and raised edges is suggestive of

    _____   _____.

    *Strepto-
    coccus
    pneumoniae*

    b. A small to medium size, smooth, opaque, cream to gold pigmented colony, often surrounded by a zone of beta hemolysis which is fuzzy at its outer edge is suggestive of _____ _____.

   Staphylo-
   coccus
   aureus

  c. A small, circular, translucent colony surrounded by
     a wide, well-defined zine of beta hemolysis is prob-
     ably a member of the genus _____.

   Strepto-
   coccus

260. Name four genera of pathogenic bacteria which have microscopically visible capsules.

   See p. 386

261. In Gram stained smears from blood broth, pneumococci
usually resemble streptococci.   T   F

   T

262. When pneumococci are mixed with specific immune serum
there occurs, in addition to agglutination, a swelling of the
cell capsules. This swelling ("quellung") phenomenon is
the:
   a. Weil-Felix reaction
   b. Freund's reaction
   c. Neufeld's reaction
   d. Cross-reaction

   c

263. *Streptococcus pneumoniae* is also known as:
   a. *Gonococcus*
   b. *Staphylococcus*
   c. *Meningococcus*
   d. *Pneumococcus*

   d

264. *Streptococcus pneumoniae* may cause:
   a. Pneumonia
   b. Meningitis
   c. Pericarditis
   d. Endocarditis
   e. All of the above
   f. None of the above

   e

265. The most frequent etiologic agent of pneumonia in adults
is:
   a. *Hemophilus influenzae*
   b. Beta streptococci
   c. *Klebsiella-Enterobacter*
   d. *Pneumococci*

   d

266. There are 75 or more pneumococcus types. For each, the
capsular polysaccharide (SSS) is:
   a. Immunologically similar to the other types
   b. Immunologically different from the other types

   b

267. Gram-positive, lancet-shaped encapsulated diplococci in
stained direct smears of CSF could be:
   a. Staphylococci
   b. Streptococci
   c. *Cryptococcus neoformans*
   d. Pneumococci

   d

268. Pneumococci are desoxycholate-soluble, whereas other alpha streptococci are not.   T   F   **T**

269. Distinguish between pneumococci and other alpha streptococci.   See p. 386

270. Briefly describe the characteristic appearance of pneumococcus colonies on surface of defibrinated sheep blood agar plates.   See p. 386

271. Sodium lauryl sulfate is used in differentiating _____ from other alpha streptococci.   pneumococci

272. The most accurate test for the identification of pneumococci is:
    a. Bile-solubility
    b. Serologic typing (Neufeld-Quellung reaction)   **b**
    c. Optochin sensitivity
    d. Sodium lauryl sulfate

NEISSERIA

273. "Ophthalmia neonatorium":
    a. Is an inflammation of the optic nerve and is generally caused by a staphylococcus
    b. Is an infection of the eye due to *N. gonorrhoeae*   **b**
    c. Is caused by the Morax-Axenfeld bacillus and generally infects the conjunctiva
    d. Can be effectively treated with neomycin

274. In picking from G.C. medium (Difco), successful pure subcultures are obtained by:
    a. Picking colonies that are translucent, sometimes with undulant margins, which closely resemble oxidase-positive colony morphology observed on another part of the plate   **a**
    b. Picking colonies which have already turned black
    c. Picking colonies which are opaque white
    d. Using a loop to pick with and inoculating a sample from each type of peroxidase-positive colony all onto a single nutrient agar slant
    e. Inoculating on a nutrient agar slant from a peroxidase positive colony which is still in the "pink" stage

275. Gram-negative cocci include the genus:
    a. *Micrococcus*
    b. *Neisseria*   **b**
    c. *Sarcina*
    d. *Aerococcus*

276. _____ basal medium is the one recommended for determining sugar fermentation reactions of gonococcus and meningococcus.   C.T.A.

277. The gonococcus and meningococcus can best be differentiated by their:
    a. Fermentation of dextrose and lactose
    b. Fermentation of dextrose and maltose   b
    c. Fermentation of maltose and lactose
    d. Fermentation of maltose and sucrose

278. Give two characteristics which differentiate *Mimae* from *N. gonorrhoeae*. See p. 386

279. Preseumptive identification of *N. gonorrhoeae*, based only upon finding oxidase-positive colonies is subject to a high rate of false-positive diagnosis. Name two other organisms which might be mistaken for gonorrheae upon this basis alone.

Micro-
    coccus
luteus &
Mimea
polymorpha
var. oxidans

280. What two general criteria must be fulfilled for the positive diagnosis of gonorrhea? See p. 386

281. If a Neisseria were isolated from the blood, how would you determine whether it is *N. meningitidis* or *N. gonorrhoeae*? See p. 386

282. The oxidase test on colonies containing Gram-negative diplococci, if positive, will identify:
    a. Neisseria as a group   a
    b. Only *N. gonorrhoeae*
    c. Only *N. gonorrhoeae* and *N. meningitidis*
    d. *N, gonorrhoeae* but not *N. meningitidis*
    e. Certain diphtheroids normally found in the urethral tract.

283. To increase chances of detection, the specimen material submitted for the cultivation of *N. gonorrhoeae* should be:
    a. Held at room temperature for 24 hours before inoculation
    b. Mailed into a central laboratory for initial inoculations
    c. Allowed to dry out before inoculation
    d. Held at 37°C. (incubation temperature) for 72 hours
    e. Inoculated directly onto the surface of Thayer-Martin medium contained in a Transgrow transport bottle.   e

284. A report of *N. gonorrhoeae* present depends upon the finding of:
    a. Gram-negative diplococci intracellularly in exudates
    b. Oxidase-positive colonies in culture
    c. A pure culture of Gram-negative diplococci which produce biochemical reactions typical of *N. gonorrhoeae*   c
    d. Coagulase-positive micrococci

    e. Diplococci which produce beta hemolysis on medium containing rabbit blood

285. Name the three most common etiologic agents of meningitis.

N. meningitidis
H. influenzae
S. pneumoniae

286. Epidemic cerebrospinal meningitis is caused by _____ _____. Laboratory diagnosis of this disease is based upon_____
_____.

See p. 386

287. Characterize the genus *Neisseria*.

See p. 386

288. Give the scientific names of three Gram-negative diplococci which may be found in the nasopharynx.

Branhella catarrhalis
Neisseria meningitidis
N. sicca

289. The medium of choice for isolation of *N. gonorrhoeae* is prepared from _____ base medium and enriched with _____ and _____. Selectivity is enhanced by the addition of the antimicrobials _____, _____, and _____. Spreading colonies of *Proteus* may be controlled with the addition of _____ _____.

GC
supplement B
& hemoglobin;
vancomycin,
colistimethane
& nystatin;
tri-methaprime
lactate

290. Gonococcal bacteremia occurs more frequently than meningococcemia. T F

F

291. A *Neisseria* species isolated from joint fluid is likely to be:
    a. *Neisseria meningitidis*
    b. *Neisseria sicca*
    c. *Neisseria flavescens*
    d. *Neisseria gonorrhoeae*

d

292. Indicate sugar fermentation:

	Dextrose	Maltose	Lactose	Sucrose
N. gonorrhoeae	+	—	—	—
N. meningitidis	+	+	—	—
B. catarrhalis	—	—	—	—
N. sicca	+	+	—	—

293. What test is used for the presumptive identification of the genus *Neisseria*?

Oxidase test on Thayer-Martin

294. The genus *Neisseria* requires moisture for growth. T F

T

295. Indicate a suitable medium for the transport of *Neisseria gonorrhoeae* and *Neisseria meningitidis*:

    a. Tinsdale's
    b. Lester-Martin's Transgrow   b
    c. Löeffler's blood serum
    d. Thayer-Martin

296. Which of the following *Neisseria* will grow on simple, un-
enriched media:
    a. *Neisseria gonorrhoeae*
    b. *Neisseria meningitidis*
    c. *Neisseria sicca*   c

297. Gram-negative, intracellular coffee bean-shaped diplococci
with the adjacent slides flattened in a stained direct smear
of CSF would be:
    a. Streptococci
    b. Staphylococci
    c. Neisseria   c
    d. Pneumococci

298. Mention at least six organisms which may be found in CSF
in infections.   See p. 386

299. Gram-stained direct smears of the sediment after centrifugation are of little value in the bacteriologic examination
of CSF.   T   F   F

300. When meningococcus colonies on solid media are sprayed
with tetramethylparaphenylenediamine hydrochloride they
rapidly turn black. This test is known as the:
    a. Catalase test
    b. Oxidase test   b
    c. Neisser's test
    d. Ascoli test

301. The commonest complication of meningococcemia is ____
_____.   meningitis

302. The portal of entry for meningococci is:
    a. Mouth
    b. Nasopharynx   b
    c. Skin
    d. Genitalia

303. Droplets may spread all of the following except:
    a. Measles
    b. Meningococcal meningitis
    c. Yellow fever   c
    d. Whooping cough
    e. Herpes simplex

304. The gonococcus is technically called:
    a. *Branhella catarrhalis*
    b. *Neisseria gonorrhoeae*   b
    c. *Neisseria sicca*
    d. *Neisseria meningitidis*
    e. *Mimea polymorpha*

305. The meningococcus is technically called:
    a. *Branhella catarrhalis*
    b. *Neisseria gonorrhoeae*
    c. *Malleomyces mallei*
    d. *Neisseria sicca*
    e. *Neisseria meningitidis*   e

306. *Neisseria gonorrhoeae* grows best when incubated:
    a. Aerobically
    b. Under 10% CO_2 b
    c. Under 10% NO
    d. Anaerobically

307. Explain why CSF must always be examined immediately.   See p. 386

308. The various species of the genus *Neisseria* are:
    a. Strict aerobes   a
    b. Strict anaerobes
    c. Facultative aerobes
    d. Facultative anaerobes

ENTEROBACTERIACEAE

309. Enteric pathogens associated with food poisoning epidemics,
    in the *Salmonella* and *Shigella* group, are:
    a. Gram-negative bacilli which will ferment glucose
       with or without gas   a
    b. Gram-positive bacilli which will ferment glucose
       with or without gas
    c. Gram-negative bacilli which will ferment lactose
       with or without gas
    d. Gram-negative bacilli which will ferment sucrose
       with or without gas

310. The preliminary identification of enterobacteriaceae is
    made by:
    a. Biochemical methods   a
    b. Serological methods
    c. Direct microscopic examination
    d. Extreme resistance to antibacterial agents

311. Why is it customary to distinguish between members of the
    Escherichia and *Enterobacter* divisions of the colon group?   See p. 386

312. Name the materials or specimens you would want for the
    following, the test or medium you would use for identifi-
    cation, and what constitutes a positive test:
    a. Typhoid fever (second week of illness)   See p. 386
    b. Typhus fever (second week of illness)   ”

313. From what sources and at what times during the course of
    typhoid fever is *Salmonella typhi* isolatable?   See p. 387

314. An enteric organism which ferments dextrose with gas,
    grows in KCN broth, does not ferment lactose or sucrose,
    and gives a negative reaction on urea agar after 24 hours
    incubation would probably be classified as:
    a. *Citrobacter*   a
    b. *Salmonella*
    c. *Shigella*
    d. *Proteus*
    e. *Pseudomonas*

315. Salmonellosis, caused by members of the *Salmonella* genus, is an illness which can be attributed to food poisoning and is universally considered to be:
    a. Of parasitic origin
    b. An intoxication
    c. A true infection
    d. Of chemical origin

c

316. The public health sanitarian is aiding in the search for the source of infection in a presumably milk-borne food epidemic of typhoid fever. The least likely specimen to be examined would be:
    a. Feces from the milker
    b. A blood culture from the milker's wife who has been ill two weeks
    c. A representative daily sample of milk
    d. Feces from a helper in the milk house

c

317. List two properties which the following have in common and one difference between them: *Salmonella typhi* and *Shigella sonnei*.

See p. 387

318. A Gram-negative curved rod, motile by single polar flagellum, capable of using inorganic nitrogen, gelatin liquified, nitrates reduced, indol produced, milk not coagulated, pathogenic, is most likely:
    a. *Proteus vulgaris*
    b. *Shigella boydii*
    c. *Salmonella cholerasuis*
    d. *Vibrio cholera*

d

319. A non-motile Gram negative rod which ferments dextrose without gas, does not ferment mannitol or produce H_2S, and is citrate positive, is most likely to be:
    a. *Salmonella typhi*
    b. *Shigella dysenteriae*
    c. *Salmonella paratyphi* A
    d. *Salmonella paratyphi* B

b

320. Name three genera of bacteria which can cause enteritic infection.

Salmonella
Shigella
Vibrio

321. A principal characteristic used in the laboratory for distinguishing intestinal pathogens from other enterobacteriaceae is:
    a. Mannitol fermentation
    b. Production of acetyl-methyl-carbinol
    c. Animal pathogenicity
    d. Rate of growth
    e. Lactose fermentation

e

322. Gram-negative, nonsporulating rods, intestinal inhabitants, ferment no carbohydrates: _____ _____.

Alcaligenes fecalis

323. How may *Klebsiella pneumoniae* be distinguished from *Escherichia coli*? See p. 387

324. Friedlander's bacillus closely resembles:
    a. Coliform bacilli
    b. *Yersinia pestis*
    c. *Corynebacterium diphtheriae*
    d. *Enterobacter aerogenes*   d

325. Differentiate between "food infection" and "food intoxication." See p. 387

326. Differentiate between "endotoxin," "exotoxin," and "enterotoxin." See p. 387

327. Name three or more genera of bacteria, resembling non-lactose fermenters, that are ordinarily non-pathogenic intestinal inhabitants in man. See p. 387

328. To what family does *Klebsiella pneumoniae* belong?   enterobacteriaceae

329. Assume you have isolated a Gram-negative, motile, lactose-negative, encapsulated rod from a stool specimen in the "S" form. After a few biochemical determinations, you observe that your culture has dissociated to the "R" form.
    a. Will the organism from "R" colonies be motile?   yes
    b. Will the organisms from "R" colonies be as virulent as the original "S" colonies were?   no
    c. Will they be able ("R" colonies) to sporulate at room temperature?   no

330. Why do typical colonies of *E. coli* have dark centers on EMB? See p. 387

331. Red colonies of SS agar indicate that the organisms have:
    a. Fermented sucrose
    b. Produced hydrogen sulphide
    c. Produced indol
    d. Fermented lactose   d
    e. Fermented salicin

332. In a search for carriers of *Salmonella typhi,* the plating medium of choice is:
    a. SS
    b. BS   b
    c. BG
    d. EMB
    e. DCLS

333. In a search for cases of Shigellosis, the plating media of choice are:
    a. EMB and SS   a
    b. SS and BS
    c. BG and MacConkey's and BS
    d. BG and BS
    e. BS and MacConkey's

334. Red colonies on SS agar indicate that the organisms have:
    a. Fermented sucrose
    b. Produced hydrogen sulfide
    c. Fermented lactose   c
    d. Fermented dextrose

335. One chemical constituent of the EMB medium used for
    enteric work which is not present in the EMB medium
    (Levine's) used in water analysis is:
    a. Sucrose   a
    b. Eosin
    c. Galactose
    d. Urea
    e. Lactose

336. The fermentable carbohydrate present in Selenite F enrich-
    ment medium is:
    a. Lactose   a
    b. Dextrose
    c. Mannite
    d. Salicin
    e. Sucrose

337. How can one distinguish between *S. typhi* and *Sh. dysen-
    teriae* on the basis of cultural characteristics in TSI agar?   See p. 387

338. Mannite is used in biochemical studies of suspected enteric
    pathogens in order to:
    a. Determine indol production
    b. To test for the presence of the enzyme urease
    c. Exclude possible Shigella-like organisms as non-
        pathogens
    d. Classify possible salmonellas tentatively into
        smaller groups and exclude or confirm possible
        shigellas
    e. Confirm or eliminate salmonella-like organisms
        and to subdivide shigella into smaller groups   e

339. Members of the shigella group react to produce an alkaline
    slant and acid butt when grown on T.S.I. medium because
    they ferment:
    a. Sucrose
    b. Lactose
    c. Glucose   c
    d. Salicin
    e. Sorbitol

340. A pure culture of a Gram-negative bacillus isolated from a
    stool specimen may be excluded from further study as an
    enteric pathogen when after 24 hours incubation at 37°C.
    it ferments:
    a. Mannitol
    b. Glucose
    c. Sucrose   c

      d. Mannite
      e. Dextrose

341. A typical aerogenic *Salmonella* strain, grown on TSI medium, will show:
      a. Alkaline slant, acid butt, no gas, H_2S
      b. Alkaline slant, alkaline butt, no H_2S
      c. Acid slant, acid butt, gas, H_2S
      d. Alkaline slant, acid butt, gas, H_2S d
      e. Acid slant, alkaline butt, gas, H_2S

342. A pure culture of a Gram-negative bacillus isolated from a food infection specimen may be excluded from further study as an enteric pathogen when after 24 hours incubation at 37°C. it ferments:
      a. Mannitol
      b. Glucose
      c. Sucrose   c
      d. Dextrose

343. A typical aerogenic *Salmonella* strain grown on Russell's double sugar agar will show:
      a. Alkaline slant, acid butt, no gas   a
      b. Alkaline slant, alkaline butt, no gas
      c. Alkaline slant, acid butt, gas
      d. Acid slant, alkaline butt, gas

344. Which one of the following reactions will be produced by *Shigella dysenteriae* in a slant of TSI:
      a. Neutral or alkaline butt, acid slant
      b. Acid butt, neutral or alkaline slant   b
      c. Acid and gas in both the butt and the slant
      d. Acid and gas in the butt, neutral or alkaline slant

345. All members of the family Enterobacteriaceae ferment:
      a. Lactose
      b. Dulcitol
      c. Glucose   c
      d. Sucrose
      e. Mannitol

346. Fill in the appropriate organisms from the numbers listed:

	RDS	Urea	Motility	H_2S	
——	Alk/A	−	−	−	5
——	Alk/Alk	+	−	−	3
——	Alk/AG	+	+	+	4
——	Alk/AG	−	+	+	2
——	A/A	−	+	−	1

        1. Coliform
        2. *Salmonella*
        3. *Alcaligenes*
        4. *Proteus*
        5. *Shigella*

347. *E. aerogenes* does not produce acid, which is the reason
for the negative MR test.   T   F   F

348. The negative reaction produced by *Shigella* in Falkow ly-
sine broth is a result of the following:
    a. Production of acid from the fermentation of glucose
       and lack of production of cadaverine due to the ab-
       sence of the enzyme lysine decarboxylase   a
    b. Decarboxylation of lysine to cadaverine and the pro-
       duction of acid from the fermentation of glucose
    c. Deamination of lysine to cadaverine and the produc-
       tion of acid from the fermentation of glucose
    d. Production of acid from the fermentation of lactose
       and lack of production of cadaverine due to the ab-
       sence of the enzyme lysine decarboxylase
    e. Decarboxylation of lysine to cadaverine and produc-
       tion of acid from the fermentation of lactose

349. The urea in Christensen's agar is hydrolyzed in three hours
at 37°C. by:
    a. *Salmonella typhi*
    b. *Salmonella boydii*
    c. *Shigella flexneri*
    d. *Proteus vulgaris*   d
    e. *Salmonella enteritidis* var. enteritidis

350. The organisms, isolated from stool specimens, which may
be excluded from further study as possible enteric pathogens by a positive reaction on urea are:
    a. *Arizona paracoli* and *E. coli*
    b. Providence group
    c. *Strep. fecalis*
    d. *Alcaligenes fecalis*
    e. Bethesda-Ballerup and Proteus groups   e

351. The production of phenylpyruvic acid from phenylalanine
is useful in the identification of:
    a. *Klebsiella pneumoniae*
    b. *Klebsiella ozaenae*
    c. *Salmonella*
    d. *Providence*   d
    e. *Escherichia coli*

352. *Salmonella typhi* is the only member of the *Salmonella*
group D that:
    a. Contains flagellar d antigen   a
    b. Ferments glucose with the production of gas
    c. Forms indol
    d. Will grow on Simmon's citrate agar
    e. Ferments lactose without producing gas

353. In the grouping of *Shigella* organisms, agglutination by
group C antiserum indicates that species is:
    a. *Dysenteriae*

b. *Alkalescens*
c. *Boydii*   c
d. *Flexneri*
e. *Sonnei*

354. Both the *Salmonella* and *Escherichia* have certain antigens
in common with:
  a. *Arizona*   a
  b. *Proteus*
  c. *Corynebacteria*
  d. *Shigella*
  e. *Mycobacteria*

355. What information can you give for the antigenic formula
of *S. typhi,* which is IX, XII, Vi; d; —?   See p. 387

356. How can you explain the fact that the serum from a patient suffering from typhoid fever agglutinates both *S. typhi*
and *S. paratyphi* B antigens to a high titer?   See p. 387

357. "If the freshly isolated culture agglutinates with anti-Vi
serum but fails to do so with *Salmonella* polyvalent antiserum and upon being boiled agglutinates with group D
antiserum but fails to do so with anti-Vi antiserum, a diagnosis of typhoid fever is to be made." Justify this statement.   See p. 387

358. *Escherichia coli* serotypes associated with infantile diarrhea number:
  a.   3
  b.   11   b
  c.   47
  d. 130

359. What single biochemical test best differentiates *Proteus*
from *Salmonella* and *Shigella*?   urease

360. *Salmonella* and *Shigella* are always urease-negative.
     T   F   T

361. The abbreviation IMViC stands for _____
_____.   See p. 387

362. Fill out:

Organism	Indol	Methyl Red	Voges-Proskauer	Citrate
E. coli	+	+	—	—
Enterobacter aerogenes	—	—	+	+

363. The production of acetylmethylcarbinol from dextrose
constitutes the basis for the following test:
  a. Neufeld-Quellung
  b. Cholera red
  c. Voges-Proskauer   c
  d. Oxidase

364. What do the following standard abbreviations stand for:
    a. IMViC; BBL; EMB; SS   See p. 388
    b. BS; PPD; VP   "
    c. SIM; TSI; MLD; GC   "
    d. M colony; S colony; R colony; AFB   "

365. On the basis of the IMViC reaction, the members of the
    coliform group of bacteria may be divided into three bio-
    chemical types which are known as:
    a. _____   See p. 388
    b. _____   "
    c. _____   "

366. Sodium citrate is utilized by *Escherichia coli* as the only
    source of carbon.   T   F   F

367. Using Simmons citrate agar slants, a positive test, showing
    alkaline reaction and utilization of citrate, would be indi-
    cated by the following color:
    a. Orange
    b. Yellow
    c. Red
    d. Blue   d

368. Sodium citrate is utilized by nonfecal organisms (such as
    Enterobacter aerogenes) as the only source of carbon.
    T   F   T

369. The genus *Alcaligenes* is composed of those Gram-negative
    intestinal bacilli which:
    a. Ferment carbohydrates
    b. Fail to ferment carbohydrates   b

370. The indicator employed in TSI agar and urease test medium
    is:
    a. Phenol red   a
    b. Bromcresol purple
    c. Bromthymol blue

371. Triple sugar iron (TSI) agar containing 1% lactose, 1%
    sucrose, 0.1% glucose, and _____   ferrous ammo-
    _____ is used to demonstrate H₂S production.   nium sulfate

372. The use of TSI agar and urease test medium is sufficient to
    identify the various genera of enterobacteriaceae.   T   F   F

373. A single tube differential medium, employed for the iden-
    tification of enteric pathogens and serving as an indicator
    of lactose, sucrose, and glucose fermentation as well as
    H₂S production is:
    a. Triple sugar agar
    b. Triple sugar-iron (TSI) agar   b
    c. Russell's double sugar (RDS)
    d. Kligler's iron agar (KIA)

374. Enteric pathogens (*Shigella-Salmonella*) are most easily
    differentiated from normal intestinal Gram-negative rods

by their failure to ferment:
  a. Glucose
  b. Mannitol
  c. Xylose
  d. Lactose   d

375. *Protus, Alcaligenes, Pseudomonas,* and *Providencia*
  bacilli ferment lactose.   T   F   F

376. TSI agar tubes should be closed with a tight-fitting stopper
  or screw cap.   T   F   F

377. *Shigella sonnei* ferment lactose:
  a. Rapidly
  b. Slowly   b

378. Certain strains of *E. coli,* previously designated as Alka-
  lescens-Dispar and *Shigella sonnei:*
  a. Ferment lactose rapidly
  b. Ferment lactose slowly   b
  c. Do not ferment lactose

379. A single tube differential medium, employed for the identification of enteric pathogens, and serving as an indicator
  of lactose and glucose fermentations as well as H_2S production is:
  a. Triple sugar agar
  b. Glucose phosphate
  c. Lactose-glucose-iron agar   c
  d. Koser citrate

380. A single tube differential medium, employed for the identification of enteric pathogens, and serving as an indicator
  of lactose, sucrose, and glucose fermentation but not H_2S
  production is:
  a. Triple sugar agar   a
  b. Triple sugar-iron agar
  c. Glucose-phosphate
  d. Lactose-glucose-iron agar

381. On EMB agar the colonies of *Alcaligenes fecalis* resemble
  those of:
  a. Enteric group   a
  b. Coliform group
  c. Staphylococci
  d. Enterococcus group

382. Indicate at least two suitable media for the isolation of
  the various strains of *Escherichia coli.*   EMB; Mac-
                                                                Conkey;
                                                                sorbitol
                                                                agar

383. On desoxycholate, desoxycholate-citrate, EMB, SS, and
  MacConkey agar the members of the Shigella-Salmonella
  group produce small colonies which are:

a. Black
b. Green
c. Pink
d. Colorless   d

384. In desoxycholate-citrate agar (a selective medium for the enteric pathogens), the purpose of the ferric ammonium citrate is to inhibit the growth of:
   a. The Gram-positive organisms
   b. *Escherichia coli* and other Gram-negative rods that predominate in the normal intestine   b

385. For the isolation of *Salmonella typhi* the best single medi-ium is:
   a. Eosin-methylene blue (EMB) agar
   b. Endo
   c. Bismuth-sulfite (BS) agar (Wilson-Blair medium) c   c
   d. MacConkey agar

386. When a stool specimen is best inoculated into an enrich-ment medium (such as selenite-F or tetrathionate broth) it must be subcultured within:
   a. 18–24 hours   a
   b. 24–36 hours
   c. 36–48 hours
   d. 48–72 hours

387. Classify as: Enrichment medium (1), differential medium (2), selective medium (3):
   a. Selenite-F broth   1
   b. Blood agar   1
   c. Desoxycholate, Endo, EMB, MacConkey   2
   d. Desoxycholate-citrate, SS, BS   3
   e. Bacto tryptose   1
   f. Bacto tryptose with thionin   2
   g. Bacto tryptose with fuchsin   2
   h. Brain heart infusion (BH) agar   1
   i. Kligler iron agar   2
   j. Dextrose cystine agar   1
   k. Blood tellurite agar   3

388. On BS agar the colonies of *Salmonella typhi* are charac-teristically:
   a. Pink
   b. Black with metallic silver sheen   b
   c. Green
   d. Colorless

389. *Escherichia coli* is never pathogenic.   T   F   F

390. It is possible to differentiate between the various members of the group of intestinal Gram-negative rods on the basis of:
   a. Blood agar plate growth
   b. Morphology on smears

    c. Both of these

    d. None of these   d

391. Name at least eight organisms which may be isolated from the urine in infections. See p. 388

392. Name at least six organisms which may be present in normal urine. See p. 388

393. Briefly describe appearance of *Klebsiella* colonies. See p. 388

394. Typhoid fever organisms disappear from the blood after two weeks.   T   F   T

395. The commonest cause of urinary tract infection is:
    a. Streptococci
    b. Staphylococci
    c. Coliforms   c
    d. Diphtheroids

396. Asiatic cholera is caused by:
    a. *Streptococcus pneumoniae*
    b. *Vibrio cholera*   b
    c. *Spirillum minus*
    d. *Listeria monocytogenes*

397. *Klebsiella pneumoniae* may cause:
    a. Diphtheria
    b. Meningitis
    c. Subacute endocarditis
    d. Respiratory tract infection   d

398. *Klebsiella pneumoniae* is also known as:
    a. Klebs-Loeffler bacillus
    b. Friedlander's bacillus   b
    c. Koch-Weeks bacillus
    d. Morgan.s bacillus

399. Which species of *Shigella* produces a powerful endotoxin?   *S. dysenteriae*

400. The first species of *Salmonella* to be linked to food infection was:
    a. *Salmonella typhimurium*
    b. *Salmonella enteritidis*   b
    c. *Salmonella schottmuelleri*
    d. None of these

401. *Salmonella schottmuelleri* is also known as:
    a. *Salmonella paratyphi* A
    b. *Salmonella paratyphi* B   b
    c. Typhoid bacillus
    d. *Salmonella paratyphi* C

402. The organism usually encountered in positive bile cultures is:
    a. *Streptococcus hemolyticus*
    b. *Salmonella typhi*   b
    c. *Streptococcus pneumoniae*
    d. *Myobacterium tuberculosis*

403. Oysters bred in polluted water may be infected with:
    a. *Entamoeba histolytica*
    b. Botulinus bacilli
    c. Typhoid bacilli   c
    d. Typhus rickettsiae

404. Coliform bacteria are never pathogenic.   T   F   F

405. Cholera is spread primarily through polluted water.   T   F   T

406. Bacillary dysentery is an infectious disease caused by organ-
    isms of the following group:
    a. *Proteus*
    b. *Salmonella*
    c. *Shigella*   c
    d. *Providencia*

407. Plate growth of enteropathogenic *Escherichia coli* strains
    may sometimes be detected by the odor.   T   F   T

408. The spreading of *Proteus* may be inhibited by:
    a. Lactic acid
    b. 95% ethyl alcohol   b
    c. Glycerin
    d. Sodium chloride

409. Capsules occur more frequently in *Enterobacter* than in
    Escherichia.   T   F   T

410. In *Escherichia* capsules occur:
    a. Frequently
    b. Rarely   b
    c. Never

411. It is difficult to detect the presence of enteric pathogens in
    a stool specimen when the number of organisms present is
    small.   T   F   T

412. The growth of *Proteus* species on the surface of most solid
    media can easily be differentiated from that of any other
    organisms by its characteristic:
    a. Hemolysis
    b. Spreading   b
    c. Color
    d. Thinness

413. Voges-Proskauer tests for production of _____   acetylmethyl-
    _____ from _____.   carbinol; dex-
                                                                trose

414. Distinguish between *Escherichia* and *Enterobacter*.   See p. 388

415. A simple medium, used in the performance of the Methyl
    Red and Voges-Proskauer tests, is:
    a. Triple sugar agar
    b. Triple sugar-iron agar
    c. Glucose-phosphate   c

      d. Lactose-glucose-iron agar
      e. Koser citrate

416. A differential tube medium employed as an aid in the identification of *Escherichia coli* and *Enterobacter aerogenes* is:
      a. Triple sugar agar
      b. Triple sugar-iron agar
      c. Glucose-phosphate
      d. Lactose-glucose-iron agar
      e. Koser or Simmon's citrate   e

417. The basis of the Methyl Red test, used in differentiating
Escherichia coli from *Enterobacter aerogenes,* is the production of:
      a. Citric acid
      b. A high acidity   b
      c. Acetylmethylcarbinol
      d. Hydrogen sulfide

418. Distinguish between *Enterobacter* and *Klebsiella.*   See p. 388

419. *Vibrio cholerae* is also called:
      a. *Borrelia muris*
      b. *Vibrio comma*   b
      c. Pneumococcus
      d. *Bacterium monocytogenes*

420. Stool cultures for *S. typhi* are of great value during the
early stages of typhoid fever.   T   F   F

PSEUDOMONAS

421. Pseudomonadaceae are distinguished from Achromobac-
teriaceae on the basis of:
      a. Flagellation
      b. Pigment production   b
      c. Temperatures of growth
      d. Gram stain

422. On solid media Flavobacterium (a nonmotile Gram-negative bacillus which ferments no sugars) produces a pigment
which possesses the following color:
      a. Brown
      b. Yellow   b
      c. Red
      d. Blue

423. The "blue pus" organism is technically called:
      a. *Serratia marcescens*
      b. *Proteus mirabilis*
      c. *Proteus vulgaris*
      d. *Pseudomonas aeruginosa*   d

424. On the surface of blood agar plates the colonies of *Pseudomonas aeruginosa* may be recognized by their appearance

and by their:
  a. Typical burned gunpowder odor
  b. Characteristic grape-soda odor   b

MYCOBACTERIA

425. Into what four groups has Runyon classified the acid-fast
  bacilli other than *M. tuberculosis?* On what basis were these
  four groups established?   See p. 388

426. _____ is the only organism found in the   *M. tubercu-*
  sputum which will produce large amounts of niacin in the   *losis*
  Konno (or niacin) test.

427. The finding of a single acid-fast bacillus in a smear should
  be reported:
  a. Positive
  b. Negative
  c. As suspicious, needing further investigation   c
  d. As "insignificant number of AFB present"

428. The N-acetyl-L-cysteine component of the NALC-NaOH
  reagent for the treatment of sputum specimens prior to
  culture has the function of:
  a. Killing mold contaminants
  b. Decontamination of the specimen permitting use of
     less concentrated NaOH for digestion
  c. Liquefaction of mucus   c
  d. Detoxifying NaOH

429. The standards for the photochromogenicity test are: "Expose the young, actively growing culture to a ____ watt   60 watt
  lamp for ____ minutes at a distance of ____ cm. Then re-   60 min.; 60 cm.
  incubate for ____ hours to allow development of new cells 24 hrs.
  that will show the color."

430. The Von Pirquet skin test is for:
  a. Tuberculosis   a
  b. Scarlet fever
  c. Diphtheria
  d. Brucellosis

431. *Mycobacterium leprae* is synonymous with:
  a. Hoffman's bacillus
  b. Hansen's bacillus   b
  c. Klebs-Loeffler bacillus
  d. Morax-Axenfeld bacillus

432. *M. smegmatis* is non-pathogenic.   T   F   T

433. Acid-fast, Gram-positive, nonsporulating thin rods; some
  are pathogenic: _____.   *Mycobac-*
                                                             terium

434. One of the digesting reagents used for the concentration of
  the tubercle bacillus in sputum contains:

a. Bromthymol blue
b. Sodium hydroxide   b
c. Potassium alum
d. All of the above

435. *Mycobacterium leprae* are included with the mycobacteria
because:
    a. Of their acid-fast staining characteristics and their
      morphological resemblance to the tubercle bacilli   a
    b. They are motile and produce spores
    c. Both *Mycobacterium tuberculosis* and *M. leprae* were
      discovered by Hansen
    d. All of the above

436. The acid-fast property of tubercle bacilli is due to:
    a. The presence of a waxy or lipoid substance   a
    b. Their presence in "caseous particles"
    c. Both of the above
    d. Neither of the above

437. The most optimum atmosphere for incubation of mycobacteria can be achieved by:
    a. Enclosing cultures in mylar bags and then in poly-
      ethylene bags and introducing a mixture of CO_2 in
      air into the polyethylene bag
    b. Enclosing cultures in polyethylene bags and then in
      mylar bags and introducing a mixture of CO_2 in air
      into the mylar bag   b
    c. Enclosing cultures in either polyethylene bags or
      mylar bags and introducing CO_2
    d. Incubation in a candle jar

438. The Adansonian system of classification of mycobacteria
is based on:
    a. A statistical analysis of the reactions of a large
      number of strains to many tests   a
    b. Niacin, tween hydrolysis, nitrate reduction, and
      semiquantitative catalase tests
    c. Pigment and rate of growth
    d. Cellular and colony morphology, acid-fastness,
      photochromogenicity, rate of growth, and niacin
      production

439. Name three saprophytic species in the genus *Mycobacterium.* | *M. smegmatis*
M. phlei
M. fortuitum

440. Tubercle bacilli producing a brittle, dry, granular, thick,
yellowish growth with a wrinkled surface belong to the
type:
    a. Hominis
    b. Bovine
    c. Avian
    d. Atypical   d

441. Concentration methods for acid-fast bacilli include:
    a. Digestion of mucous with alkali
    b. Digestion with bleach
    c. Centrifugation
    d. All of the above   d

442. The bovine tubercle bacilli are:
    a. Shorter than the human bacilli
    b. Pathogenic for man
    c. Slow growing
    d. All of the above   d

443. Sputum specimens should be collected in a sterile glass jar containing no preservatives because:
    a. These substances dissolve out the tubercle cells
    b. These substances are frequently inhibitory to growth of tubercle bacilli   b
    c. These substances are injurious to the media used
    d. All of the above

444. *Mycobacterium tuberculosis* stains readily with:
    a. Gram's stain
    b. Papanicolaou stain
    c. Ziehl-Neelsen stain   c
    d. Wayson's stain

445. The mycobacteria are acid-fast because:
    a. They are easily stained
    b. Once stained they are not decolorized by acid   b
    c. They cannot be stained with acids
    d. None of the above

446. *Mycobacterium leprae:*
    a. Occurs singly
    b. Is found within the endothelial cells of blood vessels or in mononuclear cells
    c. Has a tendency to occur in clumps or packets   c
    d. All of the above

447. The skin form of tuberculosis is:
    a. Miliary tuberculosis
    b. Lupus vulgaris   b
    c. Mesenteric tuberculosis
    d. The "Gohn" complex

448. The concentrates of treated sputum specimens containing *M. tuberculosis* are "washed" in order to:
    a. Remove the chemical used in pre-treatment to avoid killing *M. tuberculosis* by too long contact   a
    b. Remove contaminants and cellular debris
    c. Neutralize the acidity or alkalinity of the sediment
    d. Remove toxic pH indicators
    e. Prevent killing of animals by inoculation of acid suspensions.

449. Treatment of sputum specimens with "caroid":
    a. Dissolves the mucus but does not kill contaminants   a
    b. Kills contaminants but not *M. tuberculosis*
    c. Kills both contaminants and *M. tuberculosis*
    d. Dilutes out contaminants
    e. Is preferred when animals are to be inoculated

450. Any medium used for the isolation of *M. tuberculosis* must
    contain:
    a. Whole eggs
    b. Potato flour
    c. Asparagine   c
    d. Milk
    e. Malachite green

451. In the primary isolation of *M. tuberculosis,* the use of
    glycerine in the medium tends to enhance the growth of
    human strains which show the characteristic colonies of a:
    a. Dysgonic culture
    b. Eugonic culture   b
    c. Pathogenic culture
    e. Eugenic culture

452. The common disadvantage of the direct smear and culture
    methods in the diagnosis of tuberculosis is that they:
    a. May be complicated by overgrowth of contaminants
    b. Fail to distinguish bovine from mammalian types
    c. Do not distinguish pathogenic from nonpathogenic
       organisms   c
    d. Are very time-consuming
    e. Are very expensive laboratory procedures

453. The typical cord formation in colonies of virulent *M. tuber-
    culosis* is most readily observed in:
    a. Petragnani's medium
    b. Loeffler's medium
    c. Human blood agar medium
    d. Dubos' oleic-albumin medium   d
    e. Brain heart infusion agar

454. List two advantages of using Middlebrook's 7H10 medium
    in tuberculosis work.   See p. 388

455. Where is serpentine cord formation best observed?   See p. 388

456. Distinguish between "acid-fast organisms" and nonacid-
    fast organisms."   See p. 388

457. When an acid-fast bacillus fails to produce lesions in a
    guinea pig it can safely be concluded that the organism is
    not pathogenic.   T   F   F

458. INH-resistant human tubercle bacilli are often:
    a. Catalase-positive
    b. Catalase-negative   b

459. Pathogenic tubercle bacilli are morphologically similar to nonpathogenic species of *Mycobacterium*.   T   F   T

460. Before discarding a culture as negative for *Mycobacterium tuberculosis*, it should be incubated and examined every week for at least:
  a. 2 weeks
  b. 1 month
  c. 2 months   c
  d. 4 months

461. Malachite green is usually added to media for the cultivation of *Mycobacterium tuberculosis* in order to:
  a. Show a pH charge
  b. Confer a particular color to these media
  c. Speed up growth of tubercle bacilli
  d. Prevent growth of contaminating organisms   d

462. A strong acid or alkaline (such as 4% NaOH) solution will not kill the majority of tubercle bacilli but is likely to destroy all other bacteria that may be present in a given clinical specimen.   T   F   T

463. *Mycobacterium leprae* will not multiply on bacteriological culture medium.   T   F   T

464. Acid-fast bacilli are rarely found, in cases of tuberculous meningitis, in stained direct smears of CSF sediment.   T   F   T

465. Indicate advantage of Kinyoun's method over Ziehl-Neelsen method of acid-fast staining.   former requires no heat

466. What group of organisms is Kinyoun's stain used for?   acid-fast bacilli

467. Which of the following are acid-fast?
  a. *Hemophilus influenzae*
  b. *Mycobacterium tuberculosis*   b
  c. *Francisella tularensis*
  d. *Mycobacterium leprae*   d

468. Tubercle bacilli may be present in gastric contents (or gastric washings) in cases of pulmonary tuberculosis.   T   F   T

469. Indicate a suitable medium for the cultivation of *Mycobacterium tuberculosis*:
  a. 7H10   a
  b. Petragnani's   b
  c. Dubos oleic acid   c
  d. Lowenstein-Jensen   d

470. What two organisms of unrelated genera require glycerol?   *Bordetella pertussis & Mycobacterium tuberculosis*

471. Describe in detail the examination of a specimen of spinal
fluid for the presence of the tubercle bacillus.   See p. 388

472. What is the Gaffky scale?   See p. 388

473. *Mycobacterium tuberculosis* and *Mycobacterium leprae*
belong in the following Class:
    a. Eubacteriales
    b. Actinomycetales   b
    c. Spirochetales
    d. Rickettsiales

474. Leprosy is an infectious disease.   T   F   T

475. Hansen's disease is caused by:
    a. *Corynebacterium hoffmani*
    b. *Mycobacterium leprae*   b
    c. *Clostridium septicum*
    d. *Hemophilus pertussis*

476. What is the BCG vaccine?   See p. 389

477. All of the following have been used for the prevention and
treatment of tuberculosis except:
    a. Widal test   a
    b. Tuberculin test
    c. Milk pasteurization
    d. BCG vaccine

478. All of the following may be spread by droplet infection
except:
    a. Tuberculosis
    b. Pneumonia
    c. Typhus   c
    d. Whooping cough

479. In the following list, indicate bacterial diseases of animals:
    a. Tuberculosis   e. Rabies   a
    b. Syphilis   f. Yellow fever
    c. Tularemia   g. Salmonellosis   c, g
    d. Toxoplasmosis   h. Listerellosis   h

480. Distinguish between "human tuberculosis" and "bovine
tuberculosis."   See p. 389

481. A reagent, often used for the digestion and concentration
of sputum, pus and other thick, tenacious tuberculous materials, is:
    a. Diaphane
    b. Antiformin   b
    c. Schaudinn's solution
    d. 5% formic acid.

482. What is essential, in addition to gross pathology, for a
diagnosis of tuberculosis by guinea pig inoculation?   See p. 389

483. Avirulent strains of human tubercle bacilli will take up
neutral red in alkaline aqueous medium.   T   F   F

484. How is the catalase test performed? What media cannot be used? See p. 389

485. Virulent strains of human tubercle bacilli are cord-forming. T F T

486. Human type strains of *Mycobacterium tuberculosis* are niacin-negative. T F F

487. What is the niacin test employed for? See p. 389

488. The niacin test of Konno is a virulence test. T F T

489. Four (other than animal inoculation) frequently performed virulence tests for the tubercle bacillus are:
   1. _____ serpentine cord formation
   2. _____ neutral red test
   3. _____ catalase test
   4. _____ niacin test

490. Give names of laboratory animals used in the isolation of the etiologic agents for the following:
   a. Tuberculosis guinea pig
   b. Coccidoidomycosis guinea pig & mouse
   c. Pneumonia mouse
   d. Diphtheria guinea pig & rabbit
   e. Tetanus guinea pig & mouse
   f. Botulism guinea pig & mouse

CORYNEBACTERIA, LISTERIA, ERYSIPELOTHRIX

491. Diphtheria toxin will flocculate with diphtheria antitoxin in an *in vitro* virulence test only when:
   a. Antitoxin and toxin are present in approximately equivalent concentrations as "units" a
   b. The iron concentration in the medium is in excess
   c. The serum used in the diffusion column is Difco horse serum
   d. The surface of the medium is broken before the organism is inoculated
   e. The preparation of the toxin to antitoxin is in "units" 8–1

292. The *in vitro* virulence test for *C. diphtheriae* does not require:
   a. Diphtheria antitoxin in optimal concentration
   b. Medium which facilitates the growth of *C. diphtheriae*
   c. Medium enriched with serum to facilitate diffusion of both toxin and antitoxin

    d. Pure cultures of the strain to be tested
    e. A strain known to be capable of starch utilization   e

493. In principle, all positive virulence tests for *C. diphtheriae* depend upon:
    a. The flocculation of diphtheria toxin by specific anti-toxin *in vitro*
    b. Typical "target" lesions of the skin of a guinea pig inoculated intracutaneously with a suspension of virulent organisms
    c. The presence of cherry red adrenals in a guinea pig inoculated intraperitoneally with *C. diphtheriae*
    d. The presence of diphtheria toxin in the test suspension as determined by the Ramon flocculation test
    e. Evidence of the production of diphtheria toxin identified by its reaction with specific diphtheria anti-toxin   e

494. When a single guinea pig is used for virulence tests in *C. diphtheriae*, the dose of antitoxin is administered:
    a. 24 hours after the tests are injected
    b. After the "control" set of injections is made
    c. Intracutaneously 5 hours after the test injection
    d. Before any injections are made
    e. Subcutaneously 4–5 hours after the test set of injections is made   e

495. The characteristic metachromatic bodies in *Corynebacterium diphtheriae* are called:
    a. Rideal-Walker bodies
    b. Babes-Ernst bodies   b
    c. Koch-Weeks bodies
    d. L.D. bodies

496. The final diagnosis of diphtheria is made from:
    a. Cultures
    b. Morphological characteristics
    c. Virulence test   c
    d. Serological typing

497. *C. diphtheriae* may be distinguished from other members of the genus by the fact that it:
    a. Ferments lactose and not dextrose
    b. Ferments dextrose and not saccharose   b
    c. Ferments saccharose and not dextrose
    d. Ferments both dextrose and saccharose

498. There is no biochemical difference between *C. diphtheriae* and diphtheroids.   T   F   F

499. Toxoid is used in diphtheria prophylaxis.   T   F   F

500. Symptoms of diphtheria are due to the effect of exotoxins.   T   F   T

501. *C. hoffmanni* has an unstained central segment called a "mesial septum."   T   F   T

502. *C. diphtheriae* are:
    a. Less readily decolorized in Gram stain than diphtheroids
    b. More likely to be arranged in packets than diphtheroids
    c. More pleomorphic than diphtheroids   c
    d. More frequently found in exudates from well persons than are diphtheroids
    e. Less frequently virulent than diphtheroids

503. It is essential that isolates suspected of being *C. diphtheriae* be subjected to virulence testing before a final report is sent out. What procedure is most commonly used for virulence testing?

                                                       Frobisher *in vitro* virulence test

504. *Corynebacterium diphtheriae* may:
    a. Be either toxigenic or non-toxigenic   a
    b. Hydrolyze urea and reduce nitrates
    c. Produce acid from sucrose only and be non-toxigenic
    d. Be toxigenic, fail to reduce nitrates, and hydrolyze urea

505. Which of the following is not a toxin caused disease:
    a. Botulism
    b. Tetanus
    c. Diphtheria
    d. Rabies   d

506. The definitive laboratory diagnosis of both *C. diphtheriae* and *Salmonella* species is based on:
    a. The use of group specific antiserum
    b. Carbohydrate fermentation   b
    c. Animal inoculation
    d. Characteristic morphology of organisms observed in stained smear preparations
    e. Colonial morphology on selective medium

507. Nonsporulating, Gram-positive pleomorphic rods with prominent granules, aerobic, human parasites: _____ _____,   *C. diph – theriae*

508. Reactions which are characteristic of *Listeria monocyto genes* are:
    a. Catalase-positive; motile; V-P positive; do not produce acid from mannitol
    b. Catalse-positive; non-motile; V-P positive; do not produce acid from mannitol   a
    c. Catalase-negative; motile; V-P negative; do not produce acid from mannitol
    d. Catalase-negative; motile; V-P positive; produce acid from mannitol

509. What single cultural characteristic will aid in differentiating *Listeria* from diphtheroids?

Motility (tumbling motility in cultures at 18–20°C.)

510. Vincent's angina infections may be differentiated from diphtheria infections by:
   a. Indoculating a swab onto Loeffler's medium and making a smear from the growth for organisms morphologically resembling "*B. vincenti*"
   b. By observing the presence of Gram-positive, tightly coiled spirochetes in a direct smear
   c. By the observation of an increased number of Gram-positive fusiform bacilli and polymorphonuclear leukocytes in a direct smear
   d. By the presence of diphtheroids and the absence of organisms morphologically resembling *C. diphtheriae* in a smear taken from a 24 hour Loeffler's slant, inoculated with a throat swab
   e. Observation of large numbers of *Borrelia vincenti* and fusiform bacilli in a direct smear taken before antibiotics are given

e

511. Distinguish between "diphtheria bacillus" and "diphtheroid bacilli."

See p. 389

512. What does KLB mean? What animal is KLB virulent in? How else may virulence be tested for (other than animals)?

Klebs-Loeffler bacillus; guinea pig; Ramon flocculation test or Frobisher *in vitro* test

513. Diphtheroid organisms may be pathogenic.   T   F

T

514. To carry out an *in vitro* test of virulence for diphtheria bacilli a mixed culture should be used.   T   F

F

515. State the scientific name for the following and indicate a suitable isolation medium for each:
   a. Diphtheria bacillus   e. Tubercle bacillus
   b. Tetanus bacillus   f. Gonococcus
   c. Whooping cough bacillus   g. Typhoid bacillus
   d. Paratyphoid B

See p. 389

516: Erysipeloid in man is due to infection with:
   a. *Klebsiella pneumoniae*
   b. *Spirillum minus*
   c. *Erysipelothrix rhusiopathiae*
   d. *Listeria monocytogenes*

c

517. In 1931 Anderson et al. divided diphtheria bacilli (on the basis of morphologic appearance and cultural characteristics) into three varieties called:
    a. *C. diphtheriae* var. _____   gravis
    b. *C. diphtheriae* var. _____   mitis
    c. *C. diphtheriae* var. _____   intermedius

518. Indicate media suitable for the cultural diagnosis of diphtheria:
    a. Loeffler's blood serum
    b. Tinsdale's   b
    c. Blood agar
    d. Cystine-tellurite-blood agar

519. It is impossible to make a final diagnosis of diphtheria on the basis of stained direct smears alone.   T   F   T

520. In order to confirm a presumptive laboratory diagnosis of diphtheria, what two important steps must be carried out?   See p. 389

521. A Gram-stained smear from an aerobic blood agar plate growth shows slender Gram-positive bacilli of variable length. These organisms are pleomorphic and possess a barred, granular or club-shaped appearance. They are arranged parallel to each other or in V or Y formation. The species is likely to be:
    a. *Hemophilus influenze*
    b. *Corynebacterium diphtheriae*   b
    c. *Bacillus subtilis*
    d. *Klebsiella pneumoniae*
    e. None of these

522. On tellurite medium the colonies of *Corynebacterium diphtheriae* are opaque, raised, convex, and:
    a. White
    b. Cream-colored
    c. Green
    d. Gun metal in color   d

523. The smallest amount of diphtheria toxin which, when injected subcutaneously, will kill a 250 gram guinea pig within four days is the:
    a. MLD   a
    b. L+ dose
    c. L_0 dose
    d. L_f dose

524. The smallest amount of diphtheria toxin which, when mixed with one unit of antitoxin and injected subcutaneously into a 250 gram guinea pig, will produce death within four days is the:
    a. L_f dose
    b. L+ dose   b
    c. L_0 dose
    d. MLD

525. To confirm a laboratory diagnosis of diphtheria it is essential to:
    a. Grow characteristic colonies in special media
    b. Find typical granular staining bacilli in smears

c. Demonstrate toxin production   c
d. Study biochemical behavior

526. Distinguish between "endotoxin" and "exotoxin."   See p. 389

527. Distinguish between "toxin" and "toxoid."   See p. 390

528. Fill out the following chart:

	Endotoxins	Exotoxins
Method of Production		
Toxicity		
Specificity		
Antigenic Properties		
Thermal Behavior		
Effect of Treatment with Formalin		

See p. 390

BRUCELLA, PASTEURELLA, YERSINIA, FRANCISELLA

529. *Francisella tularensis* is essentially a parasite of rodents transmitted by:
  a. The fly, Chrysops
  b. The tick, Dermacentor
  c. The rabbit louse   c
  d. All of the above

530. Specimens most generally submitted to lab for culture when suspecting tularemia include:
  a. Repeated blood cultures
  b. Sputum   b
  c. Urine
  d. All of these

531. A selective medium for *Francisella tularensis* is:
  a. Blood glucose cystine agar   a
  b. Cystine tellurite blood agar
  c. Desoxycholate citrate, lactose, sucrose agar
  d. Castanada media

532. Tularemia resembles the bubonic plague in:
  a. Development of ulcerated lymph nodes   a
  b. Development of hemorrhages under the skin which turn black
  c. Its high rate of mortality
  d. All of the above

533. Tularemia can be transmitted to man from rabbits. T F   T

534. *F. tularensis* will not grow on nutrient agar.   T   F   T

535. Tularemia is primarily a human infection.   T   F   F

536. Indicate a practical way to diagnose *Francisella tularensis*.   See p. 390

537. *Francisella tularensis* will not grow on any medium exept cystine-glucose blood agar.   T   F   T

538. Briefly explain why animal inoculation is not practical in the laboratory diagnosis of *Francisella tularensis*.   See p. 390

539. Indicate suitable medium for the cultivation of *Francisella tularensis:*
     a. Glucose-cystine agar   a
     b. Glycerin-potato-blood agar
     c. Petragnani
     d. EMB

540. One infection with *F. tularensis* confers lasting immunity.
     T   F   T

541. *Yersinia pestis* is a parasite of:
     a. Fleas
     b. Rodents   b
     c. Cattle and swine
     d. Birds

542. Cultural characteristics of *Yersinia pestis* are:
     a. Fermentation of carbohydrates
     b. Non-hemolytic on blood agar
     c. No liquefaction of Loeffler's blood serum medium
     d. All of the above

543. *Yersinia pestis* when stained shows:
     a. Metachromatic granules
     b. Bipolar staining   b
     c. Gram-positive reaction
     d. All of the above

544. *Yersinia pestis* produces a variety of diseases, including:
     a. Bubonic plague
     b. Pneumonic plague
     c. Septicemic plague
     d. All of the above   d

545. The stain which best brings out the characteristic "safety pin" appearance of *Yersinia pestis* is:
     a. Gram's stain
     b. Wright's stain
     c. Wayson's stain   c
     d. Dorner's stain

546. Non-motile, non-sporulating, pleomorphic Gram-negative rods having bipolar staining are:
     a. *Pseudomonas aeruginosa*

b. *Yersinia pestis*   b
c. *Corynebacterium diphtheriae*
d. *Brucella suis*

547. The plague bacillus is technically known as:
   a. *Yersinia pestis*   a
   b. *Pasteurella multocida*
   c. *Francisella tularensis*
   d. None of these

548. Bubonic plague is caused by a:
   a. Rickettsia
   b. Protozoan
   c. Virus
   d. Bacterium   d

549. Unbroken skin is sometimes permeable to the following
   disease agents:
   a. Tubercle bacillus   d. *Staphylococcus aureus*
   b. *Treponema pallidum*   e. Anthrax bacillus   b
   c. Plague bacillus   f. Strongyloides larvae   c, f

550. Species of pathogenic bacteria requiring an increased
   amount of CO_2 in the atmosphere of the culture are:
   a. *Brucella abortus*   a
   b. *Francisella tularensis*
   c. Both of the above
   d. Neither of the above

551. Undulant fever is contracted from milk only.   T   F   T

552. *Brucella abortus* is differentiated from the other *Brucella*
   species by:
   a. Its growth in thionine, and not in basic fuchsin
   b. Its growth in basic fuchsin, and not in thionine   b
   c. Its growth in both thionine and basic fuchsin
   d. Its growth in neither thionine nor basic fuchsin

553. *Brucella abortus* grows best in:
   a. The presence of 10% CO_2 at 37°C.
   b. Castaneda's medium
   c. Both of these   c
   d. Neither of these

554. CO_2 is required for the growth of:
   a. *Brucella melitensis*
   b. *Brucella suis*
   c. *Brucella abortus*   c
   d. All of the above

555. In brucellosis, the specimen most often producing a positive culture is:
   a. Blood   a
   b. Tissue
   c. CSF
   d. Urine

556. Malta fever is spread to man by means of goat's milk infected with:
    a. *Brucella abortus*
    b. *Brucella suis*
    c. *Brucella melitensis*   c
    d. All of these

557. Brucellergin is used:
    a. To prevent the spread of *Brucella abortus* in cows
    b. As a skin test for brucellosis in man   b
    c. To differentiate the species of *Brucella*
    d. As a most specific diagnostic aid in determining brucellosis.

558. Ruling out cross-agglutination with the *Brucella* group, a positive reaction for tularemia would be:
    a. 1:20
    b. 1:40
    c. 1:80   c
    d. 1:160

559. Match the following:

1. *Brucella suis*	a. Typically infects cattle	1. b & d
2. *Brucella melitensis*	b. Typically infects swine	2. c & d
3. *Brucella abortus*	c. Typically infects goats	3. a & d
	d. Causes undulant fever in man	

560. Pasteurization will kill any *Brucellae* that may be present in the milk.   T   F   T

561. Brucellosis is primarily a human disease.   T   F   F

562. Which *Brucella* species require 10% CO_2? What species of a different genus grow better under reduced oxygen tension?   *B. abortus; Neisseria gonorrhoeae & N. meningitidis* Also see p. 390

563. *Brucella melitensis, Brucella abortus,* and *Brucella suis* may cause:
    a. Glanders
    b. Soft chancre
    c. Relapsing fever
    d. Undulant fever   d

564. The genus *Brucella* is Gram-positive.   T   F   F

565. Trypticase soy broth may be used for the isolation of *Brucella, Pasteurella,* and leptospira from the blood.
    T   F   F

566. Indicate suitable medium for the cultivation of *Brucella abortus:*
    a. Sabouraud's agar
    b. Loeffler's blood serum
    c. Trypticase soy broth and agar   c

d. Cystine-tellurite-blood agar

567. Chart biochemical differences between species of *Brucella:*

	CO$_2$ required for growth	H$_2$S formation	Pathogenicity for guinea pigs
B. abortus			
B. melitensis			
B. suis			

See p. 390

	Growth on media with 1:25,000 basic fuchsin	Growth on media with 1:50,000 Thionin	Growth on media with 1:100,000 Pyronin
B. abortus			
B. melitensis			
B. suis			

568. State temperature and oxygen requirements for:
    a. *Brucella abortus*
    b. *Brucella melitensis*
    c. *Brucella suis*

See p. 390
       "
       "

HEMOPHILUS, BORDETELLA

569. The phenomenon of "satellitism" is illustrated by:
    a. *Staphylococcus aureus*
    b. *Hemophilus influenzae*
    c. *Bacillus megatherium*
    d. *Yersinia pestis*

b

570. The satellite phenomenon is an example of:
    a. Symbiosis
    b. Parasitism
    c. Commensalism
    d. Saprophytism

c

571. List 2 properties which the following have in common (a); and one difference between them (b):

    Hemophilus influenzae and *Neisseria meningitidis*

See p. 391

572. A Gram-negative cocco-bacillus isolated from CSF, blood, sputum, and urine which rarely grows on EMB, produces a hemolytic colony on BAP, and is often resistant to antibiotics is most likely:
    a. *Bartonella bacilliformis*
    b. *Hemophilus influenzae*
    c. *Mimea* spp.
    d. *Neisseria meningitidis*

c

573. An organism which must be isolated from a medium containing egg-yolk which produces a venereal disease in which aspirates of the inguinal nodes are found to contain Gram-negative bacillus with a distinct capsule is most likely:
   a. *Klebsiella pneumoniae*
   b. *Hemophilus ducreyi*
   c. *Donovani granuloma*   c
   d. *Neisseria gonorrheae*

574. Which of the following species of *Hemophilus* do not require both the X and V factors:
   a. *H. influenzae*
   b. Koch-Weeks bacillus
   c. *H. suis*
   d. None of the above   d

575. Why was the influenza bacillus given the generic name *Hemophilus*?   See p. 391

576. With what disease is *Hemophilus ducreyi* associated?   chancroid
                                                                  or soft
                                                                  chancre

577. What is the disease with which *Hemophilus influenzae* is most often associated?   meningitis

578. *Hemophilus ducreyi* has the following characteristics:
   a. Is the cause of a venereal disease
   b. Is an intracellular organism resembling a cigarette package
   c. Requires freshly drawn rabbit blood in the culture media
   d. All of the above   d

579. *Hemophilus influenzae* requires a media containing:
   a. X factor
   b. Y factor
   c. Both of the above   c
   d. Neither of the above

580. The satellite phenomenon works on the basis that:
   a. Beta-streptococcus supplies the X factor necessary for the growth of *H. influenzae*
   b. Staphylococcus supplies the coenzyme, BAP the X factor necessary for the growth of *Hemophilus*   b
   c. Staphylococcus supplies the hemin factor, chocolate the V factor
   d. Staphylococcus will provide all the necessary nutrients for the growth of *Hemophilus* on any type of media

581. Factor V, a heat-labile substance used in culturing certain fastidious organisms, is found in:
   a. Serum
   b. Yeast   b

      c. Hemoglobin
      d. All of these

582. Match the following organisms and their characteristic
     colonies on defibrinated sheep blood agar plates:

1. *Hemophilus hemolyticus*	a. Soft, pearly, translucent with zone of alpha hemolysis.	1—a
2. *Hemophilus influenzae*	b. Small, white, rather opaque, usually quite firm. Beta hemolysis	2—c
3. Beta streptococci	c. Small, colorless, dew-drop. No hemolysis or alpha hemolysis. Grows 1-2 days.	3—b

583. *Hemophilus influenzae* may cause respiratory tract infec-
     tions as well as:
      a. Enteric fever
      b. Food poisoning
      c. Meningitis   c
      d. Subacute infectious conjunctivitis

584. Name two members of the hemoglobinophil (grows only on
     media containing blood) group of bacteria.   *Hemophilus (influenzae, ducreyi) & Bordetella pertussis*

585. *Hemophilus hemolyticus* is pathogenic.   T   F   F

586. Epidemic influenza is due to infection with:
      a. *Hemophilus pertussis*
      b. *Klebsiella pneumoniae*
      c. *Hemophilus influenzae*
      d. None of these   d

587. Soft chancre is due to infection with:
      a. *Staphylococcus aureus*
      b. *Neisseria sicca*
      c. *Hemophilus ducreyi*   c
      d. *Moraxella lacunata*

588. Match the following:

1. *Hemophilus* of Morax-Axenfeld	a. Causes pseudomembranous conjunctivitis	1—c
2. *Corynebacterium diphtheriae*	b. Causes infectious conjunctivitis ("pink eye")	2—a
3. *Hemophilus* of Koch-Weeks	c. Causes blepharoconjunctivitis	3—b

589. The genus *Hemophilus* is Gram-negative.   T   F   T

590. *Hemophilus influenzae*, as well as other hemoglobinophils,
     will grow well on:
      a. Chocolate agar with yeast extract   a
      b. Lowenstein-Jensen medium
      c. Rabbit blood agar with yeast extract   c

d. Desoxycholate agar

591. Briefly state cultural difference(s) between *Hemophilus influenzae* (a Gram-negative bacillus) and *Bacteroides* (also a Gram-negative bacillus). See p. 391

592. The V factor (coenzyme I or II) is:
  a. Heat labile
  b. Heat stable

a

593. The Pfeiffer's bacillus is technically called:
  a. *Bordetella pertussis*
  b. *Hemophilus influenzae*
  c. *Mycobacterium leprae*
  d. *Hemophilus ducreyi*

b

594. *Bordetella pertussis* requires:
  a. K tellurite agar
  b. Blood-cystine agar
  c. Ascitic fluid agar
  d. Potato-blood-glycerol agar

d

595. *Bordetella pertussis* is also called:
  a. Bordet-Gengou bacillus
  b. Ducrey's bacillus
  c. Morgan's bacillus
  d. Koch-Weeks bacillus

a

596. Whooping cough is caused by:
  a. *H. influenzae*
  b. Friedlander's bacillus
  d. *Bordetella pertussis*
  d. Koch-Weeks bacillus

c

597. Bordet-Gengou agar base with fresh blood is used for the isolation of:
  a. *Hemophilus influenzae*
  b. *Corynebacterium diphtheriae*
  c. *Bordetella pertussis*
  d. *Listeria monocytogenes*

c

598. On infusion media *Bordetella parapertussis* produces a characteristic pigment which possesses the following color:
  a. Brown
  b. Yellow
  c. Red
  d. Blue

a

599. Morphologically, *Bordetella pertussis* is very similar to:
  a. *Proteus morgani*
  b. *Pseudomonas aeruginosa*
  c. *Klebsiella pneumoniae*
  d. *Hemophilus influenzae*

d

600. Name two species, other than *Bordetella pertussis*, which may be responsible for whooping cough.

B. parapertussis
B. brochiseptica

601. On glycerin-potato-blood agar the colonies of *Bordetella pertussis* are small and resemble:
    a. Dew drops
    b. Maple syrup droplets
    c. Mercury droplets   c
    d. None of the above

602. Indicate suitable medium for the cultivation of *Bordetella pertussis:*
    a. Loeffler's serum
    b. Glycerin-potato-blood agar   b
    c. Bordet-Gengou agar   c
    d. Corn meal agar

603. Glycerin-potato-blood agar is also called:
    a. Bordet-Gengou medium   a
    b. Petragnani's medium
    c. Loeffler's medium
    d. Sabouraud's medium

604. *Bordetella pertussis* requires factors X and V for growth
    T   F   F

CLOSTRIDIA

605. Which species of pathogenic *Clostridium* is best described by the following statement:
"This organism produces no significant local infection but general intoxication produced by a toxin so powerful that even a slight lodgement of the organism in the host tissue is dangerous. Terminal spores are usually produced which swell the vegetative cell."   *Clostridium tetani*

606. Gram-positive sporulating rods, motile, anaerobic, some are pathogenic: _____.   *Clostridium*

607. The best anaerobic conditions are obtained in an anaerobe jar through the:
    a. Replacement of the air with CO_2 and inert N_2 a
    b. Burning of a candle
    c. Replacement of the air with H_2, CO_2, and inert N_2
    d. Burning of hydrogen

608. *Cl. tetani* is readily distinguishable from other members of the *Clostridium* genus by its:
    a. Production of indol
    b. Distinctive sporulating form   b
    c. Presence in the intestine of horses
    d. All of the above

609. List two properties which the following have in common (1) and one difference between them (b):
    Clostridium tetani and *Corynebacterium diphtheriae*   See p. 391

610. Name three organisms and/or products mainly responsible for food poisoning. See p. 391

611. *Clostridium perfringens* is a normal inhabitant (constantly present in small numbers) of the human intestine.   T   F   T

612. Tetanus is caused by:
   a. *Clostridium perfringens*
   b. *Clostridium tetani*   b
   c. *Clostridium histolyticum*
   d. *Clostridium novyi*

613. Gas gangrene may be caused by:
   a. *Clostridium septicum*
   b. *Clostridium novyi*
   c. *Clostridium perfringens*
   d. *Clostridium histolyticum*
   e. All of these   e
   f. None of these

614. Food poisoning (botulism) is caused by a toxin which is produced in improperly canned or preserved foods by:
   a. *Clostridium tetani*
   b. *Clostridium botulinum*   b
   c. *Clostridium perfringens*
   d. *Clostridium histolyticum*

615. Indicate suitable medium for the cultivation of spore-forming anaerobes *(Clostridium* group), anaerobic streptococci, and *Bacteroides:*
   a. Petragnani
   b. Anaerobic blood infusion agar   b
   c. Lowenstein-Jensen
   d. Bordet-Gengou

616. *Clostridium perfringens* will grow under strict anaerobic conditions only.   T   F   F

617. Stormy fermentation of milk is due to the activity of:
   a. *Flavobacterium synxanthum*
   b. *Serratia marcescens*
   c. *Alcaligenes viscosus*
   d. *Clostridium perfringens*   d

618. The species of *Clostridium* most frequently isolated from clinical materials through anaerobic cultures is:
   a. *Clostridium botulinum*
   b. *Clostridium tetani*
   c. *Clostridium perfringens*   c
   d. *Clostridium histolyticum*

619. A member of the genus *Clostridium* which will not, as a rule, form spores unless it is grown in a sugar-free medium is:
   a. *Clostridium botulinum*
   b. *Clostridium tetani*

  c. *Clostridium perfringens*   c

  d. *Clostridium histolyticum*

620. In solid media and in thioglycollate broth, *Clostridium tetani* produces spores which are:
  a. Round and terminal   a
  b. Oval and eccentric
  c. Oval and subterminal
  d. Usually absent

621. In solid media and in thioglycollate broth, *Clostridium perfringens* produces spores which are:
  a. Round and terminal
  b. Oval and eccentric
  c. Oval and subterminal
  d. Usually absent   d

622. To confirm a laboratory diagnosis of tetanus it is essential to:
  a. Grow characteristic colonies through anaerobic cultures
  b. Find typical sporulating bacilli in smears
  c. Demonstrate toxin production   c
  d. Study biochemical behavior

623. The members of the genus *Clostridium* are:
  a. Obligate aerobic spore-formers
  b. Obligate anaerobic spore-formers   b
  c. Facultative anaerobic spore-formers

624. *Clostridium perfringens* was formerly known as:
  a. *Bacillus oedematiens*
  b. *Bacillus tetani*
  c. *Bacterium welchii*   c
  d. *Bacillus histolyticus*

BACTEROIDES

625. *Bacteroides* is a non-sporogenous, anaerobic Gram (negative, positive) rod tending to produce filaments. negative

626. *Bacteroides* has been isolated from the following cases:
  a. Puerperal infections   a
  b. Urinary tract infections
  c. Appendicitis   c
  d. Food poisoning

627. On blood agar, *Bacteroides melanogenicus* produces a pigment which is:
  a. Blue
  b. Black   b
  c. Yellow
  d. Green

628. *Bacteroides* species will grow aerobically as well as anaerobically.   T   F | F

629. Choose organism which is anaerobic, Gram-negative, and culturally fastidious:
    a. *Escherichia coli*
    b. *Bartonella bacilliformis*
    c. *Bacteroides* | c
    d. *Corynebacterium diphtheriae*

MORAXELLA

630. *Moraxella lacunata* is a Gram-negative diplobacillus.   T   F | T

631. Organisms belonging to the *Moraxella* genus are:
    a. Gram-negative | a
    b. Anaerobic
    c. Motile rods
    d. Non-pathogenic to man

632. The toxin produced by the glander's bacillus is called:
    a. Mallein | a
    b. Tuberuclin
    c. Toxoid
    d. Anatoxin

633. "Glanders" is due to infection with:
    a. *Moraxella lacunata*
    b. *Malleomyces mallei* | b
    c. *Streptococcus pyogenes*
    d. *Bacillus anthracis*

634. The etiologic agent of subacute infectious conjunctivitis is:
    a. *Hemophilus ducreyi*
    b. *Moraxella lacunata* | b
    c. *Clostridium perfringens*
    d. *Streptobacillus moniliformis*

PPLO OR MYCOPLASMA

635. Characterize the pleuropneumonia group of organisms. | See p. 391

636. PPLO (pleuropneumonia-like organisms) are characterized by:
    a. Absence of cell wall | a
    b. Presence of cell wall
    c. Inability to grow on artifical media
    d. Requirement of living (viable) culture medium (tissue culture)

637. PPLO (pleuropneumonia-like organisms) require the presence of living cells for growth.   T   F | F

BACILLUS

638. The only pathogenic *Bacillus* is _____.   *B. anthracis*

639. What disease to you associate with the aerobic spore-
forming bacilli?   Anthrax
                                                          (B. anthracis)

640. The Ascoli test is used for the diagnosis of:
    a. *Malleomyces mallei*
    b. *Bacillus anthracis*   b
    c. *Yersinia pestis*
    d. *Ascaris lumbricoides*

641. A Gram-positive, non-hemolytic organism producing a
grayish colony resembling a medusa-head is most likely:
    a. *Staphylococcus epidermidis*
    b. *Bacillus anthracis*   b
    c. *Clostridium histolyticum*
    d. *Corynebacterium diphtheriae*

642. "Medusa head" colonies are characteristic of _____.   *B. anthracis*

643. "Medusa head" growth (agar culture) is characteristic of:
    a. *Bacillus anthracis*   a
    b. *Francisella tularensis*
    c. *Salmonella cholerasuis*
    d. *Brucella abortus*

644. The only spore-bearing aerobic organism of medical importance is _____.   *B. anthracis*

645. A test used for the diagnosis of anthrax in animals dead of
the disease, or to detect contamination of hides by *B. an-*
thracis, is known as:
    a. Schick test
    b. Mallein test
    c. Ascoli precipitation test   c
    d. Ramon flocculation test

646. Will *B. subtilis* grow when streaked over the surface of an
EMB plate? Explain.   No. See p. 391

647. *Bacillus subtilis* is commonly called:
    a. Hay bacillus   a
    b. Acne bacillus
    c. Blue pus bacillus
    d. Smegma bacillus
    e. Loeffler's bacillus

648. A gram-stained smear from an aerobic blood agar plate
growth shows large, straight Gram-positive (easily decolorized) bacilli in chains. The organism is:
    a. *Streptococcus pneumoniae*
    b. Bordet-Gengou bacillus
    c. *Hemophilus hemolyticus*
    d. *Corynebacterium diphtheriae*
    e. *Bacillus subtilis*   e

FUNGI

649. What is the causative organism in each of the following diseases?
   a. San Joaquin valley fever *Coccidioides immitis*
   b. Torulosis *Cryptococcus neoformans*
   c. Thrush *Candida albicans*
   d. Lumpy jaw *Actinomyces bovis*

650. What are two diagnostic procedures for detecting active infection with *Coccidioides immitis*? coccidioidin skin test & serology (C-F)

651. The life cycles of many of the fungi causing systemic mycoses are biphasic. The organism appear as _____ in the tissues and are _____ when grown on media at room temperature. yeasts mycelial

652. Match the following:
   1. Asexual spores borne internally within a sac called "sporangium" a. Thallospores 1—d
   2. Asexual spores borne externally (not within a sac) b. Conidia 2—b
   3. Actively reproducing cells formed by segmentation of a mycelium c. Chlamydospores 3—a
   4. Enlarged, resting spores surrounded by a thick wall (formed by segmentation of a mycelium) d. Sporangiospores 4—c

653. Budding yeast cells of *Candida albicans* are Gram-negative. T F F

654. In an unstained wet smear of feces it is difficult to differentiate between red blood cells and budding yeast cells of *Candida albicans.* T F T

655. At what temperature should fungi be incubated? Both at room T° (25°C.) & at 37°C.

656. The various filaments composing the fungal thallus are called:
   a. Mycelium
   b. Conidia

      c. Hyphae   c
      d. Blastospores

657. Asexual spores formed by simple segmentation of hyphae
are called:
      a. Ascospores
      b. Arthrospores   b
      c. Basidiospores
      d. Oidia

658. Asexual spores formed by condensation of the protoplasm
of a cell of the fungal thallus into a swollen body with a
thickened membrane are called:
      a. Arthrospores
      b. Blastospores
      c. Oidia
      d. Chlamydospores   d

659. Chromoblastomycosis is usually due to infection with the
following fungus:
      a. *Coccidioides immitis*
      b. *Sporotrichum schenckii*
      c. *Hormodendrum pedrosoi*   c
      d. *Blastomyces dermatitidis*

660. In fecal smears, red blood cells may best be differentiated
from the budding yeast cells of *Candida albicans* on the basis of:
      a. Morphology in wet preparations
      b. Reaction to Gram stain   b
      c. Rouleaux formation
      d. Test for occult blood

661. A differential medium, employed as an aid in the identification on the basis of pigment production of *Trychophyton rubrum* and *Trychophyton mentagrophytes* is:
      a. Dextrose-cornmeal agar   a
      b. Cornmeal agar
      c. Dextrose-potato agar
      d. Sabouraud's agar

662. The medium of choice for the general cultivation of fungi
is:
      a. Nickerson's
      b. Sabouraud's   b
      c. Bordet-Gengou
      d. Loeffler's blood serum

663. At what temperature should dermatophytes be incubated?   See p. 391

664. Corn meal agar is suitable medium for the production of
chlamydospores by:
      a. *Clostridium botulinum*
      b. *Francisella tularensis*
      c. *Candida albicans*   c
      d. *Brucella abortus*

665. Indicate suitable media for the cultivation of *Candida*,
Cryptococcus, and other fungi:
    a. Sabouraud's agar   a
    b. Brain heart infusion (BH) agar
    c. Bordet-Gengou
    d. Dorset's egg medium

666. A differential medium supporting the growth of *Micro-*
sporum canis and *Microsporum gypseum* but not of *Micro-*
sporum audouini is:
    a. Corn meal agar
    b. Rice medium   b
    c. Eosin-methylene blue agar
    d. Dextrose-cornmeal agar

667. Oroya fever is also known as Carrion's disease and:
    a. Yaws
    b. Pinta
    c. Perruga peruana   c
    d. Ornithosis

668. Thrush is due to infection with the following fungus:
    a. *Torula histolytica*
    b. *Epidermophyton inguinale*
    c. *Blastomyces hominis*
    d. *Candida albicans*   d

669. *Candida albicans* was formerly known as _____ *albicans*.   *Monilia*

670. All of the following are transmitted by insects except:
    a. Yellow fever
    b. Kala-azar
    c. Coccidioidomycosis   c
    d. Bubonic plague

671. A fungus cannot manufacture its own food because it lacks:
    a. Vitamins
    b. Chlorophyll   b
    c. Minerals
    d. Enzymes

672. An allergic reaction, manifested by a generalized skin erup-
tion, to a particular fungus infection:
    a. Trichophytid   a
    b. Pfeiffer's reaction
    c. Epidermophytosis
    d. Anamnestic reaction

673. Distinguish between "endothrix" and "exothrix."   See p. 391

674. Distinguish between "hyphae" and "mycelium."   See p. 391

675. India ink preparations of CSF sediment are the best way
to demonstrate:
    a. *Hemophilus influenzae*
    b. Pneumococci
    c. Budding *Cryptococcus*   c

d. *Neisseria meningitidis*

676. The genus *Nocardia* belongs in the following group:
    a. Eubacteriales
    b. Actinomycetales   b
    c. Spirochaetales
    d. Rickettsiales

SPIROCHETES

677. Relapsing fever is caused by a spirochete.   T   F   T

678. What are the etiologic agents (genus and species) of:
    a. Relapsing fever   *Borrelia recurrentis*
    b. Infectious jaundice (Weil's disease)   *Leptospira icterohaemorragiae*

    c. Leprosy   *M. leprae*
    d. Q fever   *Coxiella burnetti*

679. What is Vincent's angina, and what is the nature of its
     etiology?   trench mouth *Borrelia vincenti*, a spirochete

680. The spirochete of Vincent's angina can be cultivated on
     blood agar.   T   F   F

681. Rat-bite fever is caused by which of the following organisms:
    a. *Malleomyces mallei*
    b. *Yersinia pestis*
    c. *Streptobacillus moniliformis*
    d. *Spirillum minus*   d

682. Two diseases for which the dark-field is diagnostic are:
    a. _____   syphillis *(T. pallidum)*
    b. _____   trench mouth *(B. vincenti)*

683. An observable difference between a spirillum and a spirochete in the dark-field is _____
    _____
    _____.   See p. 391

684. *Borrelia* is a:
    a. Tissue spirochete
    b. Blood spirochete   b

685. *Spirillum minus* is also known as:
    a. *Bacillus cholerae*
    b. *Borrelia muris*   b

    c. *Spirilum duttoni*
    d. *Leptospira icterohaemorrhagiae*

686. Vincent's angina (trench mouth) is caused by *Bacillus fusi-formis* and:
    a. *Borrelia recurrentis*
    b. *Borrelia vincenti*   b
    c. *Borrelia duttoni*
    d. *Borrelia novyi*

687. *Borrelia, Treponema,* and *Leptospira* belong in the following group:
    a. Eubacteriales
    b. Actinomycetales
    c. Spirochaetales   c
    d. Rickettsiales

688. Rat-bite fever is due to infection with:
    a. *Listeria monocytogenes*
    b. *Streptococcus pyogenes*
    c. *Vibrio cholerae*
    d. *Spirillum minus*   d

689. Relapsing fever may be caused by:
    a. *Borrelia recurrentis*
    b. *Borrelia duttoni*
    c. *Borrelia novyi*
    d. *Borrelia berbera*
    e. All of these   e
    f. None of these

690. European relapsing fever is caused by:
    a. *Borrelia recurrentis*   a
    b. *Borrelia duttoni*
    c. *Berrelia novyi*
    d. *Borrelia berbera*

691. The causative agent of yaws is:
    a. *Treponema pallidum*
    b. *Treponema pertenue*   b
    c. *Treponema caratum*
    d. *Borrelia berbera*

692. In syphilitic lesions of mouth or throat a dark-field examination may reveal:
    a. *Treponema pallidum*   a
    b. *Borrelia vincenti*
    c. *Leptospira icterohaemorrhagiae*
    d. *Treponema microdentium*

693. Spirochetes may reach the fetus through the placenta of a syphilitic mother.   T   F   T

694. Spirochetes have:
    a. Thick, rigid walls
    b. Thin, flexible walls   b
    c. No walls

695. The routine laboratory diagnosis of Vincent's angina is made through:
    a. Stained direct smears   a
    b. Special cultures
    c. Animal inoculation

696. Weil's disease may affect animals as well as man.   T   F   T

697. Infectious jaundice is also called:
    a. Chagas' disease
    b. Weil's disease   b
    c. Dutton's disease
    d. Nicolas' disease

698. Infectious jaundice is due to infection with:
    a. *Borrelia carteri*
    b. *Treponema pertenue*
    c. *Actinomyces israeli*
    d. *Leptospira icterohaemorrhagiae*   d

RICKETTSIAE

699. Give (1) the etiologic agent, (2) the common name of the arthropod vector and, (3) a reservoir host of the following rickettsial infections
    a. Rocky Mountain spotted fever
        1. Etiologic agent: _____   *Rickettsia rickettsii*
        2. Arthropod vector: _____   tick
        3. Reservoir host: _____   rodents
    b. Rickettsial pox
        1. Etiologic agent: _____   *R. akari*
        2. Arthropod vector: _____   mites
        4. Reservoir host: _____   rodents
    c. Epidemic typhus
        1. Etiologic agent: _____   *R. prowazekii*
        2. Arthropod vector: _____   human body louse
        3. Reservoir host: _____   man
    d. Tsutsugamushi fever
        1. Etiologic agent: _____   *R. tsutsugamushi*
        2. Arthropod vector: _____   mites
        3. Reservoir host: _____   rodents

700. In what geographical area of the United States is one most likely to see rickettsial pox infections?   Northeast

701. The rickettsiae are an unusual group of organisms, _____ (smaller or larger) than bacteria, which _____ (can, cannot) be cultivated on artificial media and require an _____ vector for their dissemination.   smaller
                                                            cannot
                                                            insect

702. Which one of the following is not a rickettsial disease:
    a. Epidemic typhus   a
    b. Scrub typhus
    c. Colorado tick fever   c
    d. Boutonneuse fever

703. What is the etiologic agent of Brill-Zinsser disease?   *Rickettsia*
                                                    prowazekii

704. What kinds (not specific names) of vectors are concerned
in the transmission of:
    a. Yellow fever   mosquito
    b. Rocky Mountain spotted fever   tick
    c. Tularemia   fleas
    d. Epidemic typhus fever   body louse
    e. Equine encephalomyelitis   mosquito

705. A stain suitable for the staining of rickettsial bodies in
smears from infected tissues is:
    a. Fontana stain
    b. Giemsa stain
    c. Macchiavello's stain   c
    d. Neisser's stain

706. Rocky Mountain spotted fever is an infectious disease.
    T   F   T

707. *Lymphogranuloma inguinale* is a:
    a. Bacterial disease
    b. Fungal disease
    c. Viral disease   c
    d. Rickettsial disease

708. *Lymphogranuloma inguinale* is due to infection by a species
of the genus:
    a. *Rickettsia*
    b. *Coxiella*
    c. *Bartonella*
    d. *Miyagawanella*   d

709. Parrot fever ("psittacosis") is caused by a species of the
following genus:
    a. *Rickettsia*
    b. *Coxiella*
    c. *Bartonella*
    d. *Miyagawanella*   d

710. What is the best culture medium for rickettsiae?   suspension
                                                   of yolk sac
                                                   from chick
                                                   embryos

711. Briefly describe detail of procedure using Macchiavello's
stain.   See p. 391

712. The Frei antigen is used as an aid in the diagnosis of:
    a. *Herpes simplex*

      b. *Herpes zoster*
      c. *Lymphogranuloma inguinale*   c
      d. Rubella (German measles)

713. *Lymphogranuloma inguinale* and *Lymphogranuloma vene-*
    reum are one and the same disease.   T   F   T

714. *Bartonella bacilliformis* belongs in the following group:
      a. Eubacteriales
      b. Actinomycetales
      c. Spirochaetales
      d. Rickettsiales   d

715. Epidemic typhus is caused by:
      a. *Rickettsia prowazekii*   a
      b. *Rickettsia rickettsii*
      c. *Rickettsia akari*
      d. *Rickettsia tsutsugamushi*

716. Rocky Mountain spotted fever is caused by:
      a. *Rickettsia prowazekii*
      b. *Rickettsia rickettsii*   b
      c. *Rickettsia akari*
      d. *Rickettsia tsutsugamushi*

717. Scrub typhus is caused by:
      a. *Rickettsia prowazekii*
      b. *Rickettsia rickettsii*
      c. *Rickettsia tsutsugamushi*   c
      d. *Rickettsia typhi*

718. Rickettsial pox is caused by:
      a. *Rickettsia rickettsii*
      b. *Rickettsia tsutsugamushi*
      c. *Rickettsia akari*   c
      d. *Rickettsia prowazekii*

719. *Rickettsia rickettsii* is transmitted by:
      a. The body louse, *Pediculus corporis*
      b. A tick, *Dermacentor andersoni*   b
      c. The harvest mite, *Trombicula akamushi*

720. The etiologic agent of Q fever is:
      a. *Rickettsia quintana*
      b. *Rickettsia rickettsii*
      c. *Rickettsia akari*
      d. *Coxiella burnetii*   d

721. *Coxiella burnetii* belongs to the following group:
      a. Eubacteriales
      b. Actinomycetales
      c. Spirochetales
      d. Rickettsiales   d

722. The etiologic agent of Oroya fever is:
      a. *Coxiella burnetii*   a
      b. *Bartonella bacilliformis*

c. *Rickettsia akari*
d. *Miyagawanella psittaci*

723. In suspected lymphopathia venereum cases the best diagnostic laboratory procedure is:
    a. Direct smears from lesions
    b. Dark-field examination
    c. Complement-fixation
    d. Frei test   d

724. A genital lesion, usually diagnosed by finding intracellular
"Donovan bodies" in ciopsied material or in smears from
the ulcerating buboes, is:
    a. Chancroid
    b. *Lymphogranuloma venereum*
    c. *Granuloma inguinale*   c
    d. Inclusion conjunctivitis

725. Epidemic typhus is milder and has a lower mortality rate
than endemic typhus.   T   F   F

726. Which of the following diseases may be diseeminated by
ticks?
    a. Typhoid fever
    b. Malaria, yellow fever
    c. Bacillary dysentery
    d. Rocky Mountain spotted fever   d

727. Which of the following diseases may be disseminated by
lice?
    a. Typhoid fever
    b. Malaria, yellow fever
    c. Typhus fever   c
    d. Rocky Mountain spotted fever

728. Most rickettsial species will pass through a porcelain filter.
    T   F   F

729. Rickettsiae are:
    a. Larger than viruses but smaller than bacteria   a
    b. Larger than bacteria
    c. Smaller than viruses

730. Rickettsiae differ basically from bacteria in that they:
    a. Are smaller
    b. Are nonmotile
    c. Are intracellular
    d. Require presence of living cells for growth   d

731. Most rickettsial species are visible under the high power
of the microscrope.   T   F   T

VIRUSES

732. Influenza antibodies can most frequently be demonstrated
by:

a. Agglutination test
b. Hemolysis
c. Hemagglutination-inhibition test   c
d. Precipitin test

733. When a clear zone appears in an opaque film of bacterial growth on a nutrient agar plate in the presence of phage, it is called:
a. Plaque   a
b. Hemolysis
c. No growth
d. None of the above

734. Viruses that attack bacteria are called:
a. Virocytes
b. Bacteriophages   b
c. Neutropic viruses
d. Dermotropic viruses

735. When viruses multiply in tissue culture they:
a. Produce visible growth
b. May produce a cytopathogenic change in the cells   b
c. Produce a color change
d. Do not require a fluid medium
e. Do require an overlay of nutrient agar over the cells

736. *Herpes simplex* frequently produces:
a. Diarrhea
b. Vomiting
c. Fever blisters   c
d. Pneumonia
e. Encephalitis

737. Yellow fever is transmitted from person to person by:
a. Aedes mosquito   a
b. A mite
c. Fleas
d. Flies
e. Body louse

738. Negri bodies are cytoplasmic inclusions in nerve cells found in:
a. Rabies   a
b. Influenza
c. Psittacosis
d. Trench fever
e. Measles

739. One way of preventing the spread of Q fever is by:
a. Drinking only certified milk
b. Mosquito control
c. Adequate pasteurization of milk   c
d. Chlorination of drinking water
e. Through control of selling contaminated meat

740. The causative agent of primary atypical pneumonia associated with the development of cold agglutinins is:
    a. *Rickettsia*
    b. *Mycoplasma*   b
    c. Fungus
    d. Virus
    e. *Streptococcus*

741. Each of the following viruses except one should be considered as a possible cause of viral meningitis. Which of the following is not commonly associated with viral meningitis?
    a. Rhinovirus   a
    b. Mumps virus
    c. Poliovirus
    d. Coxsackie virus, group B
    e. Echovirus

742. For serologic diagnosis of viral diseases it is important to collect blood specimens at the proper time, which is:
    a. At peak of clinical symptoms
    b. At onset of illness and again after 2-3 weeks
    c. As soon as possible after onset of illness
    d. At onset of illness and again after 7 days
    e. Approximately 2 weeks after onset of illness

743. The specimen of choice for recovery of poliovirus by culture from a living patient is:
    a. Spinal fluid
    b. Blood clot
    c. Buffy coat
    d. Throat washings
    e. Feces   e

744. Why do viruses require specific hosts or tissues, whereas most other microorganisms can multiply in or on a variety of substances?   See p. 391

745. List three techniques which may be used for determining the size of viruses.   filtration; electron micrographs; ultracentrifugation

746. The occurrence of disease due to ultramicroscopic living agents was postulated in Pasteur's time.   T   F   T

747. Some viruses may be demonstrated as "inclusion bodies" in the cells of infected animals.   T   F   T

748. Epidemiological evidence points to the mosquito as the vector of Western equine encephalomyelitis from horse to man.   T   F   T

749. *Herpes simplex* may be the cause of encephalitis.   T   F   T

750. Western equine encephalomyelitis virus is classified as ARBOR virus, group A.   T   F

    T

751. Outbreaks of epidemic pleurodynia are frequently caused by group A Coxsackie viruses.   T   F

    T

752. Immunological studies indicate that the viruses of varicella and herpes simplex are the same or very closely related. T   F

    F

753. In general, characterize the Picornavirus group or describe the characteristics of the viruses contained in this group.

    See p. 391

754. Name the members of the Picornavirus group.

    See p. 391

755. Low hemagglutination titers can be obtained when the virus suspension contains too many incomplete particles. T   F

    T

756. A susceptible cell can be infected by an animal virus without manifesting infection.   T   F

    T

757. The "D" phase of influenza virus does not hemagglutinate chick red blood cells.   T   F

    F

758. The hemagglutination test is an antigen-antibody reaction. T   F

    F

759. The hemagglutination test measures the amount of virus present in a suspension, but not the infectivity of the suspension.   T   F

    T

760. The assay of the potency of a virus suspension by the application of the formula of Reed and Muench makes possible an accurate determination in an economical manner. T   F

    T

761. Each type of influenza virus is specific in that infection or immunization with one will not protect against the other types.   T   F

    T

762. Serological tests for the diagnosis of viral infections must demonstrate a four-fold rise in titer in order to be diagnostically significant.   T   F

    T

763. The first information necessary in the selection of diagnostic techniques is the type of virus infection suspected. T   F

    T

764. Data as to onset of illness is of paramount importance in the laboratory diagnosis of viral diseases.   T   F

    T

765. The determination of potency of virus suspensions by the LD 50 method is more accurate than the determination of an LD 100.   T   F

    T

766. Mumps encephalitis is never a primary infection but follows classical mumps infection.   T   F

    F

767. Complement-fixation tests cannot be used to determine the type of influenza virus occurring in an individual patient. T   F

    F

768. In influenza, the hemagglutination test is more strain-specific than is the complement-fixation test.   T   F   T

769. Hemagglutination tests, using chicken cells, have been devised for use in the laboratory diagnosis of all viruses causing disease in man.   T   F   F

770. Elution of myxoviruses from red blood cells occurs most rapidly at 4°C.   T   F   F

771. Whole blood to be examined for complement-fixing antibodies should be frozen and shipped to the laboratory on dry ice.   T   F   F

772. Pouring is the best method of transferring a viral suspension from one container to another.   T   F   F

773. Filtration is a poor method of removing bacterial contaminants from suspensions of clinical materials to be examined for the presence of viruses.   T   F   T

774. Interference occurs between every combination of viruses whether or not they are immunologically related.   T   F   F

775. For serologic diagnosis of mumps virus infections, viral complement-fixing antigens are generally of greater value than soluble complement-fixation antigens.   T   F   F

776. The property of hemagglutination is associated with the "soluble" antigen of influenza.   T   F   F

777. The protein moiety of a virus is responsible for infectivity.
T   F   F

778. What is the best evidence for the suggestion that viral nucleic acid is responsible for the replication and genetic continuity of infective viral progeny?   See p. 392

779. What is thought to be the mechanism of adaptation?   See p. 392

780. What is meant by the term "adaptation" as applied to viruses?   See p. 392

781. Calculate the number of milligrams of a dried viral preparation needed to cause a positive response in 50% of the hosts. The answer may be left in log units.

Dose of virus inoculated (mg.)	No. of deaths	No. of survivors
1.25	2	3
2.5	1	4
5.0	5	0
10.0	4	1
20.0	5	0

See p. 392

Note: log of 1.25 is 0.09   log of 2.0 is 0.30
        log of 2.5   is 0.40   log of 5.0 is 0.70
        log of 10.0 is 1.0   log of 20.0 is 1.3

782. Indicate four ways in which the chick embryo is useful in the study of virus infections. Indicate two advantages and two disadvantages in the use of chick embryos in such studies. See p. 392

783. What is the significance of the neutralization index? See p. 392

784. What is meant by the term "titer" as applied to a virus suspension? See p. 392

785. Explain the meaning of the nomenclature of the following influenza virus isolate: A3/Detroit/5/71. See p. 392

786. Give two ARBOR viruses which may be etiological agents of human encephalitis in the Central and Imperial valleys of California.
    1. _____

    2. _____

St. Louis equine encephalitis
Western equine encephalitis

787. Five diseases, known to be caused by viruses, are:
    1. _____
    2. _____
    3. _____
    4. _____
    5. _____

measles
mumps
poliomyelitis
influenza
chicken pox
Also see p. 393

788. Viruses which attack bacteria are called _____.

bacteriophages

789. "Councilman bodies" are thought to be pathognomonic of:
    a. Rabies
    b. Yellow fever
    c. Smallpox
    d. Poliomyelitis

b

790. "Councilman bodies" are formed by degeneration of cytoplasm of:
    a. Liver cells
    b. Kidney cells
    c. Brain cells
    d. Pancreatic cells

a

791. Molluscum contagiosum is a benign skin lesion caused by a:
    a. Bacterium
    b. Virus
    c. Spirochete
    d. Fungus

b

792. No inclusion bodies have been demonstrated for:
    a. Viral hepatitis
    b. Molluscum contagiosum
    c. Herpes simplex

a

d. Herpes zoster

793. Infectious mononucleosis is caused by a virus. T F   T

794. Poliomyelitis virus can pass the placental barrier. T F   T

795. Infectious hepatitis is caused by a:
    a. Bacterium
    b. Fungus
    c. Virus   c
    d. Spirochete

796. What is the meaning of the term "viremia"?   presence of a
                                                        virus in the
                                                        bloodstream

797. What are viruses chiefly composed of?   See p. 393

798. No animal virus has ever been cultivated in a cell-free medium. T F   T

799. Many small viruses behave like chemicals in that they can
be crystallized. T F   T

800. Bacteria are, in general, more stable and more resistant to
physical agents than are viruses. T F   F

801. Yellow fever is essentially:
    a. An enteric disease
    b. An eruptive disease
    c. A liver disease   c
    d. A viremia

802. The name of Walter Reed is associated with pioneer experimental work in the field of:
    a. Yellow fever   a
    b. Malaria
    c. Rocky Mountain spotted fever
    d. American trypanosomiasis

803. Influenza virus disease can be proven by serological studies.
T F   T

804. Infectious hepatitis is an enteric infection. T F   T

805. Serum hepatitis infection can only be acquired through the
injection of (or contamination with) the blood of patients
or carriers. T F   T

806. Serum hepatitis infection may be acquired through the use
of contaminated needles and syringes. T F   T

807. Serum hepatitis is a contagious disease. T F   F

808. Yellow fever virus is one of the largest viruses. T F   F

809. A smear is taken from Ammon's horn. What disease?   rabies

810. The finding of Negri bodies in certain brain cells is diagnostic of:
    a. Chickenpox
    b. Smallpox

      c. Trachoma

      d. Rabies   d

811. Distinguish between "viruses" and "rickettsiae." See p. 393

812. Distinguish between "street virus" and "fixed virus." See p. 393

813. Which of the following stains would not be suitable for the staining of elementary bodies in smears from infected materials:

      a. Paschen (carbol-Fuchsin) stain

      b. Methyl violet

      c. Victoria blue

      d. Lactophenol cotton blue   d

814. Serum hepatitis and infectious hepatitis are one and the same condition.   T   F   F

815. Serum hepatitis and infectious hepatitis are clinically:

      a. Very similar   a

      b. Very different

816. The distribution of yellow fever is world-wide.   T   F   F

817. Common cold virus disease can be proven by laboratory means.   T   F   F

818. The "exanthemata" group includes:

      a. Typhoid fever

      b. Measles   b

      c. Chickenpox

      d. Mumps

819. Most animal viruses range in size between:

      a. 0.001–0.04 microns

      b. 0.01–0.4 microns   b

      c. 0.1–4.0 microns

      d. 1–40 microns

820. Viruses resemble living things in that they:

      a. Are motile

      b. Are crystalline

      c. Grow

      d. Reproduce   d

821. Which are the best known cellular lesions caused by various viruses?   their inclusion bodies

822. Twort and d'Herelle discovered:

      a. Bacteriophage   a

      b. Rickettsiae

      c. Filterable viruses

      d. Fluorescent antibody microscopy

823. A filter-passing agent capable of killing and (transmissible lysis) dissolving living bacteria is called:

      a. Penicillin

   b. Streptomycin
   c. Opsonin
   d. Bacteriophage ("phage")   d

824. Trachoma is caused by a:
   a. Fungus
   b. Virus   b
   c. Bacterium
   d. Spirochete

825. A venereal disease which is caused by a filterable virus is:
   a. Lymphopathia venereum   a
   b. Granuloma inguinale
   c. Gonorrhea
   d. Chancroid

MILK, WATER, FOOD, UTENSILS

826. List eight diseases commonly transmitted by milk to man. Name the genus and species of the causative agent and indicate whether the pathogen originated from the cow or a milk handler.   See p. 393

827. Milk that is not adequately pasteurized may be detected by:
   a. Phosphatase test   a
   b. Sediment test
   c. Manurial pollution test
   d. Methylene blue reduction test
   e. Plate count

828. What is meant by pasteurization?   See p. 393

829. State the two main purposes of pasteurization.   kill pathogens; decrease bacterial numbers

830. Briefly indicate the purpose and principle underlying the presumptive test.   See p. 393

831. What is meant by 2 X lactose broth and why is it used in the presumptive test?   See p. 393

832. Why is the search for *E. coli* in water preferable to a search for the pathogens themselves?   See p. 393

833. Why is not the search for *E. coli* ended when there is evidence that gas is formed in lactose broth fermentation tubes?   See p. 393

834. What two diseases of the water-borne epidemics are most likely to occur?   typhoid fever & polio

835. How can it be possible for a fermentation tube with 0.1 ml. of water sample to be positive when five tubes with 10 ml. portions were all negative?   chance

836. What kind of water supply might have consistently a high colony count yet a low "MPN" for *E. coli*?

     well water

837. Would you regard as preferable the thorough examination of one sample of water or a more superficial examination of a series of samples taken weekly? Explain your answer.

     See p. 393

838. How many coliforms need to be present before drinking water need be considered dangerous?

     one

839. Why is *E. coli* referred to as an indicator organism in water analysis?

     because it is the symbol of fecal contamination

840. Why are brilliant green and bile salts added to the BGBL broth?

     inhibitors of G-neg. rods other than coliforms

841. Before a bacterial count can be made, the free chlorine present in a sample of swimming pool water is neutralized by:
   a. Tween 80
   b. Sodium thiosulfate
   c. Azolectin
   d. Tamol-N
   e. Buffered salt solution

     b

842. According to the USPHS standards, the number of samples necessary for adequate testing of a water supply is determined by the:
   a. Potability of the water
   b. Size of the plant
   c. Per capita consumption of the water
   d. Findings of the sanitary/survey
   e. Size of the population served

     e

843. The test sample of swimming pool water should be:
   a. Taken when the pool water is fresh
   b. Taken into a clean, not necessarily sterile, container
   c. Taken into a bottle containing Tween 80 to neutralize chlorine
   d. Taken at the time of a "peak load" of swimmers in the pool
   e. Incubated at body temperature until it reaches the laboratory

     d

844. According to the USPHS Drinking Water Standards, the standard sample for the bacteriological test shall consist of:
   a. 3 standard portions of either 1 ml. or 10 ml. each
   b. 5 standard portions of either 1 ml. or 10 ml. each
   c. 5 standard portions of either 10 ml. or 100 ml. each
   d. 10 standard portions of either 5 ml. or 10 ml. each

     b

345. In the United States, sanitation of water supplies has been largely responsible for the decline of:
    a. Diphtheria
    b. Septic sore throat
    c. Tuberculosis
    d. Salmonellosis
    e. Brucellosis

    d

846. In the bacteriological analysis of water, the confirmed test consists of:
    a. Demonstration of Gram-negative, non-sporulating rods from an agar slant
    b. Gas in a lactose tube
    c. Typical coliform colonies on EMB agar plates
    d. Acid and gas in lactose tubes

    c

847. List five diseases commonly transmitted to man via water. Name the genus and species of the etiologic agents.

See p. 394

848. From the list below, fill in the appropriate letter(s):

	BGBL	EMB	
Indicator(s)	_____	_____	none/e, g
Differential Substance(s)	_____	_____	f/f
Selective Substances	_____	_____	b, d/e, g
Energy Source(s)	_____	_____	f/f
Growth Source(s)	_____	_____	a, h/a, h

    a. Peptone   f. Lactose
    b. Bile   g. Methylene blue
    c. Dextrose   h. Beef extract
    d. Brilliant green i. Glucose
    e. Eosin   j. Sucrose

849. What advantages does the membrane or molecular filter technique offer for bacteriological analysis of water?

    ability to test greater volume of water

850. Which of the following pathogens is *not* commonly transmitted by water:
    a. *Salmonella*
    b. *Shigella*
    c. *Pasteurella*
    d. *Vibrio*

    c

851. Which of the following media could not be used in the confirmed test in water analysis:
    a. EMB agar
    b. Endo's agar
    c. BGBL broth
    d. Lactose broth

    d

852. The outstanding characteristic of *Escherichia* on EMB agar is its:
    a. Large size

b. Green sheen   b
c. Mucoid state
d. Irregular margin

853. MPN means most probable number of *E. coli* per ml.   T   F   T

854. A qualitative test of water is more important than a quantitative test.   T   F   F

855. In the examination of water, we look for an indicator group
or organisms called the _____ group. The group is   coliform
made up of Gram (positive, negative) rods which ferment   negative
(glucose, lactose, sucrose) with the production of (acid,   lactose
acid and gas, NH₄OH) within (24, 48, 72) hours   acid & gas; 48

856. In carrying out examination of potability of water, three
major tests are conducted. These are called the _____   presumptive;
test, the _____ test, and the _____ test.   confirmed;
                                                              completed

857. The swab-rinse technique used in the evaluation of the
sanitation of eating utensils is:
    a. A presumptive test for coliform organisms
    b. A test for *Streptococcus salivarius*
    c. An index of the disinfection accomplished in the
       dishwashing process
    d. An index of the effectiveness of washing, rinsing, and
       handling of the eating utensils tested   d
    e. A test required by law in all cities

858. The *most ideal* procedure, but *not the most practical* procedure, to use in determining whether or not eating utensils have been rendered free from bacteria harmful to man
by the washing and drying process would be:
    a. To examine for an oral index organism
    b. A procedure in which the exact number of organ-
       isms present could be determined by a plate count
    c. A procedure where the presence or absence of hu-
       man pathogens was determined   c
    d. To perform coliform counts on rinse water
    e. To enumerate the number of organisms present by
       counting a direct smear

859. In the sanitary analysis of water, which of the following is
most indicative of pollution:
    a. High chloride
    b. High plate count
    c. *Escherichia coli*   c
    d. *Enterobacter aerogenes*

860. How would you confirm a presumptive water test?   See p. 394

BACTERIOLOGY & ALLIED FIELDS ANSWERS CONTINUED

1. pH — Hydrogen-ion concentration
   pK — Constant at which pH indicator changes color
   Eh — Redux indicator or oxidation/reduction potential

2. **Thermoduric bacteria:** Resist high temperatures but do not grow at these high temperatures
   Thermophilic bacteria: Growing at temperatures up to 80°C.

3. **Cell wall:** a. Cell wall stain   b. Cell shape
   Cytoplasmic membrane: a. Prepare protoplasts and stain. b. Semipermeable membrane and respiratory enzymes located here.
   Ribosomes: a. Electron micrographs   b. Protein synthesis
   Fimbriae: a. Electron micrographs   b. Assist in transport of nucleic acid from one bacterium to another during conjugation

4. They do possess a mitochondrial system as the respiratory enzymes are found in the cytoplasmic membrane. No mitochondria are present however as we know them in other cells.

9. Selenite contains all the ingredients necessary to support the growth of most bacteria, plus sodium selenium and lactose. Sodium selenium is converted to selenous acid in an acid pH and is toxic to actively metabolizing bacteria. All lactose fermenting bacteria are actively metabolizing therefore they are directly affected by the selenous acid. Non-lac bacteria are only mildly affected therefore the non-lac bacteria are enriched, e.g., survive.

10. Heating the smear over flame of Bunsen burner gently enough not to distort cellular structure but enough to cause sufficient protein degradation so that the bacteria adhere to the microscope slide. Fixing the smear in this manner *does not* guarantee killing of the bacteria.

11. Prevents distortion of the bacterial cell, therefore excellent stains for studying morphology and grouping. Negative staining does not stain the bacteria but rather the background.

12. Aid in recognition of genus *Corynebacterium* and possibly species within genus.

22. Neither. KH_2PO_4 is an alkaline buffer while K_2HPO_4 is an acid buffer.

29. Prevent water of condensation from accumulating over the surface of the agar thus preventing the development of well isolated colonies.

43. No. Protein (tryptone) is not readily used in the presence of a fermentable carbohydrate (glucose); e.g., protein-sparing effect.

44. No. Phenol red is a pH indicator not a redux indicator.
    The greater the number of organisms the more rapid the reduction or decolorization of the methylene blue.

50. The procedure, used for cells or structures which are difficult to stain directly, employs an acidic dye (nigrosine, a black dye, is frequently employed to stain the background, leaving the cells contrastingly colorless.

54. Para-aminobenzoic acid (PABA) (5 mg. for each 100 ml.).

63. **Fermentation:** The decomposition of compounds (chiefly carbohydrates) by the action of enzymes produced by microorganisms.

Putrefaction: The decomposition of nitrogenous compounds (protein) by the action of microorganisms.

64. **Cocci** (singular: coccus) are round or spherical bacteria, 0.15 to 2 microns in diameter.
Bacilli (singular: bacillus) are the rod-shaped bacteria.

66. **Sterilization:** The destruction of all microbial life on or in an object. The term **disinfection** is employed more particularly to designate the use of chemicals in destroying bacteria.

67. **Disinfection:** See the preceding answer.
Asepsis: The prevention of the access of microorganisms.

68. **Thermolabile:** Easily altered or destroyed by heat.
Thermostable (thermostabile): Not easily altered or destroyed by heat.

69. **Aerobic organisms:** Organisms (obligate aerobes) that require oxygen for their growth or (facultative aerobes) may grow either in the presence or in the absence of oxygen.
Microaerophilic organisms: Organisms that grow best at a low oxygen tension.

70. **S colonies:** Colonies that possess round, even margins. Smooth, convex, glistening surfaces. Cells show normal morphology. Encapsulated species have capsules and flagellated ones are usually motile. Somatic and type antigens are present (flocculent agglutination). S colonies are usually obtained in active disease conditions and are sensitive to bacteriophage, resistant to phagocytosis.
R colonies: These possess irregular margins. Flat, uneven, granular surfaces. Cell morphology often is abnormal. Motility, when present, is poor. No encapsulated forms occur. Only somatic antigens are present (granular agglutination). R colonies are usually obtained in convalescents and carriers and are less sensitive to bacteriophage, susceptible to phagocytosis.

71. **Bacteriostatic:** Said of any agent which, without causing actual death to living bacteria, nevertheless prevents their growth and multiplication.
Bactericidal: Said of any agent that destroys bacteria.

72. **In vivo:** In the living body.
In vitro: In a test tube outside the human or the animal body.

73. **Bright-field microscopy** (used for all routine purposes). Makes use of transmitted light.
Dark-field microscopy (used for the study of spirochetes in exudates from syphilitic lesions): Employs special condensers, i.e., condensers which do not allow any light rays, reaching object(s) to be magnified, to directly enter the microscope objective. Thus any light entering the microscope tube is reflected rather than transmitted.

74. **Antibacterial serums:** Horses are immunized by inoculation. First with dead cultures and short intervals (every other day); and, second, with increasing doses of living, virulent cultures of the specific microorganisms until their blood contains substances (bacteriolysins, agglutinins, precipitins, or opsonins) that directly or indirectly destroy either the life or the activity of the specific bacteria. The horses are bled in the same way as are antitoxin horses.

Bacterial vaccines: These are suspensions of killed pathogenic bacteria in physiological salt solution to which a preservative has been added. A bacterial vaccine contains no preformed protective antibodies. It is the same protein that causes the disease, so modified that it will not produce the disease yet so little altered that it will stimulate the body cells to form the substances which will promptly destroy the infective agent.

A bacterial vaccine is said to be *polyvalent* when several strains of the same microorganism are embodied in it. *Autogenous vaccines* are prepared from a culture of microorganisms recovered from a particular patient and intended for the treatment of that patient.

75.   Bacterial **Synergism** occurs when two bacterial species, growing together, produce a reaction or effect which cannot be produced by either species growing alone.

76.   **Active immunity:** That immunity which results from the presence of antibodies developed within the body in response to, and as a result of, direct antigenic stimulation.

   Passive immunity: Acquired immunity produced by administration of preformed antibodies.

77.   RNA (ribonucleic acid) is a cytoplasm component whereas DNA (desoxyribonucleic acid) occurs in nuclei for the most part. Chromosomes contain large (up to 92%) amounts of DNA-nucleoprotein. This fact suggests that DNA is important in heredity. RNA, on the other hand, plays a role in protein synthesis within cells.

   Viruses are, at least in part, nucleoprotein. Plant viruses are of the RNA type while bacteriophages (the bacterial viruses) are of the DNA type. Animal viruses are more complicated. They can either have RNA- or DNA-nucleoprotein and they may also contain other compounds such as carbohydrates or lipids.

   Because of the lability of the purine N-glycoside bonds, when either DNA or RNA is hydrolyzed under mildly acid conditions, the purine bases leave the molecule. If, after removal of the purine bases, basic fuchsin (Schiff's aldehyde reagent) is added, the desoxyribose (in DNA), but not the ribose (in RNA), gives a pink color. This reaction is presumably due to the greater aldehydic properties of desoxyribofuranose as compared to ribofuranose. *This test for DNA is called the Feulgen test.*

78.   **Aerobic organisms** are organisms that (obligate aerobes) require oxygen for their growth or (facultative aerobes) may grow either in the presence or in the absence of oxygen.

   Anaerobic organisms are organisms that (obligate anaerobes) can only grow in the absence of oxygen or (facultative anaerobes) may grow either in the absence or the presence of oxygen.

81.   1. Isolate organism
   2. Inject isolate into laboratory animal
   3. The animal becomes ill due to bacterium
   4. Re-isolate the bacterium in pure culture

82.   Glucose 1%; lactose 10%. The principle of the test reaction is based upon the rate the carbohydrates are fermented. Those organisms growing on the slant reproduce at a faster rate than those that were stabbed into the butt

of the slant. Therefore, for a Gram-negative, glucose +, lactose-rod, the glucose near the slant will be used up in 6–8 hours, while the glucose in the butt will not be used up even after 24 hours. The slant will show an acid reaction for the first 4–8 hours and then will revert to an alkaline reaction as the bacteria break down the protein to alkaline end-products. These same organisms in the butt will still be using the carbohydrate after 24 hours thus an acid butt reaction is noted. A gram-negative, glucose +, lactose-rod gives an alkaline slant with acid butt reaction. However, if a Gram-negative rod ferments both glucose and lactose, the reaction will be acid slant with acid butt because of the excessive concentration of lactose present in the medium. A gram-negative rod that ferments neither sugar will have an alkaline slant with alkaline butt reaction after 24 hours at 37°C.

85. a. Blood agar plate, EMB, thioglycollate, 7H10
     b. Thioglycollate, thiol, BHI broth
     c. Sabouraud's, Petragnani, 7H10, blood agar plate, Tinsdale's, Staph 110, thioglycollate
     d. EMB, MacConkey's, HE, XLD, SS, BiS, anaerobic media for *Bacteroides*
     e. Blood agar plate, Thayer-Martin, chocolate agar, anaerobic media

88. 1. Growth requirements
     2. Hemolytic patterns

96. Typhoid and paratyphoid fevers, diphtheria, bacillary dysentery, poliomyelitis, meningococcal meningitis, strep throat, coagulase-positive staph infections.

104. **Pyelitis:** Inflammation of pelvis or kidney.

113. Typhoid fever, pneumonia, bacterial endocarditis, generalized *Salmonella* infections, peritonitis, puerperal sepsis, wound infections, etc.

118. **Bacteremia:** The presence, without multiplication, of bacteria in the bloodstream.
     Septicemia: The presence *and multiplication* of microorganisms in the bloodstream.

119. **Pyelitis:** Inflammation of the *pelvis* of the kidney.
     Pyelonephritis: Inflammation of the kidney *and* its pelvis.

120. **Boil (furuncle):** A cutaneous abscess occurring as the result of infection by pyogenic organisms (usually *Staphylococcus aureus*) of a hair follicle or of the ducts of cutaneous glands.
     Abscess: A localized collection of pus anywhere in the body.

121. **Furuncle:** See the preceding answer.
     Carbuncle: Carbuncles differ from boils in that they are larger and have a flat surface discharging pus from multiple drainage points.

124. **Food poisoning** Is due to ingestion of food contaminated with harmful bacterial exotoxins such as those of *Clostridium botulinum* or certain staphylococci.
     Ptomaines (cadaverine, putrescine, etc.) are products of protein decomposition whose oral administration produces no harmful effect. Therefore the term "ptomaine poisoning" should not be used to indicate food poisoning.
     Food-borne infections include the *Salmonella* infections (here the symp-

toms are similar to those of food poisoning), typhoid fever, cholera, and dysentery. Ingestion of food contaminated with harmful bacteria.

128. **Somatic:** Pertaining to the body or "soma." The O antigens.
Capsular: The capsule (pneumococcus, *Klebsiella*) surrounding the bacterial cell contains a capsular antigen which is a type-specific polysaccharide (identification of various serological types by means of the Neufeld-Quellung reaction). The K antigens.

129. **Somatic:** See preceding answer.
Flagellar: Pertaining to the flagella, i.e., to the long filaments which surround the body of motile bacteria, filaments which move with a wave-like motion. In peritrichous bacteria (*Salmonella typhi*, for instance), the entire organism is surrounded by flagella. The flagellar antigen is called "H" antigen.

131. An inflammatory reaction in ganglion cells of the brain is called **encephalitis.** If the inflammation is in the spinal cord the term is **myelitis.**

133. Lactose (a disaccharide) would be decomposed to its two monosaccharides, glucose and galactose. Medium could not be used because there would be no lactose, only glucose and galactose, therefore it would be glucose fermentation and not lactose fermentation.

135. Non-synthetic because it is not chemically defined.

151. Most media are sterilized at 15 pounds (pressure per sq. inch) for 15 minutes at 120 degrees Centigrade. Decontamination of contaminated materials is 15 pounds, 120°C., 30 min.

156. 1. Hot-air oven or,
2. Autoclave for 45 minutes at 121°C.

158. **Chocolate agar** (used for the cultivation of *Neisseria*) is agar to which blood has been added and heated until it turned dark-brown or chocolate in color. **Plain blood agar,** on the other hand, utilizes unheated (i.e., unchanged) blood.

163. 1. Filtration with Seitz or Millipore filters
2. Autoclave, 121°C., 15 lbs., 15 min.
3. Inspissation
4. Gaseous, ethylene oxide
5. Tyndallization

164. Confluent streak the bacteria over the surface of supportive agar medium. Place a filter disc impregnated with the disinfectant on the surface of plate. Incubate. Note zones of inhibition of growth about the disc. Using a sterile loop, obtain an inoculum from the area of no growth and subculture to a supportive medium. If the bacterium grows, the agent was bacteriostatic. If the bacterium does not grow, the agent was bactericidal.

168. Add 99 ml. sterile broth to 1 ml. stock solution.

171. **Antibiotic:** A bacteriostatic substance (bacitracin, Aureomycin, erythromycin, etc.) produced by microorganisms. Some (Chloromycetin, for instance) may be synthetically prepared.
Chemotherapeutic agent: A chemical (sulfonamides, Furadantin, etc.) used for the treatment ("chemotherapy") of various diseases. Chemothera-

peutic agents are toxic to particular disease-producing organisms but relatively harmless to man.

181. 1. Alpha toxin
     2. Beta toxin
     3. Gamma toxin
     4. Delta toxin
     5. Enterotoxin
     6. Leucocidin

182. Coagulase test: Add approximately 0.5 ml. of 24 hour broth culture of isolate to approximately 0.5 ml. rabbit plasma. Mix. Place tube in 37°C. water bath. Examine for clot formation every 15 minutes for a period of 3 hours.
     Fibrinolysis test: Add $CaCl_2$ to rabbit plasma. Allow for clot formation to take place. Add an aliquot of 24 hour broth culture of isolate. Mix. Place in 37°C. water bath. Examine for lysis of the clot every 15 mintues for a period of 3 hours.

184. Because the red blood cells possess catalase and when the hydrogen peroxide is added to the colony, a false-positive reaction may occur.

190. 1. Anaerobic, high-protein conditions so *Cl. botulinum* could replicate and release exotoxin.
     2. Aerobic, high-carbohydrate medium, so *Staph.* spp. could replicate and release enterotoxin.

191. Rabbit plasma because of the high concentration of coagulase-reacting factor (CRF).

193. Both colony types may be beta hemolytic. However, staphylococcus colony exhibits a larger colony (5-6 mm. diameter) with a narrow zone of hemolysis while streptococcus colony is small (2-4 mm. diameter) with a wide zone of hemolysis.

201. To differentiate the pathogen, *S. aureus,* from the opportunist, *S. epidermidis.*

206. 1. Lysogenized group A beta hemolytic streptococcus
     2. Group A beta hemolytic streptococcus
     3. Group A beta hemolytic streptococcus
     4. Group A beta hemolytic streptococcus
     5. Group D viridans group streptococci

214. No. Hemolytic patterns, of diagnostic value, are dependent upon:
     a. The base medium used as the blood agar base
     b. The pH of the base medium
     c. The animal species of red blood cells used
     d. The concentration of red blood cells used
     e. The method of incubation, e.g., whether aerobic or anaerobic methods used, and
     f. Bacteria, other than streptococci may produce hemolysins

215. 1. Grouping of beta hemolytic streptococci according to the C-carbohydrate of Lancefield.
     2. Typing of group A beta hemolytic streptococci according to the M-protein.

3. T-typing of group A beta hemolytic streptococci according to the T-antigen(s).

216. 1. Sheep. Prevent confusion of colony types of beta hemolytic streptococci and *H. hemolyticus*, which also produces beta hemolytic colonies on blood plates other than sheep.
2. 10% defibrinated. Because hemolysis is dependent upon nucleotides and serum or plasma proteins that are present in the defibrinated blood.
3. ACD solution contains citrate which inhibits growth of streptococcus dextrose which inhibits synthesis of streptolysin S. Also, streptococcal antibodies may be present which may inhibit the growth of streptococci.

218. *Strep. fecalis* following abdominal surgery or viridans streptococci following dental work.

220. 1. Bile solubility: *S. salivarius* is bile-insoluble while *S. pneumoniae* is bile-soluble.
2. Optochin sensitivity: *S. salivarius* is optochin-insensitive and *S. pneumoniae* is optochin-sensitive.

222. Streptococci: Chains of cocci (resulting from cocci dividing in one plane). Staphylococci: Grape-like clusters of cocci (resulting from cocci dividing in multiple planes).

237. *Hemophilus influenzae;* pneumococci; *Staphylococcus aureus;* alpha and gamma streptococci (also beta streptococci of serologic group other than A); *Branhella catarrhalis;* coliform bacteria; *Candida;* diphtheroids.

238. Beta hemolytic streptococci (group A); *Neisseria meningitidis; Corynebacterium diphtheriae; Bordetella pertussis;* coliform bacteria; predominance of *Hemophilus influenzae; Staphylococcus aureus; Candida albicans.*

244. Schick test: A skin test for diphtheria.
Dick test: A skin test for scarlet/fever.
Neufeld test (capsular swelling or quellung test): The determination of pneumococcus types employing type-specific antisera. Also meningococcus, *Hemophilus pertussis* serotypes.

246. Alpha streptococci: This group of streptococci includes the strains which, on blood agar plates, produce a greenish coloration in the medium and partial hemolysis around the colonies.
Beta streptococci: This group of streptococci includes those strains which, on blood agar plates, produce colonies which are surrounded by clear, colorless zones of complete hemolysis.

247. Alpha streptococci: See the preceding answer.
Gamma streptococci: This group produces no hemolysis on blood agar plates.

251. Gram-positive: *Strep. pyogenes, S. pneumoniae*
Gram-negative: *Hemophilus influenzae, Neisseria meningitidis*

252. 1. Bile solubility: Pneumococcus is bile-soluble and other alpha streptococci are bile-insoluble.
2. Inulin fermentation: Pneumococcus ferments inulin and other alpha streptococci do not ferment inulin.
3. Optochin disc sensitivity: Pneumococcus is sensitive to optochin and other alpha streptococci are insensitive to optochin.

253. Presence of a capsule that is anti-phagocytic.

254. 1. Microscopic: Neufeld-Quellung reaction
     2. Macroscopic: Slide agglutination

255. The elaboration of a greater quantity of capsular material.

257. "R" form is a rough form, avirulent form, devoid of the capsule.
     "S" form is a smooth form, virulent form, and the capsule is present.

260. 1. *Streptococcus pneumoniae*
     2. *Hemophilus influenzae*
     3. *Neisseria meningitidis*
     4. *Klebsiella pneumoniae*

269. On defibrinated sheep blood agar plates, **surface colonies of pneumococci** are small, shiny, flat, and transparent and appear green as a result of discoloration of the medium. Type III colonies are larger, green, raised, mucoid, and confluent. They resemble oil drops.
     On defibrinated sheep blood agar plates, **surface colonies of streptococci** are small, raised, convex, usually more opaque and surrounded by narrow zone of green hemolysis.
     Deep colonies of both pneumococci and alpha streptococci have similar appearances. They may be differentiated on a serological (Neufeld-Quellung, capsular swelling) basis or on a biochemical basis (pneumococci are desoxycholate-soluble, sodium lauryl sulfate-soluble, bile-soluble and inulin-fermenting. Their growth is inhibited by optochin [ethylhydrocupreine hydrochloride]).

270. Small, shiny, transparent colonies which appear green because of discolorization of the blood agar.

278. *Mimae* are Gram-negative diplobacilli.
     Mimae grow on EMB and MacConkey's agar

280. 1. Isolate an oxidase-positive, Gram-negative diplococcus.
     2. Demonstrate that the isolate ferments glucose only.

281. Set up appropriate fermentations. *N. gonorrhoeae* ferments only glucose.
     N. meningitidis ferments glucose and maltose only.

286. *N. meningitidis*
     Demonstrating a positive quellung reaction using type-specific immune sera or by isolating the organism, demonstrating the isolate to be an oxidase-positive, Gram-negative diplococcus, with sero-specificity to typing antisera.

287. Gram-negative, diplococci, that appear as kidney-beans with flattened sides adjacent, some require CO_2 for growth, all are oxidase-positive. Species are differentiated according to the fermentation of various carbohydrates.

298. *Neisseria meningitidis;* pneumococci; beta streptococci; staphylococci; *Hemophilus influenzae; Mycobacterium tuberculosis; Cryptococcus neoformans.*

307. Meningococci and pneumococci, when present, usually autolyze rapidly.

311. *Escherichia* is of animal origin. *Enterobacter* is of soil origin.

312. a. Typhoid fever (2nd week of illness): Stool; bismuth sulfide agar; pure

cultured identified with group-specific immune sera.

b. Typhus fever (2nd week of illness): Serum for tube agglutination tests using OX_{19}, OXK, and OX_2 (Weil-Felix test). Positive titer with OX_{19}.

313. 1. First week: Whole blood and possibly urine.
2. Second week: Feces.

317. a. Gram-negative and bacilli; non-lac fermentors; anaerogenic.
b. *S. typhi* is motile; produces H_2S.

323. 1. Presence of a capsule
2. *K. pneumoniae* is urease-positive
3. *K. pneumoniae* is V-P positive

325. 1. Food infection is ingestion of contaminated food or water. The organisms must replicate in sufficient amount for the release of enough endotoxins to cause symptoms.
2. Food intoxication is the ingestion of preformed toxin.

326. Endotoxin: Toxin contained in the cell body and given off only after the death of the bacteria; e.g., typhoid endotoxin.
Exotoxin: Soluble toxin discharged into the medium surrounding the cells; e.g., diphtheria or tetanus toxin.
Enterotoxin: A toxin produced by *Staphylococcus aureus*. It gives rise to typical symptoms of food poisoning when absorbed by the cells of the intestinal mucosa.

327. 1. *Alcaligenes fecalis*
2. *Proteus vulgaris*
3. *Providencia* spp.
4. *Klebsiella* spp.

330. Because EMB has eosis, methylene blue, lactose and sucrose. *E. coli* ferments sugars to lower the pH. With lowering of pH, the eosin and methylene blue are precipitated in the colony.

337. *S. typhi:* Alkaline slant, acid butt, no gas, small amount of H_2S.
Sh. dysenteriae: Alkaline slant, acid butt, no gas, no H_2S.

355. IX, XII = somatic, cell wall antigens
Vi = capsule
d; — = monophasic with group-specific flagellar antigen only

356. 1. *S. typhi* has the antigenic formula IX, XII, Vi, d; —.
2. *S. paratyphi B* has the antigenic formula I, IV, V, XII; b; 1, 2
3. Cross reactions occur because of the common somatic antigen "XII"

357. The Vi antigen masks the somatic antigens therefore with fresh isolates only the Vi antigen is exposed to the anti-Vi serum. No reaction takes place with *Salmonella* polyvalent antiserum because these somatic "O" are masked. The Vi antigen is heat-labile therefore boiling removes it, thus exposing the somatic "O" antigens.
S. typhi is in Kauffman-White Scheme Group D, therefore should now react with *Salmonella* polyvalent and Group D antisera.

361. Indol production; Methyl Red reaction; Voges-Proskauer reaction (production of acetylmethylcarbinol from dextrose); citrate utilization as the only source of carbon.

364. a. Indol-Methyl Red/Voges-Proskauer/Citrate; Baltimore Biological Laboratory; Eosin Methylene Blue; *Shigella-Salmonella.*
      b. Bismuth Sulfite; Purified Protein Derivative (a form of tuberculin); Voges-Proskauer reaction.
      c. Sulfide-Indol-Motility; Triple Sugar-Iron Agar; Minimum Lethal Dose; Gonococcus.
      d. Mucoid colony; Smooth colony; Acid-Fast bacilli.

365. 1. *Escherichia* ++−−
      2. *Enterobacter* −−++
      3. *Citrobacter* −+−+

391. Coliform bacilli; *Proteus, Pseudomonas;* enterococci; *Candida albicans;* beta streptococci; coagulase-positive staphylococci; *Mycobacterium tuberculosis; Salmonella.*

392. Diphtheroids; coliform bacilli; coagulase-negative staphylococci: *Proteus* sp.; alpha and beta streptococci; saprophytic yeasts; enterococci; aerobic spore-forming bacilli.

393. Large and very mucoid. They tend to coalesce with prolonged incubation.

414. **Escherichia coli** is indol and methyl red positive; Voges-Proskauer and citrate negative.
      Enterobacter is indol and methyl red negative; Voges-Proskauer and citrate positive.

418. It is practically impossible to distinguish between *Enterobacter* and *Klebsiella* on a cultural (on blood agar, EMB, MacConkey, etc., capsular strains produce colonies which have a similar appearance) basis, on a biochemical (IMViC reaction) basis or, in most cases, on a morphological (both species are short Gram-negative bacilli) basis. Serological methods (Neufeld-Quellung reaction) are required.

425. Group I: Photochromogens — require exposure to light for pigmentation.
      Group II: Scotochromogens — colonies produce pigment with or without light.
      Group III: Nonphotochromogens — colonies with no pigmentation with light.
      Group IV: Rapid Growers — colonies appearing in less than one week.

454. 1. More rapid development of colonies
      2. Observe cord formation

455. In smears made from condensation water positive for tubercle bacilli egg media slants. Middlebrook 7H10 colonies using low power ocular.

456. **Acid-fast organisms** resist decolorization (**nonacid-fast organisms,** on the other hand, are promptly decolorized) by acid-alcohol after being stained with basic fuchsin.

471. 1. Acid-fast stained smear of sediment or of the fluid after concentration
      2. Examine fluid at intervals for pellicle formation
      3. Acid-fast stained smears of pellicle when this is present
      4. Culture in Petragnani's special medium
      5. Tryptophane test (probably of little value) is used for Tb meningitis

472. A method of reporting (I to X) the number of acid-fast bacilli present in

a smear containing these organisms.

476. **Bacillus Calmette-Guerin vaccine.** A vaccine prepared with attenuated strain of *Mycobacterium bovis.* Used to confer artificial, active immunity against this disease.

480. **Human tuberculosis (M. tuberculosis):** Long, slender, acid-fast rods. Not pathogenic to calves or fowls. Mildly pathogenic to rabbits. On first isolation, satisfactory growth on glycerin broth, egg, glycerin-egg or glycerin-potato. The pH of inoculated glycerol medium increases first then decreases. pH of tuberculin is acid.
Mycobacterium bovis: Usually shorter, thicker, acid-fast rods. Highly pathogenic to rabbits and calves but not pathogenic to fowls. Growth in above media is more difficult. pH of inoculated glycerol medium steadily increases. pH of tuberulin is, as a rule, alkaline.

482. The demonstration of presence of acid-fast bacilli in smears and cultures from these lesions.

484. A drop of reagent is added to colonies of tubercle bacilli. Catalase-positive colonies will give bubbling of nascent oxygen. Blood agar, and other catalase-containing media, should not be used for this test or false-positives may occur.

487. To distinguish human type strains of *Mycobacterium tuberculosis* from the non-human varieties.

511. Fermentation reactions (see chart below) and virulence tests (diphtheroids are nonpathogenic to man and guinea pigs) are more reliable means of differentiation than the study of the morphology on stained smears.

	Dextrose	Maltose	Lactose	Saccharose	Dextrin	Mannite
C. diphtheriae	+	+	–	–	+	–
C. hoffmanni	–	–	–	–	–	–
C. xerose	+	+	–	+	–	–

515. **Diphtheria bacillus:** *Corynebacterium diphtheriae;* Loeffler's serum, Tinsdale's, or potassium tellurite.
Tetanus bacillus: *Clostridium tetani;* anaerobic blood agar plate.
Whooping cough bacillus: *Bordetella pertussis;* Bordet-Gengou medium.
Paratyphoid B: *Salmonella schottmuelleri;* EMB, SS, MacConkey agar.
Tubercle bacillus: *Mycobacterium tuberculosis;* Petragnani's medium.
Gonococcus: *Neisseria gonorrhoeae;* chocolate agar (10% CO_2) or Thayer-Martin.
Typhoid: *Salmonella typhi;* EMB, SS, MacConkey.

520. 1. Organism *(Corynebacterium diphtheriae)* must be isolated (culture in Loeffler's serum slants, cystine-tellurite-blood agar plates, or Tinsdale's plates)
2. Virulence tests

526. **Endotoxin:** A toxic substance (intimately associated with the cell wall) formed by bacteria, especially the enteric bacilli and other Gram-negative organisms. Upon autolysis endotoxins, which are heat-stable lipopolysaccharides, are liberated into the enfironment. They may produce fever, irreversible shock and many other pathophysiological effects.

Exotoxin: A toxic, and also highly specific, substance secreted into the medium by certain Gram-positive (rarely Gram-negative) bacteria. Exotoxins are heat-labile, protein in nature and possess antigenic properties. By treatment with formalin, heat, or through prolonged storage, toxins may be converted into *toxoids* (nonpoisonous).

527. Diphtheria toxin may be converted into toxoid, which is nontoxic but has the same combining power with antitoxin as does the toxin from which it is derived. The conversion is accomplished by heat or by treatment with various percentages of formaldehyde (anatoxin Ramon). Diphtheria toxoid treated or precipitated by alum has been found to be an effective immunizing agent. Toxoid preparations do not contain animal serum, are stable and do not become toxic. Toxoid does, however, cause considerable local and even general reaction in subjects who are sensitive to diphtheria bacillus protein.

528.

	Endotoxins	**Exotoxins**
Method of Production	Released through autolysis only	Excreted from living organisms
Toxicity	Weak	High
Specificity	Relatively non-specific	Usually specific
Antigenic Properties	Weakly antigenic	Highly antigenic
Thermal Behavior	Heat-stable*	Heat-labile†
Effect of Treatment With Formalin	Not converted to nontoxic antigenic toxoid	Converted to nontoxic antigenic toxoid

*They withstand more than 120°C. for one hour
†Inactivated at 60–80°C.

536. 1. A saline suspension of organisms (from growth on cystine-glucose blood agar slant) is either heated for 30 minutes at 60°C. or added 0.5% formalin.
   2. Agglutination tests are then set up with this bacterial suspension and *Francisella tularensis* antiserum.

538. Danger of infection to laboratory workers is very high.

562. 1. *Brucella abortus* is microaerophilic. It requires 25% CO_2 on primary isolation and 10% on subsequent transfers.
   2. *Neisseria gonorrhoeae* and *N. meningitidis.*

567.

Organism	CO_2 required for growth	H_2S formation	Pathogenicity for guinea pigs	Growth on media with 1:25,000 basic fuchsin	Growth on media with 1:50,000 thionin	Growth on media with 1:100,000 pyronin
B. abortus	+	++	+	+++	–	+++
B. melitensis	–	±	++	+++	+++	+
B. suis	–	++++	++	–	+++	–

568. *Brucella abortus:* Optimum 37°C. Microaerophilic (requires 10% CO_2).
   Brucella melitensis: Optimum 37°C. (20–40 degree range). Aerobic (re-

quires no CO_2 for growth).
Brucella suis: Optimum 37°C. Aerobic (requires no CO_2 for growth).

571. a. Gram-negative; both attribute virulence to the presence of type-specific capsule.
   b. *H. influenzae* is a bacillus while *N. meningitidis* is a diplococcus.

575. The members within the genus have an affinity for blood.

591. *Hemophilus influenzae* is aerobic, requires blood for growth. *Bacteroides* is an obligate anaerobe and does not require blood for growth.

609. a. 1. Gram-positive
       2. Bacilli
   b. 1. *Cl. tetani* is a sporulating rod
       2. *C. diphtheriae* is a non-sporulating rod that possesses characteristic metachromatic granules

610. a. Enterotoxin-producing *S. aureus*
   b. Exotoxin of *Cl. botulinum*
   c. Exotoxin of *Cl. perfringens*

635. Members of the pleuropneumonia group of organisms belong to the family Mycoplasmataceae. Pathogenic, parasitic, and saprophytic species exist. One of the six species found in man is pathogenic. This species, *Mycoplasma pneumoniae*, is associated with primary atypical pneumonia and bronchitis. *M. hominis* may occasionally invade the bloodstream. All species lack cell walls, Gram-negative, pleomorphic, nonmotile, non-encapsulated, and non-sporulating. Aerobic to facultative anaerobic, grow on media enriched with serum, ascitic fluid, whole blood, or egg yolk.

646. No. Presence of methylene blue which inhibits Gram-positive bacteria.

663. At 37°C. (Sabouraud's medium and blood agar) for several days and at 22°C. for 2–3 weeks.

673. Endothrix: Said of *Trichophyton* species which invade the hair shaft.
   Exothrix: Said of *Trichophyton* and other fungi which grow mostly on the outside of the hair shaft.

674. Hyphae (singular: Hypha): Any one of the filaments of a fungal thallus.
   Mycelium: A network or mass of branched hyphae.

683. The mode of motility, and the degree of tightness of the coil. Spirochetes are tightly coiled while spirilium is very loosely coiled.

711. A rickettsial stain. Smears are fixed by heat then stained with basic fuchsin followed by decolorization in citric acid and counterstain with methylene blue. Rickettsiae stain red and tissue elements blue. Macchiavello's stain may be used for the elementary bodies of viruses of the psittacosis and lymphogranuloma venereum group.

744. Complete enzyme systems are lacking therefore they require specific host cells with appropriate enzyme systems to carry on viral requirements of replication and synthesis.

753. RNA, single-stranded, 7–30 millimicrons, cubical in shape, no envelop or peplos, ether-resistant, icosohedril, 32 capsomeres.

754. Enteroviruses are Poliovirus, Coxsackie, and ECHO, and the Rhinoviruses.

778. Hershey-Chase experiment with T-2 phage and *E. coli.*

779. Spontaneous mutation with selection of these new mutants which are more adapted to grow in the new environment. Takes place during serial blind passage.

780. Refers to a change in a virus to a new host other than from that originally isolated. The new host can be a new species or just a different organ or tissue of the same host. The virus which could not originally grow in the new host is adapted in such a way that it can grow and multiply in the new host.

781.

				Accumulation			
Dose (mg.)	log	Death	Survivors	Death	Survivors	Ration	%
1.25	0.09	2	3	2	3	2/10	20
2.5	0.40	1	4	3	5	3/8	37
5.0	0.70	5	0	8	1	8/9	90
10.0	1.0	4	1	12	1	12/13	92
20.0	1.3	5	0	17	0	12/17	100

$$\frac{\% \text{ above } 50\% - 50\%}{\% \text{ above } 50\% - \% \text{ below } 50\%} = \frac{90 - 50}{90 - 37} = \frac{40}{53} = 0.76$$

Cal. factor = 0.76
log dil. factor = 0.3

.228 ∴ log 0.4 + 0.228 = 0.628 or log 0.628 is 5% LD.

782. Ways in which chick embryo are useful:
a. For neutralization tests
   2. For production of vaccines
   3. For titrations of antigen potency
   4. For primary isolations
   Advantages:
   1. Has no latent virus
   2. Has not the ability to produce antibodies
   3. Cheap
   4. Readily accessible
   5. No animal caretaker
   6. No cages
   Disadvantages:
   1. Must have bacteriological sterile material—thus must add antibiotics to preparations
   2. Not all viruses can be cultured in eggs
   3. Interference phenomenon

783. Neutralization index gives a numerical value which can be used as a measure of the virus-neutralizing capacity of a given set of serum samples, e.g., acute vs. convalescent. If the serum index shows a 1.7 log difference between acute and convalescent serum then the index is significant.

784. The smallest amount of virus suspension causing a manifestation in a host per unit volume is considered to be a unit of infectious particle. Therefore, titer is the reciprocal of the highest dilution of infectious particles/unit volume.

785. A2 means Influenza A type with subtype of strain 2

Detroit means place of isolation
5 means the number of passages before finally isolated
71 means the year isolated

787. Also shingles, fever blister, keratitis, smallpox.

797. Nucleic acid (DNA or RNA) nucleus and protein coat (capsid). Some possess a capsule called an envelop and still others possess appendages called "spicules."

811. **Viruses:** Disease-producing agents smaller than the bacteria (filterable viruses can pass through bacteria-proof filters). Viruses are obligate parasites and they require living cells (chick embryo, etc.) for their cultivation. Inclusion bodies (Negri bodies of rabies, elementary bodies of vaccinia) produced by viruses within living cells often have a diagnostic significance. **Rickettsiae:** These are also intracellular parasites of size intermediate between the bacteria and the filterable viruses. Morphologically rickettsiae resemble small bacteria (cocci, diplococci, short bacilli) and are Gram-negative. Giemsa appears to be the best general stain for them. None of the rickettsiae is easily cultured. The well-known rickettsial diseases usually fall into three types: Typhus fever, spotted fevers, and tsutsugamushi.

812. **Street virus:** A term commonly employed (rabies) to designate the virus as it exists in the natural infection in dogs or other animals.
Fixed virus: Street virus, when passed through the brain of rabbits, rapidly becomes "fixed" in virulence for this animal (incubation six to seven days) and vaccines prepared from "fixed virus" are commonly used for the prevention of rabies in man.

826.

Disease	Genus & Species	Cow/Man
Strep throat	*Strep. pyogenes*	Cow & man
Diphtheria	*C. diphtheriae*	Cow & man
Strep throat	*Strep. lactis*	Cow
Typhoid	*S. typhi*	Man
Dysentery	*S. dysenteriae*	Man
Polio	Polio virus	Man
Cholera	*V. cholerae*	Man
Q fever	*C. burnetii*	Man

828. Heating for a sufficient time and temperature necessary to kill pathogens.

830. Purpose is to locate coliforms and this is done by adding water to lactose fermentation tubes. Coliforms ferment lactose with acid and gas in 24–48 hours. Presumptive evidence that *E. coli* is present and presumptive evidence of fecal contamination.

831. Twice the concentration of lactose per tube. When an equal amount of water is added single (1 X) strength remains.

832. Pathogens may be in such few numbers it is possible to miss them; also, *E. coli* is an index of fecal pollution.

833. Synergism; also, other bacteria than *E. coli* will give this reaction, e.g., *E. aerogenes.*

837. More superficial because of the greater recovery with multiple samplings.

847. | Disease | Etiologic Agent |
|---|---|
| 1. Salmonellosis | *Salmonella* spp. |
| 2. Shigellosis | *Shigella* spp. |
| 3. Cholera | *Vibrio cholerae* |
| 4. Typhoid | *Sal. typhi* |
| 5. Polio | Polio virus |

860. Streak EMB plates with material from the tubes (lactose broth tubes) which have shown gas formation in the previous test.

Section III MICROBIOLOGY

Subsection III: SEROLOGY & IMMUNOLOGY

SEROLOGY & IMMUNOLOGY EXAMINATION

Edited by Arthur Simmons, Immunohematology Director, MetPath, Inc.

1. What is serum? | See p. 427

2. To obtain a specimen of serum, an anticoagulant must be added to the blood.   T   F | F

3. What is serology? | See p. 427

4. How does serum differ from plasma? | See p. 427

5. How does serum differ from whole blood? | See p. 427

6. What are "agglutinins"? In what fraction of the serum do they occur? | See p. 427

7. The fraction of the serum which includes most of the protein antibodies is:
   a. Alpha 2 globulin
   b. Alpha-1 globulin
   c. Beta globulin
   d. Gamma globulin | d

8. What are "agglutinogens"? In what fraction of the blood do they occur? | See p. 427

9. Antigenic specificity is a function of the chemical structure of an antigen.   T   F | T

10. Antibodies which act upon bacterial invaders so that they will be more readily ingested and digested by certain white blood cell corpuscles ("phagocytes") are called:
    a. Agglutinins
    b. Precipitins
    c. Opsonins
    d. Bacteriolysins | c

11. How to opsonins act? | See p. 428

12. Opsonins are bacteriotrophins.   T   F | T

13. What is the "opsonocytophagic test"? | See p. 428

14. An antibody which differs from antitoxin in that instead of neutralizing soluble toxin it kills and dissolves the bacterial cell itself is called:
    a. Agglutinin
    b. Precipitin
    c. Opsonin
    d. Bacteriolysin | d

15. Phagocytosis by reticuloendothelial cells is greatly enhanced by:
    a. Hemolysins
    b. Opsonins
    c. Specific antitoxins
    d. Protective (neutralizing antibodies | b

397

16. A reaction in which antibodies which had previously existed and had disappeared from the blood are redeveloped upon injection of a nonspecific antigen is called:
    a. Prozone reaction
    b. Gruber-Widal reaction
    c. Cross-reaction
    d. Anamnestic reaction   d

17. A local inflammatory reaction of the skin (more marked in tuberculous subjects than in normal persons) following inoculation with tuberculin is known as:
    a. Prausnitz-Küstner reaction
    b. Pirquet's reaction   b
    c. Schultz-Charlton reaction
    d. Noguchi's luetin reaction

18. An inflammatory reaction following an injection of protein in the skin of a sensitized animal is known as:
    a. Danysz phenomenon
    b. Schultz-Charlton phenomenon
    c. Arthus phenomenon   c
    d. Shwartzman reaction

19. Antigens which show cross reactions when the species from which they are derived are remotely related are called:
    a. Natural antigens
    b. Mixed antigens
    c. Heterophilic antigens   c
    d. Forsmann antigens

20. An antigen substance suitable for serological tests but incapable of stimulating antibody formation is called:
    a. Reagin
    b. Receptor
    c. Hapten   c
    d. Opsonin

21. 0.002 gram/10 ml. is the same as dilution:
    a. 1:200
    b. 1:2,000
    c. 1:5,000   c
    d. 1:20,000
    e. 1:50,000
    f. None of these

22. What do the following standard abbreviations stand for:
    a. ASTO — CRP — PPD   See p. 428
    b. STS — VDRL — FTA — TPI   ”
    c. TPA — TPIA — TPCF — TPMB   ”
    d. RPCF — KRP — CNL — CSL   ”

23. A single positive agglutination test is sufficient to prove existence of active disease.   T   F   F

24. List at least three different applications of precipitin tests.   See p. 428

25. An antibody which renders its antigenic microorganism (usually a virus) noninfective is:
    a. A lysin
    b. A precipitin
    c. A neutralizing antibody   c
    d. An opsonin

26. Capillary blood cannot be used for typing of blood.   T   F   F (although it is not recommended)

27. Blood type O contains the following agglutinogens in its red cells:
    a. A
    b. B
    c. Both A & B
    d. Neither A nor B   d

28. Blood type A contains the following agglutinogen in its red cells:
    a. A   a
    b. B
    c. Both A & B
    d. Neither A nor B

29. Blood type B contains the following agglutinogen in its red cells:
    a. A
    b. B   b
    c. Both A & B
    d. Neither A nor B

30. Blood type AB contains the following agglutinogens in its red cells:
    a. A
    b. B
    c. Both A & B   c
    d. Neither A nor B

31. Blood type O contains the following agglutinins in its plasma (or serum):
    a. Anti-A
    b. Anti-B
    c. Both anti-A & anti-B   c
    d. Neither anti-A nor anti-B

32. Blood type A contains the following agglutinin in its plasma (or serum):
    a. Anti-A
    b. Anti-B   b
    c. Both anti-A & anti-B
    d. Neither anti-A nor anti-B

33. Blood type B contains the following agglutinin in its plasma (or serum):
    a. Anti-A   a

    b. Anti-B
    c. Both anti-A & anti-B
    d. Neither anti-A nor anti-B

34. Blood type AB contains the following agglutinins in its
    plasma (or serum):
    a. Anti-A
    b. Anti-B
    c. Both anti-A and anti-B
    d. Neither anti-A nor anti-B   d

35. A_2B blood occasionally has the following antibody in the
    plasma:
    a. Anti-B
    b. Anti-A_1 b (20–25%
    c. Anti-A_2 of all A_2B
    d. Anti-H   bloods)

36. A potent anti-H is obtained from the seeds of *Ulex euro-
    paeus* (Gorse) and this reacts most strongly with:
    a. A_1 cells
    b. A_2 cells
    c. A_3 cells   c
    d. B cells

37. Anti-H agglutinates A_1 cells.   T   F   F

38. The red cells of blood type O are not agglutinated by the
    serum of any blood type.   T   F   T

39. The serum of type O will agglutinate the red cells of the
    other three types.   T   F   T

40. Blood type O occurs in the following percentage of the Cau-
    casian population:
    a. 40%
    b. 4%
    c. 43%   c
    d. 13%

41. Blood type A_2B occurs in the following percentage of the
    Caucasian population:
    a. 10%
    b. 9%
    c. 3%
    d. 1%   d

42. The serum of type AB will not agglutinate the red cells of
    the other three types.   T   F   T

43. Blood type A_2 occurs in the following percentage of the
    population:
    a. 34%
    b. 10%   b
    c. 3%
    d. 43%

44. Blood type A_1B occurs in the following percentage of the population:
    a. 40%
    b. 3%   b
    c. 13%
    d. 43%

45. Agglutination of red blood cells with anti-B serum but not with anti-A serum indicates that these cells belong to group:
    a. AB
    b. A
    c. B   c
    d. O

46. Agglutination of red blood cells with anti-B serum and with anti-A serum indicates that these cells belong to group:
    a. AB   a
    b. A
    c. B
    d. O

47. The substances that characterize the ABO blood groups are present:
    a. In the blood only
    b. In most body tissues   b

48. What is meant by "blood group secretor"?   See p. 428

49. Is the Rh factor an antigen or an antibody?   See p. 428

50. The Rh factor is present in the following percentage of all persons:
    a. 43%
    b. 55%
    c. 75%
    d. 85%   d

51. For routine Rh typing of patients it is best to use:
    a. Anti-Rh" (anti-E)
    b. Anti-Rh' (anti-C)
    c. Anti-Rh$_0$ (anti-D)   c

52. An Rh-negative person may develop agglutinins against the Rh factor after receiving Rh-positive blood.   T   F   T

53. An Rh-negative woman married to an Rh-positive man can expect all of her children to be Rh-positive if the husband is heterozygous.   T   F   F

54. All human bloods fall into either type M, N, or MN.
    T   F   T

55. Naturally occurring anti-M agglutinins are found in human sera:
    a. Quite frequently
    b. Occasionally   b
    c. Rarely
    d. Never

56. In the following list of diseases, underline those which may be transmitted through blood transfusion:
   a. Tuberculosis — cancer — syphilis
   b. Scarlet fever — pneumonia — rubella (German measles)
   c. Brucellosis — malaria — viral hepatitis
   d. Rheumatic fever — typhoid fever

See p. 428
"
"
"

57. Why is it necessary to crossmatch donor and patient after it has been determined that they both belong to the same type and Rh?

See p. 428

58. In crossmatching, what is the point of major importance?

See p. 428

59. Hemoglobin may be present in the urine following an incompatible blood transfusion.   T   F

T

60. The mother of a newborn infant afflicted with hemolytic disease due to anti-Rh is likely to have a severe reaction if administered Rh-positive blood.   T   F

T

61. In cases of erythroblastosis due to Rh incompatibility, exchange transfusion is often indicated.   T   F

T (also see p. 428)

62. In cases of erythroblastosis due to ABO incompatibility exchange transfusion is usually indicated.   T   F

F (also see p. 428)

63. Determination of blood group can prove that a certain man is the father of a child.   T   F

F (also see p. 428)

64. Explain the heredity pattern when the mother is type A, the father is type A; when the mother is type O, the father is type B. What type could children not be in this case?

See p. 429

65. Children of type A father and type B mother may belong to any of the four major blood types.   T   F

T

66. Children of type AB father and type AB mother cannot belong to type O.   T   F

T

67. Dark-field examinations are of value in the laboratory diagnosis of late syphilis.   T   F

F

68. The Reiter Protein Complement Fixation (RPCF) test for the detection of syphilis, employs:
   a. Living spirochetes
   b. A protein extract of a suspension of nonpathogenic spirochetes
   c. A suspension of treponemes of the Nichol's strain of T. pallidum.

b

69. The *Treponema pallidum* Immobilization Test is (can):
   a. Not as sensitive as most STS procedures
   b. Useful in detecting latent and tertiary syphilis
   c. Be used in clarifying biological false positives occurring in the performance of most STS

a
b
c

70. The antigen used in the Fluorescent Treponemal Antibody Test (FTA) is a suspension of treponemes of the Nichol's strain of *Tr. pallidum.*   T   F   T

71. Advantages of the FTA test over the TPI test include:
    a. Shorter time to carry out the test   a
    b. Using a stable antigen   b
    c. Using only a phosphate buffer of pH 8.5

72. The *Treponema pallidum* Hemagglutination test utilizes:
    a. Sheep red cells
    b. Tanned turkey red cells   b
    c. Horse red cells
    d. Tanned human red cells

73. The RPR (Rapid Plasma Reagin) test is similar to the VDRL except:
    a. That the antigen is modified by the addition of charcoal and choline chloride   a
    b. That the patient's serum is not inactivated   b
    c. That the results are read on disposable cards   c

74. The antigen used in the RPR test is delivered through an 18 gauge needle, delivering 45 drops per ml.   T   F   T

75. The RPR test should be rotated at 180 rpm for:
    a. 2 minutes
    b. 4 minutes   b
    c. 6 minutes
    d. 8 minutes

76. A 1+ fluorescence result in the FTA test indicates that the test is:
    a. Non-reactive
    b. Reactive   b
    c. Not diagnostic

77. In the FTA test, sera is used:
    a. Without inactivation
    b. After inactivation at 56°C. for 15 minutes
    c. After inactivation at 56°C. for 30 minutes   c

78. All syphilitic flocculation test are based on the reaction of the antigen cardiolipin (a cholesterolized alcohol solution of beef-heart lipids) with antibody reagin in the patient's serum.   T   F   T

79. Flocculation tests are more sensitive than complement fixation tests.   T   F   T

80. The pH of the distilled water and saline solution used in the Kline test is:
    a. 4.5
    b. 6.0   b
    c. 7.5
    d. 8.0
    e. 9.4

81. Kline and VDRL slide tests should be rotated on a flat surface for:
    a. 30 seconds
    b. 1 minute
    c. 2 minutes
    d. 4 minutes   d
    e. 5 minutes

82. The antigen used in the VDRL slide test is an alcoholic solution containing 0.03% _____, 0.9% _____,   cardiolipin;
    and sufficient purified _____, to produce standard   cholesterol;
    (0.21% plus or minus 0.01%) reactivity.   lecithin

83. The saline diluent used in the VDRL slide test is buffered
    to the following pH:
    a. 4.5 plur or minus 0.1
    b. 5.0 plus or minus 0.1
    c. 6.0 plus or minus 0.1   c
    d. 7.5 plus or minus 0.1
    e. 8.4 plus or minus 0.1

84. Quantitative serologic tests for syphilis may be carried out
    by testing _____ _____ of the patient's serum.   serial dilu-
                                                                   tions

85. Contaminated serum may be sterilized by _____ be-
    fore using in complement-fixation or neutralization test.

86. Mention at least eight common causes of biological false-
    positive reactions in serologic tests for syphilis.   See p. 429

87. What is the usual source of complement?   See p. 429

88. Why must *pooled* guinea pig serum be used in serological
    tests for syphilis?   See p. 429

89. Complement is always diluted with cold saline. Why?   See p. 429

90. Complement, especially when diluted, deteriorates rapidly
    at room temperature.   T   F   T

91. Complement prepared by freezing guinea pig serum and de-
    hydrating it rapidly under high vaccum is called _____   lyophile
    serum.

92. Three methods of preserving complement are:
        a. _____   salting
        b. _____   freezing
        c. _____   drying

93. "Anticomplementary" activity can sometimes be chekced
    by _____ or _____ the serum.   heating or
                                                                   diluting

94. The phenomenon of complement-fixation was discovered
    by:
    a. Kolmer
    b. Bordet-gengou   b

c. Eagle
d. Pasteur
e. Wassermann

95. The addition of complement to sensitized bacteria (i.e., bacteria plus immune antibody or amboceptor) will result in:
a. Bacteriolysis   a
b. Hemolysis
c. Proteolysis
d. None of these

96. Naturally occurring anti-N agglutinins are found in human sera:
a. Quite frequently
b. Occassionally
c. Rarely   c
d. Never

97. In flocculation tests the visible reaction is the result of the combination of reagin in the serum of the patient with components of the antigen, namely, particles of lipid-coated cholesterol with or without cardiolipin.   T   F   T

98. In reporting results of serologic tests for syphilis the correct terminology is:
a. Reactive, Weakly Reactive, Nonreactive   a
b. Positive, Weakly Positive or Doubtful, Negative

99. A positive complement-fixation test gives no hemolysis.
T   F   T

100. The Kolmer test is:
a. A complement-fixation test   a
b. An agglutination test
c. A flocculation (precipitation) test
d. A hemagglutination-inhibition test

101. The Kolmer test is based upon a specific antigen-antibody reaction.   T   F   F

102. Inactivation (i.e., heating of serum at 56°C. for thirty minutes) is carried out for the following purpose:
a. To destroy native complment   a
b. To check any hemolysis that might be present
c. To prevent the occurrence of prozone reactions
d. To destroy any bile pigment that might be present

103. When inactivation (i.e., heating of fresh sera for thirty minutes at 56°C.) was carried out more than two hours before a test, serum should be rehated for:
a. 30 minutes at 56°C.
b. 30 minutes at 37°C.
c. 10 minutes at 37°C.
d. 10 minutes at 56°C.   d

104. Briefly explain why it is unnecessary to inactivate, by heating at 56°C., spinal fluid to be used in complement-fixation

tests.   See p. 429

105. Kolmer saline solution contains, in 1,000 ml. of freshly distilled water, 8.5 grams of dry CP sodium chloride and 0.1 gram of anhydrous:
    a. Calcium chloride
    b. Magnesium sulfate   b
    c. Barium sulfate
    d. Potassium carbonate

106. When not in use complement and hemolysin should be stored in:
    a. A refrigerator   a
    b. The dark at room temperature

107. The sheep cell suspension which (0.5 ml. per tube) is used in complement-fixation test is:
    a. 0.5%
    b. 1.0%
    c. 2.0%   c
    d. 4.0%
    e. 5.0%

108. The cardiolipin antigen for complement-fixation test should be stored in:
    a. The refrigerator
    b. The dark at room temperature   b

109. The optimal dilution of cariolipin complement-fixation antigen (this dilution remains constant because the ratio cardiolipin : lecithin : cholestrol is fixed in successive lots of antigen) has been set at:
    a. 0.5 ml. antigen + 99.5 ml. Kolmer saline
    b. 1.0 ml. antigen + 130.0 ml. Kolmer saline   b
    c. 2.0 ml. antigen + 98.0 ml. Kolmer saline
    d. 2.5 ml. antigen + 128.5 ml. Kolmer saline

110. Once diluted, cardiolipin complement-fixation antigen may be used:
    a. Only during day prepared   a
    b. For up to one week
    c. For up to two weeks
    d. For up to 22 days
    e. Indefinitely

111. Nonspecific fixation of complement may sometimes occur when using the Kolmer antigen.   T   F   T

112. Nonspecific fixation of complement may sometimes occur when using cardiolipin complement-fixatior antigen.
    T   F   F

113. How is the antisheep hemolysin (amboceptor) used in the Kolmer test prepared?   See p. 429

114. What is glycerinized hemolysin?   See p. 429

115. How is a 1:1,000 dilution of hemolysin prepared from stock 1:100 dilution? See p. 429

116. How is the 1:30 complement dilution (used in both hemolysin and complement titrations) prepared? See p. 429

117. In the hemolysin titration procedure, constant amounts of complement, saline, and sheep cells are added to varying amounts of hemolysin.   T   F   T

118. The correct order of adding reagents in a hemolysin titration is:
    a. Complement (0.3 ml., 1:30) — saline (1.7 ml.) — hemolysin dilution (0.5 ml.) — sheep cells (25)
    b. Hemolysin — complement — saline — sheep cells   b
    c. Saline — sheep cells — complement — hemolysin
    d. Sheep cells — hemolysins — saline — complement

119. How is the unit of hemolysin determined? See p. 429

120. Both in complement-titration and in complement-fixation the following number of units of hemolysin are used:
    a. 2   a
    b. 4
    c. 6
    d. 8
    e. 10

121. How is hemolysin diluted for the Kolmer test? See p. 429

122. Diluted hemolysin is stable:
    a. For two hours
    b. For a day   b
    c. For a week
    d. For a month
    e. Indefinitely

123. Saline to be used for the dilution of complement and the dilution of hemolysin should, before use, be brought to the following temperature:
    a. Room temperature
    b. 37°C.
    c. 60°C.
    d. 43°C.
    e. Refrigerator temperature   e

124. How would you prepare a 1:6,000 dilution of hemolysin? See p. 429

125. The complement titration procedure utilizes constant amounts of complement.   T   F   F

126. Explain detail of procedure in setting up a Kolmer complement titration. See p. 430

127. In the Kolmer complement titration, what is:
    a. The exact unit See p. 430
    b. The full unit   "
    c. The dose   "

128. In a complement titration, the tube containing 0.20 ml. of a 1:30 complement dilution was first tube giving complete hemolysis in given volume of sheep cells. Therefore, to have two full units per ml. complement should be diluted:
    a. 1:25
    b. 1:40
    c. 1:50
    d. 1:60
    e. 1:100

    d

129. How would you prepare a 1:60 dilution of complement?   See p. 430

130. What are "sensitized cells"?   See p. 430

131. Name, in their correct order, the four control tubes in Kolmer complement-fixation test.   See p. 430

132. When a certain serum turns out to be anticomplementary (i.e., the serum control, which contains no antigen, fails to show complete hemolysis) a new specimen should be obtained and tested.   T   F

    T

133. In complement-fixation tests, the use of noninactivated (or insufficiently inactivated) serum may cause a:
    a. False-positive reaction
    b. False-negative reaction

    a

134. The use of overinactivated serum in a complement-fixation test may cause:
    a. False-positive reaction
    b. False-negative reaction

    b

135. Complement-fixation test difficulties are, in the large majority of cases, due to the following:
    a. Antigen
    b. Hemolysin
    c. Complement
    d. Sheep cells

    c

136. The use of too weak an antigen for a complement-fixation test may result in a:
    a. False-positive reaction
    b. False-negative reaction

    b

137. The use of weak hemolysin in a complement-fixation test may result in:
    a. False-positive reaction
    b. False-negative reaction

    a

138. The presence of strong hemolysis in a serum to be used for a complement-fixation test may cause a:
    a. False-positive reaction
    b. False-negative reaction

    a

139. The use of too weak a complement in a complement-fixation test may result in a:
    a. False-positive reaction
    b. False-negative reaction

    a

140. The use of too strong a complement for a complement-fixa-
     tion test will result in a:
     a. False-positive reaction
     b. False-negative reaction   b

141. The use of too strong a suspension of cells in a complement-
     fixation test may result in a:
     a. False-positive reaction   a
     b. False-negative reaction

142. Briefly explain why bloody spinal fluid specimens are un-
     satisfactory for the complement-fixation test.   See p. 430

143. Mention at least three different applications (other than the
     laboratory diagnosis of syphilis) of complement-fixation
     tests.   See p. 430

144. Briefly describe the technique of the *Treponema pallidum*
     immobilization test (TPI).   See p. 430

145. What is the greatest advantage of the TPI over routine diag-
     nostic STS?   See p. 430

146. Briefly explain the principle of *Treponema pallidum* immune
     adherence phenomenon (TPIA).   See p. 430

147. A satisfactory colloidal gold solution should have the fol-
     lowing color:
     a. Light amber
     b. Deep orange-red   b
     c. Light blue
     d. Green
     e. Yellow

148. The saline solution employed for making serial dilutions of
     spinal fluid for the colloidal gold test is:
     a. 0.1% NaCl
     b. 0.2% NaCl
     c. 0.4% NaCl   c
     d. 0.9% NaCl
     e. 1.5% NaCl

149. In the colloidal gold test, what is the purpose of tube No.
     11?   See p. 431

150. What is the basic difference between the Lange's colloidal
     gold test and the so-called "mastic test"?   See p. 431

151. What is meant by "prozone reaction"?   See p. 431

152. What are "febrile antigens"?   See p. 431

153. What is the Rapid Slide Test using diagnostic febrile anti-
     gens primarily intended for?   See p. 431

154. What is the Tube Test using diagnostic febrile antigens pri-
     marily intended for?   See p. 431

155. The Widal test was originally a microscopic slide test for
     the diagnosis of:

    a. Tularemia
    b. Brucellosis
    c. Dysentery
    d. Typhoid fever   d
    e. Syphilis

156. Typhoid carriers usually give a positive Widal test.   T   F   F

157. The "H" (Hauch) antigen is the:
    a. Somatic antigen
    b. Flagellar antigen   b
    c. Neither of these

158. The somatic (")") antigen is species-specific.   T   F   F

159. The somatic antigen is prepared by suspending a bacterial
    growth from agar in saline containing 0.5% formalin.
    T   F   F (also see
                                                       p. 431)

160. The somatic antigen is thermolabile.   T   F   F

161. The flagellar antigen is thermolabile.   T   F   T

162. A thermolabile somatic antigen which occurs either as a
    capsule or as an envelop surrounding the bacterial cell is
    the:
    a. O antigen
    b. H antigen
    c. K antigen   c

163. The Vi antigen of *Salmonella typhi* is:
    a. Somatic (O) antigen
    b. Somatic (K) antigen   b
    c. Flagellar (H) antigen

164. Somatic K antigens are thermolabile.   T   F   T

165. The most fundamental serologic subdivisions of a biochem-
    ical group are made on the basis of the:
    a. O antigens   a
    b. H antigens
    c. K antigens

166. Identification of enteropathogenic *Escherichia coli* sero-
    types may be carried out with the following variety of so-
    matic K antigen:
    a. B variety   a
    b. L variety
    c. Vi variety

167. Serum containing antibodies capable of reacting specifically
    and individually with the O antigen and with the B variety
    of the K antigen is called ____ _____.   OB serum

168. Briefly explain why the thermolabile (B) structure of *Escher-
    ichia coli* (and *Shigella*) must be inactivated by heating be-
    fore the somatic (O) antigen can be determined or tested for.   See p. 431

169. How are the results of the Rapid Slide Test recorded and reported.   See p. 431

170. How is the titer of a serum determined from the results of a Rapid Slide Test?   See p. 431

171. A single negative agglutination test is sufficient to exclude infection.   T   F   F

172. A single positive agglutination test is not diagnostically significant unless the titer is unusually high.   T   F   T

173. Persistent low titers are diagnostically significant in typhoid fever and in chronic brucellosis provided previous tests were negative.   T   F   T

174. Under what conditions can conclusive laboratory data be arrived at from bacterial agglutination tests?   See p. 431

175. What is a "cross-reaction"?   See p. 431

176. Mention at least three examples of cross-reaction.   See p. 431

177. The Weil-Felix reaction is used for the laboratory diagnosis of:
    a. Bacterial diseases
    b. Rickettsial diseases   b
    c. Viral diseases
    d. Mycotic diseases
    e. Allergic conditions

178. What culture of *Proteus* is used for typhus fever (epidemic and murine) agglutination testing?   See p. 431

179. Only the agglutination of the O antigen is diagnostic of typhus fever.   T   F   T

180. In Q fever agglutinins are formed which will agglutinate the following antigen or antigens:
    a. *Proteus* OX_{19}
    b. *Proteus* OX_2
    c. *Proteus* OXK
    d. All of the above
    e. None of the above   c

181. In scrub typhus (Tsutsugamushi fever) agglutinins are formed which will agglutinate the following antigen(s):
    a. *Proteus* OX_{19}
    b. *Proteus* OX_2
    c. *Proteus* OXK   c
    d. None of these
    e. All of these

182. Although both agglutinins and hemolysins for sheep cell blood cells occur in normal persons they rarely reach a titer above:
    a. 1:7   a
    b. 1:28

       c. 1:56
       d. 1:112
       e. 1:224

183. The inactivated serum of patients with infectious mononucleosis will, in dilutions beyond 1:56, agglutinate sheep red
cell corpuscles. This phenomenon is called:
       a. Gruber-Widal reaction
       b. Pfeiffer's reaction
       c. Much's reaction
       d. Paul-Bunnell reaction   d
       e. Anamnestic reaction

184. Infectious mononucleosis is also called:
       a. Valley fever
       b. Glandular fever   b
       c. Rheumatic fever
       d. Mediterranean fever
       e. Q fever

185. Why must the patient's serum be inactivated for the heterophil (Sheep cell) antibody test? See p. 431

186. The saline solution employed to make serial dilutions of the
patient's serum in the heterophil antibody test is:
       a. 0.5%
       b. 0.4%
       c. 0.85%   c
       d. 1.0%
       e. 4.0%

187. Get 0.5 ml. packed sheep cells in 15 ml. centrifuge tube.
How much saline has to be added to obtain:
       a. A 2% suspension   24.5 ml.
       b. A 3% suspension   16.16 ml.

188. The suspension of sheep cells used in routine heterophil
antibody testing is:
       a. 0.5%
       b. 1.0%
       c. 2.0%   c
       d. 3.0%
       e. 5.0%

189. The Forssman heterophil antibody found in normal serum
is absorbed by:
       a. Guinea pig kidney antigen   a
       b. Beef erythrocyte antigen
       c. Both of these
       d. None of these

190. The heterophil antibody of infectious mononucleosis is
absorbed by:
       a. Guinea pig kidney antigen
       b. Beef erythrocyte antigen   b

    c. Both of these
    d. None of these

191. The Forssman antibody found in serum sickness is absorbed by:
    a. Guinea pig kidney antigen
    b. Beef erythrocyte antigen
    c. Both of these   c
    d. None of these

192. The Forssman heterophil antibody found in normal serum is absorbed by beef erythrocyte antigen.   T   F   F

193. The origin of cold agglutinins is:
    a. Known
    b. Unknown   b

194. Cold agglutinins often occur in:
    a. Infectious mononucleosis
    b. Atypical pneumonia   b
    c. Rheumatoid arthritis
    d. Rheumatic fever
    e. Tularemia

195. Mention at least three conditions, other than virus pneumonia, in which a high (above 1:32) titer of cold agglutinins may occur.   See p. 432

196. Cold agglutinins will agglutinate group O human erythrocytes at the following temperature:
    a. Body temperature (37.5°C.)
    b. Refrigerator temperature (4°C.)   b
    c. Room temperature (20°C.)

197. How soon after it has been set up can a cold agglutination test be read and reported?   See p. 432

198. Finding persistently high antistreptolysin-O titers (above 125 Todd units) suggests recurrent infection with:
    a. Staphylococcus aureus
    b. Influenza virus
    c. Polio virus
    d. Beta hemolytic streptococci   d
    e. Mycobacterium tuberculosis

199. Streptolysin-O is:
    a. An antigen
    b. An antibody   a
    c. Neither a nor b

200. Streptolysin-O has the ability to hemolyze human and rabbit erythrocytes.   T   F   T

201. Antibodies against streptolysin-O are called _____   antistrep-
    _____ antibodies.   tolysin-O

202. Antistreptolysin-O antibodies are usually present in the serum of patients with:

a. Rheumatic fever | a
b. Lupus erythematosus
c. Rheumatoid arthritis
d. Infectious mononucleosis
e. Brucellosis

203. Rheumatic fever usually affects persons over 20 years of age.   T   F | F

204. When streptolysin-O antigen combines with its specific (i.e., antistreptolysin-O) antibody is loses its _____ activity. | hemolytic

205. How is the Todd unit defined? | See p. 432

206. What reagents, and in what order, are needed to carry out an ASTO test? | See p. 432

207. Hemolyzed serum cannot be used for an ASTO test.   T   F | T

208. Chylous serum may be used for an ASTO test provided it contains no hemolysis.   T   F | F

209. The patient's serum must be inactivated before it can be used in an ASTO test.   T   F | F

210. Inactivated serum cannot be used in an ASTO test.   T   F | F

211. The suspension of human or rabbit cells used in routine ASTO tests is:
a. 1%
b. 2%
c. 3%
d. 4.5%
e. 5% | e

212. A positive ASTO reaction shows none or partial hemolysis.   T   F | T

213. What is C-reactive protein? | See p. 432

214. C-reactive protein is a modified:
a. Albumin
b. Alpha globulin
c. Beta globulin
d. Gamma globulin | c

215. C-reactive protein is specific antibody.   T   F | F

216. The C-reactive protein test is based upon the following type of reaction:
a. Complement-fixation
b. Agglutination
c. Precipitation
d. Hemagglutination-inhibition | c

217. How is C-reactive protein antiserum usually prepared? | See p. 432

218. A positive C-reactive protein test would be expected in patients having active _____ processes. | inflammatory

219. The C-reactive protein test is never diagnostic.   T   F   T

220. In asthma the antigen usually:
    a. Is injected
    b. Is inhaled   b
    c. Is ingested
    d. Comes in contact with skin

221. Tests for the rheumatoid factor using latex and bentonite are:
    a. Agglutination tests   a
    b. Preciptin tests
    c. Complement-fixation tests
    d. Hemagglutination-inhibition tests

222. The serum of patients with rheumatoid arthritis will frequently agglutinate sheep cells.   T   F   T

223. Fibrinogen deficiency is common.   T   F   F

224. Fibrinogen deficiency is never congenital.   T   F   F

225. Flagellar antigens will withstand treatment with:
    a. Alcohol
    b. Heat
    c. Formalin   c
    d. Phenol
    e. All of these
    f. None of these

226. Somatic antigens will withstand treatment with:
    a. Alcohol
    b. Heat
    c. Formalin
    d. Phenol
    e. All of these   e

227. In typhoid fever, agglutinins to not appear in the blood until:
    a. 1–2 days after onset of clinical symptoms
    b. 2–4 days after onset of clinical symptoms
    c. 4–5 days after onset of clinical symptoms
    d. 8–10 days after onset of clinical symptoms   d

228. Briefly explain why *Salmonella* and *Shigella* antigens are not available for routine testing.   See p. 432

229. *Proteus* OX_{19}, OX_2, and OXK antigens (Weil-Felix) are prepared from:
    a. Motile strains of *Proteus*
    b. Nonmotile strains of *Proteus*   b
    c. A bacillus other than *Proteus*

230. In the preceding questions, what does the letter X stand for? the letter O?   See p. 432

231. Agglutination of *Proteus* OX_{19} alone is sufficient to distinguish the two types (i.e., epidemic and murine) of typhus

fever from Rocky Mountain spotted fever.   T   F | F

232. The Kingsbury strain of *Proteus* is:
    a. *Proteus* OX_{19}
    b. *Proteus* OX_2
    c. *Proteus* OXK | c

233. What is meant by "sensitivity" of a STS? | See p. 432

234. What is meant by "specificity" of an STS? | See p. 432

235. What is the purpose of adding cholesterin to various antigens? | See p. 432

236. The term complement denotes a complex system of _____ and other factors found in normal serum. Some components have _____ activity. | proteins
     | enzymatic

237. What is tuberculin? | See p. 432

238. How is Koch's old tuberuclin (OT) prepared? | See p. 432

239. What is tuberculin "purified protein derivative" (PPD)? | See p. 432

240. The Vollmer test is a:
    a. Tuberculin patch test | a
    b. A skin test using 0.1 mg. OT (for 0.0002 mg. PPD)

241. How is the anti-human serum for use in the anti-globulin test (Coombs test, developing test) prepared? | See p. 432

242. Explain difference(s) between "thermostabile" and "thermolabile." | See p. 432

243. Explain difference(s) between "heterologous serum" and "homologous serum." | See p. 432

244. Explain difference(s) between "natural antibodies" and "acquired antibodies." | See p. 432

245. Explain difference(s) between "agglutinin" and "glutinin." | See p. 433

246. Explain difference(s) between "agglutination" and "conglutination." | See p. 433

247. Explain difference(s) between "agglutinin" and "agglutinoid." | See p. 433

248. Explain difference(s) between "complement-fixation" and "complement-deviation." | See p. 433

249. Explain difference(s) between "natural immunity" and "acquired immunity." | See p. 434

250. Explain difference(s) between "active immunity" and "passive immunity." | See p. 434

251. Explain difference(s) between "direct Coombs test" and "indirect Coombs test." | See p. 434

252. Explain difference(s) between "exclusion antigen" and "diagnostic antigen." | See p. 435

253. Explain difference(s) between "opsonic power" and "op-

| | sonic index." | See p. 435 |

254. Explain difference(s) between "Forssman antibody" and the "heterophil antibody" of infectious mononucleosis. See p. 435

255. Explain difference(s) between "warm agglutinins" and "cold agglutinins." See p. 435

256. Explain difference(s) between "Widal reaction" and "Weil-Felix reaction." See p. 435

257. Explain difference(s) between "Arthus phenomenon" and "anaphylactic reaction." See p. 435

258. What is a "universal blood donor"? See p. 436

259. What is a "universal recipient"? See p. 436

260. What is the definition of "titer"? See p. 436

261. What is the "Rose-Waaler test"? See p. 436

262. What are "coated-particle" agglutination reactions? See p. 436

263. List seven causes of false-positive antiglobulin tests. See p. 436

264. List five causes of false positive antiglobulin tests. See p. 436

265. Indicate the possible diseases that can cause false-positive antiglobulin tests. See p. 436

266. Name the five drugs that have been reported as causing false-positive antiglobulin tests. See p. 436

267. Broad-spectrum antiglobulin reagents contain antibodies to some proteins that are not immunoglobulins. Red cells coated with these proteins will also react with the antiglobulin serum to produce a positive test. What are the two commonest proteins that cause such a reaction? See p. 437

268. What is "zeta potential"? See p. 437

269. Which of the following diseases may be transmitted by blood transfusion?
    a. Brucellosis   a
    b. Hepatitis   b
    c. Malaria   c
    d. Influenza

270. A positive anti-globulin test may be found in an individual:
    a. Whose serum gives a negative antibody detection test   a
    b. Due to coating of the red cells by complement components   b
    c. Without detectable evidence of in vivo hemolysis   c
    d. Who appears healthy and has no manifestations of disease   d

271. A patient's red cells are grouped as AB. The reverse grouping using the patient's serum indicates that the patient is group B. This discrepancy should be investigated by:
    a. Testing the cells with anti-A, B
    b. Testing the cells with anti-A₁   b

    c. Carrying out a direct anti-globulin test

    d. Testing the serum against A_1 cells   d

272. A patient whose type is group O may receive large quantities of cryoprecipitate of group:

    a. O   a

    b. A   b

    c. B   c

    d. AB   d

273. Antiglobulin sera used to test cord bloods must:

    a. Possess anti-complement activity   a

    b. Be made in goats

    c. React with both IgA and IgE antibodies

    d. React with presensitized (coated) red cells   d

274. Delayed hemolytic transfusion reactions are occasionally associated with antibodies of the

    a. Kell system

    b. Kidd system   b

    c. ABO system

    d. Lewis system

275. Typing for the presence of ABO antigens can be carried out without significant error on a:

    a. 95 year old male   a

    b. Newborn   b

    c. 6 month old child   c

    d. 3 month old infant   d

276. Which of the following foils will result in the temporary rejection of a blood donor (for 6 months)?

    a. Recent tattoo   a

    b. Removal from a plasmapheresis program because of a lowered serum protein

    c. Anti-malarial drugs, discontinued 6 months previously

    d. Contact with hepatitis 7 months previously

277. What is the correct storage temperature for fresh frozen single donor plasma having an expiration date of one year? $-18°C.$

278. What is the correct storage temperature of leucocyte-poor packed red cells? $1-6°C.$

279. A patient is known to have acquired autoimmune hemolytic anemia of the warm type. His serum is tested with each of the cells listed below. Which of these cells would be expected to give the weakest reaction?

    a. i

    b. CcDee

    c. $Fy^{(a-b+)}$

    d. Rh_{null} d

280. An Rh negative mother is known to be sensitized to D. She delivers a baby who is typed Rh negative. The baby's direct antiglobulin test is 4+; the cord bilirubin is 3.7 mg.%;

the cord hemoglobin is 10.5 gm.%. The baby probably has:
   a. Erythroblastosis due to Jk^a incompatibility
   b. Physiologic jaundice
   c. Erythroblastosis due to Anti-D   c
   d. Erythroblastosis due to ABO incompatibility

281. The concentration of red cells used in red cell antigen-anti-
     body reactions should not be higher than that recommended
     by the anti-serum manufacturer, because higher concen-
     trations may cause:
   a. False positives due to oversensitivity of red cells
   b. False positives due to the "rouleaux-like" appearance
      of red cells
   c. False negatives due to adsorption of antibodies   c
   d. False negatives due to elution of antibodies

282. "Non-specific" cold antibodies usually possess specificity
     of:
   a. Anti-N
   b. Anti-I   b
   c. Anti-PP_1p^k (Tj^a)
   d. Anti-D

283. A patient is found to be group A, with an antibody which
     agglutinates A_2 cells but not A_1 cells. The most likely anti-
     body specificity is:
   a. Anti-D
   b. Anti-Fy^a
   c. Anti-H   c
   d. Anti-i
   e. Anti-A_2

284. Which cells possess the greatest amount of H substance?   Group O

285. Which of the following are correct statements concerning
     IgM antibodies?
   a. React best at 37°C.
   b. Molecular weight of 150.000
   c. Inactivated by 2-mercaptoethenol   c
   d. Sedimentation coefficient of 19S   d
   e. Inactivated by dithiothetrol   e

286. If Rh negative (cde/cde, rh) cells are transfused into an Rh
     positive person of the genotype CDe/CDe (Rh_1 Rh_1), the
     antibody most likely to be developed is:
   a. Anti-c   a
   b. Anti-d
   c. Anti-e
   d. Anti-D

287. Lewis antibodies have not been implicated in hemolytic
     disease of the newborn because their:
   a. Antibodies are not usually hemolytic
   b. Antibodies are always 7S in form
   c. Antigens are not developed on the red cells of new
      borns   c

d. Antigens are not soluble plasma substances

288. In the process of identifying an antibody, a 2+ reaction
with 3 of the 8 cell panel was observed after immediate
spin. The reaction disappeared at 37°C. and after the
Coombs phase. The antibody is most likely:
  a. Anti-Fy^a
  b. Anti-D
  c. Anti-c
  d. Anti-M   d
  e. Anti-Xg^a

289. The following units of blood are available for transfusion.
Which would be your first choice to transfuse to an A Rhesus negative female of child-bearing age?
  a. AB Rh positive
  b. O Rh negative with anti-A hemolysins of 1:8
  c. B Rh positive
  d. A Rh positive
  e. O Rh negative with an immune anti-A titer of 1:1
     and an immune anti-B titer of 1:64   e

290. What is the major disadvantage of enzyme treated red cells
for serological studies?   Pan-agglu-
                                                                tination
                                                                may occur

291. The Hubener-Thomsen-Friedenrich effect is not:
  a. An in vivo phenomenon
  b. Related to T-receptor site activation
  c. An in vitro phenomenon   c
  d. A cause of agglutination

292. Mother is A Rh negative; baby is B Rh positive. An exchange transfusion is indicated. There is no time to determine the cause of the jaundice. What type of blood would
you choose with only the following types available:
  a. O Rh positive
  b. A Rh negative
  c. B Rh negative
  d. O Rh negative   d
  e. B Rh positive

293. When a Coombs titer is carried out on a pregnant woman
who possesses a known antibody capable of causing erythroblastosis:
  a. A titer of 1:8 is always significant
  b. A titer of 1:1024 is sufficient evidence that the baby
     will be born with severe erythroblastosis
  c. An increase in titer during pregnancy is cause for
     concern   c
  d. The results are sufficient to diagnose the condition
     of the fetus and the amniotic tap procedure need not
     be done.

294. Which of the following would *not* be necessary information
to have before issuing Rhogam (immune gamma globulin)?
    a. Group and type of the mother
    b. Identification of the antibody if present
    c. Titer of the antibody if present   c
    d. Group and type of the baby
    e. D^u if the mother appears Rhesus negative

295. During shipment, the temperature of whole blood should
not rise above:
    a. 5°C.
    b. 6°C.
    c. 10°C.   c
    d. 15°C.
    e. 20°C.

296. An antibody that reacts more strongly against homozygous
positive cells exhibits _____ _____.   dosage
                                                effect

297. A woman is given two pints of blood during surgery without compatibility testing. A study of her blood reveals
anti-Fy^a in her pretransfused serum. Her posttransfused
serum fails to reveal any antibody (it fails to react against
Fy$^{(a+)}$ cells), because the antibody is:
    a. Removed by the spleen
    b. Absorbed   b
    c. Inactivated
    d. Removed by the liver
    e. Diluted

298. The saliva of an adult whose red cells are shown to be
group A Le$^{(a-b+)}$ is expected to contain:
    a. A substance only
    b. A, H, and Le^a substances
    c. A and H substances
    d. A, H, Le^a and Le^b substances   d
    e. A and Le^b substances

299. Which of the antigens listed belong to the Kell blood group
system?
    a. Kp^a a
    b. Js^a b
    c. Be^a
    d. Kam
    e. Kp^b e
    f. Js^b f
    g. Ul^a g

300. Why cannot group O Rhesus negative blood be transfused
to a patient who is "Bombay" positive? See p. 437

301. Which specific antibody has been associated with paroxysmal
cold hemoglobinuria?   Anti-P

302. Which disease syndrome is often associated with the presence of Anti-e?

Warm auto-immune hemolytic anemia

303. Infectious mononucleosis is often associated with:
    a. Anti-A₁
    b. Anti-I
    c. Anti-i
    d. Anti-nl
    e. Anti-pdl

c

304. When should "saline" anti-D typing sera be used?

See p. 437

305. Enzyme treatment of cells is useless for the detection of antibodies in the:
    a. Rhesus system
    b. MN system
    c. Lewis system
    d. Kidd system

b

306. Which sugar is responsible for B specificity?

D-galactose

307. Bacterial infections will often expose a red cell antigen of what specificity?
    a. I
    b. P
    c. T
    d. Tn
    e. Rh

c

308. Which system is best understood by thinking of its antigens as genetically determined body fluid substances which under certain circumstances attach to red cells?
    a. Kell
    b. I
    c. Duffy
    d. ABO
    e. Lewis

e

309. Activation of T receptor sites on red cells results from the activity of:
    a. Chloroacidinidase
    b. Hydroaminidase
    c. Neuraminidase
    d. A T Pase

c

310. In erythroblastosis of the newborn (hemolytic disease of the newborn) caused by ABO incompatibility, the peripheral blood often shows the presence of _____.

spherocytosis

311. Human serum is injected into rabbits to produce antibodies against human globulins. The "raw" serum obtained from the animals cannot be used directly as Coombs reagent but must first:

a. Be heated to 56°C. to destroy complement
b. Be absorbed to remove anti-species anti-A, anti-B and anti-H
c. Be blended with both rabbit and goat sera to ensure its "broad spectrum"
d. Be diluted with a high protein diluent to afford maximum economy

b

312. Bromelin is an enzyme used in blood banking produced from:
a. Papaya
b. Pineapple stems
c. Figs
d. Hog stomach

b

313. The presence of Le^b substance in body fluids depends upon the interaction of which of the genes listed below?
a. Le and h
b. Se and le
c. le and H
d. H and Se
e. se and le

d

314. The indirect antiglobulin test is applicable in all of the following tests *except:*
a. The test for D^u on apparent Rhesus negative (Rh$_0$ or D negative) individuals
b. The major and minor crossmatches
c. Antibody screening of obstetrical patients
d. Testing cord blood for antibody fixed *in vivo*
e. Testing the serum of patients with autoimmune diseases

d

315. How does Anti-I react?

See p. 437

316. An individual who is O$_h^A$ would differ from a group O person in that:
a. There is a small amount of group A specific substance in the cells
b. He secretes soluble H substance
c. He possesses the gene H
d. One of his parents are group A
e. He does not possess anti-A$_1$ in his serum

d

317. Rhesus antibodies are:
a. Complement dependent
b. Naturally occurring
c. Destroyed by enzyme action
d. IgG and IgM mixtures
e. Reactive in a majority of situations at 37°C.

e

318. IgM antibodies usually:
a. Cross the placenta
b. React at 37°C.
c. Possess a molecular weight of 900.000 to 1,000.000

c

      d. Have a sedimentation constant of 3.5 S

      e. Possess alpha, kappa and lambda heavy chains

319. When a patient's serum is tested for antibodies, a reaction is observed with the screening cells at room temperature only. The antibody probably is:

      a. Anti-A

      b. Anti-Jk

      c. Anti-M   c

      d. Anti-K

      e. Anti-V

320. Mrs. X is admitted with a bleeding gastric ulcer. An emergency crossmatch is requested and the following results obtained in blood typing:

Anti-A	Anti-B	Anti-A, B	A_1 Cells	B Cells	O Cells
++	++++	++++	+	0	0

This discrepancy should be further investigated with (by):

      a. Additional A_1 and O cells

      b. *Dolichous biflorus* lectin   b

      c. O cord cells

      d. Incubation at 37°C.

      e. Serum electrophoresis

321. An extract of *Ulex europeus* seeds is used to:

      a. Enhance agglutination of weak reacting type A cells

      b. React with H substance   b

      c. Inhibit complement

      d. Distinguish group A_1 cells from weaker subgroups of A

      e. Inactivate cold agglutinins

322. Which amongst the following would be suitable for absorbing cells in the preparation of specific anti-D sera from serum donated by a group O Cde mother with anti-D:

      a. O cde/cde

      b. O Cde/cde

      c. AB CDe/cde

      d. AB cde/cde   d

323. The gene R^2 gives rise to the "blood factors":

      a. Rh_0, hr', rh''   a

      b. Rh_0, rh', rh''

      c. Rh_0, hr', hr''

      d. Rh_0, rh', hr''

324. For each of the patients listed in Column A, a request has been received for a transfusion. From Column B select the most appropriate choice. Each product can be used only once:

	Column A		Column B	
1.	12 year old male with classic hemophilia	a.	Whole blood	
		b.	Packed red cells	1—c
2.	35 year old male with acquired hemolytic anemia due to anti-e (Hb 10.1 gm.)	c.	Cryoprecipitate	
		d.	Fresh frozen plasma	
		e.	Reconstituted frozen red cells	2—h
3.	4 year old female with leukemia and bruising	f.	Fresh whole blood	
		g.	Platelet concentrate	3—g
4.	68 year old female with heart failure (Hb 6.0 gm.)	h.	No transfusion required	
				4—b
5.	25 year old male waiting a kidney transplant			5—e

325. In the formula $\dfrac{K_1}{K_2}$ = K, if K is increased, you would expect:

a. The dissociation of antibody-antigen to be increased, the avidity not being involved

b. The dissociation of antibody-antigen to be decreased and the avidity to be increased   b

c. The dissociation of antibody-antigen to be decreased and the avidity to be decreased

d. The dissociation of antibody-antigen to be increased and the avidity to be increased

e. No effect on the antigen complex

326. Fresh serum is used for antibody screening and compatibility testing. The serum must be less than 48 hours old to preserve:

a. Calcium

b. Complement   b

c. Labile serum antibodies

d. Chelating agents

e. Labile red cell antigens

327. A patient's red cells give the following reactions with Rh antisera:

Antiserum	Reaction
Anti-C	Positive
Anti-D	Positive
Anti-E	Positive
Anti-c	Positive
Anti-e	Positive

The most probably Rh genotype of the individual is:

a. R_1r

b. R_1R_1

c. R_1R_2 c

d. R_2R_2

328. If Rh negative red cells (cde/cde) are transfused into an Rh positive person of the genotype CDe/CDe, the antibody *most* likely to be developed is:

    a. Anti-c   a
    b. Anti-d
    c. Anti-e
    d. None, since the donor is Rh negative

329. An EDTA blood sample is received in the blood bank lab-
     oratory with a request for an indirect antiglobulin test to
     be carried out. This sample is *unsatisfactory* because:
     a. EDTA covers the antigenic receptor sites
     b. EDTA chelates with antigen-antibody complexes,
        preventing their agglutination
     c. EDTA prevents magnesium from adding C2 to the
        C4 complex
     d. EDTA binds calcium which is necessary for comple-
        ment addition to sensitized red cells   d

330. To qualify as a blood donor:
     a. A pregnant female must be in her first trimester
     b. Anyone under 17 years must have a note from their
        mother and should have persmission from their at-
        tending physician
     c. A minimum of five years must have passed since a
        person has had hepatitis
     d. The individual's pulse should not exceed 100 beats
        per minute   d

331. A unit of two-day old blood is given to a patient. After the
     non-viable red cells are removed from the circulation, the
     remaining donor red cells will usually disappear at the rate
     of:
     a.   1%/day   a
     b.   3%/day
     c.   5%/day
     d.   10%/day
     e.   15%/day

332. The percentage of high protein *in the tube* that is optimal
     for the detection of most immune antibodies (IgG) is:
     a.   5–10%
     b.   12–18%   b
     c.   18–25%
     d.   22–30%
     e.   Over 30%

333. What are the four general classes of procedures used in the
     routine serology laboratory?   See p. 437

334. What are the two phases involved in complement fixation
     tests?   See p. 437

335. What is the basic theory of fluorescent antibody methods? See p. 437

336. Antibodies to thyroglobulin are found in 80% of patients
     with _____ disease.   Hashimoto's

337. What are the four main patterns of fluorescence in anti-

nuclear antibody testing?	See p. 437
338. What is the nucleolar pattern seen in ANA testing?	See p. 437
339. What is a speckled pattern in ANA testing?	See p. 437
340. Which diseases, other than syphilis, can cause reagin reactivity?	See p. 438
341. What are the pitfalls in the use of the FTA-ABS test?	See p. 438
342. What end-point is usually considered evidence of infectious mononucleosis in the ox cell hemolysin test?	1:40 or greater
343. Immunoglobulins can be quantitated by the use of radial immunodiffusion techniques. In which conditions are these tests useful in diagnosis?	See p. 438
344. Anti-serum which produces rapid and clear agglutination with the appropriate cells is said to have a high degree of _____ and titer.	avidity
345. The only direct way of detecting an antigen is through reaction with an antibody. The d antigen cannot be detected in this way because _____.	anti-d has not been found
346. During pregnancy, the placenta provides a means for exposure to a _____ _____ of Rh antigens.	sensitizing dose

SEROLOGY & IMMUNOLOGY ANSWERS CONTINUED

1. The clear amber fluid remaining after blood has clotted. Serum contains all of the coagulation factors present in plasma except fibrinogen, factor V, and factor VIII, which are normally consumed in the synthesis of the clot.

3. Study of antigen antibody reactions.

4. Blood coagulation is the final result of a cyclic reaction involving at least 12 coagulation enzymes and chemicals which are present in the normal plasma. When blood clots, some of these substances are consumed in the formation of the clot, and are then absent from the resulting serum. Fibrinogen, factor V, and factor VIII are consumed in this way.

5. Normal serum contains no fibrinogen, factor V, or factor VIII, and no formed cellular elements (red blood cells, white blood cells, and blood platelets).

6. Natural or acquired serum antibodies which may react with antigens ("agglutinogens") in the red cells, thereby causing the agglutination or clumping of these cells.

8. Antigens in the red cells which may react with the corresponding antibodies ("agglutinins") in the serum with resulting agglutination or clumping of these cells.

11. They lower the resistance of bacterial invaders to the phagocytizing action of leukocytes.

13. The opsonic power of a patient's blood may be demonstrated by mixing the patient's fresh citrated blood with a suspension of bacteria and comparing the degree of phagocytosis with that of controls. Opsonocytophagic tests, though still used occasionally in brucellosis, are of doubtful diagnostic value.

22. a. Anti-streptolysin-O; C-reactive protein; purified protein derivative (a form of tuberculin)
    b. Serological test(s) for syphilis; Venereal Disease Research Laboratory; fluorescent treponemal antibody test; *Treponema pallidum* immobilization
    c. *Treponema pallidum* agglutination; *Treponema pallidum* immune adherence; *Treponema pallidum* complement fixation; *Treponema pallidum* methylene blue
    d. Reiter protein complement-fixation (Kolmer test with Reiter protein antigen); Kolmer test with Reiter protein antigen (Reiter protein complement-fixation); cardiolipin natural lecithin; cardiolipin synthetic lecithin

24. a. Typing of beta-hemolytic streptococci
    b. Diagnosis of syphilis
    c. Identification of blood stains
    d. Diagnosis of certain parasitic, bacterial, and mycotic diseases

48. Certain individuals may secrete, in soluble aqueous form, the A, B, or H antigen ("substance") in their saliva, gastric juice, and other body fluids.

49. An agglutinating antigen ("agglutinogen").

56. Syphilis, brucellosis, malaria, viral hepatitis may be transmitted through blood transfusion (theoretically any disease characterized by the presence of any sort of microorganism in the blood could be transmitted by transfusion).

57. Because there are other blood group systems, which the patient could be sensitized to from either a previous transfusion or from a previous pregnancy. In addition, naturally occurring antibodies (anti-Lewis and anti-P, etc.) could be present in the patient's plasma and could react against the donor's cells, although these reactions are not usually considered as dangerous and harmful as those IgG antibodies detected in the patient and reacting against the donor's cells.

58. The patient's serum must not agglutinate or hemolyze the donor's cells either at room temperature or at 37°C. using both a saline and high protein crossmatch, and an indirect Coombs test.

61. The clinical criterion for exchange transfusion is dependent upon several factors (indirect bilirubin level of the infant's serum, hemoglobin level of infant, speed of bilirubin build-up, and age of the infant).

62. In ABO disease, exchange transfusions are only infrequently given, as the disease, although probably more frequent than Rh disease, is more often undiagnosed and usually milder in severity. This is partly due to the presence of ABH substances in the infant's tissues that complex with any antibody crossing the placenta.

63. Exclusion in "paternity" blood typing can be accomplished if it is proven that the infant possesses antigens not possessed by either the mother or the accused father. It is not possible to prove that because the infant possesses antigen sites on his red cells that are the same as the accused fathers's, those sites were derived from the accused. They could have come from many other people.

64. a. Mother A, father A. Possible children: O and A. Impossible children: B, AB.
    b. Mother O, father B. Possible children: O and B. Impossible children: A, AB

86. Yaws, pinta, bejel (50–100% cases); Leprosy (40–70% cases); Infectious mononucleosis (10–50% cases); Malaria (10–40% cases); All the collagen diseases; Any fever of long standing; Following anesthesia or alcohol intoxication.

87. Fresh guinea pig serum is the usual source of complement (it has to be used fresh or otherwise kept frozen since it is labile or unstable).

88. The serum of a single guinea pig may happen to be resistant to fixation. Pool fresh sera from at least three normal guinea pigs.

89. Nine components of complement (C-1, C-2, C-3, C-4, C-5, C-6, C-7, C-8, C-9) have been identified by physical or chemical characteristics. C-3 deteriorates rapidly when serum stands at room temperature, partly because of its sensitivity to pH changes.

104. CSF does not contain enough native complement to justify inactivation. Fluids three days old or older and fluids which are contaminated by bacteria may be heated at 56°C. for 15 minutes to destroy any thermolabile anticomplementary factors that may be present.

113. By injecting the specific antigen (i.e., washed sheep red blood cells) into rabbits. After rabbits have become immunized the animals are bled, the blood is allowed to clot and the serum is obtained.

114. The 1:1 solution of hemolysin in glycerin (glycerin and phenol are hemolysin preservatives). Two ml. of this glycerinized hemolysin are mixed with 94 ml. of Kolmer saline solution and with 4 ml. of 5% phenol in Kolmer saline to prepare the 1:100 stock solution of hemolysin (to avoid precipitation of the hemolysin by the 5% phenol both phenol and saline should be mixed prior to adding the glycerinized hemolysin).

115. Add 4.5 ml. Kolmer saline for each 0.5 ml. of stock (1:100) dilution.

116. Add 5.8 ml. of Kolmer saline (brought to refrigerator temperature) for each 0.2 ml. complement (fresh or restored lyophilized).

119. The highest dilution of hemolysin that gives complete hemolysis at one hour incubation in 37°C. water bath represents the unit of hemolysin. Good hemolysin will give complete hemolysis with 0.5 ml. of a 1:4,000 (or higher) dilution.

121. Hemolysin is so diluted that 2 units are contained in 0.5 ml. If the unit is 0.5 ml. of the 1:5,000 dilution then 2 units will be contained in 0.5 ml. of a 1:2,500 dilution.

124. Add 59 ml. of Kolmer saline to 1 ml. of the 1:100 stock dilution of hemolysin.

126. Complement, antigen, and Kolmer saline (step #1) are added to eight clean Kolmer tubes as follows:

	Complement (1:30)	Antigen dilution	Kolmer saline
Tube 1	0.20 ml.	0.5 ml.	1.3 ml.
2	0.25	0.5	1.3
3	0.30	0.5	1.2
4	0.35	0.5	1.2
5	0.40	0.5	1.1
6	0.45	0.5	1.1
7	0.50	0.5	1.0
8	none	none	2.5

After one hour incubation in 37°C. water bath tubes 1–7 each receives (step #2) 0.5 ml. (2 full units) of hemolysin, then all 8 tubes are added 0.5 ml. of 2% sheep cell suspension and incubated for another hour to 37°C. water bath. The *exact unit* of complement may then be determined.

127. a. The smallest amount of complement giving complete hemolysis is the **exact unit.**

b. The **full unit** is the next larger quantity and it contains 0.05 ml. more complement.

c. The **dose** for complement-fixation test should contain 2 full units in 1 ml.

129. Add 59 ml. Kolmer saline to 1 ml. complement (fresh or restored lyophilized.

130. Cells (i.e., an antigenic substance) which have become combined with specific antibody (hemolytic amboceptor or hemolysin) but which will not actually hemolyze unless free complement is present.

131. a. Antigen control
b. Hemolysin control
c. Sheep cell control
d. Serum (both known positive and known negative) controls

142. Positive reactions might be due to the activity of the serum rather than the spinal fluid itself.

143. a. Diagnosis of amebiasis (Craig test)
b. Gonorrhea
c. Yaws and pinta
d. Histoplasmosis and coccidioidomycosis

144. Serial dilutions of the patient's serum each are added a drop of suspension of actively motile *Treponema pallidum* (freshly obtained from the testicular chancre of an infected rabbit). A normal serum control is always included. Examination (dark-field) under microscope is then carried out to determine the highest dilution of serum which quickly checks spirochetal movement. This dilution represents the titer of *Treponema* immobilizing antibody.

145. The TPI test can conclusively differentiate between true syphilitic positive reactions and biological false positive reactions as it measures syphilitic antibody (syphilitic "reagin") against the specific antigen (i.e., *T. pallidum*)/

rather than against a nonspecific one (such as beef heart muscle extract with added cholesterol and lecithin).

146. Killed spirochetes will adhere to human red blood cells only when syphilitic antibody (syphilitic reagin) is present. Complement is a factor in the reaction.

149. The 11th tube is a control and contains no spinal fluid.

150. The mastic test replaces the gold chloride solution by a gum mastic reagent. The latter is easier to prepare but less sensitive.

151. The absence of agglutination in the lower dilutions of a serum which shows agglutination in the higher dilutions.

152. They are bacterial antigens that have been designed for use by either the rapid slide agglutination test or the conventional tube agglutination test procedure.

153. The Rapid Slide Test is primarily intended as a screening procedure and is especially useful when the examination of large number of serum specimens is involved.

154. The Tube Test is useful for the accurate determination of the variation in serum antibody titers that occur during the various stages of infection.

159. The *flagellar* antigen is prepared that way.

168. Because K antigens have the ability to mask the O agglutinability of living cultures.

169. Complete agglutination . . . . 4 plus (++++)
Approximately 75% agglutination . . . . . . 3 plus (+++)
Approximately 50% agglutination . . . . . . 2 plus (++)
Approximately 25% agglutination . . . . . . 1 plus (+)
Less than 25% agglutination . . . . Trace (±)
No agglutination . . . . Negative (−)

170. The smallest quantity of serum that exhibits a 2 plus (++) or 50% degree of agglutination is considered as the "endpoint" of serum reactivity or as the serum "titer."

174. When a rise in titer (twofold or greater) is observed between successive serum specimens taken several days apart.

175. Agglutination due to antibodies formed against a certain species of microorganism but which react with an entirely different species.

176. a. Rickettsial infections may produce agglutinins which react with *Brucella abortus*
b. Tularemia agglutinins may agglutinate *Br. abortus* also
c. *Brucella* agglutinins may react with *P. tularensis*.

178. For routine testing, *Proteus* OX$_{19}$ is used (if positive, set up agglutinations with *Proteus* OX$_2$ and *Proteus* OXK). In typhus fever a strong positive reaction with *Proteus* OX$_{19}$, a weak positive reaction with *Proteus* OX$_2$, and a negative reaction with *Proteus* OXK are obtained. Titers of 1:80 are suspicious, 1:60 positive.

185. The presence of native complement may cause hemolysis. Inactivate by heating at 56°C. for 30 minutes.

195. Blackwater fever; African trypanosomiasis; leishmaniasis

197. Read after two hour (or overnight) refrigeration).

205. The Todd unit is the reciprocal of the volume of serum in ml. necessary to neutralize a standard amount of streptolysin-O antigen.

206. a. Patient's serum
     b. Buffer solution
     c. Streptolysin-O reagent
     d. Cell (human or rabbit) suspension

213. It is a protein present in the serum of certain patients and which will react with the somatic C polysaccharide of pneumococcus.

217. By immunizing rabbits with this protein then obtaining their serum.

228. Infections with the *Shigella-Salmonella* group are usually acute and there is not enough time for the patient to develop antibodies. Laboratory diagnosis is made by isolating the organism.

230. "X" indicates that the relationship to *Proteus vulgaris* is not known. "O" stands for somatic antigen (the flagellar antigen is known as the "H" antigen).

233. "Sensitivity" means the ability of the test to detect the syphylitic altered globulin present in the serum of syphilitic persons.

234. "Specificity" refers to the ability of the test to give no false positive reactions with the serum of nonsyphilitic persons.

235. Cholesterin is added to antigen to coarsen the antigen particles and thereby increase its avidity for antibody per unit of surface or mass, It thus increases the sensitivity of antigen. Other influencing factors are variations in temperature, speed of mixing, optimum type of emulsion, etc.

237. The name "tuberculin" embraces all the products made from the tubercle bacillus *(Mycobacterium tuberculosis)* which contain its bacterial proteins. It produces definite reactions in tuberculous subjects.

238. A pure culture of tubercle bacilli of six weeks' growth in 5% glycerin broth, evaporated to 1/10 of its volume and filtered. It contains all the soluble products of the tubercle bacillus in 50% glycerin solution. It is standardized by the British method.

239. This is the name that designates the product obtained by Seibert (*Am. Rev. Tuberc.*, 1932, 25:724) from Standard Bureau of Animal Industry (B.A.I.) synthetic tuberculin. It is used for diagnostic testing.

241. It is prepared from the serum of rabbits or goats immunized with the globulin fraction of human serum.

242. **Thermostabile (thermostable):** Not easily changed or destroyed by heat. **Thermolabile:** Easily changed or destroyed by heat. For instance, by heating serum at 56°C. for 20–30 minutes, its native complement becomes inactive.

243. **Heterologous serum:** A serum obtained from a different species. **Homologous serum:** A serum obtained from the same species.

244. **Natural antibodies:** Antibodies which occur naturally in the serum. They

are inherited and not acquired as a result of stimulation by an antigen. **Acquired antibodies:** Antibodies developed in the serum as a result of stimulation by an antigen.

245. **Agglutinins** are complete ("bivalent") antibodies responsible for immobilization of motile organisms and for cell clumping. Agglutinins are relatively thermolabile, do not pass through the placenta and may clump cells suspended in either saline media or in high molecular weight colloids or proteins.

Glutinins are incomplete ("univalent") "blocking" antibodies which are relatively thermostable and readily pass the placental barrier. Many will "coat" specific cells when these cells are suspended in a saline medium but actual clumping will not take place unless high molecular weight colloids or proteins are also present.

246. **Agglutination:** The clumping of a particulate antigen (cells or bacteria in suspension) when acted upon by a serum ("antiserum") containing the specific (and complete) antibodies (specific "agglutinins"). Also see the preceding answer.

Conglutination: The clumping of cells which have been sensitized or "coated" by glutinins (these are incomplete, univalent, "coating" or "blocking" antibodies) will not take place unless *conglutinin* (a colloidal aggregate of serum proteins related to complement) is also present. Conglutinin is easily dissociated by diluting with salt solution. Therefore, the use of saline in conglutination tests is to be avoided. By adding 30% bovine albumin to plasma (1/4 to 1/3 its volume) so-called "fortified conglutinin" is obtained.

247. **Agglutinin:** A particular type of serum antibody (agglutinins are complete or bivalent antibodies; there are natural and acquired agglutinins) which may react with specific antigens in cells and cause agglutination or clumping of these cells.

Agglutinoid: A modified agglutinin. Agglutinoids can still combine with their corresponding agglutinogens but do not cause actual agglutination reactions.

248. **Complement-fixation:** The test depends upon two phenomena, bacteriolysis and hemolysis; and both of these, in turn, depend upon the presence of *complement*. When red blood cells remain in suspension in a fluid the fluid has an opaque color. If hemolysis occurs, the hemoglobin leaves the corpuscles and the fluid becomes transparent and of a deep red color. The hemolytic antibody combines with the stroma of the cell, increases the permeability of the latter and sets free the hemoglobin (red coloring substance of the cell) into the surrounding fluid or media.

Bacteriolysis is dependent upon a similar mechanism but it is not visible to the naked eye. Therefore, in making the complement-fixation test two systems are used: the hemolytic, to produce visible results (blood corpuscles and amboceptor) in specific hemolytic serum; and the bacterial system consisting of antigen, the suspected antibacterial serum (amboceptor) and complement.

Antigen plus suspected serum plus complement are incubated at 37°C. for an hour to give time for the amboceptor and complement to interact. Then red cells and hemolytic serum are added and the entire mixture again incubated for a like period. At the end of this time, the presence or absence or hemolysis is noted (preliminary reading). If hemolysis has occurred, there is no amboceptor in the suspected serum to fix complement with the antigen. Complement remains free to act with the hemolytic system during the second incubation. The result is negative. If no hemolysis has occurred, the presence of the immune body has led to the absorption of all of the complement, thus leaving none to take part in the hemolysis of the red cells (positive reaction).

1. Antigen
   +
2. Immune antibody   Incubated at 37°C.
   (suspected serum)   for one hour
   +
3. Complement

4. Red blood cells
   +
5. Hemolytic amboceptor

   (If 2 present, no hemolysis; if 2 not present, hemolysis)

Complement-deviation: This phenomenon, discovered by Neisser and Wechsberg in 1901, takes place when complement combines with an excess of antibody which is present and is thus prevented from reacting with the antigen-antibody complex.

249. **Natural immunity:** The resistance which exists normally in an animal or human being is termed "natural immunity." Certain persons appear to have a definite resistance to scarlet fever and diphtheria, although they have never had the disease; others repeatedly pass through epidemics of various infections, such as measles, without becoming infected. Man is immune to fowl cholera, swine plague, etc.
Acquired immunity: The resistance to a disease which exists:
a. After an attack of the disease or exposure to repeated small doses of infective material.
b. After vaccination against it with a specific vaccine or virus.
An example of the first is the immunity following a smallpox attack or the immunity that comes in later years of youth and adult life to diphtheria; of the second, the immunity following vaccination against smallpox and diphtheria.
There are two types of acquired immunity: Active and passive.

250. **Active immunity:** The immunity developed by the individual himself because he has had the disease or because the immunity to it has been artificially produced. The latter is carried out with attenuated cultures, virus changed by animal passage, immunization with dead bacteria and immunization with bacterial products.
Passive immunity: A form of immunity that depends upon defensive factors not originating in the person or animal protected but is passively acquired by the injection of serum from another that has acquired an active immunity to the disease or infection in question.

251. **Direct Coombs:** This test determines whether the patient's cells have been sensitized "in vivo" by circulating antibodies. In infants they have reached

the fetus through the placenta. Infant's cells (cord blood cells previously washed three times in normal saline) will, if sensitized, agglutinate upon addition to them of antihuman globulin serum (Coombs' serum). The direct Coombs tests the patient's cells for the presence of antibody. It frequently is positive in cases of acquired hemolytic anemia of unknown etiology.

Indirect Coombs: It tests for the presence or absence of circulating antibodies in the patient's serum. If erythroblastosis is suspected the mother's serum is incubated with known Rh-positive cells. If circulating antibodies are present in this serum the cells will become sensitized *in vitro* and will later agglutinate upon addition (cells are washed in normal saline three times before this step) of antihuman globulin serum (Coombs' serum). The indirect Coombs test tests the patient's serum for the presence of "unbound" antibodies free in the serum.

252. **Exclusion antigens** (used in screen tests for syphilis) have greater sensitivity but less specificity than **diagnostic antigens.**

253. **Opsonic power:** This is the power of the blood of an individual to phagocytize any particular microorganism.
Opsonic index: This is the opsonic power of a patient's blood (i.e., the number of bacteria taken up by the phagocytes in the presence of the patient's serum) compared with the opsonic power of normal blood (i.e., the number of bacteria taken up in the presence of normal serum).

254. The **Forssman heterophil antibody** of serum-sickness is absorbed both by guinea pig kidney antigen and by beef erythrocyte antigen. The Forssman heterophil antibody of normal serum is absorbed by guinea pig kidney antigen but not by beef erythrocyte antigen.
The **heterophil antibody of infectious mononucleosis** is absorbed by beef erythrocyte antigen but not by guinea pig kidney antigen.

255. **Warm agglutinins:** These are agglutinins whose thermal optimal temperature is 37°C.
Cold agglutinins: These are agglutinins whose thermal optimal temperature is between 4 and 20°C.

256. **Widal reaction:** This was originally a microscopic slide agglutination test for the laboratory diagnosis of typhoid fever employing the patient's serum or (agglutinins are not destroyed by drying) the patient's dried blood and, as the antigen, a suspension of motile *Salmonella typhi.*
Weil-Felix reaction: An agglutination test for the laboratory diagnosis of various rickettsial diseases. The following strains of *Proteus* are used as antigen: *Proteus* OX_{19}, *Proteus* OX_2, and *Proteus* OXK.

257. Although **Arthus phenomenon** (a local, immediate type of reaction which may occur when animals are subcutaneously or intracutaneously injected at intervals with the same antigen) is accompanied by changes similar to those of systemic anaphylaxis, the following differences may be noted:
Arthus reaction:
a. Can be passively transferred by precipitating antibody only and the amount of this antibody required for transfer is relatively large.
b. After passive transfer of antibody no latent period is necessary before injection of antigen can give rise to reaction.

    c. Injection of histamine is unable to duplicate the symptoms of the reaction.

Systemic anaphylaxis:

    a. Can be passively transferred either by precipitating or by non-precipitating antibody and the amount of these antibodies required for transfer is very small.

    b. After passive transfer of antibody a latent period is necessary before the injection of antigen can produce the reaction.

    c. Injection of histamine *will largely duplicate the symptoms of the reaction.*

258. This term is now obsolete and should not be retained. It is used to refer to a group O blood donor. Since O is not normally antigenic to A, B, or AB people, it was formerly believed that group O could be given to any patient. However, group O bloods are dangerous when transfused into patients of other groups, if they possess hemolysins levels that are high and active against either A or B cells.

259. The term "universal recipient" is a misnomer, an obsolete term for a group AB patient.

260. The titer of an antiserum is a measure of the number of antibody units per unit volume of the original serum; thus if the last tube showing a reaction contains 1 ml. volume and is diluted 1/128 of the original serum, the titer of the serum is 128 units of antibody per ml. of serum.

261. The Rose-Waaler test is a test using sheep red blood cells sensitized with rabbit anti-sheep serum that are agglutinated by the sera of 75% of patients with rheumatoid arthritis.

262. Inert particles of polystyrene latex, collodion, and bentonite, and red cells both treated with tanic acid and untreated, can be coated with a variety of protein antigens, and in the case of untreated red cells, with polysaccharide antigens. They can be used for the detection of antibodies, as shown by the agglutination of the coated particle. Examples of such coated particular tests are the L.D. test and the R.A. test.

263. a. Failure to add antiglobulin serum
    b. Inadequate washing of the red cells
    c. Inactivation of the antiglobulin serum by exogenous gamma globulin
    d. Weak or inactive antiglobulin serum
    e. Lack of a broad-spectrum reactivity
    f. Fibrin clot in the cell suspension
    g. Dirty test tube

264. a. Colloidal silica
    b. Wax from either straw or test tube stoppers
    c. Overcentrifugation
    d. Bacterial contamination of cells, serum or reagents
    e. Over zealous reading

265. Lymphoma; lymphocytic leukemia; collagen diseases (L.E.); liver disease; infectious mononucleosis; Boeck's sarcoid; virus infections; Kaposi's sarcoma; Gaucher's disease; ulcerative colitis; galactosemia; *E. coli* enteritis.

266. Stibophen; Quinidine; Quinine; Phenacetin; Penicillin; Aldomet; Keflin.

267. Transferrin and complement. Transferrin is a beta globulin that transports iron in the blood. During the maturation of red cells, iron is delivered to them by a process in which transferrin becomes bound to the cell surface. Reticulocytes in particular have a high proportion of surface-bound transferrin and produce a false-positive antihuman globulin test if the serum used is rich in anti-beta globulin. The reaction between red cells and cold agglutinins is usually accompanied by a reaction between at least one component of complement and the same red cell. The complement-binding is stable so that warming and washing which removes the antibody does not affect the complement coating. Antiglobulin sera that either anti-beta or anti-complement activity may react to give a weak positive direct test.

268. Red cells have a negative electrical charge that arises from the ionization of carboxyl groups of siliac acid residues on the cell surface. The charge is equal on all red cells because like charges repel, red cells in suspension do not come into contact with each other. When suspended in electrolytes, such as sodium chloride, the cell attracts an "ionic cloud", the intensity of which varies depending upon the intrinsic red cell charge and the ionic constitution of the suspending medium. The electrical activity of this "ionic cloud" is the zeta potential, and is the force that must be overcome before agglutination can take place. Usually, the zeta potential is sufficient to keep red cells separated by a space of 1,000 Å. Before agglutination takes place in such a situation either the antibodies should be over 1,000 Å in length or the zeta potential should be reduced so that antibodies of shorter length can act as bridges between the red cells.

300. Because the red cells of the donor contain H antigens which react with anti-H found in the serum of the "Bombay" patient.

304. When the blood sample has a positive direct antiglobulin test.

315. More strongly with adult cells then with cord cells, at 4°C.

333. Agglutination; precipitation; complement fixation; fluorescent antibody.

334. The first phase is the incubation of the patient's serum with the appropriate antigen to be tested and a specified amount of complement. The second phase is the indicator phase in which the presence of an antigen-antibody reaction in the first phase is indicated by the fact that complement is "fixed" to these complexes and is no longer free in the system.

335. The fluorescent antibody procedures are based upon a fluorescent dye, such as fluorescein isothiocyanate or rhodamine B isothiocyanate being conjugated with antibody. Thus, antibody attachment to antigen can be identified under the fluorescent microscope.

337. Homogenous pattern; peripheral pattern; speckled pattern; nucleolar pattern.

338. The nucleolar pattern is believed to result from antibody directed against a specific RNA configuration of the nucleolus or antibody specific for proteins necessary for maturation of nucleolar RNA. This pattern is seen by itself, usually in patients with progressive systemic sclerosis.

339. This results from antibody directed against different nuclear antigens. Antibody against soluble material, a nonchromatin antigen extracted from nuclei with dilute phosphate buffer, is found in some S.L.E. patients.

Patient's with Raynaud's phenomenon and progressive systemic sclerosis may give a speckled pattern with antibody directed against nuclear material other than soluble antigen.

340. Acute or chronic infections, such as malaria, leprosy, infectious mononucleosis, and upper respiratory diseases, as well as collagen and immunological diseases such as rheumatoid arthritis and lupus erythrematosus can produce false positive reagin tests.

341. The test does not distinguish between syphilis and other treponematoses such as pinta, yaws and bejel. It is not useful in measuring the effectiveness of therapy.

343. Walderstom's macroglobulinemia; agammaglobulinemia; certain myelomas; dysgammaglobulinemia; certain liver diseases; hyperimmunization; and a wide variety of infections.

Section IV

REVIEW OF HISTOLOGY TECHNIQUE

REVIEW OF HISTOLOGY TECHNIQUE

Edited by Ron Otta, Dept. of Laboratory Medicine, University of Nevada at Reno

BOARD EXAMINATION QUESTIONS AND ANSWERS

1. The sliding microtome is used for:
   a. Cutting celloidin and large paraffin materials   a
   b. Cutting routine paraffin sections
   c. Cutting unembedded, formalin-fixed tissue
   d. Cutting celloidin and unembedded tissues

2. The usual thickness for routine paraffin sections is:
   a. 1 to 2 microns
   b. 3 to 4 microns
   c. 5 to 6 microns   c
   d. 8 to 10 microns

3. The usual thickness for routine cryostat sections is:
   a. 1 to 2 microns
   b. 3 to 4 microns
   c. 5 to 6 microns
   d. 8 to 10 microns   d

4. If ribbons break off and curl, the cause may be:
   a. Nicks in knife edge   a
   b. Knife edge dirty   b
   c. Too much knife tilt   c
   d. Dull knife   d

5. What melting temperature of paraffin is best for routine histology?
   a. 52 to 53°C.
   b. 54 to 55°C.
   c. 56 to 57°C.   c
   d. 58 to 59°C.

6. What is the optimum temperature for paraffin bath with paraffin melting point of 56°C.?
   a. 60°   a
   b. 62°
   c. 65°
   d. 70°

7. How do you examine the cutting edge of the knife for nicks?
   a. With the microscope under high power objective
   b. With the microscope under low power objective   b
   c. With the naked eye

441

8. If Zenker's solution is used, what must one do to remove the fixative salts from the tissue before staining?
   a. Immerse the slides in alcoholic iodine after the paraffin has been removed from the sections   a
   b. Fixative salts removed by washing in water   b
   c. Mercuric salts removed by iodine   c
   d. Mercuric salts removed by water

9. The most common fixative for special stain is:
   a. Bouin's fluid
   b. Flemming's fluid
   c. Zenker's solution   c
   d. Formalin ammonium bromide solution

10. How do you deformalinize tissue slides for sections?
    a. Deformalinize in ammonia water for one hour   a
    b. Wash in water for one hour   b
    c. Fix in Zenker's or Helly's fluid for one hour   c
    d. Wash in water for one hour
    e. Stain

11. Which of the following is a good dehydrator for routine histology?
    a. Isoproperol   a
    b. Acetone   b
    c. Xylene
    d. Dioxane   d

12. Which of the following are commonly used as decalcifying solutions?
    a. Formic acid 5%   a
    b. Picric acid 10%
    c. Trichloroacetic acid (TCA)   c
    d. Nitric acid   d

13. What does prolonged decalcification do to the bone structure?
    a. The bone structure will swell   a
    b. Good results can be expected
    c. The soft tissues of bone damaged   c
    d. Good results cannot be expected   d

14. Which may be used to neutralize tissue after decalcification?
    a. Lithium carbonate   a
    b. Potassium bromide
    c. Potassium ferrocyanide
    d. HCl

15. Which is the best fixative for bone prior to decalcification?
    a. Carnoy's
    b. 10% formalin   b
    c. Alcohol
    d. Trichloroacetic acid

16. Can sulfosalicylic acid be used alone as a decalcifier or in combination with other acids?

a. It could be used only in combination with other acids
b. It could either be used alone or in combination with other acids   b
c. It could be used only in combination with an alkali
d. It could be used with acid or alkali

17. Orth's fluid is:
    a. A decalcifying solution
    b. A dehydrating solution
    c. A clearing solution
    d. A fixative   d

18. How long can tissues be left in Zenker's fluid without producing substantial damage?
    a. 2 hours
    b. 6 hours
    c. 24 hours   c
    d. Indefinitely

19. Which of the following dissolves collodion?
    a. Xylene
    b. Ethyl alcohol   b
    c. Ether   c
    d. Chloroform

20. Which fixative is best used for preservation of lipids?
    a. Osmic acid   a
    b. Formalin
    c. Alcohol 95%
    d. Ether-alcohol

21. Fat is better demonstrated in:
    a. Paraffin sections
    b. Celloidin sections
    c. Frozen sections   c
    d. None of these

22. What mounting medium is best used for temporary mounting:
    a. Cedar oil
    b. Kaiser's glycerin jelly   b
    c. Colophonium
    d. Glycerin

23. A good clearing reagent for celloidin is:
    a. Oil of origanum
    b. Oil of bergamot
    c. Carbolxylol
    d. Xylol   d

24. Vital staining and supravital staining differ from each other in that:
    a. Vital stain is employed to stain living cells in the body
    b. Vital stain is employed to stain dead cells in the body
    c. Supravital stain is employed to stain living cells in the body   c

d. Supravital stain is employed to stain living cells immediately after removal from the body

25. If most synthetic mounting media become too thick, they may be thinned with:
    a. Ether
    b. Alcohol 95%
    c. Xylol   c
    d. Ether-alcohol

26. Fixatives for tissues are usually used at:
    a. 56°C.
    b. Room temperature   b
    c. —15°C.
    d. —5°C.

27. Absolute ethyl alcohol is:
    a. A dehydrating agent   a
    b. A clearing agent
    c. A fixing agent
    d. A decalcifying agent

28. The freezing microtome uses:
    a. Compressed carbon dioxide   a
    b. Compressed carbon monoxide
    c. Compressed oxygen
    d. Compressed nitrogen

29. Unfixed tissues may be examined by means of:
    a. Paraffin sections
    b. Celloidin sections
    c. Frozen sections   c
    d. None of these

30. Xylol is a solvent for:
    a. Celloidin
    b. Paraffin   b
    c. Acid alcohol
    d. Ether

31. Dioxane will mix with:
    a. Paraffin   a
    b. 5% formic acid
    c. 10% formalin   c
    d. Water   d

32. The chief causes of artifacts on Papanicolaou smears are:
    a. Poor fixation   a
    b. Old stain
    c. Improper agitation   c
    d. Poor dehydration

33. In the hematoxylin and eosin method of staining, two reagents that will cause fading of the nuclei are:
    a. Xylol
    b. Eosin

    c. Acid alcohol   c
    d. Ammonia water   d

34. Van Gieson stain is used for demonstrating:
    a. Collagen fibers   a
    b. Cellulose
    c. Muscle   c
    d. Carbohydrate

35. The periodic acid Schiff's stain demonstrates:
    a. Cellulose   a
    b. Chitin   b
    c. Carbohydrate   c
    d. Mucoprotein   d
    e. Nerve cells and fibers   e

36. A good fixative for amyloid stain is:
    a. Formalin 5%
    b. Formalin 10%   b
    c. Absolute alcohol   c
    d. Alcohol 70%

37. State which of the following dyes are basic dyes, which are acid dyes, and which are neither:
    1. Hematoxylin is a:
        a. Basic
        b. Acid
        c. Neither   c
    2. Fast green is:
        a. Basic
        b. Acid   b
        c. Neither
    3. Methyl green is:
        a. Basic   a
        b. Acid
        c. Neither
    4. Gentian violet is:
        a. Basic   a
        b. Acid
        c. Neither
    5. Orange green is:
        a. Basic
        b. Acid   b
        c. Neither
    6. Sudan black is:
        a. Basic
        b. Acid
        c. Neither   c

38. Fontana solution is made up from:
    a. Gold chloride acid solution A
    b. Uranium nitrate solution
    c. Silver nitrate solution   c
    d. 0.5% periodic acid solution

39. Potassium ferrocyanide and hydrochloric acid may be used
    to demonstrate:
    a. Hemosiderin   a
    b. Fungi
    c. Hemofuchsin
    d. Melanin

40. Eosin solution should be:
    a. Neutral
    b. Alkaline
    c. Acid   c

41. In Schiff's staining method the periodic acid must be:
    a. 1%
    b. 0.5%   b
    c. 10%
    d. 5%

42. Gridley's stain for fungi is oxidized in:
    a. 6% chromic acid for one hour
    b. 2% periodic acid solution for two hours
    c. 4% gold chloride acid solution for one hour
    d. 4% chromic acid for one hour   d

43. Is Permount a good mounting medium for Gridley's stain?
    a. Yes   a
    b. No

44. The Autotechnicon is a mechanical and electrical device
    which can carry out the process of:
    a. Staining
    b. Fixation   b
    c. Dehydration   c
    d. Infiltration   d

45. Which of the following are appropriate in routine Auto-
    technicon processing:
    a. Formalin-alcohol (I, II, III) = Fixation and dehy-
                                        dration   a
    b. Alcohol 95% (I, II)   = Dehydration   b
    c. Absolute alcohol (I, II)   = Dehydration   c
    d. Acetone & dririte (I, II)   = Remove alcohol,
                                        clearing
    e. Paraffin bath (I, II, III)   = Infiltration   e

46. "Gross" is a:
    a. Microscopic examination
    b. Macroscopic examination and description of specimen
       surgically removed   b
    c. Microscopic examination of intracellular bodies
    d. Microscopic examination for disease

47. The main functions of a fixative are:
    a. Preserve shape and size of the parts of organs or
       tissues   a
    b. To set intracellular bodies

   c. To arrest postmortem, autolytic, osmotic, and other
      changes in the tissues   c
   d. To bring out differences in the refractive indices of
      parts of organs   d
   e. To render insoluble as many constituents of the cells
      as possible   e

48. Important properties for a fixative are:
   a. Rapid penetration   a
   b. Rapid dehydration
   c. Stabilization of structure   c
   d. Cell killing   d

49. Blocks should be:
   a. Thin enough   a
   b. More than 0.5 cm. thick
   c. Not more than 0.5 cm. thick   c
   d. Immersed in 10 times their volume of fixative
   e. Immersed in 20 times their volume of fixative   e

50. Washing before staining is needed for:
   a. Acetic acid and picric acid only for some strains   a
   b. Not at all
   c. All osmic, chromic, and platinic liquids   c
   d. Oxalic acid and alcohol-chloroform

51. Do not require washing out before staining:
   a. Acetic and picric acid only for some stains
   b. Alcohol   b
   c. All osmic, chromic, and platinic liquids
   d. Formaldehyde   d
   e. Sublimate   e

52. The fixative most widely used is:
   a. 10% formalin   a
   b. Zenker's fluid
   c. 5% acetic acid
   d. Carnoy's fluid

53. Formalin or formol is:
   a. The common name for the combination of the 50%
      formaldehyde and alcohol
   b. The common name for the combination of the 5%
      formaldehyde and ether-alcohol
   c. The commercial name for the combination of the
      gas formaldehyde and water   c
   d. The commercial name for the combination of the
      alcohol and gas formaldehyde

54. An excellent fixative for brain tissue is:
   a. Formalin ammonium bromide   a
   b. Acetone
   c. 10% acetic acid
   d. 70% formalin solution

55. An excellent fixative for nuclear studies is:
    a. Acetone
    b. 5% acetic acid
    c. Zenker's followed by washing and storage in 80% alcohol
    d. 50% formalin solution

    c

56. As fixatives for bacteria, glycogen, and some of the enzymes, the following are also commonly used:
    a. Alcohol
    b. Acetone
    c. Ether
    d. Potassium bromide

    a
    b

57. Which of the following are steps in the removal of mercuric salts from microscopic section?
    a. Deparaffinize and run down to water
    b. Place slides in Lugol's iodine for 10 minutes
    c. Place slides in 5% sodium thiosulfate for 5 minutes
    d. Wash in distilled water
    e. Stain, beginning with the hematoxylin

    a
    b
    c
    d

58. Fixatives are:
    a. 10% formalin solution
    b. 10% formalin-alcohol solution
    c. Buffered neutral formalin solution
    d. Formalin ammonium bromide
    e. Zenker's fluid
    f. Zenker's-formalin solution
    g. Bouin's fluid
    h. Flemming's fluid
    i. Carnoy's fluid
    j. Absolute alcohol
    k. Acetone
    l. 5% acetic acid
    m. All of the above

    m

59. Fixatives can be classified into:
    a. Enzymatic fixatives
    b. Non-enzymatic fixatives
    c. Coagulating fixatives (e.g., ethanol)
    d. Non-coagulating fixatives (e.g., formaldehyde)

    c
    d

60. Although formalin is widely used as a fixative, a better fixative for preserving tissue structure is:
    a. Glutaraldehyde
    b. Acetone
    c. 5% acetic acid
    d. Absolute alcohol

    a

61. The major fixing agent in Zenker's is:
    a. Acetic acid
    b. Mercuric chloride
    c. Potassium dichromate
    d. Water

    c

62. The usual concentration of formaldehyde in formalin is:
    a. 35-40%
    b. 37-40%   b
    c. 38-45%
    d. 32-38%

63. The most commonly used decaclcifying fluid is:
    a. 5% acetic acid
    b. 5% formalin solution
    c. 5% formalin ammonium bromide
    d. 5% formic acid   d

64. Carnoy's fixing fluid contains:
    a. Absolute alcohol, 60 ml.   a
    b. Chloroform, 30 ml.   b
    c. Acetic acid, glacial, 10 ml.   c
    d. Acetone, 10 ml.

65. 5% acetic acid is widely used as a fixative in conjunction
    with other fixatives to utilize its noted property of pre-
    serving:
    a. Enzymes
    b. Cytoplasm   b
    c. Nucleus   c
    d. Fats

66. How long must tissue be fixed in formalin?
    a. Depends on the size of the tissue   a
    b. Depends on the density of the tissue   b
    c. The rate of penetration of the fixing fluid   c
    d. The temperature at which it is fixed   d
    e. It takes roughly 6-48 hours to fix tissue adequately   e

67. Fixatives for tissues are used at room temperature.   T   F   T

68. Absolute ethyl alcohol is a dehydrating agent.   T   F   T

69. The freezing microtome uses compressed carbon monox-
    ide.   T   F   F

70. Unfixed tissues may be examined by means of frozen sec-
    tions.   T   F   T

71. Xylol is a solvent for paraffin.   T   F   T

72. Dioxane will not mix with water.   T   F   F

73. The plane-wedge knife is used for paraffin sections and for
    frozen sections.   T   F   T

74. The plano-concave knife is usually used for celloidin sec-
    tions.   T   F   T

75. The motion for stropping the knife is from toe to heel.
    T   F   T

76. One-quarter teaspoon of gelatin should be added to the
    cold bath in the mornings.   T   F   T

77. The paraffin bath should be from 3-5 degrees higher than the melting point of the paraffin.   T   F   T

78. Each specimen is given a Pathology Number.   T   F   T

79. It is most important to place the right number with the right specimen.   T   F   T

80. Formalin is poured on the gross specimens and the jars are then capped.   T   F   T

81. The tissue receptacles are placed in receptacle baskets.   T   F   T

82. All work tables and cutting boards should be rinsed with a 12% solution of Amphyl.   T   F   F

83. Frozen sections are used for rapid diagnosis.   T   F   T

84. Biopsies with a suspicion of a malignancy are rushed.   T   F   T

85. Preparation of 10% formalin is accomplished by mixing 100 ml. of 37-40% formaldehyde with 900 ml. of water.   T   F   T

86. When a stain for glycogen is anticipated, fresh tissue should be fixed in alcohol.   T   F   T

87. In the study of enzymes in histochemistry, best results are usually obtained when slides are made from paraffin technice.   T   F   F

88. For photography work, a tissue specimen that has been fixed in formalin with a resulting loss of natural color may regain some of its vital color by immersing the specimen in alcohol.   T   F   T

89. Formalin pigment forms in tissues when formalin is unbuffered.   T   F   T

90. Tissue specimen intended for frozen section preparation need not be fixed before it is sectioned.   T   F   T

91. Fresh tissue specimen may be kept moist under refrigeration for short periods of time.   T   F   T

92. Formalin is a coagulating type fixative.   T   F   F

93. Tissue section stored in alcohol becomes very hard.   T   F   T

94. Acetic acid alone may be used as a fixative.   T   F   T

95. Schaudinn's solution contains acetic acid and ether.   T   F   F

96. When ready to use, Zenker's solution is a very active, decalcifying agent.   T   F   F

97. Mercuric chloride is corrosive and poisonous.   T   F   T

98. When a tissue specimen is soft and spongy when sectioned on the microtome it may indicate incomplete fixation.   T   F   T

99. Smears may be fixed in a solution of equal parts of alcohol
and ether. T F   T

100. The characteristics of a good fixative are:
   a. The ability to penetrate and kill tissue quickly and
      harden   a
   b. Stabilize it so that it will not be significantly altered
      by the various processes of dehydration, embedding,
      staining, clearing, and mounting   b
   c. The production of increased transparency with refer-
      ence to both blocks and sections
   d. Will dry quickly and have a suitable index of refraction

101. 10% formalin gives good penetration, is stable, economical,
and not too dangerous to use. It contains:
   a. Formalin (30% formaldehyde) . . . . 20 ml.
   b. Full-strenth formalin (37-40% formal-
      dehyde) . . . . 10 ml.   b
   c. Absolute alcohol . . . . 90 ml.
   d. Distilled water . . . . 90 ml.   d

102. Since excess fixing fluid must be removed from the tissue,
explain how you would remove it from tissue fixed in each
of the following:
   1. Zenker's fluid:
      a. Wash out excess fixative thoroughly in running water   a
      b. Wash out excess fixative thoroughly in alcohol 70%
      c. To remove mercuric chloride crystals, immerse the
         slide in alcoholic iodine after the paraffin has been
         removed from the sections   c
      d. Immerse the slide in water for one hour
   2. 10% formalin:
      Deparaffinize the sections and place in:
      a. Solution I: Ammonia water, 28% . . .   2 ml.
                     Alcohol, 70% . . . . . . 100 ml.   a
      b. For 30-60 minutes, wash thoroughly in tap water and
         stain as desired   b
      c. Solution II: Hydrogen peroxide, 3% aq. . 50 ml.
                      Acetone . . . . 50 ml.
                      Ammonium hydroxyide, 28%   1 ml.   c
      d. For 5-10 minutes, wash thoroughly in running water
         and stain as desired   d
   3. Bouin's solution:
      a. Wash in several changes of 25% and 45% alcohol for
         2-4 hours
      b. Wash in several changes of 50% and 75% alcohol for
         4-8 hours   b
      c. Store in absolute alcohol
      d. Store in 70% alcohol   d

103. When sending tissue through the mail, the following fixative
is recommended:
   a. Acetone

b. 10% formalin-alcohol
c. Zenker's fluid
d. 10% formalin   d
e. Buffered neutral formalin   e

104. Hematin is:
    a. The active coloring agent in hematoxylin   a
    b. The product of oxidation from mercuric oxide
    c. A blood pigment   c
    d. The product of reduction from mercuric oxide

105. Hemosiderin is:
    a. Bright yellowish-brown granules   a
    b. Dark blue-black granules
    c. Does not react to iron stain
    d. A blood pigment   d

106. Hemofuchsin is:
    a. A blood pigment occurring as very dark granules
    b. A blood pigment occurring as light brown granules   b
    c. It will not react with iron stain   c
    d. It will react with iron stain

107. Lipoid is:
    a. Substance resembling fat in appearance and solubility   a
    b. An active coloring agent
    c. Bright yellowish-brown granules
    d. A clearing reagent for celloidin

108. Melanin is:
    a. A temporary mounting medium
    b. A mordant in the hematoxylin
    c. A dark-brown natural pigment found in cells, usually
       of the skin, as brown or black granules   c
    d. A very bright artificial pigment found in the bone

109. Metachromasia is:
    a. An iron compound of protoporphyrin
    b. A change of color. Tissue reaction color different
       from that of stain used   b
    c. The scientific study of cells, their origin, structure,
       and functions
    d. The removal and usually microscopic examination of
       tissue.

110. "Miscible" means:
    a. Capable of being mixed   a
    b. Capable of being separated
    c. Capable of being a living body
    d. Capable of being a mordant

111. By "mordant" is meant:
    a. The production of increased transparency with refer-
       ence to blocks and sections
    b. Requiring very thin sections
    c. Enters with dye linking it with object to be dyed   c

d. An antiseptic and disinfectant

112. The micron is:
    a. 1/25,000 of an inch   a
    b. 0.001 mm.   b
    c. 10^{-3} millimeter   c
    d. 10^{-6} meter   d

113. Biopsy is:
    a. The removal and examination, usually microscopic, of tissue or other material from the living body for purposes of diagnosis   a
    b. The removal and examination, usually microscopic, of tissue or other material from the dead body for purposes of diagnosis.
    c. A macroscopic examination of the dead body
    d. A macroscopic and microscopic examination of the dead eye

114. Cytology is:
    a. A general study of the embedding process
    b. The scientific study of cells, their origin, structure, and functions   b
    c. The scientific study of mordants
    d. The scientific study of solutions for the Technicon

115. Polychrome, or polychromic, means:
    a. Exhibiting one color
    b. Exhibiting polysaccharides
    c. Exhibiting two colors
    d. Exhibiting several colors   d

116. The reagents for the Technicon are:
    a. Formalin alcohol   a
    b. 95% alcohol   b
    c. Absolute alcohol   c
    d. Xylene   d
    e. Paraffin   e

117. Hematin is:
    a. A passive coloring agent in most hematoxylin stains
    b. An active coloring agent in most hematoxylin stains
    c. Formed by oxidation   c
    d. The result of a process which takes a number of days or weeks and is spoken of as "ripening"
    e. A blood pigment   e

118. Zenker's fluid contains:
    a. Absolute alcohol
    b. Potassium dichromate   b
    c. Mercuric chloride   c
    d. Distilled water   d
    e. Acetic acid, glacial   e

119. Give three reagents that may be used for clearing:
    a. Xylene (dimethylbenzene $C_6H_4[CH_3]_2$)   a

        b. Levulose
        c. Chloroform   c
        d. Benzene   d

120. Why is it necessary that we have different fixatives?
        a. Different fixative used for fixing old tissues
        b. Different fixatives used for fixing fresh tissue possess
           in various degrees the characteristics of penetrating,
           killing, and hardening   b
        c. Some fixatives have the disadvantage of inhibiting or
           interfering with dye reactions   c
        d. Some fixatives also act as mordants to insure certain
           staining results   d

121. For staining purposes, metals are combined with hematoxy-
     lin for the following reason:
        a. Hematoxylin is a neutral dye   a
        b. Hematoxylin alone bind very weakly to tissue   b
        c. Hematoxylin when used alone is a nonspecific stain   c
        d. Hematoxylin's selective staining power is dependent
           upon the metals with which it is combined   d

122. Progressive staining means:
        a. The dye is taken up by the good technician, it is not
           removed
        b. The dye is taken up by the tissue. It is not removed   b
        c. Differentiation in progressive staining relies on the
           selective affinity of tissue elements for the dye   c
        d. Differentiation in progressive staining depends on
           partial destaining

123. Regressive staining means:
        a. The tissue is first overstained and then partially de-
           colorized   a
        b. Differentiation is usually controlled by examination   b
        c. Differentiation is usually controlled without exami-
           nation
        d. When regressive staining is employed, a sharper de-
           gree of differentiation is obtained   d

124. What are the characteristics of a good mounting medium?
        a. As the slide dries, most of the solvent from the
           mounting medium evaporates, leaving the sections
           enclosed in an almost solid substance   a
        b. A good mounting reagent will dry quickly   b
        c. A good mounting reagent should have a suitable in-
           dex of refraction   c
        d. A good mounting reagent will not discolor   d
        e. A good mounting reagent will not fade tissue sections   e

125. Embedding processes include:
        a. Water (distilled)
        b. Paraffin (can be cut with safety razor blades)   b
        c. Celloidin (very thin section could be cut)   c
        d. Gelatin (slow process)   d

126. Which are desirable for routine paraffin processing?
    a. Preferred paraffin melting point 55 to 56°C.   a
    b. Tissue blocks not over 2 cm. wide   b
    c. Tissue blocks not over 2-3 mm. thick   c
    d. Sections not over 7 microns in thickness. Use about
       44°C. warm water to remove all wrinkles   d
    e. Eliminate most of the ethyl alcohol before embed-
       ding in paraffin   e

127. Dioxane is:
    a. 1:4 diethylene dioxide   a
    b. A dehydration agent used in paraffin embedding   b
    c. Miscible with paraffin and water   c
    d. Miscible with paraffin but not with water
    e. Tissue may be stored for long periods (2-3 years)
       without imparing its ability to take up stain or caus-
       ing it to harden   e

128. Steps of embedding in celloidin are:
    a. Alcohol 95% for 24 hours   a
    b. Alcohol 100% for 24 hours   b
    c. Alcohol 100% and ether for 24 hours   c
    d. Celloidin thin and celloidin thick from 24 hours to
       one week   d
    e. Mount on blocks of vulcanized fiber   e

129. Cutting of celloidin section:
    a. Cut as large as possible
    b. Cut as thin as possible, 10–16 microns   b
    c. Cut for bone, 20–22 microns   c
    d. Cut for bone, 10–16 microns

130. Celloidin section can be stained:
    a. By almost any method, without the necessity of re-
       moving the celloidin   a
    b. By one method only, removing the celloidin
    c. By two methods, it being necessary to remove the
       celloidin
    d. By cellosolve alone

131. The celloidin is removed:
    a. From dioxane and ether for 2–4 minutes and then
       back to dioxane and 70% alcohol
    b. From absolute alcohol into oil of cloves   b
    c. Or toluene and benzine for 2 hours and then back to
       toluene and benzine
    d. Or absolute alcohol and ether for 5–10 minutes and
       then back to absolute alcohol into 95% alcohol   d

132. Glycerin:
    a. Stains and distinguishes collagen from reticulum
    b. Dehydrates   b
    c. Clears   c
    d. Serves as a mounting medium   d

133. Clearing reagents for celloidin:
    a. Variety of clearing reagents are used   a
    b. Dioxane only is satisfactory
    c. Cellosolve clearing reagent only one used
    d. There is no clearing reagent for celloidin

134. Clearing reagents for paraffin:
    a. Potassium acetate
    b. Levulose
    c. Xylol   c
    d. Toluol   d

135. Dehydrating reagent for celloidin and paraffin is:
    a. Dioxane
    b. Alcohol   b
    c. Pyridine
    d. Acetone

136. Clearing reagents are:
    a. Xylol (tissue with brittle, most rapid clearing)
    b. Terpincol (lilacine). It does not dissolve celloidin
    c. Oleum origani cretici
    d. Weigert's carbox-xylol
    e. Weigert's aniline-xylol
    f. Aniline
    g. Cedarwood oil (not hardening enough)
    h. Benzene (best)
    i. Toluene (very satisfactory)
    j. Chloroform (for large pieces)
    k. Butyl alcohol tertiary
    l. Cajeput oil
    m. Cellosolve
    n. Dioxane
    o. Ethylene glycol
    p. All of the above   p

137. The fluid mounts are:
    a. Glycerine   a
    b. Potassium acetate   b
    c. Levulose   c
    d. DuNoger's lanolin-colaprory mixture   d
    e. Kaiser's glycerine jelly (1880)   e

138. Dehydrating agents are:
    a. Ethyl alcohol (95% commercially and absolute)
    b. Acetone
    c. Dioxane
    d. Isopropyl alcohol
    e. Tertiary butyl alcohol
    f. Methyl alcohol
    g. Pyridine
    h. All of the above   h

139. Dehydration is quite satisfactorily carried out at the following temperature:
    a. Room temperature   a
    b. 100°C.
    c. 50°C.
    d. −5°C.

140. Paraffin and nitrocellulose are:
    a. Soluble in water
    b. Insoluble in water   b
    c. Soluble in distilled water
    d. Soluble in distilled water and water mixture

141. Tissue fixed in absolute alcohol:
    a. Needs dehydration
    b. Does not need dehydration   b
    c. Needs very strong dehydration
    d. Needs very little dehydration

142. Dehydration is sufficient when:
    a. No more than 5–6% of water remains in the tissue
    b. No more than 6–7% of water remains in the tissue
    c. No more than 7–8% of water remains in the tissue
    d. No more than 3–4% of water remains in the tissue   d

143. The rate of diffusion is approximately proportional:
    a. To the square root of the distance travelled by the
       fluid   a
    b. To the cubic of the distance travelled by the fluid
    c. To the square and the cubic of the distance travlled
       by the fluid
    d. It is not proportional to the square of the distance
       travelled by the fluid

144. The speed of diffusion is only slightly accelerated by:
    a. A decrease in temperature
    b. A decrease in humidity
    c. An increase in temperature   c
    d. An increase in humidity

145. Acid dyes usually stain:
    a. Basic components (cytoplasm)   a
    b. Acid components
    c. Neutral components
    d. Acid and neutral components

146. Solvents are:
    a. Ethyl alcohol (ethanol)
    b. Methyl alcohol (methanol)   b
    c. Acetone
    d. Phenol (0.5–5% solution)
    e. Aniline water

147. Hematoxylin is:
    a. $C_8H_{10}O_{12}$
    b. $C_6H_4O_6$

    c. $C_{16}H_{24}O_6$

    d. $C_{16}H_{14}O_6 + 3\ H_2O$ d

148. Basic dyes usually stain:
    a. Basic components (cytoplasm)
    b. Acid components (nuclei)
    c. Basic components only   c
    d. It does not stain at all

149. Hematin is:
    a. $C_{16}H_{14}O_6$
    b. $C_{34}H_{32}O_4 \cdot FeOH$ b
    c. $C_{16}H_{12}O_8$
    d. $C_6H_{12}O_6$

150. By clearing is meant:
    a. The production of increased transparency with reference to both blocks and sections   a
    b. The production of decreased transparency with reference to both blocks and sections
    c. The production of increased transparency with reference to blocks only
    d. The production of decreased transparency with reference to the sections only

151. "Cleared specimens" should be:
    a. Embedded in dioxane
    b. Embedded in xylol
    c. Embedded in paraffin   c
    d. Embedded in hematin

152. Embedding in nitrocellulose:
    a. Requires elimination of alcohol
    b. Does not require the elimination of alcohol   b
    c. Requires the elimination of gelatin
    d. Does not require the elimination of polyethylene glycol

153. Embedding is:
    a. The process of adding a supporting medium to the interstices of a block of tissue   a
    b. The process of taking away a supporting medium from the interstices of a block of tissue
    c. The production of increased transparency with reference to both blocks and sections
    d. The process of adding 5% formic acid to the hematoxylin

154. Embedding masses are:
    A. *Water soluble:*
        a. Gelatin   a
        b. Vegetable gums   b
        c. Carbowax   c
        d. Nonex   d
        e. Polyethylene glycol   e

        f. Agar   f
   B. *Water insoluble:*
        a. Nitrocellulose   a
        b. Pyroxylin   b
        c. Plastics   c
        d. Paraffin   d
155. Embedding masses should have a melting point under:
        a. 95°C.
        b. 85°C.
        c. 75°C.
        d. 65°C.   d
156. Properties of paraffin embedding:
        a. Shrinkage during the subsequent drying   a
        b. The paraffin block can be cut by safety razor blades   b
        c. The paraffin block cannot be cut by razor blades
        d. The paraffin block can be cut as thin as possible
157. Fatty components of tissues are preserved by:
        a. Water   a
        b. Soluble embedding masses, such as gelatin, agar,
           polyethylene glycol   b
        c. Xylol
        d. Nitrocellulose
158. Nitrocellulose is not recommended for work requiring:
        a. Very big sections
        b. Very long sections
        c. Very small sections
        d. Very thin sections   d
159. Nitrocellulose used for embedding:
        a. Brain   a
        b. Spinal cord   b
        c. Decalcified bone   d
        d. Muscle   d
        e. Tendon   e
160. Water-soluble medium may be used for embedding:
        a. Brain tumors   a
        b. Papillomas   b
        c. Granulation tissue   c
        d. Curettings   d
161. Agar may be used as an embedding mass for:
        a. Paraffin sections   a
        b. Frozen sections   b
        c. Celloidin sections
        d. Water-soluble materials
        e. Oil soluble materials   e
162. Water-soluble mounting media are:
        a. Glycerol (1–2 days are good only)   a
        b. Glycerol-jelly (Kaiser's)—(gelatin, dist. water, glycerol,
           phenol)   b

    c. Zwemer's glychrogel   c
    d. Apathy's gum syrup   d
    e. Concentrated solution of levulose (fructose)   e

163. Vital staining takes place when:
    a. Dead tissues absorb coloring matter
    b. Living and dead tissues absorb coloring matter
    c. Coloring occurs during the transition between the normal living conditions and death
    d. Living tissues absorb coloring matter   d

164. Supravital staining takes place when:
    a. Living tissues absorb coloring matter
    b. The coloring occurs during the transition between the normal living conditions and death   b
    c. Dead tissues absorb coloring matter
    d. Living and dead tissues absorb coloring matter

165. Organic staining reagents are:
    a. Synthetic dyes   a
    b. Neutral or charged coloring matter   b
    c. Sulfides
    d. Insoluble salts

166. Inorganic staining reagents:
    a. Neutral coloring matter
    b. Metal precipitates   b
    c. Metallic oxides   c
    d. Sulfides   d
    e. Insoluble salts   e

167. Staining reactions are influenced by:
    a. The concentrated solution of levulose (fructose)
    b. The hydrogen-ion concentration (pH) of staining solution   b
    c. The concentration of salts   c
    d. Tissue fixation   d

168. Oil-soluble dyes:
    a. Are soluble in water
    b. Are soluble in a lot of water
    c. Are not soluble in water   c
    d. Are never soluble

169. Overstaining by eosin in hematoxylin-eosin stain can be corrected by:
    a. Immersing the sections in 0.1% ammonia water in 95% alcohol   a
    b. Immersing the sections in 1% ammonia water in 70% alcohol
    c. Immersing sections in 10% ammonia water in 59% alcohol
    d. Immersing section in 15% ammonia water in 90% alcohol

170. A mordant is:
   a. Only one substance, which can be used to decrease the affinity of tissue for a dye or stain
   b. Only one substance, which can be used to increase the affinity of tissue for a dye or stain
   c. Any substance which can be used to decrease the affinity of tissue for a dye or stain
   d. Any substance which can be used to increase the affinity of tissue for a dye or stain   d

171. Mordants are:
   a. Salts of iron
   b. Salts of chromium
   c. Salts of aluminum
   d. Phosphotungstate
   e. Phosphomolybdate
   f. Tannic acid (organic compound)
   g. Picric acid (organic compound)
   h. Aniline (organic compound)
   i. Formaldehyde (organic compound)
   j. All of the above   j

172. Alcohol that has an acid reaction is routinely neutralized by:
   a. Adding 5 Gm. of sodium (Na) bicarbonate to a liter
   b. Adding 1.5 Gm. of sodium bicarbonate to a liter
   c. Adding 0.5 Gm. of sodium bicarbonate to a liter   c
   d. Adding 0.05 Gm. of sodium bicarbonate to a liter

173. Alcohol with a pH of 4.0 could be alkalinzed for use with a basic dye by:
   a. Adding 5-10 drops of strong ammonium hydroxide to each liter of alcohol   a
   b. Adding 10-15 drops of strong phenol to each liter of alcohol
   c. Adding 2-5 drops of strong acetic acid glacial to each liter of alcohol
   d. Adding 5-10 drops of strong ammonium hydroxide to each 5 liters of alcohol

174. The celloidin method is used for:
   a. Small objects
   b. Large objects   b
   c. Central nervous system   c
   d. Decalcified bone   d

175. Celloidin-pyridine method is:
   a. A rapid method of dehydrating, clearing, embedding, use of alcohols and the consequent hardening of tissues   a
   b. A slow method of dehydrating, clearing, embedding. Use of alcohols and the consequent hardening of tissues
   c.. A medium method of clearing and embedding
   d. No use at all

176. Frozen-section method used for:
    a. Identification of bones in tissue
    b. Identification of fat in tissues
    c. Central nervous system
    d. Tumors

177. Gelatin embedding utilizes:
    a. Ethyl alcohol 95%
    b. Chloroform 2.5%
    c. 5% gelatin (10%, 15%, 20%, 1%)
    d. 1% phenol

178. L.V.N. (low viscosity nitrocellulose) is:
    a. 20% nitrocellulose
    b. Used for embedding tissues, 25% nitrocellulose
    c. Used for embedding tissues
    d. Used as dehydrating agent

179. Dehydration is:
    a. Addition of water to the fixed tissue
    b. The removal of the extractable water from fixed
       tissue
    c. Addition of a little water to the unfixed tissue
    d. The removal of the extractable formalin from fixed
       tissue
    e. Addition of as much water as possible to the fixed
       tissue

180. Average length of time for processing paraffin-embedded
    tissue on the Autotechnicon cycle:
    a. 70% alcohol 1 hr.
    b. 80% alcohol 1 hr.
    c. 95% alcohol 1 hr.
    d. 100% alcohol (or dioxane) 1 hr.

181. When absolute alcohol is used as the final dehydrant the
    tissue must be:
    a. Dealcoholized after infiltration with paraffin
    b. Dealcoholized before infiltration with formic acid
    c. Dealcoholized after infiltration with cellosolve
    d. Dealcoholized (usually in xylol) before infiltration
       with paraffin

182. Dehydrating agents are:
    a. Alcohol (shrinkage, overhardening of tissue
    b. Dioxane
    c. Acetone
    d. Cellosolve
    e. Triethyl phosphate (does not harden tissue)
    f. Tetrahydrofuran (dehyrates and clears, insoluble in
       water, nontoxic, odor)

183. Butyl alcohol is:
    a. Nonmiscible with paraffin
    b. Partially miscible with paraffin

176. b c d
177. c d
178. a
179. b
180. a b c d
181. d
182. a b c d e f
183. b

    c. Completely miscible with paraffin

184. The chief disadvantage of dioxane is:
    a. It is toxic to humans   a
    b. It is not toxic to humans
    c. It can be used only in a well-ventilated room   c
    d. It can be used only in a small room

185. Acetone dehydrates:
    a. Very slowly
    b. Very little
    c. Little
    d. Very rapidly   d

186. After acetone dehydration tissues should be transferred as follows:
    a. Alcohol to be cleared prior to infiltration
    b. Cellosolve to be cleared prior to infiltration
    c. Dioxane to be cleared prior to infiltration
    d. A paraffin solvent to be cleared prior to infiltration   d

187. Cellosolve is:
    a. Ethylene glycol monoethyl ether   a
    b. Dehydrates rapidly   b
    c. Has no harmful effect on the tissue   c
    d. Dehydrates very slowly

188. Triethyl phosphate is soluble in:
    a. Alcohol   a
    b. Benzene   b
    c. Ether   c
    d. Chloroform   d
    e. Xylene   e

189. Most commonly used dehydrating agent:
    a. Xylol
    b. Dioxane
    c. Ethyl alcohol   c
    d. Chloroform

190. Diethylene dioxide ("dioxane") is commonly used as a:
    a. Substitute for absolute alcohol   a
    b. Substitute for celloidin
    c. Substitute for carbowax
    d. Substitute for formalin 10%

191. Alcoholic-formalin 10% contains:
    a. Formalin, full strength (37–40% formaldehyde) 10%   a
    b. 80% alcohol . . . . 90%   b
    c. Formalin, full strength 0.5%
    d. 80% alcohol 70%

192. We speak of "clearing" in two places:
    a. Embedding process of tissue   a
    b. Mounting procedure after tissue sections have been stained   b

    c. Dehydration process of tissue
    d. Fixation process of tissue

193. Commonly used clearing agents are:
    a. Xylol   a
    b. Dioxane   b
    c. Chloroform   c
    d. Oil of cedarwood   d
    e. Acetone (not miscible with paraffin, very low boil-
       ing point)   e

194. The most used clearing agent in mounting is:
    a. Xylol   a
    b. Canada balsam
    c. Permount
    d. Gum dammar
    e. Abopon

195. Infiltrating substances (two embedding methods) are:
    a. Gelatin   a
    b. Paraffin   b
    c. Carbowax   c
    d. Celloidin   d

196. A more recent embedding medium is:
    a. A water-soluble wax preparation known as H.E.M.
       (Harleco embedding medium)   a
    b. A water-soluble substance known as "carbowax"   b
    c. Ethyl alcohol
    d. Isopropyl alcohol

197. Stock celloidin solution:
    a. Thick (12%) preferred   a
    b. Celloidin will go into solution much more rapidly if
       it is soaked in absolute alcohol first and then ether
       is added   b
    c. This solution may be diluted for higher concentration
    d. 30 grams of parlodion in 50 ml. of equal parts of
       ether and chloroform

198. The solutions on the Technicon are:
    a. 10% formalin-alcohol . . Fixation, dehydration
                                  (3 changes) 5 hours   a
    b. 95% alcohol . . . . . Dehydration (2 changes)
                                  2 hours   b
    c. Absolute alcohol . . . . Dehydration (2 changes)
                                  3 hours   c
    d. Xylene . . . . Clearing, 1 hour   d
    e. Paraffin . . . . . . Infiltration, 4 hours   e

199. Embedding procedure:
    a. After infiltration remove tissue from the capsule   a
    b. Fill an embedding mold with melted paraffin   b
    c. Place the tissue at bottom of paraffin   c
    d. Label the molds with correct number   d
    e. Place the molds on the cold plate and remove the
       block   e

200. Slow cooling results in:
    a. Silver crystals
    b. Paraffin crystals   b
    c. Sets or fixes the parts of tissues
    d. Intracellular bodies in the organs

201. The tissue blocks' thickness is about:
    a. 5 cm.
    b. 4 cm.
    c. 0.1 cm.
    d. 1.0 cm.   d

202. Dry the section in a:
    a. Slide dryer at 65–85°C. for 7–10 minutes
    b. Slide dryer at 52–82°C. for 7–10 minutes
    c. Slide dryer at 56–58°C. for 7–10 minutes   c
    d. Slide dryer at 56–58° for 1–2 minutes

203. Advantages of paraffin method:
    a. Cheap   a
    b. Thin sections   b
    c. Rapid process   c
    d. Serial sections can be obtained   d
    e. Easily and indefinitely stored   e

204. Disadvantages of paraffin method:
    a. Prolonged treatment causes shrinkage, hardening of tissue, brittleness caused by heat   a
    b. To infiltrate, long immersion is necessary   b
    c. Thin sections
    d. Rapid process

205. Celloidin embedding is used for:
    a. Soft materials
    b. Hard materials   b
    c. Small objects
    d. Large objects   d
    e. Delicate materials   e

206. Three celloidin embedding processes are:
    a. Wet celloidin method   a
    b. Dry celloidin method (for eye)   b
    c. Hard celloidin method (for heart)
    d. Double embedding processes (celloidin-paraffin)   d
    e. Soft embedding processes (for brain)

207. Dry celloidin method of embedding is recommended for:
    a. Large objects
    b. Central nervous system only
    c. Bone marrow
    d. Eyes   d

208. Cut dry celloidin with:
    a. Knife edge horizontal to the block
    b. Knife edge parallel to the block   b
    c. Knife edge parallel to the technician

d. Knife edge parallel to the table

209. 12% stock solution of celloidin:
    a. 12 Gm. of parloidon in 150 ml. of ether and absolute alcohol
    b. 21 Gm. of parloidon in 100 ml. of ether and absolute alcohol
    c. 12 Gm. of parloidon in 100 ml. of ether and absolute alcohol
    d. 12 Gm. of parloidon in 100 ml. of chloroform and benzene

c

210. Celloidin embedding blocks are cut on:
    a. A sliding microtome
    b. A freezing microtome
    c. A rotary microtome
    d. A technician microtome

a

211. With the wet celloidin technique both the block and the knife must be kept wet with:
    a. 70% alcohol
    b. 80% alcohol
    c. 95% alcohol
    d. 100% alcohol

b

212. Celloidin sections are usually cut at:
    a. 5–10 microns
    b. 10–14 microns
    c. 15–30 microns
    d. Over 35 microns

c

213. To remove the celloidin the sections must be placed in:
    a. Equal parts of absolute alcohol and ether for 5–10 min.
    b. Chloroform and benzene for 10–15 minutes
    c. Equal parts of dioxane and xylol for 20–25 minutes
    d. Formalin and methyl alcohol for 1-2 hours

a

214. Celloidin sections are stained in:
    a. Slender dishes
    b. Watch glasses
    c. Cellophane dishes
    d. Plastic dishes

a
b

215. Advantages of celloidin method:
    a. For large tissues, long periods of immersion in celloidin do not affect the consistency
    b. Embedding process is very slow
    c. Very thin sections cannot be obtained
    d. For hard to infiltrate objects celloidin provides a better support and does not crumble in sectioning

a

d

216. Disadvantages of the celloidin method:
    a. Celloidin does not crumble in sectioning
    b. No thin sections
    c. Very slow embedding process

b
c

d. Serial sections are difficult or impossible   d
e. Storage of tissue is troublesome   e

217. Celloidin-paraffin embedding process is:
   a. A double embedding process which enables one to cut serial sections by embedding celloidin blocks in paraffin mass   a
   b. Not used at all
   c. Not satisfactory
   d. This is a simple embedding process, but unsatisfactory

218. Advantage of the frozen section method:
   a. The pathologist can often make a diagnosis in a few minutes   a
   b. He could study fatty or lipoid materials   b
   c. Frozen sections required for some central nervous system stains   c
   d. It is a very long procedure

219. Totally unfixed tissues are directly (without embedding) cut on a:
   a. Carbon dioxide freezing microtome   a
   b. Carbon monoxide freezing microtome
   c. Dioxane freezing microtome
   d. Carbon tetroxide freezing microtome

220. The piece of tissue from which frozen sections are to be cut should be:
   a. Thicker than 5 mm.
   b. Not thicker than 5 mm.   b
   c. Thicker than 0.5 mm.
   d. Not thicker than 0.5 mm.

221. In what manner are frozen sections stained?
   a. Usually with metachromatic, polychrome, or fat stain   a
   b. Not the same as the cryostat procedure
   c. Usually with electrical ionization methods
   d. With ionic exchange resins methods

222. Stains used for frozen sections:
   a. Hematoxylin and eosin   a
   b. Rapid eyedropper staining method   b
   c. Rapid Gieson staining method (polychrome stains)   c
   d. Brown and Grenn Gram stain

223. What preparation is used for cover-slipping sections?
   a. Float the tissue from the slide by immersing in a dish of water. Pick up the free section on a bent glass rod and place in 10% formalin for 10-30 minutes   a
   b. Wash the section free of formalin in tap water. Place the section in a dish of 0.5% acid alcohol to remove stain. Wash in tap water   b

c. Stain with hematoxylin and eosin. Rinse quickly in water. Dehydrate in 3 changes of 95% alcohol

d. Transfer directly into oil of origanum or isopinocol to clear the tissue. If isopinocol if used, rinse with xylol before mounting. Mount section on slide and coverslip with balsam or Permount

c

d

224. Carbowax:

a. Carbowax provides a slow method for embedding tissue for histologic study

b. Carbowax provides a rapid method for embedding tissue for histologic study

c. Carbowax's advantage is that deleterious dehydrating chemicals can be avoided

d. Used for the demonstration of fat in tissue

b

c

d

225. How is infiltration accomplished?

a. If fat is not the component to be studied, the tissue can be treated with a fat solvent such as acetone prior to infiltration with water-soluble wax

b. Use: Infiltrating tissues of high lipid component with Carbowax 1000

c. Use: Infiltrating tissues of low lipid component with Carbowax 1000

d. If fat is not the constitutent to be studied, the tissue cannot be treated with a fat solvent such as acetone prior to infiltration with water-soluble wax

a

b

226. In what manner are blocks hardened?

a. By transferring the embedding container to the Histocinette for 30–40 minutes

b. By transferring the embedding container to the refrigerator for 15–30 minutes

c. By transferring the embedding container to the refrigerator for 35–45 minutes

d. By transferring the embedding container to the refrigerator for 1–2 days

b

227. Carbowax sections are cut on a:

a. Sliding microtome

b. Freezing microtome

c. Rotary microtome

d. Combination of sliding and freezing microtomes

c

228. Carbowax is:

a. A water-soluble wax preparation

b. A purified mixture of solid hydrocarbons obtained from petroleum

c. A purified form of celloidin or nitrocellulose

d. Sold under trade name as H.E.M. (Harleco Embedding Medium)

a

d

229. How are carbowax sections dried?

a. In a 73°C. oven for 12–15 minutes

    b. In a 37°C. oven for 5–10 minutes   b
    c. In a 37°C. oven for 1–2 hours
    d. in a 73°C. oven for 1–2 hours

230. In what manner are carbowax sections stained?
    a. Stain as desired   a
    b. If fat stains are used, avoid all contact with the higher
       grades of alcohol and xylol   b
    c. If fat stains are used, contact with the higher grades
       of alcohol and xylol
    d. If fat stains are used, contact with the lower grades of
       alcohol and xylol

231. Advantages of carbowax:
    a. The process is slow
    b. Fat constituents not demonstrated
    c. The process is rapid   c
    d. Fat constituents may be demonstrated   d
    e. Excellent cytologic detail   e
    f. Sections may be cut as thin as 1–3 microns   f

232. Disadvantages of carbowax:
    a. Sectioning on the microtome is difficult   a
    b. Could cut on the rotary microtome only   b
    c. Is not used routinely as yet   c
    d. The dehydration, embedding, and hydration of tis-
       sues are too long

233. Tissues are fixed:
    a. After decalcification
    b. Before decalcification   b
    c. At any time
    d. Not at all

234. Which is correct?
    a. The bone must be fixed to preserve the soft tissue
       and the cellular structures attached to it   a
    b. The bone does not have to be fixed in order to pre-
       serve the soft tissue and structure
    c. The bone must be fixed to preserve the hard tissue
       and hard structures attached to it
    d. The bone must be fixed to preserve the cytologic
       detail   d

235. Indicate three methods of decalcification:
    a. Basic method
    b. Neutral method
    c. Acid method   c
    d. Ionic exchange resin method   d
    e. Hungarian method
    f. Electrical ionization method   f

236. When acid is employed, how long is it necessary to leave
tissue in the decalcifying solution?
    a. 10–14 hours

  b. 1 day–2 weeks   b
  c. 1–2 hours
  d. 42–84 hours

237. Decalcifying solutions should be changed:
  a. Every minute
  b. Every hour
  c. From day to day   c
  d. Every week

238. After decalcification the tissues should be thoroughly washed in order to:
  a. Remove the last traces of the decalcifying solution. Wash in running water from 3–8 hours   a
  b. Remove the dust from the decalcifying solution
  c. Remove all nuclei and nucleoli from decalcifying solution. Wash in distilled water from 1–2 weeks
  d. Remove the hard structures from decalcifying solution. Wash in running water at least 2 weeks

239. Which is correct?
  a. A bone marrow may be processed as a smear or touch preparation or as a biopsy specimen   a
  b. A touch preparation may be obtained by slightly touching a clean glass slide or coverglass to the freshly cut surface of the tissue   b
  c. A bone marrow may be processed as a good nuclear stain preparation
  d. A bone marrow may be processed as a Mallory's PTAH preparation

240. Indicate fixative(s) recommended for bone marrow studies:
  a. Zenker's fluid with acetic acid   a
  b. 10% formalin-alcohol   b
  c. Zenker's formalin (Helly's fluid)   c
  d. Buffered neutral formalin   d

241. Papanicolaou smears are made for the following purpose:
  a. The cytological diagnosis of anemia
  b. The cytological diagnosis of cancer   b
  c. To determine chromosomal sex   c
  d. The effects or presence of estrogenic hormones   d
  e. The type of infection   e

242. What regions are smears taken from?
  a. Vaginal and endocervical   a
  b. Endometrial and prostatic   b
  c. Urine sediment and sputum   c
  d. Gastric aspiration and bronchial aspiration   d
  e. Pleural and peritoneal   e

243. Papanicolaou smears have the following advantage(s):
  a. The process is rapid
  b. Fat components are always demonstrated
  c. The technique of specimen collection and making

gynecological smears is simple and easy to perform   c
  d. Pap smear examinations are often followed by a sur-
     gical biopsy   d

244. What is the ideal fixing solution for these smears?
  a. Equal parts of 95% alcohol and ether   a
  b. One part of 95% alcohol and two parts of ether
  c. Two parts of ether and one part of 59% alcohol
  d. Equal parts of 59% alcohol and ether

245. How soon after preparing the smears should these be placed
     in the fixative?
  a. After a week in an ether-alcohol solution
  b. Fixation of smears before they dry is important   b
  c. These should be placed immediately in an ether-
     alcohol solution   c
  d. After 2 hours in an ether-alcohol solution

246. Weigert's stain for elastic tissue stains the latter:
  a. Green
  b. Red
  c. Blue-black   c
  d. Yellow

247. Give the complete Pap staining method in outline form:
  a. Fixation in equal parts of 95% alcohol and ether.
     Hydrate in 80%, 70%, 50% alcohols. Rinse in distilled
     water. Stain in Harris' hematoxylin   a
  b. Rinse in distilled water. Dip in a 0.25% aqueous solu-
     tion of HCl. Tap water 6 minutes. Distilled water.   b
  c. 50%, 70%, 95% alcohols. Six dips each. Stain in
     OG-6 for 1½ minutes. Rinse in 95% alcohol. Stain
     in EA-36 or EA-50 for 1½ minutes.   c
  d. Rinse in 95% alcohol, absolute alcohol (2 changes),
     xylol (3 changes). Mount in Permount   d

248. How are Papanicolaou smears prepared for mailing?
  a. Smears dried   a
  b. Wrapped in wax paper (blycerine technique)   b
  c. Smears are fixed. Remove fixative. Cover with gly-
     cerine before drying occurs   c
  d. Wrapped in silver paper (Hungarian technique)

249. The purpose in staining is to identify:
  a. The same tissue components by their color reactions
  b. Different tissue components by their color reactions   b
  c. Artifacts in the same tissue components by their
     color reactions
  d. Benhold's Congo red and acid-fast bacteria by their
     color reactions

250. A "routine stain" is:
  a. One that stains the different tissue elements with
     little differentiation except between nucleus and cy-
     toplasm   a

b. One that stains the same tissue elements with little
differentiation except between nucleus and cytoplasm

c. One that demonstrates bacteria, fungi, cell products,
and microscopic intracellular structures

d. One that demonstrates glycogen

251. A "special stain" is one that:
a. Stains the different tissue elements with little differentiation except between nucleus and cytoplasm
b. Demonstrates special features in the tissues, such as
bacteria, fungi, particular cell products, and microscopic intracellular and intercellular structures   b
c. Demonstrates only special reticulum
d. Gives optimum results in the nucleus and in bone
marrow

252. How sections are deparaffinized prior to staining:
a. Xylol, absolute alcohol, 95% alcohol   a
b. 0.5% solution of iodine in 80% alcohol, rinse in 80%
alcohol, remove iodine with 5% sodium thiosulfate
Wash in tap water
c. 50%, 70% alcohol and ether
d. 1% solution of iodine in 95% alcohol, rinse in 95%
alcohol, remove iodine with 2% sodium thiosulfate.
Wash in tap water

253. Indicate two natural dyes:
a. Orange G
b. Hematoxylin   b
c. Sudan black B
d. Congo red
e. Carmine   e

254. Indicate two metals which are used for metallic stains and
impregnations:
a. Gold chloride   a
b. Methyl violet
c. Methyl green
d. Silver nitrate   d

255. Define "basic dye":
a. A dye that is a cation   a
b. The dye which contains basic fuchsin only
c. The dye that contains silver nitrate and gold chloride
d. A dye that is an anion

256. Define "acid dye":
a. Cation contains the coloring matter
b. Anion contains the coloring matter   b
c. Both anion and cation contain the coloring matter
d. An unchanged component contains the coloring
matter

257. Acid dyes include:
a. Aniline blue and Congo red   a

    b. Methyl green and methyl violet
    c. Methyl blue and Orange G   c
    d. Cresyl violet and crystal violet
    e. Picric acid   e

258. Indicate the basic dyes:
    a. Sudan III, Sudan IV
    b. Azocarmine G and basic fuchsin   b
    c. Congo red and Sudan black B
    d. Cresyl violet and crystal violet   d
    e. Oil red O and scarlet B
    f. Methyl green and methyl violet   f

259. Fat-soluble dyes are:
    a. Oil red O and scarlet B   a
    b. Orange G and Congo red
    c. Sudan II, III, IV, and Sudan black B   c
    d. Methyl green and methyl violet

260. Natural resin mounting mediums are.
    a. Permount
    b. Canada balsam, neutral   b
    c. Diaphane
    d. Gum dammar   d

261. Synthetic resin mounting mediums are:
    a. Permount   a
    b. Gum dammar
    c. Diaphane   c
    d. Canada blasam, neutral

262. Indicate two suitable mounting reagents for frozen section
    mounts:
    a. Sudan black B
    b. Congo red
    c. Glycerine   c
    d. Gum syrup   d

263. Indicate strength at which ethyl alcohol is most effective as
    a disinfectant:
    a. 95%
    b. 80%
    c. 70%   c
    d. 60%

264. The neutral point on the pH scale is:
    a. pH 8
    b. pH 7   b
    c. pH 6
    d. pH 5

265. Marcello Malpighi (1628–1694) was:
    a. One of Italy's most distinguished scientists. One of
       the leading anatomists and histologists of history   a
    b. At age 28 a professor at the University of Pisa (Italy) b
    c. The originator of microscopic anatomy   c

  d. The discoverer (1661) of capillary vessels | d

266. Anton van Leeuwenhoek (1632–1723) is remembered for:
  a. Used microscope systematically. The size of red
     blood corpuscles | a
  b. The anatomical structure of the teeth and the study
     of blood vessels | b
  c. The eye, nerve and skin anatomy | c
  d. Microscope, 1675 | d

267. Marie Francois Xavier Bichat (1771–1802):
  a. Was one of the fathers of histology. 600 autopsies.
     Died of tuberculosis. Without aid of microscope he
     established a system of normal and pathological
     structure based on the tissues | a
  b. In 1820 invented achromatic lenses and compound
     microscope
  c. Wrote "Traite des Membranes" (1800) and "Sur la
     vie et la mort" (1800) | c
  d. Wrote "Anatomie General" (1801) | d

268. Schleiden and Schwann (1838) were:
  a. Professors of anatomy at Miami, the leaders in Am-
     erican anatomy
  b. Establishers of cell doctrine of living structures | b
  c. Describers of anatomical structures of teeth and
     blood vessels
  d. Coauthors of "Anatomie General"

269. Caspar Wistar (1760–1818):
  a. Established the cell doctrine of living structures
  b. Eye, nerve, and skin anatomy specialization
  c. Professor of anatomy in Pennsylvania, the leader in
     American anatomy | c
  d. Professor at University of Pisa (Italy)

270. The famous pathologists of the 19th century were:
  a. Robert Koch and Louis Pasteur | a
  b. Palocsay (edited review of histology technique,
     contributed neurohistology and neuropathology re-
     veiw)
  c. Rokitanszky and Helmholtz | c
  d. Bassi (micropathology) and Virchow (greatest of all
     time. His theory was "Omnis cellula e cellula") | d

271. In hematoxylin solution, alum is used as:
  a. A bacteria stain
  b. pH maintainer when other substances are added
  c. A mordant | c
  d. A dehydrating atent

272. Acid-fast bacteria in tissue can be stained:
  a. After almost any kind of fixation | a
  b. Before any kind of fixation
  c. Without fixation
  d. After fixation in water

273. Mercury crystals may be removed from tissue by immersing in:
    a.   5% iodine in alcohol
    b. 15% iodine in alcohol
    c. 0.5% iodine in alcohol
    d. 50% iodine in alcohol

    c

274. The acid in acid alcohol is:
    a. Hydrochloric acid
    b. Oxalic acid
    c. Picric acid
    d. Nitric acid

    a

275. A satisfactory clearing agent used in processing tissues for paraffin embedding must be:
    a. Not miscible with the dehydrating agent and paraffin
    b. Partly miscible with the dehydrating agent and paraffin
    c. Miscible with the dehydrating agent and paraffin
    d. Miscible with alcohol and iodine

    c

276. Best's carmine stain is used for demonstration of:
    a. Colloidal iron
    b. Fat
    c. Nucleus
    d. Glycogen

    d

277. The fixing fluid considered best for the preservation of nuclear detail is:
    a. Helly's fluid
    b. Bouin's solution
    c. Zenker's fluid-acetic acid
    d. Carnoy's fluid

    c

278. A solution is buffered in order to maintain:
    a. A given pH when other substances are added
    b. A good warm solution
    c. A good temperature in the solution
    d. A very good, cold solution

    a

279. Alcohol-formalin contains approximately:
    a. 15% formaldehyde
    b. 10% formaldehyde
    c.   4% formaldehyde
    d.   0.1% formaldehyde

    c

280. Bouin's solution contains:
    a. Picric acid, saturated aqueous solution about 1.22%
    b. Chloroform
    c. Formalin, full strength (37–40% formaldehyde
    d. Glacial acetic acid

    a

    c
    d

281. A good stain for *Entamoeba histolytica* in fecal smears is:
    a. Best's carmine stain
    b. Heidenhain's iron hematoxylin

    b

    c. Acid-fast stain
    d. Giemsa stain

282. The disadvantage of nitric acid as a decalcifier is:
    a. Staining reactions are impaired   a
    b. Staining reactions are the best
    c. Staining reactions are full of nitrogen
    d. Staining reactions contain weak ammonia water

283. In selecting a mounting medium for microscopic sections
the greatest transparency is obtained when refractive index
of the mounting medium is:
    a. Different from that of tissue section
    b. Same as that of tissue section   b
    c. Same as the color index
    d. A given pH maintainer

284. A Giemsa stain for bone marrow sections acts most satisfactorily following fixation in:
    a. Helly's fluid   a
    b. Ort's fluid
    c. Zenker's fluid
    d. Bouin's fluid

285. Formalin pigment can be removed from the tissue by immersing in:
    a. Absolute alcohol
    b. 70% alcohol
    c. Weak ammonia water   c
    d. 10% formaldehyde

286. A good fixative which contains potassium dichromate, mercuric chloride, distilled water, and full strength formalin is:
    a. Zenker's fluid
    b. Carnoy's fluid
    c. Bouin's fluid
    d. Helly's fluid   d

287. A regular laboratory incubator maintains a temperature of
about:
    a. 68°C.
    b. 58°C.
    c. 48°C.
    d. 38°C.   d

288. Tissue to be stained for glycogen should be fixed in:
    a. 70% alcohol
    b. Alcoholic formalin
    c. Picric acid
    d. Absolute alcohol   d

289. When nuclear structure is to be stained with eosin-methylene blue a good fixative is:
    a. Neutral 10% formalin   a
    b. Absolute alcohol
    c. Benzene

d. Chloroform

290. Tissue to be stained for fat should be fixed in:
    a. Flemming's fluid
    b. Bouin's fluid
    c. Formalin (and cut on freezing microtome)   c
    d. Acetone

291. The choice of paraffin is based upon which of the following principles:
    a. Paraffins with higher melting points are harder and section better
    b. Exposure of tissues to higher temperatures produces excessive shrinkage
    c. Paraffins with lower melting points are easier to section
    d. A temperature range of 56–58°C. is chosen as the best compromise between ease of sectioning and tissue artifacts   d

292. Harris' hematoxylin in tissue sections stains the:
    a. Nuclei   a
    b. Cytoplasm
    c. Collagen
    d. Nerve fibers

293. Dioxane can be used:
    a. To fix the tissues
    b. For dehydrating and clearing tissues   b
    c. For hardening of tissues
    d. To stain fat tissues

294. Ripening of hematoxylin involves the following process:
    a. Calculation
    b. Reduction
    c. Oxidation   c
    d. Dehydration

295. Celloidin is soluble in equal parts of:
    a. Absolute alcohol and ether alcohol   a
    b. 70% alcohol and chloroform
    c. 95% methyl alcohol and benzene
    d. 80% alcohol and benzol

296. One centimeter equals:
    a.   1,000 microns (μ)
    b. 100,000 microns
    c.   1 micron
    d. 10,000 microns   d

297. Tissue to be cut at 2 microns or thinner should be embedded in:
    a. Celloidin
    b. Paraffin
    c. Methacyrylate   c
    d. Sudan III and Congo red

298. A reagent unsatisfactory for dehydrating tissues is:
     a. Dioxane
     b. Acetone
     c. Benzene   c
     d. Ethyl alcohol

299. A good nuclear stain must be:
     a. Basic   a
     b. Acid
     c. Neutral
     d. Isotonic

300. One milligram per milliliter is equivalent to:
     a.   1,000 mg.%
     b.   10,000 mg.%
     c.   100 mg.%   c
     d.   .1 mg.%

301. The property of the tuberculosis bacillus upon which the
     principle of the acid-fast stain depends is:
     a. Ability of its lipoid capsule to resist decolorization
        by acid alcohol   a
     b. Ability of its capsules to resist decolorization by
        ether alcohol
     c. Ability of its capsules to resist decolorization by
        enzymes
     d. Ability of its levulose capsule to resist decolorization
        by acid alcohol

302. One micron (μ) is:
     a. One millionth part of a centimeter (1 μ = 1 mill/cm.)
     b. One millionth part of a kilometer (1 μ = 1 mill/km.)
     c. One millionth part of a millimeter (1 μ = 1 mill/mm.)
     d. One millionth part of a meter (1 μ = 1 mill/meter)   d

303. Molar solution is:
     a. A solution one liter of which contains the weight in
        grams of the solute equal to its molecular weight in
        Daltons   a
     b. A solution two liters of which contain the weight in
        grams of the solute equal to its weight in Daltons
     c. A solution ten liters of which contain the weight in
        grams of the solute equal to its molecular weight in
        Daltons

304. One kilogram (Kg.) equals about:
     a. 1.1 pounds
     b. 3.3 pounds
     c. 2.2 pounds   c
     d. 4.4 pounds

305. The staining of fat by Sudan IV or oil red is due to:
     a. Solubility of dye in fat   a
     b. Insolubility of dye in fat
     c. Temperature of dye in fat

d. The insolubility of nuclear stain in fat

306. "Micrometry" is a term applied to:
    a. Kind of microtome
    b. Kind of microscope
    c. Kind of micropreparation
    d. Kind of measurement   d

307. A chief advantage of Mallory's PTAH stain is:
    a. Its ability to stain nuclei   a
    b. Its ability to stain glycogen
    c. Its ability to stain cytoplasm
    d. Its ability to stain fat

308. One gram (gm.) equals about:
    a. 10 grains
    b. 20 grains
    c. 15 grains   c
    d. 25 grains

309. Toluidin blue is especially recommended for:
    a. Frozen sections of fresh tissue   a
    b. Paraffin sections
    c. Celloidin sections
    d. Methacylate sections   d

310. One inch equals about:
    a. 1.5 centimeter
    b. 2.5 centimeters   b
    c. 3.5 centimeters
    d. 4.5 centimeters

311. One milligram equals:
    a.   10 micrograms
    b.   100 micrograms
    c.   1,000 micrograms   c
    d. 10,000 micrograms

312. One decigram equals:
    a.   10 milligrams
    b.   100 milligrams   b
    c.   1,000 milligrams
    d. 10,000 milligrams

313. One meter equals about:
    a. 19 inches
    b. 29 inches
    c. 39 inehes   c
    d. 49 inches

314. To demonstrate nerve endings and nerve fibers, a gener-
    ally recommended stain is:
    a. Sudan IV
    b. Congo red
    c. Mallory's aniline blue
    d. Weil's   d

315. A staining method which differentiates neutral fat from fatty acids has as its principal ingredient:
    a. Nile blue sulfate   a
    b. Aniline blue
    c. Azocarmine
    d. Gum Dammar

316. Carbon may be differentiated from malarial pigment as follows:
    a. The solubility of carbon in concentrated sulfuric acid
    b. The insolubility of carbon in concentrated sulfuric acid   b
    c. The temperature of carbon in concentrated acetic acid
    d. The insolubility of malarial pigment in picric acid

317. Sections stained for fat with Sudan I V should be mounted in:
    a. Glycerine jelly   a
    b. Permount
    c. Abapone
    d. Levulose

318. The Mallory's aniline blue stain is used to distinguish:
    a. Collagen from muscle   a
    b. Nucleus from nucleolus
    c. Nucleus from cytoplasm
    d. Nerve fibers from nucleus

319. A temperature of 212°F. is equal to:
    a.   50°C.
    b. 100°C.   b
    c. 200°C.
    d. 215°C.

320. Tissue to be stained by the Cinishovsky-Marash method should be fixed in:
    a. Carnoy's fluid
    b. Bouin's fluid
    c. Zenker's fluid   c
    d. Formalin 5%

321. One cubic centimeter (cc.) is equal to:
    a. 0.1 liter
    b. 0.01 liter
    c. 0.001 liter   c
    d. 0.0001 liter

322. Elastic tissue is best demonstrated by:
    a. Weigert's stain   a
    b. Crystal violet stain
    c. Toluidine blue stain
    d. Alcian blue stain

323. Sudan III is used in staining tissue for:
    a. Collagen

      b. Muscle

      c. Glycogen

      d. Fat   d

324. The Unna differential stain is used to demonstrate the difference between:

      a. Mast cells and plasma cells   a

      b. Red blood cells and white blood cells

      c. Mast cells and red blood cells

      d. Plasma cells and malarial cells

325. The temperatture of the paraffin bath for embedding tissue should be about:

      a. 40°C.

      b. 50°C.

      c. 60°C.   c

      d. 70°C.

326. Sections stained by the Giemsa method should be mounted in:

      a. Clarite of Permount   a

      b. Glycerine

      c. Gelatin

      d. Carbowax

327. The tissue block from which frozen sections are to be cut should average approximately:

      a. 15 mm. in thickness

      b. 10 mm. in thickness

      c. 8 mm. in thickness

      d. 5 mm. in thickness   d

328. Sections to be stained for the demonstration of microglia should be cut at approximately:

      a. 5 microns

      b. 10 microns

      c. 15 microns   c

      d. 20 microns

329. A mordant is used for:

      a. Dehydrating the tissue section

      b. Fixing the stain in a tissue section   b

      c. Embedding the tissue section

      d. Clearing the stain in a tissue section

330. Most neuropathology stains can be satisfactorily used after fixation in:

      a. 50% formalin

      b. 30% formalin

      c. 10% formalin   c

      d. 5% formalin-ammonium bromide

331. To make a liter (one l.) of a 1:5,000 solution from a 10% stock solution you use:

      a. 5 ml. of stock solution to 1,000 ml.

      b. 10 ml. of stock solution to 1,000 ml.

c. 20 ml. of stock solution to 1,000 ml.
d.   2 ml. of stock solution to 1,000 ml.   d

332. The recommended fixation for tissue to be stained for glycogen is:
   a. Absolute alcohol   a
   b. Formalin-ammonium bromide
   c. Buffered neutral formalin
   d. Acetone

333. The laboratory refrigerator should have a temperature of approximately:
   a. 8°C.
   b. 7°C.
   c. 5°C.
   d. 4°C.   d

334. Dehydration of celloidin section after staining is best completed in:
   a. Ether-alcohol   a
   b. Dioxane
   c. Isopropyl alcohol
   d. Pyridine

335. To convert Fahrenheit into centigrade:
   a. Multiply by 32 and subtract 0.555
   b. Subtract 32 and multiply by 0.555   b
   c. Subtract 23 and multiply by 1.555
   d. Multiply by 32 and subtract 1.555

336. Bloch's dopa reaction demonstrates:
   a. Dopa melanin in frozen sections   a
   b. Dioxane melanin in paraffin sections
   c. The presence of fat in frozen sections
   d. Hemosiderin and hemofuchsin in hematoxylin

337. The volume of the tissue-fixing fluid should exceed the volume of the tissue by:
   a. 25–30 times
   b. 20–25 times
   c. 15–20 times   c
   d.   5–10 times

338. When Gomori's method for histochemical demonstration of acid phosphatase is used, tissues should be fixed in:
   a. Zenker's fluid
   b. Flemming's fluid
   c. Buffered neutral formalin
   d. Acetone (for 24 hours)   d

339. The active staining ingredient in a ripe alum hematoxylin solution is:
   a. Hematein   a
   b. Hemofuchsin
   c. Hemosiderin
   d. Lipoid

340. When honing a knife, oil is used on oil stone:
     a. To prevent too much knife tilt
     b. To prevent dull knife
     c. To prevent nicking of the knife   c
     d. To prevent dusting of the knife

341. The purpose in adding mercuric oxide to an alum hematox-
     ylin solution is to:
     a. Oxidize hematoxylin   a
     b. Presence of fat in tissue
     c. Obtain satisfactory results
     d. Cut thinner sections

342. Osseous tissue for histological study may be decalcified
     with:
     a. Ammonia water for one hour
     b. Zenker's fluid for one hour
     c. 5% formic acid   c
     d. Alcohol-formalin solution

343. In the Brown and Brenn modification of the Gram stain for
     tissue, Gram-positive organisms appear:
     a. Black
     b. Blue   b
     c. Brown
     d. Bronze

344. The presence of fat in tissue is best demonstrated in
     a. Celloidin sections
     b. Paraffin sections
     c. Paraffin and celloidin mixed sections
     d. Frozen sections   d

345. In a Gram stain the acetone is used to:
     a. Decolorize Gram-negative bacteria   a
     b. Demonstrate Nissl's bodies
     c. Stain reticulum
     d. Stain lipids

346. Formalin pigment does not usually form in tissues remain-
     ing in a formalin solution:
     a. Buffered to a pH below 5
     b. Buffered to a pH of 5
     c. Buffered to a pH above 5   c
     d. Unbuffered

347. In the Prussian blue reaction for ferric iron, the reacting
     solution contains:
     a. Ferrichloride
     b. Polychrome methylene blue
     c. Alcohol
     d. Potassium ferrocyanide and diluted hydrochloric acid   d

348. Ribbons from paraffin blocks should be floated on a con-
     stant temperature bath of approximately:
     a. 24°C.

b. 34°C.
c. 44°C.   c
d. 54°C.

349. When cutting paraffin embedded tissue, if the tissue seems
     hard and brittle, a source of trouble is likely to be:
     a. Overheating paraffin   a
     b. Refrigeration of paraffin
     c. The angle of the knife
     d. Tissue left in xylol too short a period of time

350. When fixing aspirated bone marrow, if it is desirable to
     preserve erythrocytes, the most satisfactory fixative
     should be:
     a. Zenker's fluid
     b. Carnoy's fluid
     c. Helly's fluid   c
     d. Bouin's fluid

351. A method recommended for demonstration of argentaffin
     granules is:
     a. Wilder's reticulum stain
     b. Terry's polychrome methylene blue stain
     c. Brown and Brenn stain
     d. Fontana silver nitrate   d

352. In a connective tissue stain using iron hematoxylin, picric
     acid and acid fuchsin muscle should appear:
     a. Blue
     b. Brown
     c. Yellow   c
     d. Red

353. In Wilder's reticulum stain collagen appears:
     a. Rose-grey   a
     b. Blue
     c. Yellow
     d. Brown

354. In order to obtain good results with amyloid stains, tissue
     should be fixed in:
     a. Zenker's fluid
     b. Helly's fluid
     c. Alcoholic formalin   c
     d. Carnoy's fluid

355. A stain highly recommended for demonstration of Nissi's
     bodies is:
     a. Giemsa
     b. Heidenhain's iron hematoxylin
     c. Alcian blue
     d. Toluidine blue   d

356. Terry's polychrome methylene blue is of particular value
     for staining of:
     a. Frozen sections of fresh material   a

  b. Argentaffin granules
  c. Uric acid crystals
  c. Celloidin sections of fresh material

357. A method especially devised for the staining of reticulum
     after Zenker's fixation is:
     a. Fontana silver nitrate
     b. Toluidine blue
     c. Wilder's reticulum   c
     d. Lithium carbonate

358. A disadvantage in using dioxane for processing tissue is:
     a. Dehydration starts during fixation
     b. Toxic   b
     c. No longer good when it turns pink
     d. Refractile particles may be seen

359. The chief objection to the use of xylene as a clearing agent
     in processing tissue is that xylene is:
     a. Likely to harden tissue   a
     b. Dissolve celloidin
     c. Affect aniline dyes
     d. Not a most rapid clearing agent

360. Schiff's reagent is no longer good when it turns:
     a. Brown
     b. Pink   b
     c. Blue
     d. Yellow

361. A normal solution is one which contains:
     a. Milligram-equivalent weight per 1,000 ml.
        $$N = \frac{mg.\ Eq.}{1\ liter}$$
     b. Kilogram-equivalent weight per 1,000 ml.
     c. Gram-equivalent weight per 1,000 ml.
        $$N = \frac{Gm.\ Eq.}{1\ liter}$$
     d. Dekagram-equivalent weight per 1,000 ml.   c

362. The angle between the level of the knife and top of the
     paraffin block is:
     a. Rake angle   a
     b. Quadrangle
     c. Triangular
     d. Polygon

363. If the temperature of the water bath is 44°C., the melting
     point (MP) of the paraffin should be:
     a. 65–85°C.
     b. 45–55°C.
     c. 56–58°C.
     d. 85–88°C.   c

364. Tubercle bacilli are stained by:

a. Bennhold's Congo red
b. Sudan III and IV
c. Best's carmine
d. Kinyoun's   d

365. A stain for cholesterol is:
a. Schultz modification, the Lieberman-Burchard   a
b. Best's stain
c. Bennhold's Congo red stain
d. Brown and Brenn stain

366. Which is correct?
a. 1 quart or 8 gills   = 1 pint = 1.9463 liter
b. 1½ quart or 10 gills = 1 pint = 2.9463 liter
c. 2 quarts or 20 gills = 1 pint = 4.9463 liter
d. ½ quart or 4 gills   = 1 pint = 0.4731 liter   d

367. Coverslips for oil immersion work should be:
a. #1   a
b. #2
c. #3
d. #4

368. The decimal equivalent of 1/16 is:
a. .0526
b. .0265
c. .0625   c
d. .0025

369. The fixative for uric acid crystals is:
a. Acetic acid
b. Potassium dichromate
c. Alcohol   c
d. Chloroform

370. The preservative for Mayer's egg albumin is:
a. Thymol   a
b. Benzene
c. Chloroform
d. Ether

371. Blood and blood forming pigments form a dark-brown pigment when fixed in:
a. Alcohol
b. Thymol
c. Acetone
d. Formalin   d

372. Starch granules generally stain:
a. Blue   a
b. Brown
c. Black
d. Red

373. After fixation with Bouin's the excess picric acid is removed by:

    a. Calcium carbonate with 50% alcohol
    b. Lithium carbonate with 80% alcohol   b
    c. Oxalic acid with 75% alcohol
    d. Ammonia 37% with 70% alcohol

374. A stain for lipids is:
    a. Brown and Brenn stain
    b. Giemsa stain
    c. Oil red O   c
    d. Acid-fast stain

375. The main advantages of using carbowax are:
    a. Cutting of thinner sections   a
    b. Preservation of lipids   b
    c. Optimum results as far as vacuum is concerned
    d. Collagen may be distinguished from reticulum

376. Celloidin sections are hardened in:
    a. Alcohol
    b. Ether
    c. Benzene
    d. Chloroform   d

377. The percentage of gold chloride for toning is:
    a. 4%
    b. 3%
    c. 2%
    d. 1%   d

378. Bouin's fixative is a good fixative for:
    a. Trichrome stain   a
    b. Schiff's stain
    c. Alcian blue stain
    d. Nissl's stain

379. An advantage of using Carnoy's fixative is:
    a. Dehydration starts after fixation
    b. Dehydration starts during fixation   b
    c. Dehydration starts before fixation
    d. Fixation starts during dehydration

380. Fixation renders protein:
    a. Soluble
    b. Very soluble
    c. Insoluble   c
    d. Increases nuclear precipitation

381. The Autotechnicon disk is set for:
    a. 2 hours
    b. 12 hours   b
    c. 24 hours
    d. 48 hours

382. To convert °C. (Celcius) to °F. (Fahrenheit):
    a. Divide by 1.8 then add 32
    b. Multiply by 32 then divide by 1.8

c. Multiply by 1.8 then add 32   c
d. Divide by 32 then add 1.8

383. In an acid-fast stain, acid is used to:
   a. Increase nuclear precipitation
   b. Stain bone marrow section
   c. Decolorize   c
   d. Remove ammonia

384. Light green is:
   a. Not a nuclear dye   a
   b. A nuclear dye
   c. The best fixative for glycogen
   d. A good stain for amyloid

385. To improve nuclear detail when staining, add:
   a. Glacial acetic acid   a
   b. Citric acid 15%
   c. Picric acid 35%
   d. Osmic acid 5%

386. Best fixative for preserving nuclear detail is:
   a. Bouin's fixative
   b. Helly's fluid
   c. Zenker's fluid   c
   d. Carnoy's fluid

387. Helly's fluid is also called:
   a. Zenker's-formol   a
   b. Zenker's-Helly's
   c. Zenker's-Helly's-formol
   d. Helly's-Zenker's-formol

388. A stain used for nerve endings and fibers is:
   a. Kossa-Bennhold
   b. Palocsay-Pauliczky
   c. Bodian   c
   d. Hale

389. In the periodic acid Schiff (P.A.S.) stain, sulfurous rinses
   are used to:
   a. Remove excess leukofuchsin   a
   b. Remove excess water
   c. Remove excess alcohol
   d. Remove excess ether

390. The objective of the microscope is at the:
   a. Upper end of the barrel
   b. Lower end of the barrel   b
   c. Center of the barrel
   d. Upper and lower end of the barrel

391. Doubly refractile particles may be observed by:
   a. Light green
   b. Decalcification
   c. Using mercuric chloride
   d. Polarized light   d

392. Fixation for Pap (Papanicolaou) smears:
    a. 70% alcohol and chloroform
    b. 50% methyl alcohol and absolute alcohol
    c. 95% ethyl alcohol and ether   c
    d. 75% butyl alcohol and ether

393. Eosin Y is:
    a. A cytoplasm stain   a
    b. A nuclear stain
    c. A good stain for amyloid
    d. A good stain for bone marrow sections

394. The best fixative for glycogen is:
    a. Ether-alcohol
    b. Absolute alcohol   b
    c. Chloroform
    d. Benzene

395. A good stain for amyloid is:
    a. Best's carmine
    b. Papanicolaou
    c. Palocsay-Pauliczky
    d. Bennhold's-Congo red   d

396. A good stain for glycogen is:
    a. Best's carmine   a
    b. Bennhold's Congo red
    c. Hale stain
    d. Fontana-Masson

397. Formalin pigment may be removed by:
    a. Vacuum
    b. Ammonia water   b
    c. Distilled water
    d. Polarized light

398. "Retro" means:
    a. Beside
    b. Like
    c. Backward   c
    d. Forward

399. "Para" means:
    a. Beside   a
    b. Backward
    c. Forward
    d. Like

400. "Osteo" means:
    a. Original
    b. Oscillate
    c. Bone   c
    d. Beside

401. To stain bone marrow section, apply:
    a. Fite-Faraco

b. Palocsay-Pauliczky stain
c. Hale stain
d. Giemsa stain   d

402. Ion-exchange resins used for:
a. Dehydration
b. Decalcification   b
c. Clearing
d. Mounting

403. "Oid" means:
a. Like   a
b. Beside
c. Bone
d. Backward

404. Dioxane may be used for:
a. Both clearing and dehydrating   a
b. Clearing only
c. Dehydrating only
d. Decalcifying only

405. Affords optimum embedding results:
a. Paraffin
b. Celloidin
c. Gelatin
d. Vacuum   d

406. In hematoxylin stain ferric chloride is employed as:
a. Mordant   a
b. Hematein
c. Chilled acetone
d. Sudanophilic

407. The mordant in Harris's hematoxylin is:
a. Eosin
b. Hematein
c. Hemoglobin
d. Alum   d

408. The oxidation product of hematoxylin is:
a. Hemofuchsin
b. Hemosiderin
c. Hematein   c
d. Hemoglobin

409. Overstaining and then decolorizing is:
a. Regressive staining   a
b. Metachromatic staining
c. Orthochromatic staining
d. Progressive staining

410. A stain which stains different elements without having
specific chemicals to stain any particular element is:
a. Iron hematoxylin
b. Chilled acetone

    c. A metachromatic stain   c
    d. An orthochromatic stain

411. Centrosomes may be stained by:
    a. Wilder's stain
    b. Fontana-Masson
    c. Iron hematoxylin   c
    d. Osmic acid

412. The best fixative for most enzymes is:
    a. Chilled acetone   a
    b. Iron hematoxylin
    c. 10% formalin
    d. Alcohol

413. If there is no hurry the optimum time for formalin fixation is:
    a. 4 days
    b. 3 days
    c. 2 days   c
    d. 1 day

414. The diameter of an average cell is:
    a. 1-2 microns
    b. 2-3 microns
    c. 3-4 microns
    d. 5-15 microns   d

415. Reticulum is stained by:
    a. Masson's
    b. Fontana's
    c. Wilder's   c
    d. Gomori's   d

416. On PTAH the addition of the following hastens oxidation:
    a. Potassium permanganate   a
    b. Oxalic acid
    c. Sodium permanganate
    d. Potassium ferrocyanide

417. Fontana-Masson is:
    a. An aldehyde-fuchsin stain
    b. Not a stain for inclusion bodies   b
    c. A fixative for soft materials
    d. A celloidin embedding material

418. Osmium tetroxide is:
    a. A fat stain (black substance formed in tissue) a
    b. A stain highly recommended for demonstration of
       Nissl's bodies
    c. A good stain for amyloid
    d. A good stain for glycogen

419. Osmium tetroxide stains tissue:
    a. In the section   a
    b. In the nuclei

c. In the blocks
d. In the mounting medium

420. Sudanophilic means:
    a. Thin
    b. Slight
    c. Having affinity for fat
    d. Having affinity for Sudan stains   d

421. Sections for myelin stains are cut at:
    a. 10 microns
    b. 15 microns   b (paraffin)
    c. 5 microns
    d. 0.5 microns

422. A good stain for muscle striations is:
    a. Gomori's stain
    b. Palocsay's stain
    c. PTAH   c
    d. Terry's stain

423. Weigert's iron keeps for:
    a. Minutes
    b. Hours
    c. Days   c
    d. Months

424. Gomori's aldehyde-fuchsin stains elastic fibers and beta
    cells of pancreas:
    a. Deep blue   a
    b. Brown
    c. Yellow
    d. Red

425. Carbol xylene is:
    a. 2 parts of xylene and 1 part of phenol
    b. 3 parts of xylene to 2 parts of phenol
    c. 2 parts of xylene to 2 parts of phenol
    d. 3 parts of xylene to 1 part of phenol   d

426. A fixative for soft friable material is:
    a. Absolute alcohol
    b. 10% formalin   b
    c. Chloroform
    d. Acetic acid

427. Bone is decalcified:
    a. Before fixative
    b. After fixative   b
    c. Never use fixative
    d. Not at all

428. Terry's polychrome methylene blue uses:
    a. Paraffin section
    b. Celloidin section
    c. Frozen section   c
    d. Paraffin and celloidin section

429. A temporary mounting medium is:
    a. Glycerin   a
    b. Apathy's gum syrup
    c. Concentrated solution of levulose (fructose)
    d. Zwemer's glychrogel

430. Helly's fluid contains:
    a. Potassium dichromate and mercuric chloride   a
    b. Acetic acid and water
    c. Picric acid and water
    d. Chloroform and acetic acid

431. A stain which distinguishes collagen from reticulum is:
    a. Van Kossa stain
    b. Palocsay-Pauliczky stain
    c. Periodic acid Schiff stain
    d. Wilder's stain   d

432. Magnesium carbonate:
    a. Is best fixative for microincineration
    b. Helps neutralize formalin   b
    c. Is a decalcifying solution
    d. The only fixative that preserves glycogen

433. Cytoplasm is stained by:
    a. Acid dye   a
    b. Basic dye
    c. Neutral dye
    d. Basic and neutral dyes

434. The acid in acid alcohol is:
    a. Sulfuric acid
    b. Nitric acid
    c. Hydrochloric acid   c
    d. Oxalic acid

435. Carbon is distinguished by:
    a. Its insolubility in sulfuric acid   a
    b. Its solubility in sulfuric acid
    c. Its red color
    d. A blue-black precipitate on hematoxylin and eosin

436. When using Hg chloride the following should be avoided:
    a. Cold distilled water
    b. Camel's hair brush
    c. Refrigerator
    d. Metal forceps   d

437. Sections should be lifted from microtome with:
    a. Metal forceps
    b. Cold distilled water
    c. Alcohol
    d. Fine camel's hair brush   d

438. Yeast organisms may be seen in:
    a. 10% formaldehyde

b. Hematoxylin
c. Dioxane
d. P.A.S. (periodic acid Schiff)   d

439. 1½ pints (pts.) are about equivalent to:
    a. 650 ml.
    b. 750 ml.   b
    c. 570 ml.
    d. 550 ml.

440. Xylene causes tissues to become brittle if:
    a. Left in alcohol too long
    b. Left in water too long
    c. Left in xylene too long   c
    d. Left in air too long

441. Paraffin used for embedding should be:
    a. The same MP as infiltrating   a
    b. Changed every 24 hours
    c. 37°C. ± 1°
    d. Mixed with acetone

442. For routine histology, nerve tissue is best embedded in:
    a. Celloidin
    b. Acetic acid
    c. Paraffin   c
    d. Frozen section

443. Best fixative for microincineration is:
    a. 10% formalin   a
    b. Absolute alcohol
    c. Acetone
    d. 5% acetic acid

444. Frozen section of fat floated on:
    a. Warm distilled water
    b. Cold distilled water   b
    c. Absolute alcohol
    d. 5% potassium hydroxide

445. Cloudy or opaque sections after staining due to:
    a. Sufficient dehydration and sufficient removal of
       ammonia water
    b. A fine camel's hair brush
    c. If left in xylene too long
    d. Insufficient dehydration and insufficient removal of
       ammonia water   d

446. Egg-albumin is stored in:
    a. A warm container
    b. Refrigerator   b
    c. At room temperature
    d. A dark container

447. Carbowax sections are best cut at:
    a. Very warm temperature

b. Humid air
c. Room temperature
d. Very cold temperature

c

448. 1 Gram (Gm.) equals:
a. 15 grains
b. 51 grains
c. 0.5 grain
d. 25 grains

a

449. Acetone:
a. Softens tissue if left too long (or poor grade of acetone)
b. Hardens tissue if left too short (or good grade of acetone)
c. Does not remove alcohol
d. Hardens tissue if left too long (or poor grade of acetone)

d

450. Decalcifying solution should be changed:
a. Every 24 hours
b. Every 4 hours
c. Every minute
d. Every hour

a

451. Picric acid is a component of:
a. Zenker's fluid
b. Bouin's solution
c. Helly's fluid
d. Carnoy's fluid

b

452. Carnoy's fluid contains:
a. Absolute alcohol
b. Chloroform
c. Acetic acid, glacial
d. Formalin, full strength

a
b
c

453. The fixative that best preserves glycogen is:
a. 10% formalin
b. Zenker's fluid
c. Absolute alcohol
d. Acetone

c

454. Shrinkage and distortion is greatest when the tissue has been fixed in:
a. 5% acetic acid
b. Flemming's fluid
c. Buffered neutral formalin
d. Alcohol

d

455. In Mallory's phosphotungstic acid-hematoxylin stain the collagen and reticulum stain:
a. Black
b. Yellowish to reddish-brown
c. Green
d. Light blue to dark blue

b

456. The best fixative for modified Gram stains on tissue is:
  a. Alcohol
  b. Zenker's fluid
  c. Bouin's fluid
  d. Formalin   d

457. Fat is best stained when fixed in:
  a. Absolute alcohol
  b. Formalin   b
  c. Zenker's fluid
  d. 5% acetic acid

458. Fibrin is differentiated by:
  a. Mayer's
  b. Palocsay-Pauliczky's
  c. Weigert's   c
  d. Masson's

459. Congo red stains:
  a. Amyloid   a
  b. Glycogen
  c. Fat
  d. Calcium

460. Formalin pigment can be removed by:
  a. 5% potassium hydroxide (KOH)   a
  b. 5% sodium chloride (NaCl)
  c. 5% acetic acid
  d. 5% picric acid

461. Frozen sections are most easily made from:
  a. Tissue fixed overnight in alcohol
  b. Tissue fixed overnight in 5% acetic acid
  c. Tissue fixed overnight in Zenker's fluid
  d. Tissue fixed overnight in 5% formalin   d

462. Formalin is a chemical compound.   T   F   F

463. Micrometry is the term given to the use of the microtome.
  T   F   F

464. Sudan IV is used for demonstrating the presence of glycogen.   T   F   F

465. 10% formalin is prepared by making 1:10 dilution of 40% formaldehyde.   T   F   T

466. Fixatives for tissues are generally used at room temperature.   T   F   T

467. Absolute ethyl alcohol is a dehydrating agent.   T   F   T

468. Decalcification is the process of removal of calcium so that bony tissue can be cut in sections.   T   F   T

469. Dioxane will not mix with water.   T   F   F

470. The freezing microtome uses compressed carbon monoxide.   T   F   F

471. In stropping the microtome knife the motion is from toe to heel of the blade.   T   F   T

472. Xylol is a solvent for paraffin.   T   F   T

473. When preparing tissue blocks for sectioning on the microtome during hot weather, a paraffin of lower melting point should be used.   T   F   F

474. Acid-alcohol is used for differentiation of certain dyes in tissue slide.   T   F   T

475. Zenker's fluid is a tissue fixative.   T   F   T

476. Color preservation of museum specimen may be accomplished by using Kaiserling's.   T   F   T

477. The letters "CC" after a dye name indicates that it has been certified by the Biological Stain Commission.   T   F   F

478. Paraffin ribbons from the microtome are floated at 58°C.   T   F   F

479. The temperature of the paraffin oven for embedding tissues should be 37°C. ± 1°.   T   F   F

480. Tissue to be decalcified should be thoroughly fixed before decalcification.   T   F   T

481. A mordant assists in binding stain to tissue.   T   F   T

482. Causes of shrinkage: Tissue allowed to become dry, too strong a fixative, improper dehydration, putting tissue in alcohol, too long in acetone.   T   F   T

483. Causes improper dehydration: Very good grade of acetone, too long exposure in acetone.   T   F   F

484. Improper infiltration: Paraffin too hot, paraffin used too long, not enough time in paraffin.   T   F   T

485. There exist two methods of decalcification.   T   F   F

486. Acids employed in decalcification methods are: Nitric acid, sulfuric acid, trichloroacetic acid, sulfosalicylic acid, formic acid.   T   F   T

487. Acid method of decalcification: Used for decalcifying with formic, nitric, trichloroacetic acids. Decalcifying time is 24–48 hours. Change solution daily. Agitation of jar will speed up process.   T   F   T

488. Ionic exchange resin method of decalcification is slower than acid method but gives better cellular detail.   T   F   T

489. Electrical ionization method of decalcification: Decalcification in electrical apparatus using ether alcohol-ether combination for 2-3 hours.   T   F   F

490. The best fixative to use for mailing of tissue purposes is Zenker's fluid.   T   F   F

491. Slide overstained with hematoxylin may be decolorized

with acid-alcohol.   T   F | T

492. Before staining sections of tissues fixed in Zenker's fluid it is necessary to use iodine to remove mercury precipitate.   T   F | T

493. To speed up ripening of hematoxylin one may add absolute alcohol.   T   F | F

494. If section stained with hematoxylin and eosin is too blue it indicates that it should have been left in acid alcohol a longer period of time.   T   F | T

495. The silver stains are usually used for impregnating or staining fat.   T   F | F

496. Dioxane is a dehydrating agent.   T   F | T

497. Tissue stored in unbuffered formalin for several months is likely to contain formaldehyde (formalin) pigment. T   F | T

498. Routine paraffin tissue sections are preferably cut at 8–10 microns.   T   F | F

499. Mayer's albumin adhesive is a mixture of albumin and methyl alcohol.   T   F | F

500. Smears for cytology to be stained by the Papanicolaou method should be fixed in equal parts of ether and 95% alcohol.   T   F | T

501. If a paraffin of 56–58 M.P. is used for embedding, the temperature of the water bath used for floating ribbons should be approximately 56°C.   T   F | F

502. A blue-black precipitate on hematoxylin and eosin stained section may be due to failure to filter hematoxylin.   T   F | T

503. Sections to be stained for fat should be fixed in acetone and cut on the sliding microtome.   T   F | F

504. The most common cause of unsatisfactory sections, when cutting sections from paraffin blocks, is improperly sharpening knife.   T   F | T

505. For optimum staining results, segments of bone of average size should be fixed in acetone and decalcified in a solution containing ether.   T   F | F

506. The volume of tissue-fixing fluid should exceed the volume of tissue by at least 25–35 times.   T   F | F

507. Van Gieson's stain is specific for connective tissue. T   F | T

508. Formalin fixation gives best results when formalin is used in a strength of 10%.   T   F | T

509. A good medium for mounting paraffin sections on slides before staining is Mayer's albumin.   T   F | T

510. Dioxane can only be used as a dehydrating agent.   T   F   F

511. The mercury is removed from Zenker's fixed tissue by an iodine solution.   T   F   T

512. If the knife digs into the paraffin block the usual cause is wrong angle of knife.   T   F   T

513. To best stain neutral fat in tissue, use Sudan III.   T   F   F

514. To decalcify bone it is customary to use 5% nitric acid.   T   F   T

515. Osmium tetroxide is a stain for some fats and Golgi apparatus.   T   F   T

516. Prussian blue stain may be used for staining of glycogen   T   F   F

517. Commercial formalin is a 25% solution of formaldehyde.   T   F   F

518. Because fat solvents are used usually in the preparation of paraffin sections, the latter are not adequate for special staining of fats.   T   F   T

519. Quick diagnosis and the staining of fat are two reasons why frozen sections are used in the histology laboratory.   T   F   T

520. Alum in hematoxylin acts as a mordant.   T   F   T

521. Paraffin infiltration should take place at 15–20 degrees above the melting point of the paraffin.   T   F   F

522. Mayer's egg albumin should be stored at room temperature.   T   F   F

523. Sudan IV or scarlet R are used in frozen sections.   T   F   T

524. The "wet method" in cutting celloidin sections is: Wet knife and block with 70% alcohol.   T   F   T

525. Before staining, mercury crystals should be removed from sections by iodine solution.   T   F   T

526. When doing a Gram's stain the tissue can be decolorized by ether.   T   F   F

527. Alcohol, dioxane, acetone, and cellosolve are dehydrating agents.   T   F   T

528. Mayer's albumin is made of albumin and glycerine.   T   F   T

529. The meaning of prefix "macro" is "large."   T   F   T

530. The formula for converting degrees Fahrenheit to degrees centigrade is (F + 32) x 5/9.   T   F   F

531. Laboratory equipment can be sterilized in hot water.   T   F   F

532. The magnification of the eyepiece times that of the objective gives the total magnification.   T   F   T

533. Brown and Brenn stain is used for bacteria in tissues: Gram-positive appear blue, Gram-negative red.   T   F   T

534. Fite-Faraco stains:
    a. Are used for acid-fast bacilli   a
    b. Acid-fast bacilli stained red, background blue. Use control slide.   b
    c. Used for Gram-negative and Gram-positive bacteria
    d. Acid-fast bacilli stained black, background is yellow

535. Gomori methenamine silver stain (G.M.S.):
    a. Stains fungi yellow, mucin is black
    b. Inner parts brown, background pale-blue
    c. Fungi delineated in black, mucin is gray   c
    d. Inner parts are rose, background pale-green   d

536. Mayer's mucicarmine stain for mucin:
    a. Mucin deep-rose to red, nuclei black, others yellow   a
    b. Mucin black, nuclei rose, others brown
    c. Solutions: Weigert's iron-hematoxylin and solution A + B   c
    d. Solutions: Sudan IV and Congo red B

537. Bennhold's Congo red for amyloid:
    a. Amyloid blue, others violet
    b. Solutions: stock crystal violet
    c. Amyloid pink to red, nuclei blue   c
    d. Solutions: Congo red and saturated lithium carbonate   d

538. Crystal violet stain for amyloid:
    a. Amyloid violet, others blue   a
    b. Amyloid pink to red, nuclei brown
    c. Solutions: stock crystal violet and working crystal violet solution   c
    d. Use Apopon for mounting medium   d

539. Giemsa stain for bacteria:
    a. Nuclei pink to rose, cytoplasm blue
    b. Nuclei blue, cytoplasm pink to rose   b
    c. Bacteria red
    d. Bacteria blue   d

540. Masson's trichrome stain for formalin-fixed tissue:
    a. Nuclei black, cytoplasm, muscle, fibers red   a
    b. Collagen and mucin blue   b
    c. Nuclei blue, cytoplasm, muscle, fibers black
    d. Collagen and mucin brown

541. Modification of Mallory's reaction stain for iron:
    a. Iron pigments red, nuclei blue
    b. Iron pigments bright blue, nuclei red   b
    c. Cytoplasm pink to rose   c
    d. Cytoplasm brown to black

542. Heidenhain's aniline blue stain:

  a. Chromatin, osteocytes, neuroglia, cytoplasm brown
  b. Collagen and reticulum blue, muscle red to yellow   b
  c. Chromatin, osteocytes, neuroglia, cytoplasm pink to
     blue   c
  d. Collagen and reticulum brown, muscle blue

543. Wilder's reticulum stain:
  a. Reticulum blue
  b. Nuclei and background black
  c. Reticulum dark-violet to black   c
  d. Nuclei and bakcground pink   d

544. Best's carmine stain for glycogen:
  a. Glycogen blue
  b. Glycogen pink to red   b
  c. Nuclei blue   c
  d. Nuclei brown

545. Heidenhain's iron-hematoxylin stain:
  a. Chromatin, nuclei, mitochondria, parts of striated
     muscle fibers black   a
  b. Other tissue elements dark-black
  c. Other tissue elements contrast stain   c
  d. Chromatin, nuclei, mitochondria, parts of striated
     muscle fibers blue

546. Toluidin blue metachromatic stain:
  a. Metachromatic tissue pink   a
  b. Metachromatic tissue brown
  c. Metachromatic tissue blue
  d. Metachromatic tissue yellow

547. May-Gruenwald-Giemsa stain:
  a. Nuclei black, cytoplasm blue
  b. Bacteria yellow
  c. Nuclei blue, cytoplasm pink to rose   c
  d. Bacteria blue   d

548. Hematoxylin and eosin stains:
  a. Nuclei pink
  b. Nuclei blue   b
  c. Cytoplasm pink   c
  d. Cytoplasm black

549. Van Gieson stain for collagen:
  a. Collagen red, muscle, epithelium yellow   a
  b. Nuclei blue to black   b
  c. Collagen blue, muscle, epithelium brown
  d. Nuclei red to pink

550. Van Kossa's stain for calcium:
  a. Calcium salts blue, nuclei black
  b. Cytoplasm brown to black
  c. Calcium salts black, nuclei red   c
  d. Cytoplasm pink to rose   d

551. Oil red O fat stain (frozen section):
    a. Fat orange to bright red   a
    b. Fat black
    c. Nuclei blue   c
    d. Nuclei brown

552. Mallory's phosphotungstic acid hematoxylin (PTAH) stain:
    a. Myofibrils deep blue   a
    b. Myofibrils orange to bright red
    c. Myofibrils black
    d. Myofibrils brown

553. Wade's modification of Fite's new fuchsin-formaldehyde method:
    a. Acid-fast bacilli deep ultramarine blue or blue black, connective tissue element (incl. reticulum) red   a
    b. Acid-fast bacilli orange to bright red, connective tissue element (incl. reticulum) blue
    c. Other elements yellowish   c
    d. Other elements pale green

554. Periodic acid Schiff (P.A.S.) reaction:
    a. Glycogen, mucin blue to black
    b. Glycogen, mucin rose to purplish-red   b
    c. Nuclei blue, fungi red, background pale green   c
    d. Nuclei red, fungi blue, bakcground brown

555. Buffer solution is:
    a. Any substance or combination of substances which, when dissolved in water, produces a solution which resists a change in its H-ion concentration upon the addition of acid or alkali   a
    b. Any substance or combination of substances which, when dissolved in alcohol produces a solution which changes in its H-ion concentration upon the addition of acid or alkali
    c. Any substance or combination of substances which, when dissolved in butyl alcohol-ether produces a solution which resists a change in its H-ion concentration upon the addition of acid or alkali
    d. Any substance or combination of substances which, when dissolved in chloroform produces a solution which changes in its H-ion concentration upon the addition of acid or alkali.

556. pH is:
    a. The P-ion concentration
    b. The symbol commonly used to express H-ion concentration. It signifies the logarithm of the reciprocal of the H-ion concentration in gram molecules per liter of solution.   b
    c. The K-ion concentration, base 100 of the reciprocal of K-ions
    d. The phosphotungstic acid hematoxylin (PTAH) concentration

557. You have 80% alcohol and wish to prepare 100 ml. of
 60% alcohol:
  a. Take 75 ml. of distilled water and add 25 ml. of
     80% alcohol. You will have 100 ml. of 60% alcohol
  b. Take 75 ml. of 80% alcohol and add 25 ml. of dis-
     tilled water. You will have 100 ml. of 60% alcohol   b
  c. The formula is:

$$100 \times \frac{X}{Y} \qquad \begin{array}{l} 100 = \text{ml. desired} \\ X = \%\text{ alcohol desired} \\ Y = \%\text{ alcohol on hand} \end{array}$$ c

  d.
$$100 \times \frac{X}{Y} = 100 \times \frac{60}{80} = 75 \text{ ml.}$$ d

558. How many grams of NaOH are needed to prepare 500 ml.
 of 0.1N solution:
  a. Molecular weight of Na = 23, oxygen = 16, hydrogen
     = 1. MW = 40   a
  b. 10 Grams/liter NaOH – 1N
     4 Grams/liter NaOH = 0.1N
     2 Grams/500 ml. NaOH = 0.1N   b
  c. 2 grams of NaOH are needed to prepare 500 ml. of
     0.1N solution   c
  d. 4 grams of NaOH are needed to prepare 500 ml. of
     0.1N solution

559. Indicate the normality of a 10% NaOH solution:
  a. Molecular weight of Na = 23, O = 16, H = 1
     MW = 40   a
  b. $\frac{100}{40} = \frac{10}{4} = 2.5N$ 10% NaOH solution is 2.5N   b

  c. $\frac{40}{100} = \frac{4}{10} = 0.4N$ 10% NaOH solution is 0.4N

  d. 10% NaOH solution is 2.9 normal

560. 832μ (microns) is the same as:
  a. 0.0832 mm.
  b. 0.832 mm.   b
  c. 8.32 mm.
  d. 83.20 mm.

561. 36.6 Celsius = how many Fahrenheit?
  a. 36.6 $\times$ 1.8 + 32 = 97.9 Fahrenheit   a
  b. 36.6 $\times$ 1.8 – 32 = 65.9 Fahrenheit
  c. 36.6 $\div$ 1.8 + 32 = 54.6 Fahrenheit
  d. 36.6 $\div$ 1.8 – 32 = –9.6 Fahrenheit

562. 97.9 Fahrenheit = how many Celsius?
  a. 97.9 + 32 $\div$ 1.8 = 72.3 Celsius
  b. 97.9 – 32 $\div$ 1.8 = 36.6 Celsius   b
  c. 97.9 $\times$ 32 $\div$ 1.8 = 17.40 Celsius
  d. 97.9 $\times$ 32 – 1.8 = 31.32 Celsius

563. 1°C. = ?, 1°F. = ?, 0°C. = ?, 100°C. = ?
    a. 1°C. = 1.8°F., 1°F. = 5/9°C., 0°C. = 32°F., 100°C.
       = 212°F.
    b. 1°C. = 218°F., 1°F. = 9/5°C., 0°C. = 2.2°F., 100°C.
       = 100°F.
    c. 1°C. = 2.8°F., 1°F. = 59°C., 0°C. = 23°F., 100°C.
       = 100°F.
    d. 1°C. = 21.8°F., 1°F. = 95°C., 0°C. = 3.2°F., 100°C.
       = 21.2°F.

a

564. One liter (l.) equals:
    a. 100 ml. = 1.1134 pt. = 0.567 qt.
    b. 1,000 ml. = 2.1134 pt. = 1.0567 qt.
    c. 10 ml. = 3.1134 pt. = 0.0567 qt.
    d. 10,000 ml. = 0.1134 pt. = 2.0567 qt.

b

565. One kilogram (Kg.) equals:
    a. 1,000 mg. = 100 gr. = 5.274 oz. = 1.204622 lb.
    b. 10,000 mg. = 1,000 gr. = 50.274 oz. = 12.04622 lb.
    c. 100,000 mg. = 10,000 gr. = 500.274 oz. = 120.4622 lb.
    d. 1,000,000 mg. = 1,000 gr. = 35.274 oz. = 2.204622 lb.

d

566. 10% NaOH means:
    a. 10 grams of NaOH is dissolved in and the volume
       made up to 100 ml. with distilled water
    b. 100 grams of NaOH is dissolved in and the volume
       made up to 1,000 ml. with distilled water
    c. 1 gram of NaOH is dissolved in and the volume made
       up to 100 ml. with distilled water
    d. 0.1 gram of NaOH is dissolved in and the volume
       made up to 100 ml. with distilled water

a

b

567. Percent (%) solution means:
    a. Volume weight to percent $\dfrac{V}{\%W}$
    b. Percent weight to volume $\dfrac{\%W}{V}$
    c. Percent to volume weight $\dfrac{\%V}{W}$
    d. Weight to volume percent $\dfrac{WV}{\%}$

b

568. Normal solution is:
    a. The gram equivalent weight of solute in a liter of
       solution
    b. The kilogram equivalent weight of solute per liter of
       solution
    c. The milligram equivalent weight of solute per liter of
       solution
    d. The dekagram equivalent weight of solute per liter of
       solution.

a

569. Make 2% ammonia (NH$_3$) water:
    a. 100 ml. of distilled water and 2 ml. of ammonia

a

   b. 1,000 ml. distilled water and 2 ml. of ammonia
   c. 10 ml. distilled water and 2 ml. of ammonia
   d. 10,000 ml. distilled water and 2 ml. of ammonia

570. Make 10% formalin solution:
   a. 95 ml. of 40% formaldehyde and 5 ml. distilled water
   b. 10 ml. of 40% formaldehyde and 90 ml. of distilled
      water   b
   c. 25 ml. of 40% formaldehyde and 75 ml. of distilled
      water
   d. 70 ml. of 40% formaldehyde and 30 ml. of distilled
      water

571. Atomic weights of:
   a. H = 1, Ca = 40, Cl = 35, C = 12, S = 32, N = 14,
      O = 16, PO_4 = 30   a
   b. H = 2, Ca = 35, Cl = 40, C = 14, S = 16, N = 32,
      O = 18, PO_4 = 40
   c. Na (sodium) = 23, K (potassium) = 39   c
   d. Na = 39, K = 22

572. Make $N/12$ H_2SO_4 solution:
   a. Dilute 1N (normal) H_2SO_4 with 11 volumes distilled
      water   a
   b. Dilute 2N H_2SO_4 with 11 volumes distilled water
   c. Dilute 3N H_2SO_4 with 11 volumes distilled water
   d. Dilute 4N H_2SO_4 with 11 volumes distilled water

573. Make N/10 solution from a stock 1N (normal) solution:
   a. Dilute 1 volume of stock solution with 9 volumes of
      distilled water   a
   b. Dilute 9 volumes of stock solution with 1 volume of
      distilled water
   c. Dilute 10 volumes of stock solution with 9 volumes of
      distilled water
   d. Dilute 19 volumes of stock solution with 1 volume of
      distilled water

574. Make 50 ml. N/50 solution from N/10:
   a. Dilute 100 ml. of N/10 solution with 4 ml. distilled
      water
   b. Dilute 1 ml. of N/10 solution with 50 ml. distilled
      water
   c. Dilute 1,000 ml. of N/10 solution with 10 ml. distilled
      water
   d. Dilute 10 ml. of N/10 solution with 40 ml. distilled
      water   d

575. Prepare one liter of 1N (normal) solution of:
   a. HCl = 36.46 Grams HCl/liter, NaOH = 40 Gm./liter   a
   b. H_2SO_4 = 98.08 Gm./liter
   c. $Ca(OH)_2$ = 37 Gm. $Ca(OH)_2$/liter   c
   d. NaCl = 59 Gm. NaCl/liter   d

576. 1N (normal) means:

    a. 1 gram equivalent/liter of solution   a
    b. 10 gram equivalents/2 liter solution
    c. 15 gram equivalents/20 liter solution
    d. 20 gram equivalents/15 liter solution

577. Make 100 ml. 1% HCl-alcohol from 25% HCl:
    a. Measure 8 ml. from the 25% HCl and add 96 ml.
       70% alcohol
    b. Measure 4 ml. from the 25% HCl and add 96 ml.
       70% alcohol   b
    c. Measure 10 ml. from the 25% HCl and add 96 ml.
       70% alcohol
    d. Measure 15 ml. from the 25% HCl and add 96 ml.
       70% alcohol

578. Make 70% alcohol from 95% alcohol:
    a. $100 \times \dfrac{X}{Y} = 100 \times \dfrac{70}{95} = 70$ ml.   a
    b. Measure 700 ml. of 95% alcohol and add 250 ml. of
       distilled water   b
    c. Measure 70 ml. of 95% alcohol and add 25 ml. of
       distilled water   c
    d. Measure 75 ml. of 95% alcohol and add 15 ml. of
       distilled water

579. Make alcoholic iodine solution:
    a. Measure 10 ml. of 95% alcohol and add 2 grams of
       iodine crystals
    b. Measure 100 ml. of 95% alcohol and add 2.5 grams
       of iodine crystals
    c. Measure 100 ml. of 95% alcohol and add 1 gram of
       iodine crystals   c
    d. Measure 10 ml. of 95% alcohol and add 0.1 gram of
       iodine crystals   d

580. Make gold chloride solution:
    a. Measure 10 ml. of 1% gold chloride and add 40 ml.
       distilled water
    b. Measure 1 ml. of 1% gold chloride and add 99 ml.
       distilled water   b
    c. Measure 2 ml. of 1% gold chloride solution and add
       99 ml. distilled water
    d. Measure 5 ml. of 1% gold chloride and add 99 ml.
       distilled water

581. Make Na (sodium) thiosulfate (hypo) solution:
    a. Measure 5 grams of sodium thiosulfate and add 100
       ml. distilled water   a
    b. Measure 5.2 grams of sodium thiosulfate and add 100
       ml. distilled water
    c. Measure 5.5 grams of sodium thiosulfate and add 100
       ml. distilled water
    d. Measure 6 grams of sodium thiosulfate and add 100
       ml. distilled water

582. Use indicator:
    a. For weak acid and strong base use indicator that
       changes on the alkaline side of 7   a
    b. For weak base and strong acid use indicator that
       changes on acid side of 7   b
    c. For strong acid and strong base use indicator at 7   c
    d. pH = ←←←←←←← 7 neutral →→→→→→→   d
             acid   alkaline

583. Myelin-staining solution contains:
    a. 10 ml. of 10% alk. hematoxylin + 90 ml. distilled
       water + 7 ml. sat. aq. lithium carbonate   a
    b. 15 ml. of 15% alk. hematoxylin + 8 ml. lithium car-
       bonate
    c. 7 ml. of 10% alk. hematoxylin + distilled water
    d. 20 ml. of 15% alk. hematoxylin + 85 ml. distilled
       water + 8 ml. lithium carbonate

584. Alcoholic solution of hematoxylin contains:
    a. 10 grams of hematoxylin crystal + 90 ml. distilled
       water + 20 ml. of 95% alcohol
    b. 0.5 gram of hematoxylin crystal + 90 ml. distilled
       water + 10 ml. of 95% alcohol   b
    c. 1.5 grams of hematoxylin crystal + 80 ml. distilled
       water + 35 ml. of 85% alcohol
    d. 2.5 grams of hematoxylin crystal + 75 ml. distilled
       water + 45 ml. of 75% alcohol

585. Ammoniacal silver solution contains:
    a. 10 ml. of 25% silver nitrate + 10 drops of 50%
       sodium hydroxide
    b. 15 ml. of 35% sodium hydroxide + 10 ml. of 25%
       silver nitrate
    c. 5 ml. of 20% silver nitrate + 5 drops of 40% sodium
       hydroxide   c
    d. 2.5 ml. of 40% silver nitrate + 7 drops of 4% sodium
       hydroxide

586. Hematoxylin according to Ehrlich contains:
    a. 2 grams hematoxylin, 100 ml. of 95% ethanol   a
    b. 100 ml. distilled water, 100 ml. glycerine   b
    c. 3 grains of potash alum, 10 ml. glacial acetic acid c
    d. 0.4 grams of sodium iodate   d

587. Weigert's iron hematoxylin A contains:
    a. 5 grams of hematoxylin and 500 ml. of 96% alcohol a
    b. 10 grams of hematoxylin and 300 ml. of 70% alcohol
    c. 2 grams of hematoxylin and 250 ml. of 50% alcohol
    d. 1 gram of hematoxylin and 600 ml. of 80% alcohol

588. Weigert's hematoxylin B contains:
    a. 20.5 ml. ferric chloride (25% in 100 ml.) + 462 ml.
       distilled water + 10 ml. of HCl (50%)
    b. 27.5 ml. of ferric chloride (20% in 100 ml.) + 467.5
       ml. distilled water + 5 ml. of HCl (25%)   b

    c. 37.2 ml. of ferrous chloride + 365 ml. distilled water + 3 ml. of HCl (10%)

    d. 50 ml. of ferrous chloride + 365 ml. distilled water + 5 ml. of HCl (35%)

589. What is xylol or xylene?
    a. $C_6H_4(CH_3)_2$ a
    b. Dimethylbenzene. An antiseptic hydrocarbon from methyl alcohol or coal tar   b
    c. Used in microscopy as a solvent and clarifier   c
    d. A group of hydrocarbons of the benzene series   d

590. What is eosin?
    a. $C_{20}H_8Br_4O_5$ a
    b. A rose-colored stain or dye. The potassium and sodium (K and Na) salts of tetrabromfluorescein   b
    c. Commercially several other red coal tar dyes are called "eosin"   c
    d. The eosins are bromine derivatives of fluorescein   d

591. Ammonia is:
    a. NH_3 a
    b. The hypothetical radical. It forms salts analogous to those of the alkaline metals. These are stimulant to the heart and respiration   b
    c. NP_4
    d. NH_4

592. Formaldehyde is:
    a. C_2CH_2O
    b. HCHO   b
    c. A powerful disinfectant gas   c
    d. Sometimes used as a disinfectant for rooms, clothing, etc.   d

593. Alcohol (ethanol) is:
    a. C_2H_5OH a
    b. A transparent, colorless, mobile, volatile liquid. Miscible with water, ether and chloroform   b
    c. Used internally as a cardiac stimulant and locally as an antiseptic and astringent   c
    d. Used for the preservation of antomical and biological specimens   d

594. Formalin is:
    a. A 40% solution of gaseous formaldehyde   a
    b. A 30% solution of formaldehyde
    c. Used as an antiseptic and disinfectant in 1:2,000 to 1:200 solutions   c
    d. Used as a fixing agent in histologic work   d

595. How do you prepare a bone section?
    a. Remove the calcium salts from bone before it can be cut   a
    b. Cut bone in small pieces   b

  c. Fix in formalin for 8–12 hours   c
  d. Wash thoroughly and decalcify   d

596. Hematoxylin is:
  a. $C_{16}H_{14}O_6 + 3\ H_2O$ a
  b. A crystalline stain   b
  c. Obtained by extracting logwood with ether   c
  d. It may be used as an indicator with a pH range of 5–6 d

597. Acetone is:
  a. CH_3COCH_3 a
  b. Dimethylketone   b
  c. Not miscible with paraffin   c
  d. It has a very low boiling point. Advantage of not
   diluting the paraffin baths   d

598. Celloidin is:
  a. A form of paraffin
  b. A form of hematoxylin
  c. A form of eosin
  d. A purified form of collodion or nitrocellulose   d

599. Stains are divided into:
  a. Bacterial stains
  b. Fungus stains
  c. Spirochete stains
  d. Connective tissue stains
  e. Reticulum stains
  f. Special nerve stains
  g. Histochemical stains
  h. All of the above   h

600. Bacterial stains are:
  a. Brown and Brenn's stain for bacteria   a
  b. Fite-Faraco stain for acid-fast bacilli   b
  c. Giemsa stain for bacteria   c
  d. Luxol fast blue stain for myelin

601. Fungus stains are:
  a. Palocsay-Paulczky
  b. Fontana-Masson
  c. Periodic acid Schiff (P.A.S.)   c
  d. Gomori methenamine silver (G.M.S.) or Grocotts d

602. The methods of spirochete staining are:
  a. Levaditti's   a
  b. Gomori's
  c. Warthin-Starry   c
  d. Steiner's silver   d

603. Connective tissue stains are:
  a. Bielchowsky
  b. Mallory's phosphotungstic acid hematoxylin (PTAH) b
  c. Palocsay-Pauliczky
  d. Heidenhein's iron-hematoxylin   d

604. Reticulum stains are:
     a. Gomori   a
     b. Bielchowsky   b
     c. Wilder   c
     d. Girdley   d
     e. Snook   e

605. Special nerve stains are:
     a. Phloxine fast green (myelin and glial fibers)
     b. Luxol fast blue (myelin)
     c. Fontana-Masson (argentaffin granules)
     d. Bodian (nerve fibers)
     e. Cajal's gold sublimate (astrocytes)
     f. Phosphotungstic acid hematoxylin
     g. All of the above   g

606. Histochemical stains are
     a. Heidenhain's iron-hematoxylin (iron)
     b. Best's carmine (glycogen)   b
     c. Periodic acid Schiff's (P.A.S.) (glycogen)   c
     d. Bennhold's Congo red (amyloid)   d
     e. Carbohydrates

607. Fat-staining method is:
     a. Cut materials in freezing microtome about 14–16
        microns. Place in distilled water.   a
     b. Stain 1½ minutes in Mayer's hematoxylin. Rinse
        for 10–20 minutes in tap water.   b
     c. Stain in Fettrot for 5 minutes. Rinse quickly in 70%
        alcohol   c
     d. Rinse in tap water, coverslip with glycerine   d

608. Cells that stain very poorly are called:
     a. Chromophobes   a
     b. Chromatin
     c. Chromosomes
     d. Chromic

609. Basophilic refers to a tissue which has an affinity for:
     a. Basophilia
     b. An acid dye
     c. A neutral dye
     d. A basic dye   d

610. Frozen sections may be made with:
     a. Fixed tissue only
     b. Fixed or unfixed tissue   b
     c. Unfixed tissue only
     d. Not at all

611. Formalin can be neutralized by adding:
     a. Absolute alcohol
     b. Ether
     c. Calcium carbonate   c
     d. Chloroform

612. Formol-alcohol:
    a. Fixes and dehydrates tissue at the same time   a
    b. Fixes tissue only
    c. Dehydrates tissue only
    d. Does not fix and does not dehydrate tissue at all

613. A polychrome stain is generally used in the:
    a. Paraffin section technique
    b. Celloidin technique
    c. Paraffin and celloidin techniques
    d. Frozen section technique   d

614. The celloidin-paraffin combination method is well-adapted
    for:
    a. Large objects containing bone
    b. Black objects containing spirochetes
    c. Small objects containing fat   c
    d. Large objects containing crystals

615. Dioxane (used for dehydrating) is miscible with water,
    xylol, and alcohol.   T   F   T

616. A 20% solution of commercial formalin is a good fixative
    agent.   T   F   F

617. Hematoxylin stains the nuclei of cells red.   T   F   F

618. Balsam (a mounting material) is miscible with water.
    T   F   F

619. Xylol is an excellent clearing agent.   T   F   T

620. Tissue to be cut should not be rigid.   T   F   F

621. The phloxine and methylene blue technique is never used
    for the staining of tissues.   T   F   F

622. Whole blood is a suitable medium to fix tissues to the slide.
    T   F   F

623. Sudan IV stain consists of Congo red, absolute alcohol, and
    xylol.   T   F   F

624. A fixing reagent should penetrate, kill, preserve, and
    harden the tissue.   T   F   T

625. Tissue should be infiltrated with paraffin before blocking
    in paraffin.   T   F   T

626. Fixatives for tissue are generally used at room tempera-
    ture.   T   F   T

627. 10% formalin is prepared by making a 1:10 dilution of
    40% formaldehyde.   T   F   T

628. Mitochondria are not well preserved by the ordinary fixing
    method.   T   F   T

629. Celloidin may be used for embedding eyes that are to be
    sectioned.   T   F   T

630. In the frozen method, if the tissue is too cold it will crumble.   T   F   T

631. Ferritin is:
    a. Brown granule
    b. Iron-containing pigment   b
    c. Will react with iron stain
    d. Does not react with iron stain   d

632. Hematein is:
    a. A passive coloring agent in most hematoxylin stains
    b. An active coloring agent   b
    c. Formed by oxidation
    d. A process which takes a number of days or weeks
       and is spoken of as "ripening"   d

633. Which fixatives produce the highest degree of tissue stabili-
    zation by cross-linking?
    a. Osmium tetroxide
    b. Potassium permanganate
    c. Formaldehyde (paraformaldehyde)
    d. Glutaraldehyde   d
    e. Acrolein

634. What is the maximum thickness for sections for trans-
    mission electron microscopy?
    a. 1 nm
    b. 10 nm
    c. 100 nm   c
    d. 500 nm

635. Which method(s) best show(s) location of specific protein
    in tissues?
    a. X-ray diffraction
    b. Immunofluorescence   b
    c. Electron microscopy
    d. PAS reaction   d
    e. Immunoperoxidase

636. Which of the following can contribute to faulty sections
    in transmission electron microscopy?
    a. Dull knife   a
    b. Improper clearance angle   b
    c. Block too large   c
    d. Knife contaminated   d
    e. Incorrect block polymerization   e
    f. Improper angle of actual knife edge   f

637. The best method of cleaning a glass or diamond knife is
    accomplished by wiping it with a cotton swab dipped in
    acetone.   T   F   F

638. Which of the following is used to stain transmission elec-
    tron microscopy thin sections?
    a. Azure B-methylene blue
    b. Lead citrate   b

c. Uranyl acetate
d. Toluidine blue

c

639. In the immunofluorescent technique for renal biopsy specimens, it is possible to store the frozen tissue for up to one
year without any damage.   T   F

F

640. Immunofluorescent antisera should be refrozen after each
use.   T   F

F

641. Tissues should be allowed to dry out after incubation with
immunofluorescent antisera.   T   F

F

642. Some of the characteristics of osmium tetroxide are:
   a. High molecular weight
   b. Fast penetration of tissue
   c. Stains tissue for transmission electron microscopy
   d. Fixes tissue

a

c
d

643. "Chatter" in transmission electron microscopy sections
may be caused by:
   a. Dull knife
   b. Too great cutting angle
   c. Knife and/or block not secured tightly
   d. Block too small
   e. Improper cutting speed

a
b
c

e

644. Desirable characteristics of embedding media for transmission electron microscopy are:
   a. Stability during electron bombardment
   b. Blocks are moderately hard but not brittle
   c. Preservation of fine structure
   d. Controllable consistency
   e. Rapid infiltration

a
b
c
d
e

645. Glutaraldehyde penetrates tissue slower than osmium
tetroxide.   T   F

F

646. At what temperature and pressue is the critical point during
CO_2 drying?
   a. 1073 psi @ 31°C.
   b. 1124 psi @ 35°C.
   c. 1200 psi @ 38°C.
   d. 1157 psi @ 41°C.

a

647. Which of the following are commonly used to stain "thick"
plastic embedded sections?
   a. Azure B-methylene blue
   b. Toluidine blue
   c. PAS
   d. Hematoxylin-eosin
   e. Wilder's reticulum

a
b
c

648. What is the usual thickness of "thick" plastic embedded
sections?
   a. Less than 100 nm
   b. 0.1–0.5 microns

    c. 0.5–2.0 microns   c

    d. 5.0–6.0 microns

    e. 15.0–20.0 microns

649. Tissue for electron microscopy is generally fixed at:
   - a. 0°C.
   - b. 4°C.   b
   - c. Room temperature
   - d. 37°C.
   - e. 56°C.

650. Which are properties of scanning electron microscopy?
   - a. Higher resolution than transmission electron micro-
     scopy
   - b. Can use larger specimens than transmission electron
     microscopy   b
   - c. Shows surface structures   c
   - d. Shows internal structures
   - e. Does not require embedding   e
   - f. Does not require specimen drying

651. Which of the following is suitable for electron microscopy?
   - a. Tissue frozen in deep freeze
   - b. Tissue quick-frozen in liquid nitrogen   b
   - c. Tissue fresh from a living organism   c
   - d. Autopsy tissue
   - e. Tissue stored in formalin

652. Which of the following are currently considered the best
   embedding plastics for routine transmission electron
   microscopy?
   - a. Methyl methacrylate
   - b. Urea-formaldehyde resins
   - c. EPON 812   c
   - d. Araldite   d
   - e. Durcopan
   - f. IB-4
   - f. Spun resin

A CURRICULUM FOR HISTOLOGIC TECHNIQUE:
INFORMAL LECTURES & DEMONSTRATIONS

Suggested duration of course: 4 weeks.

I. Orientation in the Laboratory of Histopathologic Technique

II. Processing Tissues:
   a. Fixation
   b. Dehydration
   c. Clearing
   d. Embedding:
      1. Paraplast
      2. Celloidin
      3. Carbowax
   e. Blocking

III. Routine Cutting and Staining

IV. Decalcification:
   a. Acid
   b. Ionic exchange resins
   c. Electrical ionization

V. Frozen Sections:
   a. Temporary
   b. Permanent

VI. Special Stains:
   a. Bacterial Stains:
      1. Brown & Brenn
      2. Fite Faraco
      3. Giemsa
   b. Fungus Stains:
      1. PAS
      2. GMS
   c. Spirochete Stains
   d. Connective Tissue Stains
   e. Retiruclum Stains
   f. Special Nerve Stains:
      1. Phloxine Fast Green: Myelin and glial fibers
      2. Luxol Fast Blue: Myelin
      3. Fontana Masson: Argentaffin granules
      4. Bodian: Nerve fibers
      5. Cajal's Gold Sublimate: Astrocytes
      6. Phosphotungstic Acid Hematoxylin

VII.   **Histochemical Stains:**
      a. Iron
      b. Glycogen
      c. Amyloid
      d. Carbohydrates

VIII.   **Demonstrations:**
      a. Histochemistry
      b. Cryostat Sectioning
      c. Electron Microscopy

SUGGESTED OUTLINE OF SUBJECTS
(to be covered in preparation for examination in histologic technique)

Fixatives.
Be familiar with a number of the most common fixatives, learning the ingredients and their purpose but not necessarily the quantities used. Learn the advantages of each and indications for choice of each.

Dehydrating and Clearing Agents.
Be familiar with the advantages and disadvantages of several of the most common dehydrating and clearing agents.

Decalcification Methods.
Acid Methods
Ionic Exchange Resins
Electrical Ionization

Embedding Media.
Paraffin
Celloidin
Carbowax
    (properties, solubilities, techniques involved)

Routine Staining.
Know reasons for each step in staining procedure.
Know purpose of each ingredient in various hematoxylin solutions.

Special Stains:
Be familiar with the most common methods of staining the following: Bacteria, fungi, amoebae in tissue sections; amyloid; argentaffin granules; blood and bone marrow sections; calcium; cholesterol; collagen; elastic fibers; enzymes (acid and alkaline p'tase); fat and fat-like substances; fibrin; Nissl substance; glycogen; hemoglobin; hemosiderin; melanin; mucin; muscle; myelin; nerve fibers and endings; reticulum.
Be familiar with methods of identification of common exogenous and endogenous pigments, including those listed above.

Read Booklets Accompanying Equipment Used.
Autotechnicon.

Use and Care of Microscope by Spencer Company.
Use and Care of Microtome by Spencer Company, with particular attention to chapters on knife angles, microtome knife sharpening, and difficulties encountered in cutting sections.

Preparation of Molar, Normal, Buffered Solutions.

Word Stems, Prefixes, Suffixes used in Medical Terminology.

Fixatives.
Be familiar with a number of the most common fixatives (Zenker's, Heller's, Bouin's, formalin-ammonium bromide, Carnoy's, Flemming's, alcoholic formalin, aqueous formalin), learning the ingredients, but not necessarily the quantity of various reagents used. Learn the advantages and disadvantages of the various fixatives and indications for the choice of each. Know when absolute alcohol and acetone can and should be used as fixatives.

Dehydrating and Clearing Agents.
Advantages and disadvantages of the following:

Dehydrating:	Clearing:
Alcohol (ethyl, methyl, butyl)	Xylene
Dioxane	Toluene
Acetone	Benzene
Cellosolve (ethylene glycol monoethyl ether)	Dioxane
	Amyl acetate
Triethyl phosphate	Butyl acetate
	Cedarwood oil

Decalcification Methods.
Acid methods (formic and nitric) with advantages and disadvantages.
Ionic exchange resins
Electrical ionization.

Embedding Media.
Paraffin
Celloidin
Carbowax (not too much on this—just be familiar with the nature of this medium and know reasons for its use).

Routine Staining.
Know reasons for each step in staining procedure. Know purpose of each ingredient in various hematoxylin solutions.

Metric System.

SPECIAL STAINS

This and the following pages contain a list of stains which are reliable and are commonly used. It is not necessary to actually perform all of them unless the occasion arises that they are needed, but it would be beneficial to become familiar with them and note the reagents and stains used. Those marked with an asterisk (*) are so commonly requested that the student should gain experience in actually performing them.

Bacteria.
*Kinyoun's (acid-fast), *Ziehl-Neelsen (acid-fast), *Brown and Brenn modification of Gram stain, Lillie's Gram stain.

Spirochetes.
Warthin-Starry, Levaditi.

Fungi.
*Bauer-Feulgen stain (yeast-like organisms), *Schiff's periodic acid method, *Gram-stain (see under bacteria).

Amebae.
Iron-hematoxylin, phosphotungstic acid hematoxylin.

Alpha Cells of Pancreas.
Gomori's method, chromium, hematoxylin, Mallory-Heidenhain azan stain.

Amyloid.
*Bennhold Congo red, *Lieb crystal violet.

Argentaffin Granules.
*Fontana silver nitrate.

Beta Cells of Pancreas.
Gomori's aldehyde fuchsin stain; Gomori's chromium hematoxylin stain.

Blood and Bone Marrow Cells.
Jenner-Giemsa stain (smears), *Wolbach-Giemsa stain (sections).

Calcium.
*von Kossa silver nitrate method.

Cholesterol.
Osmic acid reaction, Windaus digitonin reaction.

Collagen.
*Mallory aniline blue, *Masson trichrome, *Mallory-Heidenhain azan, *van Gieson's picric acid-acid fuchsin.

Copper.
Mallory-Parker hematoxylin stain.

Elastic Fibers.
*Gomori's aldehyde fuchsin, *Verhoeff elastic tissue stain, *Weigert's resorcin fuchsin.

Enzyme Stains.
Gomori's acid phosphatase, Gomori's alkaline phosphatase.

Fat and Fat-like Substances.
Sudan Black B (method of Chifelle and Putt), *Oil Red O in propylene glycol, Sudan IV, Osmic acid (osmium tetroxide).

Fibrin.
Weigert fibrin stain.

Glycogen.
*Bauer-Feulgen, *Best's carmine, periodic acid Schiff reaction.

Hemoglobin.
Dunn hemoglobin stain, Ralph hemoglobin stain.

Inclusion Bodies.
Giemsa stain, phloxine tartrazine stain, phloxine toluidine blue stain, Pinkerton stain, Schleifstein stain for Negri bodies.

Iron (Hemosiderin).
*Gomori iron reaction, Perl prussian blue, Turnbull blue reaction.

Malarial Parasites.
Giemsa stain, phloxine toluidine blue stain.

Melanin.
Bodian silver protein method, *Fontana stain, *Masson melanin stain, Fitzpatrick's tyrosinase reaction.

Mucin.
*Periodic acid Schiff reaction, *Mayer mucicarmine, Gomori's aldehyde fuchsin.

Muscle.
*Masson trichrome, *phosphotungstic acid hematoxylin, Bodian silver protein for striations.

Myelin.
Pal-Weigert method, Lillie's method.

Nerve Fibers and Endings.
*Bodian silver protein method, Rogers, Pappenheim, and Goetsch silver nitrate.

Nissl Substance.
Cresyl echt violet, toluidine blue stain.

Reticulum.
*Wilder ammoniacal silver nitrate, Gridley periodic acid silver nitrate, Foote reticulum.

BIOGRAPHICAL NOTES

Workers who, in the past, contributed significantly to the advancement of histology laboratory procedures include the following:

Achucarro, Nicolas. 1851–1918. Spanish histologist. A silver-tanning stain for impregnating connective tissues.

Alzheimer, Alois. 1864–1915. German neurologist. 1. A methylene blue and eosin polychrome stain for demonstration of Negri bodies. 2. Alzheimer's cells, baskets, disease, sclerosis, dementia.

Benda, Raymond. 1896– . French physician. 1. Devised many stains and staining method. 2. Test for aplastic anemia. 3. Pioneer in blood transfusion and the knowledge of blood groups, also contributed to the knowledge of pneumonia and pulmonary tuberculosis.

Bielschowsky, Max. 1869–1940. German neuropathologist. 1. An ammoniacal silver stain for demonstrating axons and neurofibrils. 2. Bielschowsky-Jansky disease.

Bouin, Paul. 1870– . French anatomist. Bouin's fixative, also called "Bouin's fluid."

Cajal, Santiago Ramon Y. 1852–1934. Noted Spanish histologist. 1. Cajal cell. 2. Cajal method of astrocyte staining, using a gold chloride-mercuric chloride compound. 3. Cajal's double method of demonstrating ganglion cells. 4. In 1906, co-winner, with Camillo Golgi, of Nobel prize in medicine.

Carnoy, Jean Baptise. 1836–1899. Carnoy's fixative, also called "Carnoy's fluid," and "Carnoy's solution."

Delafield, Francis. 1841–1915. New York pathologist. Delafield's hematoxylin (a nuclear stain).

Ehrlich, Paul. 1854–1915. German bacteriologist. 1. Acidhematoxylin. 2. Neutral stain for blood corpuscles. 3. Tri-acid stain (acid fuchsin, orange G, and methyl green) for demonstration of various formed elements in blood. 4. Ehrlich's reaction. 5. Side-chain theory. 6. "606" arsphenamine. 7. Together with Elie Metchnikoff won in 1908 Nobel prize in physiology and medicine.

Feulgen, Robert. 1884– . German physiologic chemist. Method for demonstrating chromatin and desoxyribonucleic acid (Feulgen's test).

Giemsa, Gustav. 1867–1948. Hamburg bacteriologist and chemist. The Giemsa stain.

Gieson, Ira van. 1865–1913. New York neuropathologist. van Gieson solution of trinitrophenol and acid fuchsin is used in staining of connective tissues.

Gomori, George. 1904– . Hungarian histochemist in Chicago. 1. Stain to demonstrate phosphatases, lipases, and other enzymes in tissue sections. 2. Methods for demonstration of connective tissue fibers. 3. Method for demonstration of secretion granules.

Goodpasture, Ernest William. 1896– . American pathologist. Peroxidase stain.

Gram, Hans Christian Joachim. 1853–1938. Danish physician. The Gram stain is most important bacteriological stain.

Heidenhain, Rudolph P. 1834–1897. German physiologist. 1. Heidenhain's iron hematoxylin stain. 2. Heidenhain's cell. 3. Heidenhain's rods. 4. Heidenhain's law, etc.

Hortega, Pio del Rio. 1882–1945. Spanish histologist. 1. Microglia cells. 2. Ammoniacal silver carbonate staining for microglia.

Jenner, Louis. 1866–1904. London physician. Stain for the demonstration of blood corpuscles.

Leishman, Sir William Boog. 1865-1926. English army surgeon. 1. Leishman's cells. 2. The Leishman stain (for blood and certain parasites) consists of a mixture of methylene blue and eosin.

Levaditi, Constantin. 1874–1928. Roumanian bacteriologist in Paris. Levaditi's method, using reduced silver, used for demonstration of *Treponema pallidum* in sections.

Mallory, Frank Burr. 1862–1941. Boston pathologist. 1. Mallory's bodies. 2. Mallory's stain (Mallory's acid fuchsin, orange G, and aniline blue) for demonstration of connective tissue and secretion granules. 3. Mallory's phosphotungstic acid hematoxylin. 4. Mallory's triple stain.

Marchi, Vittorio. 1851–1908. Italian physician. 1. Method for demonstration of degenerated nerve fibers. 2. Marchi's bundle. 3. Marchi's globules, etc.

Neelsen, Karl Adolph. 1854–1894. German bacteriologist. The Ziehl-Neelsen stain.

Nissl, Franz. 1860–1919. Heidelberg neurologist. 1. Nissl's stain for the study of nerve cell bodies. 2. Nissl's bodies. 3. Nissl's degeneration.

Pal, Jacob. 1863–1936. Vienna clinician. Modified Weigert's myelin sheath stain (a method for studying myelinated nerves in which the specimen is placed for several weeks in a solution containing potassium dichromate).

Papanicolaou, George N. 1883– . Greek anatomist and physician in the United States. Papanicolaou's stain is applied to the examination of exfoliated cells for early detection of cancer.

Pappenheim, Arthur. 1870–1917. German physician. Pappenheim's stain for differentiating basophilic granules and nuclear fragments in red cells.

Romanowsky, Dimitri Leonidov. Russian physician. The original eosin-methylene blue stain for blood smears and malarial parasites.

Unna, Paul Gerson. 1850–1929. Hamburg Dermatologist. 1. Unna's alkaline methylene blue for plasma cells. 2. Unna-Pappenheim stain (plasma cells and nucleoprotein). 3. Unna's dermatosis. 4. Unna's boot, etc.

Weigert, Karl. 1843–1904. German pathologist. 1. Weigert's law. 2. Weigert's fibrin stain. 3. Weigert's iron-hematoxylin stain. 4. Weigert's myelin sheath method. 5. Weigert's neuroglia fiber stain. 6. Weigert's resorcin-fuchsin stain.

Weil, Arthur. 1887– . American neuropathologist. Method of staining myelin sheaths.

Wright, James Homer. 1869–1928. American pathologist. 1. Wright's stain. 2. Wright's myelin stain. 3. First to observe origin of platelets.

Zenker, Konrad.   –1894. German histologist. Zenker's fixative, also called "Zenker's fluid" and "Zenker's solution."

Ziehl, Franz. 1857–1926. German bacteriologist. The Ziehl-Neelsen stain.

SELECTED HISTOPATHOLOGY LAB REFERENCES

1. Lillie, R.D., *Conn's Biological Stains*. The Williams and Wilkins Company, Baltimore, Maryland, 1969.

2. Lillie, R.D., *Histopathologic Technic and Practical Histochemistry*, 3rd Edition. The Blakiston Company, Inc., New York, N.Y., 1965.

3. *Manual of Histologic and Special Staining Techniques*, 2nd Edition. The Blakiston Division, McGraw-Hill Book Company, Inc., New York, N.Y., 1960.

4. Davidsohn and Henry, *Todd-Sanford's Clinical Diagnosis by Laboratory Methods*, 14th Edition. W.B. Saunders Company, Philadelphia, Penna., 1969.

5. Frankel et al., *Gradwohl's Clinical Laboratory Methods and Diagnosis*, 7th Edition. C.V. Mosby Company, St. Louis, Missouri, 1970.

6. Lynch et al., *Medical Laboratory Technology and Clinical Pathology*, 2nd Edition. Saunders Company, Philadelphia, Penna., 1969.

7. Levinson, S.A., and MacFate, R.P., *Clinical Laboratory Diagnosis*, 7th Edition. Lea and Febiger, Philadelphia, Penna., 1969.

8. AFIP: *Manual of Histologic and Special Staining Techniques*, 2nd Edition. Blakiston-McGraw, 1960.

9. Mallory, F.B., *Pathologic Technique*. 1938.

10. McManus, J.F.A., Mowry, R.W., *Staining Methods, Histologic and Histochemical.* 1960.

11. Preece, Ann, *A Manual for Histologic Technicians*, 2nd Edition. Little, Brown, 1965.

12. Richards, O.W., *The Effective Use and Proper Care of the Microscope.* American Optical Company.

13. Richards, O.W., *The Effective Use and Proper Care of the Microtome.* American Optical Company.

Section V

MISCELLANEOUS EXAMINATION QUESTIONS

MISCELLANEOUS EXAM QUESTIONS

1. Mention at least five important metabolic diseases. Also indicate particular metabolic function affected in each case. See p. 532

2. Bile plays a role in the digestion of:
   a. Fat   a
   b. Starch
   c. Sugar
   d. Protein

3. The micromol is:
   a. 1/1,000 of a mol
   b. 1/10,000 of a mol
   c. 1/100,000 of a mol
   d. 1/1,000,000 of a mol   d

4. The electron is the unit of:
   a. Positive electricity
   b. Negative electricity   b

5. The current produced by one volt acting through the resistance of one ohm is the:
   a. Ampere   a
   b. Watt
   c. Millivolt
   d. Milliwatt

6. A millivolt is:
   a. 0.1 volt
   b. 0.01 volt
   c. 0.001 volt   c
   d. 0.0001 volt

7. The electrical pressure which will cause a current of one ampere to flow through the resistance of one ohm is the:
   a. Watt
   b. Volt   b
   c. Kilowatt
   d. Millivolt

8. There are more elements than compounds in nature. T F   F

9. The normal body temperature is:
   a. 25.0 degrees centigrade
   b. 37.0 degrees centigrade   b
   c. 98.6 degrees Fahrenheit   c
   d. 96.8 degrees Fahrenheit

10. The total number of elements found in nature is:
    a. 78
    b. 82
    c. 103
    d. 185

    c

11. The gaseous elements found in nature total the following number:
    a. 2
    b. 10
    c. 80
    d. 92

    b

12. The concept of Periodic Law of classification of elements was developed by:
    a. Mendelejeff
    b. Bohr
    c. Rutherford
    c. Pasteur
    e. Einstein

    a

13. Those elements beyond uranium which have been produced artifically on earth by nuclear reactions and synthesis are known as the _____ elements.

    transuranian

14. The most abundant constituent of protoplasm is:
    a. Water
    b. Mineral
    c. Fat
    d. Carbohydrate
    e. Protein

    e

15. A term opposed to "dehydration" is:
    a. Anemia
    b. Infarction
    c. Jaundice
    d. Edema

    d

16. The visible characteristics of an individual or those which are common to a group of apparently identical individuals is the:
    a. Pedigree
    b. Genotype
    c. Phenotype
    d. Haploid

    c

17. The abnormal or excessive accumulation of fluid in tissues, cells, or body cavities is called:
    a. Edema
    b. Hyperemia
    c. Ischemia
    d. None of these

    a

18. What do the following abbreviations stand for:
    a. BP
    b. PKU

    blood pressure
    phenylketonuria

c. ACD   See p. 532
d. PVP   ”
e. T₃   ”

19. 0.01 micron is the same as:
     a.   1 millimicron
     b.   10 millimicrons   b
     c.   100 millimicrons
     d. 1,000 millimicrons

20. Amino acids serve as the building blocks for:
     a. Proteins   a
     b. Fats
     c. Carbohydrates
     d. Vitamins

21. Organisms living on dissolved substances in environment are
     said to be:
     a. Holozoic
     b. Saprophytic   b
     c. Parasitic
     d. Commensal

22. Most living organisms are:
     a. Autotrophic
     b. Heterotrophic   b

23. How would a specimen of sputum be prepared for tumor
     cell examination?   See p. 532

24. The reflex center for heart rate and breathing is:
     a. Cerebrum
     b. Cerebellum
     c. Pons
     d. Medulla oblongata   d
     e. Spinal cord

25. What are "secondary invaders"?   See p. 532

26. Pappataci fever is also called:
     a. Ornithosis
     b. Sandfly fever   b
     c. Yellow fever
     d. Oroya fever

27. "Lung stones" may be present in the sputum in:
     a. Bronchiectasis
     b. Chronic tuberculosis   b
     c. Chronic bronchitis
     d. Late pneumonia

28. Mosquitoes may spread the following except:
     a. Malaria
     b. Leptospirosis (Weil's disease)   b
     c. Dengue
     d. Yellow fever
     e. Viral encephalitis

29. The bite of *Aedes aegypti* mosquito may transmit:
    a. Dengue   a
    b. Coccidiodomycosis
    c. Malaria
    d. Botulism

30. Dengue is a:
    a. Bacterial disease
    b. Protozoan disease
    c. Viral disease   c
    d. Rickettsial disease

31. An atom which has more than its normal number of elec-
    trons is a _____ ion.   negative

32. What is the meaning of the term "biota"?   See p. 532

33. What is the meaning of the term "pathognomonic"?   See p. 532

34. Little is known concerning the microorganisms inhabiting
    the large intestine of man in health.   T   F   T

35. Forms of an element which have the same nuclear charge
    but which possess a different number of neutrons in their
    nuclei are called _____.   isotopes

36. The number of protons in the nucleus of an element is
    called the _____ _____ of that element.   atomic
                                                           number

37. The fundamental units of the *metric system* are the:
    a. _____   kilogram
    b. _____   meter
    c. _____   second

38. In the commercial affairs of the United States and England
    the British system (rather than the metric system) of mea-
    surement is used. The fundamental units of this system are
    the:
    a. _____   pound
    b. _____   foot
    c. _____   second

39. The centimeter (cm.) is the:
    a. 1/10 of a meter
    b. 1/100 of a meter   b
    c. 1/1,000 of a meter
    d. 1,100,000 of a meter

40. The time interval equal to the 1/86,400 of the mean solar
    day is the:
    a. Second   a
    b. Minute
    c. Quarter hour
    d. Hour

41. "Nosology" is:
    a. A relatively unknown word meaning "nasal pathology"

    b. The science of the classification of diseases   b

    c. The study of virus diseases of the upper respiratory
       tract

    d. The study of the geographical distribution of diseases

42. A "carcinoma" is a:
    a. Malignant epithelial cell tumor   a
    b. Benign glandular tumor
    c. Benign epithelial cell tumor
    d. Benign fatty tumor

43. Name six most important vitamins. See p. 533

44. Match the following:

1. Leydig's cells	a. Kidney	1—d
2. Küpffer's cells	b. Liver	2—b
3. Islets of Langerhans	c. Pancreas	3—c
4. Peyer's patches	d. Testis	4—g
5. Crypts of Lieberkuhn	e. Ovary	5—g
6. Bowman's capsule	f. Stomach	6—a
7. Corpus luteum	g. Intestine	7—e
8. Argentaffine cells	h. Adrenal medulla	8—g & f
9. Theca-lutein cells		9—e
10. Parietal (delomorphous) cells		10—f
11. Pheochrome cells		11—h

45. What is the most important coronary lesion? What does it
consist of? See p. 533

46. Benign tumor cells spread to adjacent or distant organs.
    T   F   F

47. Malignant cells have larger nuclei with nucleoli which stain
darker.   T   F   T

48. Reaction of tissues against an irritant is called:
    a. Inflammation   a
    b. Necrosis
    c. Trauma
    d. Abscess
    e. Infection

49. Acute catarrhal inflammations are characterized by:
    a. Presence of blood
    b. Presence of mucus   b
    c. Presence of pseudomembrane
    d. Localized collection of pus

50. Endocrine glands are ductless.   T   F   T

51. Briefly explain the meaning of the following terms:
    a. Infarction; necrosis; kink; lipoma; sarcoma;
       carcinoma See p. 533-34
    b. Metastasis; stroma; hypertension; ectopic;
       eschemia   "
    c. Anoxemia; cachexia; exophthalmia; goiter; pox,

anasarca	See p. 533–34
d. Hysterectomy; pyelography; embolus; thrombus; shock; xerophthalmia	
52. Just how toxic is Wright's stain?	See p. 534
53. What medium is used to fasten paraffin sections to slides?	egg albumin

54. Papanicolaou smears are fixed in:
    a. 5% mercury bichloride
    b. Bouin's fluid
    c. Ether-alcohol
    d. Zenker's fluid
    e. 40% formaldehyde
	c

55. Why is seminal fluid often yellow or deeply pigmented?	See p. 534

56. The normal sperm count is:
    a. 40–80 million/ml.
    b. 60–150 million/ml.
    c. 20–40 million/ml.
    d. 60–80 million/ml.
	b

57. Synovial membranes are lined by _____ cells.	columnar
58. Which factors influence the formation of pleural fluid?	See p; 534
59. Which factors may cause abnormal accumulation of pleural fluid?	See p. 534
60. How should pleural fluid be collected?	See p. 534

ANSWERS TO MISCELLANEOUS EXAM QUESTIONS CONTINUED

1. **Diabetes mellitus:** Carbohydrate metabolism.
   Gout: Purine metabolism.
   Goucher's disease: Lipid metabolism.
   Niemann-Pick's disease: Lipid metabolism.
   Porphyria: Porphyrin metabolism.
   Hemochromatosis: Inborn error of cellular iron metabolism.

18. **ACD:** Acid-Citrate-Dextrose (anticoag. solution used by blood banks).
    PVP: Polyvinylpirrolidone.
    T_3: Triidothyronine (a circulating, iodine-containing aminoacid elaborated by the thyroid gland).

23. By staining a cell block with hematoxylin and eosin or by staining a smear by the Papanicolaou technique. It is best however to examine material directly obtained from the bronchi during bronchoscopy.

25. Microorganisms that can grow and manifest themselves in an organism because of a prior diseased condition.

32. All the living things (i.e., the combined flora and fauna) of a region.

33. *Diagnostic.* Said of a sign or symptom on which a diagnosis can be made.

43. Vitamin A, Vitamin B complex, Vitamin C, Vitamin D, Vitamin E, Vitamin K.

45. a. Atherosclerosis
   b. Proliferation of the intima (or inner lining of arteries) and deposit of lipids (chiefly cholesterol and cholesterol esters). Calcification of these lesions may also occur.

51. **Infarction:** The formation of an infarct or site of coagulation necrosis in a tissue resulting from circulatory obstruction to the area.

Necrosis: Death of a cell or a group of cells surrounded by living cells.

Kink: Bend or twist (ileal kink, Lane's kink).

Lipoma: A tumor, usually nonmalignant, made up of fat cells.

Sarcoma: A malignant tumor. Nonepithelial. Histologically it resembles embryonic connective tissue.

Carcinoma: A malignant epithelial cell tumor.

Metastasis: The transfer of disease (through blood vessels or through lymph channels) from a primary focus to a distant part not directly connected with the primary focus.

Stroma: The framework or matrix of an organ or cell.

Hypertension: Hypertension usually means high blood pressure. The hypertension characterized by excessively high systolic and diastolic arterial blood pressure in patients affected with disorders (such as kidney disease) which usually raise the blood pressure is called "essential hypertension."

Ectopic: Located in an abnormal place or position.

Ischemia: Local anemia. A local and temporary diminution in the blood supply such as occurs in frostbite, angina pectoris, Raynaud's disease, etc.

Anoxemia: A reduction, below physiologic levels, in the oxygen content of the blood. It occurs in cardiac failure, high altitudes, strangling, etc.

Cachexia: Marked weakness and emaciation due to a serious disease such as tuberculosis, cancer, or syphilis.

Exopthalmos: Abnormal protrusion of the eyeball.

Goiter: The enlargement of the thyroid gland.

Pox: 1. A vesicular or pustular disease. 2. Syphilis.

Anasarca: The accumulation of serum in cellular tissues of the body. Generalized edema.

Hysterectomy: Total or partial removal of the uterus. The operation may be carried out through the abdominal wall or through the vagina.

Pyelography: X-ray studies of the renal pelvis and ureter after these structures are filled with a contrast solution.

Embolus: A plug (it may consist of a blood clot, air, cancer tissue, fat, a mass of bacteria, or even a bullet) which is carried by the circulation until it lodges in an artery or vein causing its obstruction (embolism).

Thrombus: A blood clot formed within the heart or a blood vessel and which remains at the site of its formation. Thrombi usually develop as a result of changes in the walls of the vessels, alterations of the blood, or the slowing down of the circulation.

Shock: The acute peripheral circulatory failure, resulting from the derangement of circulatory control, or the loss of circulatory fluid, and brought about by injury. Most common causes are trauma (including surgical trauma), severe burns, loss of blood, intoxications, etc.).

Xerophthalmia: A type of conjunctivitis resulting in an abnormally dry and lusterless condition of the eyeball and caused by a vitamin A deficiency.

52.   Methyl alcohol in it, especially when hot, can produce poisoning, even by contact with skin. Methyl alcohol ingestion may cause ocular disturbance and blindness.

55.   The coloration is due to the flavin content which is also responsible for the fluorescence in ultra-violet light.

58.   Pleural fluid formation is influenced by capillary wall permeability, plasma colloid osmotic pressure, and hydrostatic pressure.

59.   a. Increased capillary permeability due to inflammation.
       b. Decreased plasma colloid osmotic pressure due to hypoproteinemia.
       c. Increased hydrostatic pressure due to increased systemic and/or pulmonary venous pressure, as in congestive heart failure.
       d. Decreased lymphatic drainage due to tumor, inflammation or fibrosis involving mediastinal lymph nodes.

60.   It should be collected in three sterile anticoagulated tubes (EDTA or heparin). The first tube is used for culture and Gram's stain; the remaining tubes are used for cell count, Wright's stain, total protein, gluce, cytology, and other specialized tests if needed.

Section VI

BOARD EXAMINATION TIPS

BOARD EXAMINATION TIPS

Many well-prepared students fail to score high on board examinations because they lack "test-wisdom." The present section was prepared to serve as a guide to taking medical technology tests confidently and with skill. It is not intended as a short-cut to serious study and hard work. It is assumed that the student has already acquired satisfactory experience, thoroughly reviewed the fundamentals with the aid of the first medical technology board examination review volume, and also worked his way through the standard practice material contained in the preceding sections of the present book.

IMPORTANT DOS AND DON'TS

Always use the oil immersion lens for the identification of difficult cells and observation of protozoan parasites.

★ ★ ★ ★ ★

Always balance a centrifuge before using it.

★ ★ ★ ★ ★

Always release the tourniquet before removing needle from vein.

★ ★ ★ ★ ★

Always use aseptic techniques and special care when handling contaminated or infectious materials. Danger of laboratory infection is highest in tularemia *(Pasteurella tularensis)* and "valley fever" *(Coccidioides immitis)*. Cultures of *Coccidioides* contain highly infectious arthrospores.

★ ★ ★ ★ ★

Always autoclave (30 minutes) before washing any glassware which has been in contact with infectious (or suspected of being infectious) materials.

★ ★ ★ ★ ★

Always avoid hemolysis when obtaining or handling blood.

★ ★ ★ ★ ★

Always read opaque (or dark colored) fluids in a graduate cylinder at the top of the meniscus (or point of contact with the glass).

★ ★ ★ ★ ★

Always read fluids (other than mercury) *at the bottom of the meniscus.*

★ ★ ★ ★ ★

Always read a transparent fluid in a graduate cylinder at the bottom of the meniscus.

★ ★ ★ ★ ★

Always allow the internal pressure to drop to zero before opening a pressure vessel.

★ ★ ★ ★ ★

Always report defective cords, hot plates, or other electrical equipment so that proper repairs or replacements can be made and short-circuits or fires prevented.

★ ★ ★ ★ ★

Always keep ether, acetone, and other flammable liquids in place especially provided for them, and then only in quantities necessary for current work.

★ ★ ★ ★ ★

In storage area, always keep separate those chemicals that react together.

★ ★ ★ ★ ★

Always work under an exhaust hood when handling volatile, toxic, or flammable materials.

★ ★ ★ ★ ★

Always label a container before filling it.

★ ★ ★ ★ ★

Always use a sponge when moistening labels for samples and specimens.

★ ★ ★ ★ ★

Always be familiar with the proper means of disposal of the various substances used. Some may be diluted and poured into the sink drain, others may require disposal in special containers.

★ ★ ★ ★ ★

Always empty and rinse glassware before setting aside for cleaning.

★ ★ ★ ★ ★

Always examine glass containers and apparatus carefully for cracks or chips before using.

★ ★ ★ ★ ★

Always familiarize yourself with the safe practices (especially fire safety) to be followed in your institution or laboratory.

★ ★ ★ ★ ★

Always report defective or broken equipment to your supervisor immediately.

★ ★ ★ ★ ★

Always observe warning signs—they are for your protection.

★ ★ ★ ★ ★

Always report all injuries. Secure immediate first aid if necessary.

★ ★ ★ ★ ★

Always make sure that foreign matter on the floor is removed at once.

★ ★ ★ ★ ★

Always report immediately to your supervisor any unsafe conditions.

★ ★ ★ ★ ★

Always keep centrifuge lids on while this equipment is in use.

★ ★ ★ ★ ★

Always wipe any broken glass off counters and table tops to prevent slivers of glass cutting hands, arms, and elbows.

★ ★ ★ ★ ★

Always turn on fans in fume hood and tissue department before toxic solutions are used.

★ ★ ★ ★ ★

Needle valve on all gas cylinders must always be closed before opening master valve.

★ ★ ★ ★ ★

Always chain gas cylinders, or place them on dollies.

★ ★ ★ ★ ★

Always dispose of flammable liquids in UL approved safety cans and give to maintenance department.

★ ★ ★ ★ ★

Always return needle or blade to its proper place after use so others will not get cut.

★ ★ ★ ★ ★

Laboratory rooms should always be locked when not in use.

★ ★ ★ ★ ★

Always cotton plug bacteriology pipettes for safety or use bacteriological rubber bulbs for transferring pathogenic bacterial cultures.

★ ★ ★ ★ ★

Always maintain strict control over bacterial cultures.

★ ★ ★ ★ ★

Always decontaminate immediately with an appropriate disinfectant solution any working area that becomes contaminated.

★ ★ ★ ★ ★

After working with infectious materials always immerse hands in a disinfectant solution and then wash carefully with soap and water.

★ ★ ★ ★ ★

Always wear asbestos gloves when removing materials from sterilizing ovens and/or autoclaves.

* * * * *

Always keep reagent bottles tightly capped.

* * * * *

Always label reagent bottles with great care.

* * * * *

Always indicate very clearly the formula or name and the strength of the solution on any wash bottles containing liquid other than water.

* * * * *

Always pour acid into water and not water into acid.

* * * * *

Always store mercury in stoppered containers (mercury vapors are toxic!).

* * * * *

Always keep flames away from alcohol, ether, acetone, or combinations of these solvents.

* * * * *

Always keep the mouth of a test tube pointing away from you (and away from anyone else) while heating.

* * * * *

Always start heating a test tube gradually (to avoid breakage).

* * * * *

Always cover with a watch glass the beaker, flask, or NPN tube during digestion procedure (it will prevent loss by splattering of ebullition).

* * * * *

Always keep flames away from the valves of any tanks containing gas under pressure.

* * * * *

Always run (and make sure everyone else runs with you) if a tank containing gas under pressure ever "breaks loose."

* * * * *

Always use special lens cleaning paper in wiping off optical surfaces.

* * * * *

Always handle hot vessels with proper holders (a towel* used as a strap is unsafe).

★ ★ ★ ★ ★

Always keep face away while boiling sulfuric acid solutions.

★ ★ ★ ★ ★

Always support the bottom of a large flask while holding it.

★ ★ ★ ★ ★

Always use as small a filter paper as is practicable (the precipitate should never fill the paper and, when fitted into the funnel, the top of the paper should be about 5 mm. below the edges of the funnel).

★ ★ ★ ★ ★

Always agitate constantly while dissolving sodium or potassium hydroxide (it prevents sticking or forming of a hard mass).

★ ★ ★ ★ ★

Always have adequate ventilation whenever volatilization takes place (whether by opening a bottle, by heating a substance, or in purposeful production).

★ ★ ★ ★ ★

Always use a hot water (or steam) bath to heat an inflammable organic compound such as ether, ethyl alcohol, methyl alcohol, or benzene.

★ ★ ★ ★ ★

Always avoid prolonged breathing of volatile solvents. Most organic vapors are poisonous.

★ ★ ★ ★ ★

Always keep methyl alcohol (used in Wright's stain; for bilirubin determinations, etc.) off your hands. It is very readily absorbed by the system through the skin. Wash it off with water immediately if you happen to spill any on yourself. Even the fumes of methyl alcohol can produce blindness and even death.

★ ★ ★ ★ ★

Always place flasks and beakers over a gauze mat when heating over a Bunsen flame.

★ ★ ★ ★ ★

Always mix a urine specimen carefully before taking out a portion for centrifugation.

★ ★ ★ ★ ★

Always shake a urine sediment thoroughly before taking out a drop for microscopic examination.

---

*A large hot beaker may be safely held in both hands by using a carefully folded towel, or by wearing a pair of asbestos or soft leather gloves.

Always measure and record the total volume of a 24-hour specimen before taking out aliquot(s) for analysis.

* * * * *

Always cover urine (or other body fluids) with a coverglass before examining under microscope.

* * * * *

Always clean (special lens cleaning paper) the immersion oil objective after using it.

* * * * *

Always focus up to find the field (it will prevent damage to preparation and lenses).

* * * * *

Always wipe out the outside of a colorimeter (or a spectrophotometer) cell before taking a reading.

* * * * *

Always wear a surgical cap, gown, and mask, when entering a newborn nursery for specimen collection (or other purposes).

* * * * *

Always refrain from smoking or eating, especially in the chemistry, parasitology, and bacteriology laboratory.

* * * * *

Always write down the time a test was started, even when an automatic timer is used.

* * * * *

Always keep accurate written records of all work done in the laboratory. Never trust to memory.

* * * * *

Always maintain a professional attitude while on duty.

* * * * *

Always be friendly to patients, physicians, nurses, and coworkers.

* * * * *

Always sign or initial your own reports.

* * * * *

Always label specimens (and, in particular, blood specimens for typing and matching) with utmost care.

* * * * *

Always use only the prescribed amount of anticoagulant whenever whole blood or plasma are to be obtained for a test.

★ ★ ★ ★ ★

Always mix a tube of whole blood (blood with anticoagulant) thoroughly by inverting the vial (never by shaking it) with the stopper in place for at least ten times before obtaining an aliquot for analysis.

★ ★ ★ ★ ★

Always maintain tube in perfect upright position throughout sedimentation rate test period. Inclination of tube (this is also true of elevation in temperature) will increase the sedimentation rate.

★ ★ ★ ★ ★

Always start a CBC by putting smear to stain. It saves considerable time.

★ ★ ★ ★ ★

Always replate chamber, in counting white cells, whenever greatest variation between squares exceeds 12 cells.*

★ ★ ★ ★ ★

Always use a blood dilution greater than the routine 1:20 for the total white count when the white cells are increased above 50,000/cu. mm. such as may occur in leukemia. Use a red cell pipette to dilute (1:1,000 or greater) the blood for the white count in such cases.*

★ ★ ★ ★ ★

Always recount, using a lesser dilution, if the total white cell count is lower than 3,000 cells/cu. mm.*

★ ★ ★ ★ ★

Always clean the underside of a blood smear after staining.

★ ★ ★ ★ ★

Always count area of slide that has a single layer of cells when doing a differential leukocyte count where no abnormality (high power) in distribution is present.

★ ★ ★ ★ ★

Always note erythrocyte morphology, stain, parasites, and platelets (number and size) at the time of doing the differential leukocyte count.

★ ★ ★ ★ ★

A clean venipuncture is always important for coagulation tests.

★ ★ ★ ★ ★

Always invert Petri dishes for storage or incubating.

★ ★ ★ ★ ★

*With the widespread use of the Coulter 5 these may become obsolete

Always culture any clinical specimens promptly after collection.

* * * * *

Always obtain material for cultures prior to antibiotic treatment.

* * * * *

Always count cells in fluid within 30 minutes after spinal tap (lumbar puncture).

* * * * *

Always use care in handling spinal fluid. It often contains infectious materials.

* * * * *

Always store whole blood between 1-6°C. Always store cryoprecipitate at −20°C.

* * * * *

Always keep complement in the refrigerator, particularly if it has been diluted. Also, always use cold saline for the purpose of diluting complement.

* * * * *

Always choose donors that have the same ABO type and Rh type as that of the patient.

* * * * *

Always prepare and store platelet concentrates at room temperature.

* * * * *

Try to transfuse and use platelets as fresh as possible, but always within 48-72 hours of drawing.

* * * * *

Never pour blood clots down the sink. Only liquids, other than mercury, may be poured down the sink. When a strong reagent is poured, run a great deal of water down with it.

* * * * *

Never, unless it has been thoroughly sterilized under pressure, use the same lancet to obtain blood from a separate patient. Disposable lancets are best.

* * * * *

Never force or squeeze blood through a needle.

* * * * *

Never use Kleenex to clean or wipe off optical surfaces.

* * * * *

Never trust to memory. Always keep accurate written records of all the work done in the laboratory.

* * * * *

Never open oxygen valve until gas flame in flame photometer has been lighted.

* * * * *

Never turn off flame in flame photometer until oxygen pressure has returned to zero.

* * * * *

Never release an abnormal report until you are absolutely certain of your findings.

* * * * *

Never stuff rubber aprons into lockers. Hang them to air and dry.

* * * * *

Never weigh substances directly on scale pan.

* * * * *

Never throw waste sodium or phosphorus down the sink or drain (explosion may occur).

* * * * *

Never discard original specimen until test(s) has (have) been completed.

* * * * *

Never heat, over flame or over electric heater, an inflammable fluid in an open vessel (such as a beaker or a test tube).

* * * * *

Never breathe vapors from organic solvents (besides being unhealthy, secondary anemias have occurred).

* * * * *

Never handle with the fingers caustic soda, sodium, phosphorus or cyanides.

* * * * *

Never handle mercury with bare hands. It is toxic.

* * * * *

Never hold mercury for long in an open container (mercury vapors are toxic).

* * * * *

Never throw mercury down the sink (it will soon produce leaks in the lead pipes and traps in the plumbing).

* * * * *

Never return to the bottle a C.P. chemical removed in excess of amount needed.

* * * * *

Never ask patient "Are you Mr. John Doe?" but rather "What is your name?" (it will prevent errors in identification).

* * * * *

Never throw a solid reactive substance, such as an oxidizing agent, into a very hot solution (it will boil over).

* * * * *

Never lift or pull a tank containing a gas under pressure about by the valves.

* * * * *

Never heat a beaker or a flask directly with a flame (it may crack or its contents may be ejected).

* * * * *

Never (unless you are familiar with the actual reaction) pour a number of reactants together at once or start heating immediately.

* * * * *

Never twirl a flask containing a solution which has been quietly and strongly heated (this may cause the superheated solution to geyser out of the flask unexpectedly).

* * * * *

Never mix two or more substances unless you know in advance what will happen.

* * * * *

Never push a tube or rod into a stopper or cork or attempt to slip rubber tubing over a glass tube unless the ends are firepolished.

* * * * *

Never run water or any liquid into a porcelain vessel which is hot and dry (it will break).

* * * * *

Never, when firepolishing glass tubes, heat long enough to decrease the size of the opening.

* * * * *

Never release blood from the blood bank unless a complete crossmatch shows there is no incompatibility.

* * * * *

Never administer Rh_0 (D) positive blood to Rh-negative patients, unless in a life-saving emergency.

* * * * *

Never give high titer type O blood to patients of group A or B except in extreme emergency and then only with the physician's approval.

Never skip the fine print or the footnotes when following a laboratory procedure.

★   ★   ★   ★   ★

Never stand under a vessel while holding it up to the light.

★   ★   ★   ★   ★

Never heat soft glass too suddenly (it may crack).

★   ★   ★   ★   ★

Never heat over a flame a large* & dry (or containing dry material) evaporating dish (it may crack).

★   ★   ★   ★   ★

Never handle C.P. chemicals with your fingers (or pour them out into your hands).

★   ★   ★   ★   ★

Never heat a thermometer directly over a flame.

★   ★   ★   ★   ★

Never, even for a moment, remove for use in your own work thermometers in use anywhere (oven, constant temperature baths, etc.).

★   ★   ★   ★   ★

Never throw matches on the floor of the laboratory or in the sink.

★   ★   ★   ★   ★

Never investigate containers or dark rooms with lighted matches even though the contents are known not to be inflammable.

★   ★   ★   ★   ★

Never throw salts, dusts or powders indiscriminately into flames of any kind (violent explosions have occurred).

★   ★   ★   ★   ★

Never keep bromine, bromine water, sodium or potassium hydroxide solid or in solution and other alkaline materials in glass-stoppered bottles (otherwise the action of these materials on the glass will cause the stoppers to become permanently stuck).

★   ★   ★   ★   ★

Never pour a *hot* liquid into a bottle.

★   ★   ★   ★   ★

Never use for tests any glassware which is not in good condition.

★   ★   ★   ★   ★

---

*150 mm. or more in diameter.

Never put empty reagent bottles back in their shelves until they have been properly refilled.

★ ★ ★ ★ ★

Never milk the part (finger, ear lobe, heel, etc.) excessively when obtaining a capillary blood sample.

★ ★ ★ ★ ★

Never give out confidential medical data, except to authorized persons.

★ ★ ★ ★ ★

Never sign or initial someone else's lab reports.

★ ★ ★ ★ ★

Never use alcohol on the microscope.

★ ★ ★ ★ ★

Never, unless a physician specifically so requests it, pass a stomach tube until a Diagnex blue test has shown presumptive evidence of achlorhydria or hypochlorhydria.

★ ★ ★ ★ ★

Never pipette a cyanide solution (use a burette for the purpose). Sodium and potassium cyanides are very lethal. Just a small particle on the tip of the tongue would be almost instantly fatal.

★ ★ ★ ★ ★

Never leave cyanides exposed to air.

★ ★ ★ ★ ★

Never breath nitric acid vapors, sulfuric acid fumes, or the halogens and halogen acids. They are very corrosive to the respiratory and digestive tracts.

★ ★ ★ ★ ★

Never allow aniline dyes and coal tar derivatives to come in contact with the skin. Carcinogenic irritation may occur. Dyes should not be allowed to stain the fingers.

★ ★ ★ ★ ★

Never touch scale weights with your hands (use special pair of forceps provided).

★ ★ ★ ★ ★

Never slow by hand the revolving head of a centrifuge.

★ ★ ★ ★ ★

Never use tap water to prepare chemical solutions. It contains impurities.

★ ★ ★ ★ ★

Never rack a microscope tube downward to bring the object into focus.

★ ★ ★ ★ ★

Never allow saliva to contaminate an amylase determination. Saliva contains amylase (here called "ptyalin") and will increase test values. Avoid talking to prevent droplet contamination. Do not use blow-out pipettes.

★ ★ ★ ★ ★

Never freeze whole blood (it will result in rupture of red cells). Plasma or serum may be frozen, especially when enzyme activity is to be preserved.

★ ★ ★ ★ ★

Never use the last main division of a "serological" pipette when doing semi-quantitative work.

★ ★ ★ ★ ★

Always check a unit of blood to be given with the patient's identity bracelet. Make sure that entire name and hospital number agree.

BASIC FACTS TO IMPROVE YOUR MEDICAL TECHNOLOGY GRADES

Biochemistry Basic Facts

1 ml. = 1 cc. for all practical purposes.

1 Kg. = 2.2 lb.
1 lb. = 0.4536 Kg.

1 cm. = 0.39 in.
1 in. = 2.54 cm.

Normal body temperature is 37°C. (98.6°F.). Pathogenic bacteria grow best, or exclusively, at this temperature.
Normal room temperature is 25°C. (77°F.).

Serum separates from clotted blood. Serum may be used in any chemical test (except fibrinogen) calling for "plasma." Plasma may usually be used in a chemical test calling for "serum." Plasma is required for direct (chemical) determination of *fibrinogen*.

Fibrinogen (this protein is present in plasma but not in serum) is usually determined by calculation (total protein in plasma minus total protein in serum = plasma fibrinogen).

Capillary blood (usually obtained by finger prick* or ear lobe puncture) is essentially arterial blood.

Blood for chemical tests is frequently obtained in the fasting state. Annino and Relman (1959) however, demonstrated that the normal breakfast has no effect on the following determinations:
  Blood proteins and cholesterol
  BUN, creatinine, and uric acid
  The electrolytes (sodium and potassium, calcium, CO_2 and chloride)

---

*In babies and infants the heel or toe may be used.

The two determinations which were affected by food intake were sugar and, to an extent, phosphorus. Determinations also affected by food intake appear to be total lipids, triglycerides, and lipoprotein phenotyping.

The NPN of the blood is made up of urea (about 50% of total NPN is urea nitrogen), creatinine, uric acid, aminoacids, ammonia, and "residual" nitrogen. BUN X 2.14 = Urea.

A buffer is a solution of one or more reagents which acts to maintain a specific pH (or pH range) or otherwise resist a change in pH. There exist many buffer systems (barbiturates, phosphates, borates, etc.) that may be used for the purpose and the directions for a specific method will almost always have a formula for the preparation of the buffer needed. It is a very good rule that the final pH of a buffer should be determined with an electronic pH meter (only rarely it is satisfactory to use pH papers).

Protein-free filtrates are used in tests where presence of protein may interfere with determination of another constituent. Best filtrates for general purposes are tungstic acid (Folin-Wu) and trichloroacetic acid (Greenwald). Barium hydroxide and zinc sulfate precipitating agents produce filtrates in which glucose is the only measurable reducing substance.

Creatinine forms an intense red color when it is treated with strongly alkaline picrate. This reaction is called the "Jaffé reaction."

Both *cholesterol and cholesterol esters* react with acetic anhydride and concentrated sulfuric acid to produce (Liebermann-Bruchard reaction) a blue-green color which follows Beer's law. Present rapid methods of cholesterol determination require no saponification of esters since color develops at the same rate for both free and ester cholesterol when glacial acetic acid (rather than chloroform) is the solvent.

One-third of the *chloride in the blood* exists in the red cells; two-thirds in the plasma. Variations in red cell content when using whole blood contribute clinically significant errors in chloride determinations. When blood is exposed to air it loses CO_2 and chloride then diffuses from red cells to plasma (this is so-called "shift of chloride"). Precise plasma chloride determinations therefore require anaerobic (collect under oil or in Vacutainer) collection of blood. In the method of Schales and Schales (this is the most popular among present methods of chloride determination) serum, plasma, or protein-free filtrate is titrated with standard mercuric nitrate in acid solution using diphenylcarbanzone as indicator. After all the chloride present has combined with the mercury the excess mercury will combine with the indicator to produce a pale violet color (end-point).

Biuret methods for total protein in serum are widely employed because of speed, simplicity, and accuracy. Protein molecules contain "biuret" in specific proportions. When treated with alkaline potassium copper tartrate solution, two biruet molecules are joined to form a violet colored complex which agrees with Beer's law. The same reaction can be applied to the determination of albumin after removing the globulin from the serum (sodium sulfite 28% or sodium sulfate 26.8% removes clinically significant quantity of globulins).

Most methods for determining *uric acid* are based on the reducing power of uric acid. Normal range: 2–4 mg.% on serum or plasma (thioneine in red cells will contribute to the reduction). Same color reaction as for blood "sugar" is used here with reagent modifications to facilitate maximum reduction by uric acid.

As inorganic phosphate, *serum phosphorus* is almost exclusively determined by the method of Fiske and Subbarow:

> Trichloroacetic acid filtrate + acid molybdate =
> phosphomolybdic acid + reduction with aminonaphtholsulfonic
> acid to Mo blue

There are just a few *enzymes* important from the clinical laboratory standpoint. They are usually hydrolytic, transferring, or (dehydrogenase) oxidative. Enzymatic reactions as a rule take place best at a certain temperature and pH (hence a buffer system is included in the reagents for these tests). Enzymatic reactions are usually very specific (urease for instance acts upon urea but not upon methylurea) but may, on the other hand, have a wide range of activity (for instance, lipase will act upon *any* organic ester). General principle of enzyme determinations:

1. Enzyme incubated with proper substrate
2. Amount of change produced in substrate by enzyme (an index of enzymatic "activity") is determined by either:
   a. Quantitative determination of end product (glucose in the case of amylase) or unreacted substrate
   b. Determining the rate of utilization of a necessary coenzyme (SGOT)
   c. Measuring change in substrate concentrations (cholinesterase)

Enzymatic activity is expressed in *units*.

The BSP test is the most important test of (excretory) liver function employing an artifical agent. As a rule the test is carried out with the patient fasting (a light, low-fat breakfast may be given). A clotted blood specimen (to be used as a serum reference blank) is obtained prior to injection of the dye. Most frequently 5 ml./Kg. are injected I.V. and a serum sample (clotted blood) is removed 45 minutes later and examined* (with a photoelectric colorimeter or by comparison with artificial standards) for dye retention. With normal liver function there will remain less than 5% dye 45 minutes after its injection. No food should be eaten during the test period.

Commonly Employed Functional Tests.

Liver Function: BSP, Proteins, Cholesterol and Cholesterol Esters.
Alkaline Phosphatase, Cephalin-Cholesterol Flocculation ("ceph-floc"), Thymol (or Zinc) Turbidity, etc.
Kidney Function: Phenol Red (PSP), Mosenthal, Urea Clearance, BUN.
Pancreatic Function: Amylase and Lipase.
Thyroid Function: Iodine (PBI), T_3, T_4 and Cholesterol.
Parathyroid Function: Calcium and Phosphorus.
Adrenal Function: 17-Ketosteroids, 17-Hydroxycorticosteroids, Thorn Test.

Acid-Base Balance.†

Through a series of complex buffering systems, the hydrogen-ion concentration of serum is maintained within a narrow range, the most important buffering system being the bicarbonate-carbonic acid system.

---

*Addition of alkali (NaOH) is required to bring about purple dye color.
†The present introductory discussion to the subject has been taken from a MEDI-CHEM, Inc. test set instruction leaf.

CO_2, the most important acid end-product of metabolism, is eliminated in two ways:
1. The major portion is eliminated by the lungs, via a combination of CO_2 and certain bases (alkali reserve), and is transported as bicarbonate from the tissues to the lungs by venous blood.
2. Ammonium ions, NH_4^+, neutralize a smaller portion giving rise to urea.

In acidosis, the reserve of alkali is reduced, causing a concomitant reduction in the capacity of the blood plasma to bind CO_2. Measurement, quantitatively, of the CO_2 combining power of the blood plasma offers a most reliable method of detecting acidosis and of ascertaining its degree.

In the following MEDI-CHEM procedure, plasma bicarbonate is decomposed with acid, CO_2 liberated and the excess hydrogen-ion is titrated, as depicted below:

$$NaHCO_2 + HCl \text{ yields } NaCl + H_2O$$
$$HCl + NaOH \text{ yields } NaCl + H_2O$$

Blood gas determinations by pO_2 and pCO_2 electrodes (IL) are replacing manual measurements for determining acid-base balance.

In the *colloidal gold test using spinal fluid* four types of curves may be obtained as follows:
a. 1100000000 (normal curve; almost no change)
b. 5554321000 (paretic curve; change in zone I)
c. 0123320000 (tabetic or luetic curve; change in zone II)
d. 0001234553 (meningitic curve; change in zone III)

It should be borne in mind however that the shape of the curve is of no diagnostic significance. The last tube showing a definite color change provides a rough measure of the globulin content of the fluid.

The hottest part of a *Bunsen's flame* is its outer or oxidizing zone.

pH's below 7 are acid and pH's above 7 alkaline.

Urine is characterized by the presence of *urea*.

The specific gravity of urine normally depends largely on the concentration of *urea*.

One hydrogen atom can never combine with more than one atom of any other element. *The valence of an element* is therefore determined by the number of hydrogen atoms with which it combines or which it displaces. The valency of oxygen is two. Certain elements combine in varying proportions and thus have more than one valence.

The molecular weight of an element or compound is the number which represents the ratio between the weight of its molecule and the weight of an atom of oxygen (this has been arbitrarily set at 16.000).

The molecular weight of a substance expressed in grams represents the MOL. The "millimol" is the one-thousandth part of the mol.

A normal solution is one which contains one equivalent weight of an acid or base per liter. The "absolute reference" is replaceable hydrogen. One equivalent weight of an acid is the amount of such acid which contains one gram of replaceable hydrogen. One equivalent weight of a base is the amount of such base which will exactly neutralize one equivalent weight of an acid. For example:

Normal solution of HCl = 36.5 Gm. (molecular weight) HCl/L.
Normal solution of H_2SO_4 = 49 Gm. (½ of molecular weight) H_2SO_4/L.
Normal solution of HaOH = 40 Gm. (molecular weight) NaOH/L.

N/10 solutions are made by accurately diluting normal solutions.

Mohr or measuring pipettes consist of a straight piece of tubing (slightly constricted at the tip) sometimes graduated to tip* and sometimes graduated between two points.

Ostwald pipettes possess a round bulb and a short delivery tube. They usually come calibrated TD (to deliver) with drainage (unmarked mouthpiece). They are employed for measuring single volumes of viscous fluids such as blood.

Volumetric or transfer pipettes have an elongated bulb situated towards the center of the pipette and possess a rather long delivery tube. They are also used for measuring volumes.

Micropipettes (used in micromethods employing capillary blood) are calibrated in lambdas (λ). One lambda = 0.000001 liter (λ1.).

Litmus is red in an acid solution, blue in an alkaline one, and violet (or lilac) at neutral pH.

Methyl red (preferred for strongly acid and basic solutions) is red in an acid (4.2–6.3) pH and yellow in an alkaline one.

Phenolphthalein (preferred for weakly acid and basic solutions) is colorless in an acid pH and red in an alkaline (8.3–10.0) one.

Phenol red (phenolsulphonphthalein, PSP), is yellow in an acid pH and red in an alkaline (6.8–8.4) one. Phenol red is used in a standard test of kidney function and in Kligler's triple sugar-iron agar (TSI). The latter is of value in the bacteriological examination of feces.

Töpfer's reagent (dimethylaminoazobenzene) is red (beginning at pH 2.9) to yellow (until it reaches pH 4.0).

Gastric acidity is calculated according to the following formula:

$$\frac{\text{No. of ml. of N/10 NaOH used in titration}}{\text{No. of ml. of gastric contents titrated}} \times 100 = \text{Degrees of acidity}$$

(Since each degree of acidity equals 0.00365 Gm. of hydrochloric acid, degrees of acidity multiplied by 0.00365 equal Gm.% of hydrochloric acid).

In *photoelectric colorimeter calculations*, the following formula is applied:

$$\frac{\text{Optical Density of Unknown}}{\text{Optical Density of Standard}} \times \text{Conc. of Std.} = \text{Conc. of Unknown}$$

Optical Density (OD) = 2 −log.% Transmittance

1. To convert mg.% to mEq./L., the following formula is used:

$$\frac{\text{mg./100 ml.} \times 10}{\text{Equivalent Weight}} = \text{mEq./L.}$$

---

*"Serological" pipettes, usually calibrated TD (to deliver) with blowing (etched ring around mouthpiece).

2. To convert mEq./L. to mg.% the following formula is used:

$$mEq./L. \times \frac{Equivalent\ Weight}{10} = mg.\%$$

3. Equivalent Weight (Eq.) $= \dfrac{Atomic\ (or\ Molecular)\ Weight)}{Valence}$

4. One Gm. nitrogen represents 6.25 Gm. protein. Therefore:

Total Protein Nitrogen $\times$ 0.00625 = Gm.% Total Protein
Albumin Nitrogen $\times$ 0.00625 = Gm.% Albumin

5. Gm.% Total Protein $\times$ 2.43 = mEq./L. of Total Protein

6. Volume of Acid $\times$ Normality of Acid = Volume of Base $\times$ Normality of Base

7. $\dfrac{Normality\ Desired}{Normality\ on\ Hand} \times$ Volume Desired = Volume Needed

One degree centigrade = 1.8 degree Fahrenheit
One degree Fahrenheit = 0.54 degree centigrade

Clinical Parasitology Basic Facts

In fresh stools, *Entamoeba histolytica* trophozoites are actively motile (they show "directional" motility) and usually contain red blood cells. *Entamoeba coli* trophozoites on the other hand are sluggish, do not contain ingested red blood cells. *Entamoeba histolytica* secretes a proteolytic enzyme which digests the tissues of the host.

Mature *Entamoeba histolytica* cysts contain four nuclei with tiny central karyosomes. Mature cysts of *Entamoeba coli* contain eight nuclei with large central karyosomes.

Chilomastix mesnili has a lemon-shaped cyst. The trophozoite is pear-shaped with a twisted posterior portion.

Giardia lamblia resembles an old man with glasses.

Trichomonas vaginalis and *Dientamoeba fragilis* produce no cysts.

Smears or flotation of stool specimens are used to diagnose *Entamoeba, Chilomastix* and *Giardia.* Blood smears are used for *Plasmodium* and *Trypanosoma.*

Schüffner's dots are eosinophilic. They occur in *Plasmodium vivax* infected red cells.

Leishmania donovani causes kala-azar (visceral leishmaniasis), *Leishmania tropica* causes oriental sore (cutaneous leishmaniasis), and *Leishmania brasiliensis* causes espundia (muco-cutaneous leishmaniasis).

Nematodes are the roundworms. Cestodes are flat, ribbon-like. Flukes are flat, pear-shaped. Blood-flukes are not flat and have separate sexes.

Most common nematodes are diagnosed by flotation of stool specimens. Exceptions are *Enterobius vermicularis* (anal swab) and filarids (blood smear).

The egg of *Ascaris lumbricoides* is usually ovoid, unsegmented, and provided with a mammillated outer covering.

The egg of the pinworm *(Enterobius vermicularis)* is flattened on one side and contains a fully developed embryo. These eggs are only rarely seen in the stools (Scotch tape anal swabs are required).

The egg of the whipworm *(Trichuris trichuria)* is football-shaped and provided with a plug at each pole.

Eggs of hookworms, when found in the feces, are usually in the 4- or the 8-cell stage.

The laboratory diagnosis of *Strongyloides stercoralis* is usually made by finding the larva (rhabditiform) in the stool. Eggs are seldom found in feces.

Immunodiagnosis is valuable when parasite stages cannot be demonstrated.

The microfilariae of *Acanthocheilonema, Mansonella, Onchocerca* and *Dracunculus* are unsheathed. Those of *Loa loa* and *Wuchereria* are sheathed and, in the former, the nuclei extend to the tip of the tail.

The eggs of the liver flukes are operculated; the eggs of the blood flukes are not. The egg of *Clonorchis sinensis* (the Chinese liver fluke) is shaped like an old-fashioned electric bulb.

The egg of *Schistosoma haematobium* has a terminal spine; the egg of *Schistosoma mansoni* has a fairly large lateral spine; the egg of *Schistosoma japonicum* has only a minute lateral spine.

Eggs of *Schistosoma mansoni* and *S. japonicum* occur in stools, those of *S. haematobium* in urine.

The fish-tapeworm *(Diphyllobothrium latum)* is the longest human tapeworm. The uterus is rosette-shaped and the head (this has two longitudinal grooves and no hooks) almond-shaped.

The segments of the cat and dog tapeworm *(Dipylidium caninum,* accidentally in man) are pumpkin-seed shaped, have one genital pore on each margin.

Taenia saginata has 4 suckers but no hooklets. The gravid proglottid has 15-30 dichotomous uterine branches and lateral pores which alternate irregularly.

Taenia solium has 4 suckers and 2 rows of hooklets. The gravid proglottid has 5-10 dichotomous uterine branches and lateral pores which alternate regularly.

The egg of both *Taenia saginata* (beef tapeworm) and *Taenia solium* (pork tapeworm) is spheroid, with radially striated shell. It contains a larva with three pairs of hooklets.

The laboratory diagnosis of hydatid cyst *(Echinococcus granulosus)* should be made by serological tests. Puncturing the cyst to obtain fluid for examination is a dangerous procedure.

The egg of *Hymenolepis nana* (dwarf tapeworm) has two membranes and two hairlike processes. It contains a larva with three pairs of hooklets.

— —

Hematology Basic Facts

Review of Important Normal Values.
RBC: 5.5 million (male), 4.5 (female)
WBC: 5-10,000/cu. mm. (male or female)
Platelets: 150-350,000/cu. mm.
Reticulocytes: 0.5-1.5%
PCV: 45 ±5 males, 42 ±5 females
Hgb: 15 ±2 males, 14 ±2 females
MCV: 80-94 cubic microns
MCH: 27-32 micromcgm.
MCHC: 32-38%
ESR (Wintrobe): 0-15 mm./hr. (male
                0-20 mm./hr. (female)
Osmotic Fragility of red cells:
    Begins at 0.45-0.39% NaCl
    Complete at 0.33-0.30% NaCl
Differential Leukocyte Count:
    Myelocytes 0%
    Stab (Band) Neutrophils   0-4
    Segmented Neutrophils   54-62
    Lymphocytes   25-35
    Monocytes   4-8
    Eosinophils   1-3
    Basophils   0-1

The micron (μ or mu) is the unit of microscopic measurement. It is equal to 1/1,000 of a millimeter (approximately 1/25,000 of an inch).

The higher the magnification of a microscope objective the shortest its working distance.

Abnormal variation in size of red cells is called "anisocytosis" and abnormal variation in shape "poikilocytosis." Normal red cells are eosinophilic and stain pink. Polychromatophilic cells however stain bluish-grey. Polychromatophilia is also called "diffuse basophilia."*

In sickle cell trait or in sickle cell anemia (a hereditary anemia of blacks) the red cells will take on the shape of a sickle when they are treated with sodium metabisulfate or some other oxygen-removing substance.

The Counting Chamber is 1/10 mm. deep. Counting chamber calculations are carried out according to the following general formula:

$$\text{Cells per cu. mm.} = \text{Count} \times 10 \text{ (depth factor)} \times \text{Area Factor} \times \text{Dilution Factor}$$

The ruled area of the counting chamber is 3 mm. long $\times$ 3 mm. wide $\times$ 0.1 mm. deep.

---

*The other type of erythrocyte basophilia (i.e., "punctate basophilia" or basophilic stippling) may most commonly be seen in lead poisoning.

The red cell pipette has a larger bulb than the white cell pipette and marks at 0.5, 0.1, and 101.0.

The white cell pipette has a smaller bulb than the red cell pipette and marks at 0.5, 0.1, and 11.0.

The most common principle in use in homoglobinometry involves conversion to cyanomethemoglobin and its determination.

Hemoglobin is estimated as *oxyhemoglobin* (pink) in the following colorimetric procedures: Tallqvist, Dare, Spencer Hb meter, Evelyn-Malloy, and Sheard-Sanford.
Hemoglobin is estimated as *acid hematin (brown)* in the following colorimetric procedures: Sahli, Haden-Hauser, Newcomer and Hellige, and Osgood-Haskins.

Anemias.
Anemia refers to a substantial reduction in the oxygen carrying capacity of blood, All three concentration measurements, the PCV, Hgb concentration and RBC count, will be low. The total body RBC mass determined by the ^{51}Cr technique will also be low.

MCV (mean corpuscular volume).

$$MCV = \frac{PCV}{RBC}$$

Normal range 80–94 μ^3

MCH (mean corpuscular hemoglobin or average amount of hemoglobin per cell):

$$\frac{\text{Grams hgb./liter of blood}}{\text{RBC (million/cu. mm.)}} = MCH$$

Normal range of MCH is 27–32 picograms/cell

MCHC (mean corpuscular hemoglobin concentration or average hemoglobin concentration per unit of packed cells):

$$\frac{\text{Gm. Hgb./100 ml. of blood}}{PCV} \times 100 = MCHC$$

Normal range of MCHC is 32–36% (never exceeds 36)

Anemias may be classified on the basis of the above indices. The three most common types of anemia are listed below:

Normocytic, normochromic anemia (normal MCH, MCV, MCHC)
Macrocytic, normochromic anemia (high MCV, normal MCH and MCHC)
Microcytic, hypochromic anemia (low MCV, MCHC, MCH)

Normal *mean corpuscular diameter (MCD)* is 6.7–8.0 microns.
Price-Jones: Projection of blood film on paper and measurement of red cells. RBC sizing can now be accomplished by cell sizing devices (Coulter).

RBC mass or volume is determined by tagging RBC with ^{51}Cr. Plasma volume is determined by the use of ^{131}I tagging of albumin.

Normal *prothrombin time* is 60–100%. Generally constant in adults. Test precautions:

1. Chemically clean glassware
2. Standard conditions of temperature, time, etc.
3. Accurate pipetting of reagents
4. Avoid trauma on venipuncture

Test principle:

1. $f.X \xrightarrow{\text{Tissue thromboplastin} + f.VII + Ca^{++}} f.Xa$

2; $Prothrombin (f.II) \xrightarrow{f.Xa + Ca^{++} + f.V} Thrombin (f.IIa)$

3. $Fibrinogen (f.I) \xrightarrow{f.IIa} Fibrin (f.Ia) (clot)$

   [Calcium and Thromboplastin are added artificially (e.g., Simplastin]

Test uses:

Anticoagulant (warfarin, dicoumarol) therapy. Liver disease.

The osmotic fragility test is used to determine maximum capacity of cells to absorb aqueous solutions. In hypotonic saline, red cells increase in volume until they actually burst. Spherical cells ("spherocytes"), already contain maximum volume for surface area of cell. Any further absorption will cause rupture. Cells absorb quantitatively in relation to hypotonicity of solutions. The test is an accurate means of determining how nearly spherical the red cells actually are. Identically treated normal control should be included with every test.

Heparin anticoagulation is monitored by the Thrombin Time, the Partial Thromboplastin Time, or the whole blood activated Partial Thromboplastin Time.

Platelets can be counted accurately and directly. Counting chambers using stains or preferably phase microscopy give good results. Automated methods (Coulter counter, Technicon) are also available.

Reticulocytes require special (supravital staining. Counts may be made by the wet method or by the dry (permanent) slide method. Neither procedure is notable as concerns accuracy.
Stains: Brilliant cresyl blue, new methylene blue.

Infectious Mononucleosis (I.M.) Cells.

The cell is an atypical or transformed lymphocyte. In this condition the total leukocyte is increased, decreased or normal. The blood slide may show 60% or more mononuclear (nongranulocyte) cells of which as many as 10–25 may be atypical large lymphocytes (Downey cells). The nucleus (oval or somewhat lobulated) presents a "moth-eaten" or "tunneled" appearance. The cytoplasm (somewhat more basophilic than the normal lymphs') is "foamy" or vacuolated. The diagnosis of IM is confirmed by getting a positive heterophile agglutination or mono-spot test.

Lupus Erythematosus (L.E.) Cells.

The L.E. cell factor is a component of serum gammaglobulin. This factor reacts with cell nuclei (depolymerizes deoxyribonucleic acid) and this amorphous nuclear material is then ingested ("phagocytized") by polymorphonuclear neutrophil leukocytes. L.E. cells are usually neutrophils containing one or more masses of purplish-staining chromatin. This mass or masses fill the cell and push the nucleus to the side.

Recently the diagnosis of SLE is being made by the use of tests to detect the antinuclear antibodies which are present in the disease. One method is the fluorescent antinuclear antibody (FANA) test.

In *acute leukemia* the white count may be low or very high. The peripheral blood smear shows a preponderance of "blast" (immature) cells. Leukemias are named after the predominant cell type which is present in the peripheral blood smear or bone marrow.

Bacteriology Basic Facts

A dye is an organic compound consisting of benzene rings with **chromophore** (this confers specific color to the compound) and **auxochrome** (this is responsible for the transferring of the color to the material upon which the dye acts) groups. The auxochrome group NH_2 or $N(CH_3)_2$ is present in basic dyes. The auxochrome group SO_3H or $COOH$ or OH is present in acid dyes. A **mordant** is a substance (iodine, tannic acid, ferrous sulfate, etc.) which will fix the stain such a manner that it will be retained by the material stained. The Gram stain is a differential stain; Loeffler's methylene blue and the aniline dyes are direct stains. India ink is a negative stain (it stains the background rather than the cells). Flagella, spores, capsules, and metachromatic granules usually require special (selective) stains.

Inflammation: The reaction of the tissues to the presence of an irritant (inflammations are not always bacterial in origin).
Infection: Invasion of the body by microorganisms (bacteria, fungi, protozoa, helminths, viruses, etc.) and the reaction of the tissues to their presence and to their toxins.
Infestation: The presence of animal parasites upon the body (presence of an animal parasite within the body also constitutes an infection).

The reason why *spinal fluid cell counts* should be performed within 30 minutes after specimen collection is that meningococci, if present, must be cultured while they are still viable (meningococci usually lyse rapidly outside the body). Meningococci or *H. influenzae* may be present whenever the fluid contains polymorphonuclear leukocytes ("pus cells").

Koch's Postulates.
In order to prove that a certain microorganism is the etiological agent of a particular disease, the following conditions should be met:
1. The organism must be present in every case of the disease
2. The organism must be isolated and grown in pure culture
3. When inoculated into a susceptible animal this culture should produce an identical disease
4. The organism can be recovered from the experimentally diseased animal

Any material to be cultured should be obtained *prior to antibiotic treatment.*

A colony is a group (usually visible to the naked eye) of bacterial cells resulting from reproduction of a single cell. R (rough) colonies are composed of nonencapsulated bacteria. Encapsulated species show capsules in S (smooth) colonies. D (dwarf) colonies are quite small.

The purpose of using pressure in the autoclave is to increase the temperature of the steam beyond 100 degrees centigrade. The higher the pressure the greater the temperature that will be achieved. A high (120°C. or more) temperature kills bacteria more rapidly and also destroys spores and viruses.

Media can be enriched by adding whole blood, blood serum, carbohydrates, animal proteins, glycerin, etc. to the medium. Glycerin is used in Bordet-Gengou medium (glycerin-potato-blood agar) for *Bordetella pertussis* (whooping cough bacillus) and in Petragnani's medium for *Mycobacterium tuberculosis.*

In making blood agar plates the use of human blood should be avoided.* Large numbers of organisms are able to produce lysis on this type of blood. Using it for plates will, therefore, call for checking by smears any colonies showing hemolysis.

Cocci may occur singly (micrococci), in pairs (diplococci), fours (tetrads), short or long chains (streptococci), clusters (staphylococci), or in cubital packets resulting from cell division in three planes (Sarcinae).

Boils and furuncles are usually caused by *Staphylococcus aureus;* lobar pneumonia (about 85% of all cases) by *Streptococcus pneumoniae;* bacillary dysentery by *Shigella dysenteriae;* chancroid by *Hemophilus ducreyi;* conjunctivitis ("pink eye") by *Hemophilus aegypti;* syphilis by *Treponema pallidum;* yaws by *Treponema pertenue;* relapsing fever by *Borrelia recurrentis;* Vincent's angina (trench mouth) by *Borrelia vincenti* with a fusiform bacillus; tuberculosis by *Mycobacterium tuberculosis;* leprosy by *Mycobacterium leprae;* gonorrhea by *Neisseria gonorrhoeae;* epidemic meningitis by *Neisseria meningitidis;* botulism by *Clostridium botulinum;* tetanus (lock jaw) by *Clostridium tetani;* gas gangrene by *Clostridium perfringens;* anthrax by *Bacillus anthracis;* tularemia by *Yersinia tularensis;* plague by *Pasteurella pestis;* whooping cough by *Bordetella pertussis;* undulant fever by *Brucellae (abortus, melitensis,* or *suis):* typhoid fever by *Salmonella typhi;* scarlet fever by erythrogenic toxic producing strain of group A beta hemolytic streptococcus; diphtheria by toxigenic strain of *Corynebacterium diphtheriae;* Asiatic cholera by *Vibrio cholerae;* enteric fevers by *Salmonellae (paratyphi, schottmuelleri, enteritidis,* or *typhimurium);* thrush by *Candida albicans;* valley fever by *Coccidioides immitis;* actinomycosis by *Actinomyces bovis* or *Nocardia;* and dermatomycoses (tineas, athlete's foot, etc.) by *Microsporum, Trichophyton,* or *Epidermophyton.*

Smith and Brown's classification separates the streptococci in three groups according to their effect on horse blood agar plates:
1. *Alpha hemolytic streptococci* partially hemolyze red blood cells in the immediate vicinity of the colony and produce a greenish decoloration of the medium in this area.

---

*Sheep, horse, and rabbit blood are preferred in that order.

2. *Beta hemolytic streptococci* completely hemolyze red blood cells and show clear, colorless areas around the colonies.
3. *Gamma streptococci* produce no hemolysis of red blood cells.

In *Lancefield's classification,* the streptococci pathogenic to man are included in Group A. This group includes the streptococci responsible for scarlet fever, erysipelas, acute abscesses, tonsilitis, puerperal infection, osteomyelitis, etc.

Typical *pneumococci* are arranged in pairs (short chains may occur with the distal ends of each pair pointed or lancet-shaped. Each pair may be surrounded by a delicate capsule. Pneumococci are Gram-positive. The capsules can usually be seen by dimming the light sharply or by means of special stains.

Pneumococci are bile-soluble and other streptococci bile-insoluble.

The coliform group includes all aerobic and facultative anaerobic, Gram-negative, nonsporulating bacilli which ferment lactose with production of acid and gas in 24–48 hours. In water analysis, three different sets of tests are used to establish the presence of coliform organisms. *The presumptive test* is performed on all samples. *The confirmed test* is used if results of the presumptive test are positive. *The completed test* is used if the results of the confirmed tests are positive.

The typical IMViC (indol, Methyl Red, Voges-Proskauer, Citrate) reactions are:

Escherichia coli: + | − −
Enterobacter aerogenes: − − + +

On E.M.B. (eosin-methylene blue) agar, colonies of *Escherichia coli* are dark and with a greenish metallic sheen. On the same medium, colonies of *Enterobacter aerogenes* are large and with dark centers but do not possess this greenish metallic sheen.

Agar cultures of *Proteus* are characterized by moist, thin, and opaque growth spreading over the entire surface.

Exotoxins (true or soluble toxins) are produced by the staphylococci, the streptococci, *Corynebacterium diphtheriae, Shigella dysenteriae* and the well-known clostridia *(C. botulinum, C. tetani,* and *C. perfringens).*

The presence of Gram-negative, intracellular, coffee-bean shaped diplococci in smears made from urethral discharge constitutes a presumptive test for *Neisseria gonorrhoeae* (gonococcus).

The presence of Gram-negative, intracellular, coffee-bean shaped diplococci in smears made from the sediment of centrifuged spinal fluid constitutes a presumptive test for *Neisseria meningitidis* (meningococcus).

Corynebacterium diphtheriae (diphtheria bacillus) grows best on Loeffler's blood serum. To differentiate diphtheria from diphtheroids, Tinsdale's medium should be used. *Corynebacterium diphtheriae* reduces tellurite (diphtheroids do not) producing colonies which are distinctly black and demonstrate a brown halo of H_2S around the colony.

The finding of Gram-positive, typically barred, granular and pleomorphic bacilli in smears made from throat swabs of suspected diphtheria cases or the growth in cultures with special (Loeffler's) media constitutes only a presumptive laboratory test for the presence of the diphtheria bacillus *(Corynebacterium diphtheriae)*. For confirmation, fermentation reactions and virulence test (guinea pig inoculation or Frobisher in vitro test) are necessary.

The presence of acid-fast bacilli against a blue background in Ziehl-Neelsen stained smears from sputum or other materials constitutes a presumptive test for tubercle bacilli.

To check the growth of saprophytic acid-fast bacteria, malachite green is included in Petragnani's medium. In this medium the tubercle bacillus grows luxuriantly producing colonies which are raised, granular, cream-colored and tend to coalesce in 4–6 weeks.

Typical "Medusa-head" colonies on agar plates are produced by *Bacillus anthracis*.

Brucella abortus is microaerophilic. It requires 25% CO_2 on primary isolation and 10% CO_2 on subsequent transfers.

Hemophilus influenzae is a Gram-negative coccobacillus which requires two factors (both present in fresh whole blood) for its growth, namely "X" (heat-stable) and "V" (heat-labile) factors. The X factor may be replaced by hemoglobin or by hematin. The V factor (obtainable from yeast and other vegetable cells and from many bacteria*) may be replaced by coenzyme I or II.

Clostridium tetani is an obligate anaerobe and *Bacillus subtilis* an obligate aerobe.

The inclusion, elementary bodies *(Negri bodies)* found in rabies are diagnostic of this particular disease. These inclusion bodies occur in the ganglion cells of the midbrain, the pons, and the medulla.

Microscopically, *malignant cells* have larger nuclei and nucleoli which (hyperchromatism) stain darker.

The most common *superficial mycoses* are caused by three closely related genera of fungi imperfecti, namely, *Trichophyton, Microsporum,* and *Epidermophyton.* Many species of these dermatophytes produce conidia of two sizes, small unicellular microconidia and larger (frequently multicellular) macroconidia. Practically all will grow on Sabouraud's medium but may tend to become pleomorphic or sterile in culture.

Wet preparations from clinical materials for *Candida albicans* will, when positive, show budding yeast-like cells and, occasionally, pseudomycelium. Both yeast and pseudomycelium are Gram-positive. Nickerson's medium (Ortho) is supplied in small vials for presumptive identification of *C. albicans.* Positive *Candida* colonies exhibit a very dark brown to black appearance within two days.

Malaria, yellow fever, and dengue fever are transmitted by mosquitoes; African trypanosomiasis by tsetse flies; American trypanosomiasis (Chagas' disease) by a "kissing bug"; bubonic plague by fleas; typhus fever and infectious jaundice by lice; and Rocky Mountain spotted fever by a tick.

- -

*Certain species of staphylococci in particular.

Serology and Immunology Basic Facts

Antigens.
Antigens are usually protein in nature, however some polysaccharides possess antigenic properties. When injected into animals, antigens stimulate the formation of antibodies. Antigens are specific and react only with the antibody which they produce. Specificity is a function of the chemical structure of the antigen (see Volume I, page 675).

Anamnestic Response (Recall Phenomenon).
The rapid reappearance of an antibody in the blood following administration of an antigen to which the subject has previously developed a primary immune response.

Haptens.
Haptens or haptenes (partial antigens) are carbohydrate-like components which do not stimulate antibody formation, but nevertheless are capable of reacting with antibodies produced as the result of stimulation by the complete antigen.

Antibodies.
Antibodies are mostly gamma globulin and some beta globulins produced by the stimulation of antigens within an animal. Antibodies may be present in the serum which can be detected by their immobilization of the causative organism. This is the basis of *immobilization tests*. Used for *Treponema, Leptospira, Trypanosoma*. The following forms are recognized:

> Isoantibodies relate to antigens within the same species
> Immune antibodies
> Heterospecific antibodies, against cells of another individual in the species
> Homospecific or autoantibodies
> Heterophil antibodies relate to antigens of another species

(See Volume I, pages 672–73.)

Neutralization Tests.
Neutralization tests (most frequently applied to the diagnosis of viral infections) depend upon specific antibody neutralizing the antigen so that no infection will develop in a susceptible host (see Volume I, page 681).

Complement.
Complement is a system of plasma globulins, the main function of which appears to be that of completing the process initiated by the interaction of antibody and antigen. Present evidence indicates that there exist at least nine components in the system. (See Volume I, pages 676–77.)
Roles of Complement:

1. Lyses sensitized bacteria
2. Kills sensitized bacteria without lysis
3. Hemolyses sensitized erythrocytes
4. Combines with antigen-antibody systems
5. Usually slows aggregation of antigen-antibody complexes
6. Opsonizes sensitized bacteria
7. Activates thermostable opsonins

For certain serological tests, sera should be inactivated for 30 minutes in a 56°C. water bath. Native complement is destroyed or inhibited by this process.

Blood Groups.
Major blood groups (blood types) are named according to the antigens ("agglu-tinogens") in the red cells' lipid membranes. Approximately 400 different red cell antigens are now recognized, differentiating over 17 different groups. The clinically important groups include ABO, Rhesus, MNSs, Duffy, Kell, Kidd, Lutheran, and P Systems. Most blood group antigens are composed of a series of polysaccharides, arranged in the fluid lipid bilayer of the cell in such a way that they are in a state of agitation, the terminal "exposed" sugar determining the antigen specificity.

Rh Factor.
This is a synonym used to denote (colloquially) the various antigens found in the Rhesus blood group system. More commonly, it is used to represent the $Rh_0(D)$ antigen, the presence of which determines if an individual is Rh positive. Indivi-duals lacking this antigen are termed Rh negative. 85% of the population are either homozygous or heterozygous for the $Rh_0(D)$ antigen and are therefore Rh positive.

Crossmatching.
Major crossmatch: Patient's serum (PS) X Donor's cells (DC). The saline cross-match detects most IgM antibodies and the high protein and Coombs crossmatch most IgG antibodies. Coomb's crossmatches are carried out on the major side by washing donor's cells (after incubating with patient's serum) three times with saline. Clumping of these cells shortly after addition of Coomb's serum (anti-human globulin) indicates presence of IgG antibodies.

Coomb's Test.
This test detects human globulins, either present free in the serum (free antibody in the indirect test), or attached to the patient's red cell (bound antibody in the direct test). The serum used (anti-human globulin) is prepared by immunizing rabbits with human globulins, and subsequently adsorbing unwanted non-specific antibodies. Commercial Coombs serum is usually a mixture of antibodies against IgG immunoglobulins and C3 fraction of complement. The direct test is useful in the detection of antibodies already complexed to red cell antigens, and is posi-tive in a wide variety of clinical conditions, including hemolytic disease of the newborn, drug-induced hemolytic reactions, autoimmune disease, and following most blood transfusion reactions. The indirect Coombs test is usually positive in individuals sensitized to other blood group antigens as a result of transfusion or pregnancy, and indicates uncomplexed antibody free in the serum.

Infectious Mononucleosis.
In infectious mononucleosis a high (1:224 or higher) titer of heterophil antibodies (antibodies capable of agglutinating the red blood cells of the sheep) may be ob-served. This heterophile antibody is absorbed by beef erythrocyte, but not by guinea pig kidney, antigen (the heterophile antibody of serum sickness, on the other hand, is absorbed both by beef erythrocyte and by guinea pig kidney anti-gens). The disease is frequently accompanied by increased levels of anti-i and by increased levels of antibodies to the Epstein-Barr virus (E.B.V.).

Cold Agglutinins.
Serum from patients with primary atypical (viral) pneumonia usually agglutinates human red blood cells at refrigerator temperature (4°C.) but not at body temper-ature (37°C.). The reaction is reversible. During the course of the disease the

titer of cold agglutinins may rise from 1:14 to a:224 or higher. Rising titers are therefore diagnostically significant.

Q Fever.
This is an air-borne rickettsial disease caused by *Coxiella burneti.* Laboratory diagnosis (using both acute and convalescent sera) is usually made by complement fixation. A rise in titer has diagnostic significance.

Units of Toxin and Antitoxin.
MLD: Smallest amount of toxin which will kill a 250 Gm. guinea pig within four days when injected subcutaneously.
One unit of Antitoxin: Amount of antitoxin in 0.6 mg. standard dried anti-toxin maintained at National Institutes of Health (Bethesda, Maryland).
L_0 Dose: Greatest amount of toxin which, when mixed with 1U. of antitoxin and injected subcutaneously in a 250 Gm. guinea pig will give no reaction.
L^+ dose: Smallest amount of toxin which, when mixed with 1U. of antitoxin and injected subcutaneously in a 250 Gm. guinea pig, will produce death within 4 days.
L_f Dose: Amount of toxin that flocculates most rapidly with 1U. of antitoxin (constant toxin-varying antitoxin).

Danysz Phenomenon.
1. Toxin added to antitoxin in several fractions results in greater quantities of antitoxin required to reach an end-point.
2. The first toxin fraction apparently combines with large amounts of antitoxin (Danysz phenomenon also applies to other antigen-antibody reactions).

Tests of Antitoxic Immunity.
1. Schick Test: Diphtheria toxin, when injected, causes erythema in susceptible persons.
2. Dick Test: Scarlet fever toxin, when injected, causes erythema in susceptible persons.
3. Schultz-Charlton Reaction: Scarlet fever antitoxin causes blanched area in true disease and differentiates it from other rash-producing diseases.

OBSOLETE TOPICS

The Use of Sodium or Potassium Oxalate as Anticoagulant for Chemistry or Hematology. The Use of Lithium Oxalate as the Anticoagulant of Choice in Uric Acid Determinations. The Use of Potassium and Ammonium Oxalate Mixture of Cell Volume Determinations.
Sodium and potassium oxalates cause cell shrinkage and cannot be used in cell volume determinations. They also form interfering white precipitate with uric acid (so lithium oxalate is used for this determination). The ammonium and potassium oxalate mixture causes no cell shrinkage but, because of its ammonium content, cannot be used in nitrogen determinations requiring Nesslerization.
EDTA (ethylene diamine tetraacetate) or a stable solution of heparin is now employed as general purpose anticoagulant. Practically only one special anticoagulant is still required and this is the 3.8% solution of sodium citrate which is used for the determination of prothrombin time (½ ml. anticoagulant for every 4.5 ml. blood).

The Benedict's Qualitative Test for Urine Sugar.
This determination was time-consuming (required boiling) and false positives could be obtained with reducing sugars other than glucose. Papers impregnated with the enzyme glucose-oxidase (specific for glucose) are now used for routine testing. Semiquantitative readings of positive specimens may then be obtained with a reagent such as Clinitest.

The Preparation of Certain Reagents (such as Ehrlich's Diazo Reagent for Bilirubin in Serum Determinations) in the Routine Laboratory.
Tablets (such as the "Diazo Reagent Tablets," Camco) which require only the addition of water may now more conveniently be used for the purpose. It is important to remember that Ehrlich's diazo reagent reacts with the bilirubin of the serum and that it consists of a mixture of sulfanilic acid and sodium nitrite in dilute hydrochloric acid. The solution must be fresh to be of any value.

The Use of Phenistix for Routine PKU (Phenylketonuria) Testing of Infants.
This determination was only of relative value since by the time phenylketonuria was detected by this method an infant's brain might have already undergone some damage. The *Guthrie test* (for phenylalanine in serum) permits early detection and therefore makes it possible to institute treatment before actual damage occurs. The test uses capillary blood. It is based upon the principle that the inhibition of growth of *Bacillus subtilis* ATCC 6051 by beta-2-thienylalanine in a minimal culture medium is specifically prevented by proline, phenylalanine, phenylpyruvic acid, and phenyllactic acid. This finding has permitted the development of a convenient agar diffusion microbial assay, employing small filter paper discs impreganted with blood serum upon the agar surface.

Visual Colorimetry Using Instruments of the Duboscq Type.
Practically all clinical laboratories are equipped with a photoelectric colorimeter (uses color filters), with a spectrophotometer (uses prism or diffraction grating) or use automated equipment. Problems involving visual colorimeter calculations are unlikely to come up in future board examinations. The formula that applies is as follows:

$$\frac{\text{Reading of Standard}}{\text{Reading of Unknown}} \times \text{Concentration of Standard} = \text{Concentration of Unknown}$$

The Use of Folin-Wu Protein-Free Filtrates in Blood Sugar Determinations by the Copper Tartrate-Phosphomolybdic Acid Reagent Method.
Folin-Wu protein-free filtrates include saccharoids and other nonsugar reducing substances. At the present time, "true sugar" methods (these employ a Somogyi-Nelson protein-free filtrate) are very much the standard procedure. Somogyi-Nelson protein-free filtrates (these contain no reducing substances other than sugar) are prepared as follows: Water (8.5 ml.) + blood (0.5 ml.) + 7% copper sulfate (0.5 ml.) + 10% sodium tungstate (0.5 ml.). Centrifuge or filter to obtain blood protein-free filtrate used in the test. Normal values compare as follows:

	Folin-Wu	True Sugar
Blood	80–120 mg./100 ml.	70–92 mg./100 ml.
CSF	60–90 mg./100 ml.	50–80 mg./100 ml.

Newer tests are eliminating the need for PFF.

The Preparation in the Laboratory of the Glucose Solution for the Glucose Tolerance Test (Jannet-Isaacson Single Oral Dose Method).
Most laboratories today are using the commercially prepared products, such as Glucola or other brands.

The Van den Bergh Procedure for Serum Bilirubin.
It was formerly believed that if the color reaction took place immediately the bilirubin came from bile and that the jaundice was due to obstructive causes. If, on the other hand, the reaction was delayed, the bilirubin was the result of cell hemolysis (i.e., the jaundice was hemolytic). This theory is no longer accepted. Nowadays, bilirubin in the serum is usually determined by the method of Malloy and Evelyn. The indirect reaction (this measures the total bilirubin present in the specimen) requires the addition of methyl alcohol and approximately 20–30 minutes time for color development after addition of Ehrlich's diazo reagent (which reacts with the bilirubin of the serum to give a pink to purple colored compound or "azobilirubin"). In the direct reaction no methyl alcohol is used. Only the esterified bilirubin (bilirubin glucuronide) gives this direct reaction. When this direct-reacting bilirubin exceeds a concentration of 0.4 mg./100 ml. in the serum, bilirubin usually also appears in the urine.

BMR (Basal Metabolic Rate) as a Routine Test of Thyroid Function.
Because it is easily affected by a number of (extra-thyroidal) factors, the BMR has been replaced by more reliable tests of thyroid function such as the PBI, T_3, T_4, and the radioactive iodine uptake.

EKG (Electrocardiogram) as a Clinical Laboratory Procedure.
Electrocardiography today is a hospital and physician's office procedure but *not* a clinical laboratory procedure. As far as we know, no state certificate is required anywhere for the performance of EKGs.

The Determination of the NPN (Total Nonprotein Nitrogen) as a Routine Test of Urinary Retention (Kidney Function).
The BUN (blood urea nitrogen) test is easier to perform and therefore more accurate. Familiarity with the NPN test however, is still advisable, although this test is rarely requested at the present time.

Determination of Cholesterol Methods Requiring Saponification.
Until recently, cholesterol was extracted from the serum or plasma by means of an alcohol-ether mixture which was then filtered and evaporated to dryness over a hot plate. Subsequently the dry residue, containing the cholesterol, was dissolved in chloroform and the solution used for the Liebermann-Burchard reaction (cholesterol reacts with acetic anhydride and concentrated sulfuric acid to give a blue-green product which can be measured colorimetrically). The test was time-consuming and errors (due to excessive charring with resulting breakdown of cholesterol, etc.) were not infrequent. Newer methods require only the addition of reagents to serum and the measurement of the reasonably stable resulting color. Results thus obtained closely agree with those obtained by careful performance of the classic Bloor-Sperry method. For greater accuracy it is recommended that a cholesterol standard (in acetic acid solution of known cholesterol content) be included with every test.

The Passing of a Stomach Tube as the Initial Gastric Analysis Procedure in Determining Achlorhydria or Hypochlorhydria.

With normal kidney function the Diagnex Blue test (Squibb) should always be used first. This is a simple colorimetric test ("tubeless" gastric) using urine collected two hours after oral test-meal.

The Use of Histamine in Gastric Analysis for the Diagnosis of True Achlorhydria.
Histalog, now the stimulant of choice, is relatively free from the undesirable side effects sometimes obtained with histamine.

The Use of Rabbits, Rats, Mice, or Frogs for Pregnancy Testing.
Hemagglutination-inhibition tests (such as the UCG) for the in vitro detection of chorionic gonadotropin (sometimes as early as four days after missed menstrual period) are now the method of choice. These tests are easy to carry out and readings can be taken after two hours. These tests are just as accurate, or even more so, than the well-known biological tests (ovarial hyperemia), using experimental animals.

The Sharpening of Hypodermic Needles.
The advent of economical, disposable needles has made work easier and at the same time put a stop to the spread of infectious hepatitis through the use of contaminated specimen collection equipment. The same goes for the advent of disposable lancets for skin puncture which are now standard everywhere.

The Howell and the Morawitz Theories of Blood Coagulation.

The Tallqvist Scale for Hemoglobin Determination.
Color-matching of whole blood with lithographed standards. Errors, as high as 50%, did occur.

Haden-Hauser Erythrocytometer.
Employs light diffraction principle.

The Reporting of Hemoglobin in Percentage of Normal.
Also the Reporting of the Color Index.
Because of the different standards used in various methods of determination, the recommended procedure of reporting should be absolute figures or grams to the first decimal place only.

Wintrobe Sedimentation Rate Correction.
The problem of correction in Wintrobe's method of sedimentation rate determination has been disclaimed by Wintrobe. It still remains an unsolved problem.

Mechanical Fragility.
This is a test to determine the physical "toughness" of the erythrocytes. The cells are shaken under standard conditions and the resulting hemolysis noted. These tests are not standardized.

Thorn (Eosinophil Depression) Test.
The determination of circulating eosinophils before and four hours after the I.M. administration of ACTH is an index of adrenal cortical activity. Normally a fall of at least 50% in eosinophils is noted. Allergic eosinophilia may mask a fall in eosinophils.

Pneumococcus Typing by the Neufeld-Quellung (Capsular Swelling) Reaction.
The advent of modern antibiotics and of antibiotic sensitivity testing has rendered this procedure unnecessary except in epidemiological studies.

Animal Inoculation as the Final Proof of the Non-Pathogenic Status of an Acid-Fast Bacillus which Failed to Produce Tubercular Lesions in a Guinea Pig. Pathogenic AFB have often failed to produce TB lesions in guinea pigs. Other more reliable procedures (neutral red test, catalase test, serpentine cord formation, etc.) are now being used for the purpose. See Volume I, pp. 451-76. Guinea pig inoculation however, is still a valuable procedure in certain cases (for instance clinical materials where the number of AFB present may be exceedinly small or in untreated cases) and cannot be *totally* discarded at the present time.

CONCERNING THE ACTUAL EXAMINATION . . .

(This section contains the replies to examination-time questions most frequently asked by students.)

Q.   **Will the Test have a Time Limit?**
A.   Yes. Practically every board examination has a time-limit, usually 2, 3, or 4 hours. It is therefore important to keep a steady pace and, at the same time, be accurate. Budget your time. Conserve your energy. When every question is worth the same number of points (and this is usually the case) the easiest questions should be answered first. Once you are through answering all of the easiest questions in the test, go back and answer the more difficult, or time-consuming, ones. Try to answer all the set questions—it's easier to get some marks for each attempt than to get extra marks by spending more time on a few only.

Q.   **What Supplies Should I Bring With Me to the Test?**
A.   Bring a watch, pen, pencil (IBM marking pencil) and, in case you are not permitted to mark the test sheet or booklet, some scratch paper as well. The use of a small electronic calculator, if permissible, will save considerable time and energy in the case of questions containing problems and requiring somewhat lengthy calculations. Do not dress formally but do wear comfortable clothes. And do not overlook bringing a package of pocket tissues or a handkerchief. It is never advisable to bring textbooks to the examination. Last minute reviews are seldom advantageous and, as a rule, create or increase nervous tension.

Q.   **Will the Examination be Written, Oral, or Both?**
A.   Board examinations usually consist of a written test only. More advanced tests (such as the California bioanalyst examination) may be oral and practical in addition to written. For specific information write to the particular state or licensing board where you will be taking your own test.

Q.   **Will the Examination Consist of Multiple Choice Questions?**
A.   The large majority of board examinations consist mainly or exclusively of multiple choice questions. Always, when you are confronted with a multiple choice question, read through *all* the choices before you answer, and make sure you understand the instructions. Usually only one choice is the correct one but (occasionally) more than one choice may apply (in this case mark these all) or (rarely) none of the choices is correct (in this case

leave all choices unmarked unless other directions are given). Even though the multiple choice type of questions is by far the most frequently encountered, you should know the subject well enough to be able to answer the same question under any of a number of common forms. Here, for instance, are examples of the four most commonly encountered styles in objective examination items:

1. Multiple Choice:
   Mature cysts of *Entamoeba histolytica* as a rule contain:
   a. One nucleus
   b. Two nuclei
   c. Four nuclei
   d. Eight nuclei
2. True False (or Yes-No or Right-Wrong):
   A mature cyst of *Entamoeba histolytica* usually contains three nuclei.
   T   F
3. Sentence Completion:
   Mature cysts of *Entamoeba histolytica* usually contain _____ nuclei.
4. Matching:
   1. *Entamoeba coli* mature cysts
   2. *Entamoeba histolytica* mature cysts

   a. Usually contain 4 nuclei
   b. Usually contain 8 nuclei
   c. Usually contain glycogen
   d. Usually contain splinter-shaped chromatoid bodies

Read the question carefully and completely! Always think before you write and be sure you understand the directions before you start. Beware of questions (or choices) containing the words "always," "never," or "sometimes." These are usually not the correct answer. In a question such as: "*Entamoeba histolytica* is always pathogenic," the answer would be "wrong."

Q. Will There be Microscopic Preparations for me to Identify?
A. This is not likely to happen unless you are taking an advanced examinations. In examinations of this type the following items are most frequently encountered:

Bacteriology:

1. AFB (TB or leprosy). Red bacilli over blue background (Ziehl-Neelsen carbol-Fuchsin staining).
2. Neisseriae (MG or GC). Gram-negative, coffee bean-shaped diplococci.
3. Pneumococci (lancet-shaped Gram-positive, encapsulated ciplococci or streptococci (Gram-positive short or long chains or pairs).
4. Staphylococci (Gram-positive cocci in irregular clusters).
5. Diphtheria. With characteristic barred appearance after staining. Gram-positive, pleomorphic, cuniforms, palisades.
6. Vincent's organisms: *Borrelia vincenti* (a spirochete) and fusiform bacilli (Gram-positive, spindle-shaped).
7. Gram-negative bacilli are indistinguishable.
8. *Clostridium tetani* (Gram-positive "drum-stick" rods).
9. *Candida albicans* (pseudomycelium; yeasts).

Biochemistry:

1. Various urinary crystals (calcium oxalate, triple phosphate, uric acid, etc.)
2. Various urinary sediment cells (r.b.c., w.b.c., epithelial) and casts.

Hematology:

1. Red cell morphology in stained films (anisocytosis, poikilocytosis, reticulocytes, Cabot rings, etc.)

2. Leukemia slides (usually myelogenous or lymphocytic).
3. L.E. cells (polymorphonuclear neutrophil leukocytes "in rosette" with L.E. body in center).
4. Infectious mononucleosis (I.M.) cells.

Parasitology:

1. Malaria smears (usually *Plasmodium vivax* trophozoites with typical Schüffner's dots).
2. Cysts of various intestinal amebas (*Entamoeba coli* and *Entamoeba histolytica, Iodamoeba bütschlii, Endolimax nana*).
3. Cysts of other intestinal protozoa such as *Giardia lamblia* or *Chilomastix mesnili.*
4. *Blastocystis hominis.*
5. The rhabditiform larva of *Strongyloides* found in feces.
6. The egg of *Schistosoma haematobium* (with a terminal spine) found in urine.
7. The eggs of the common intestinal worms such as *Ascaris lumbricoides, Trichuris trichiura* (football-shaped and with a plug at each pole), *Taenia solium* or *T. saginata* (with three pairs of hooklets), *Hymenolepis nana* (similar to the latter but with two hair-like processes), *Schistosoma mansoni* (with a large lateral spine), *Schistosoma japonicum* (with a minute lateral spine), hookworm (4- or 8-cell stages in feces), *Clonorchis sinensis* (small, operculated and shaped like an old-fashioned electric bulb).
8. Pinworm *(Enterobius vermicularis)* eggs obtained by perianal (Scotch tape) swabs.
9. Microfilariae (prelarval stages of filarial nematodes) in peripheral blood *(Dracunculus medinensis, Acanthocheilonema perstans, Wuchereria bancrofti, Mansonella ozzardi,* and *Loa loa.* It may be well to remember here that the microfilaria of *Onchocerca volvulus* does not occur in peripheral blood but rather in the skin).

Q. **Which Test (or tests) is Most Important?**
A. Because errors may be fatal, blood typing and blood crossmatching are the most important clinical laboratory procedures. Next in importance is the prothrombin test, followed by the various tests for syphilis (VDRL, etc.) which are legal premarital or prenatal requirements in various states.

Q. **Should I Memorize Normal Values?**
A. You should memorize at least the *important normal values.* For your convenience, the most important normal values are listed below:

Urinalysis:
> Routine Urinalysis:
>> pH: 4.8–7.6 (average 6)
>> Sp. Gr.: 1.015–1.025 (1.010–1.030)
>> No sugar, protein ("albumin" or Bence-Jones), acetone, or bile (unchanged bile). No more than a few w.b.c. ("pus cells"), r.b.c., or an occasional cylindroid or hyaline cast.
> Addis Count: No more than 5,000 hyaline casts in 12 hours, and less than 500,000 r.b.c., or 1,000,000 white and epithelial cells during the same period.
> Urobilinogen (a colorless compound formed in the intestines by reduction of bilirubin): Up to 2.1 Ehrlich units in 2 hours in the male

or up to 1.1 Ehrlich units in 2 hours in the female (Watson's semi-quantitative procedure).

Porphobilinogen (porphyrin precursor): 0. (Note: Both porphobilinogen and urobilinogen react with Ehrlich's benzaldehyde reagent but whereas the latter chromogen is soluble in chloroform, porphobilinogen is not.)

Porphyrins (coproporphyrin, uroporphyrin). Only small amounts. (Porphyrins require spectroscopic detection.)

Urea Clearance (C_u): 40–65 ml./min. (standard) or 60–100 ml./min. (maximal).

Blood Chemistry:

Sugar (true glucose): 70–92 mg./100 ml. (Folin-Wu higher, 80–120).

Nonprotein Nitrogen:
> Total nonprotein nitrogen (NPN): 25–35 mg./100 ml.
> Blood urea nitrogen (BUN): 12–18 mg./100 ml. (about ½ of total non-protein nitrogen)
> Creatinine: 0.7–1.5 mg./100 ml.
> Uric acid: 3–6 mg./100 ml.

Icterus (bilirubin) index: 4–8 units

Bilirubin, Quantitative:
> Direct: 0.1–0.4 mg./100 ml.
> Total: 0.2–0.8 mg./100 ml.

Calcium (total calcium): 9–11 mg./100 ml. or 4.5–5.5 mEq./L.

Phosphorus: 3–4.5 mg./100 ml. as inorganic phosphate. Children: 4–7

Phosphatase:
> Acid: 0.5–2.0 units (Bodansky or Gutman)
> Alkaline: 2.2–8.6 units (Shinowara), 5–13 (King-Armstrong), 2–4.5 (Bodansky). Children have higher values.

Amylase: 80–180 Somogyi units

Lipase: 0–1.5 units (ml. of N/20 NaOH)

Transaminase:
> SGOT: 5–40 units/ml.
> SGPT: 5–35 units/ml.

Dehydrogenase (LDH): 100–350 Berger-Broida units/ml.

Cholesterol:
> Total: 150–250 mg./100 ml.
> Ester: 60–75% of total

Protein:
> Total Protein: 6–8 Gm./100 ml.
> Albumin: 3.5–5.5 Gm./100 ml.
> Globulin: 1.5–3.0 Gm./100 ml.
> Fibrinogen (plasma): 0.2–0.4 Gm./100 ml.
> A/G: 1.5–2.5/1.0

CO_2 Combining Power: 53–64 volumes% (24–29 mEq./L.)

Chloride (NaCl), serum or plasma: 99–108 mEq./L (580–630 mg./100 m.). Lower whole blood values.

Sodium: 135–152 mEq./L. (310–350 mg./100 ml.)

Potassium: 4.1–5.6 mEq./L. (16–22 mg./100 ml.)

BSP (5 mg. per Kg., I.V.): Less than 5% retention at 45 minutes

Cephalin-Cholesterol: 0–1[+] in 48 hours

Thymol Turbidity: 0–12 units.

Spinal Fluid:

Cells: 0–5 mononuclears
Sugar (true glucose): 50–80 mg./100 ml. (Folin-Wu 60–90)
Total Protein: 15–45 mg./100 ml.
Colloidal Gold Curve: 0000110000

Gastric Analysis:

Free hydrochloric acid: 5–20 degrees fasting or 20–70 degrees after
alcohol or Histalog stimulation
Total acidity: 15–45 degrees fasting or 50–100 degrees after alcohol
or Histalog stimulation

Hematology:

RBC: 4.5–6 million, women 4-5.5/cu. mm.
WBC: 5,000–10,000/cu. mm.
Hgb: 13–17 Gm.% males, 12–16 Gm.% females
PCV (Hct.): 40–50 males, 37–47 females
Differential WBC:
Segmented neutrophils: 40–60%
Band neutrophils (stabs): 1–3%
Juveniles (metamyelocytes): 0
Myelocytes: 0
Lymphocytes: 20–25%
Monocytes: 2–6%
Eosinophils: 1–3%
Basophils: 0–1%
Sedimentation Rate (ESR), Wintrobe: 0–10 mm./hr. males or 0–20
mm./hr. females
Platelets: 150,000–350,000/cu. mm.
Reticulocytes: 0.5–1.5%
Red Cell Indices:
Mean corpuscular vol. (MCV): 80–94 cu. microns
Mean Corpuscular Hemoglobin (MCH): 30–34 picograms per RBC
Mean Corpuscular Hemoglobin Concentration (MCHC): 32–36 Gm.%
Bleeding Time (Ivy template): 3–5 min.
Partial Thromboplastin Time: 26–36 sec.
Fibrinogen: 250–400 mg.%
Red Cell Osmotic Fragility:
Beginning hemolysis: 0.45-0.35% NaCl solution
Complete hemolysis: 0.33–0.30% NaCl solution
Prothrombin: Over 60% activity

Normal values vary with methods and there are no two tables of normal
values exactly alike. Note however that, when an examination question (or
a choice within a question) is to be answered negatively, the figure is usually way off. For example in the following examination question:
Fasting blood level of true glucose is:
a.   5–15 mg./100 ml.
b.   30–50 mg./100 ml.
c.   70–92 mg./100 ml.
d.   150–250 mg./100 ml.
The correct answer (i.e., 70–92) above plainly differs from the wrong ones
(a, b, and d).

Q.   Will I be Asked to Perform Actual Analyses?
A.   This is not likely to happen.

Q.   Will Questions on BMR be Included?
A.   It is unlikely. As a clinical laboratory procedure, BMR has practically been discarded.

Q.   Will Questions on EKG be Included?
A.   EKG is not a clinical laboratory procedure. However, a certain number of (small) hospital laboratories and clinics still include EKG among their procedures. For those students who may be interested in the subject, the following observations may be made:
   1. There is a variety of direct writing electrocardiogram machines on the market and they are all similar in their operation.
   2. Standard positions for "C" or "V" leads:*

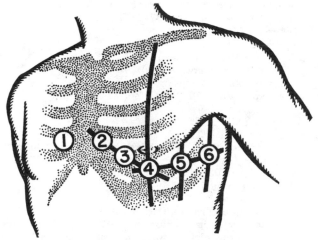

   a. Fourth intercostal space, at right border of sternum.
   b. Same interspace, at left sternal border.
   c. Midway between positions 2 and 4.
   d. At outer border of apex-beat area.†

*Sanborn Company, Cambridge, Mass.
†Position C_4, on which positions C_3, C_5, and C_6 depend, is not in the same location for all patients. If the apex beat can be located, C_4 is defined as lying over the lateral border of the apex-beat area. This places it, normally, in the mid-clavicular line at the level of the fifth interspace, as shown in the illustration. But no matter where the apex beat may be found, the line along which positions C_2 to C_6 are placed starts from the left sternal margin in the fourth interspace, proceeds from there to the outer border of the apex beat, and then becomes horizontal and continues on around the chest at the level of the apex beat. If the latter cannot be satisfactorily located, C_4 is placed arbitrarily, at the point where the mid-clavicular line crosses the center of the fifth interspace, C_5 and C_6 are at the same level, and C_3 lies midway between C_2 and C_4.
   Thus the diagram is correct for all cases in which the apex beat is in the normal position, or in which it cannot be found at all. For other cases, where it is clearly found in an abnormal location, positions C_3 to C_6 (but not C_1 and C_2) will be somewhat different from those shown.

    e. Same level as 4, in anterior axillary line.
    f. Same level as 4 and 5, in midaxillary line.
3. A common practice for marking the various leads is as follows:

Lead   I — One long line: ————
Lead   II — Two long lines: ———— ————
Lead III — Three long lines: ———— ———— ————
AVR —   Long line - short line: ———— —
AVL —   Long line - two short lines: ———— — —
AVF —   Long line - three short lines: ———— — — —
V_1 —   One short line: —
V_2 —   Two short lines: — —
V_3 —   Three short lines: — — —
V_4 —   Four short lines: — — — —
V_5 —   Five short lines: — — — — —
V_6 —   Six short lines: — — — — — —

Q. **Will Questions on Histological Technique be Asked?**

A. Usually no more than a few questions on the subject are included. It may be well to review here that tissues are most frequently fixed in 10% formalin (100% formalin is the 40% solution of the gas formaldehyde). Amebas may be fixed in Schaudinn's solution (this is a mixture of 95% alcohol and mercuric chloride). Tumor cells to be stained by the Papanicolaou technique are fixed in ether-alcohol. Heat is generally used for the fixation of bacterial cells. Before sections can be made of bone, this must be decalcified by treatment with a strong acid, usually nitric acid. Tissues may be imbedded in paraffin. A paraffin oven should be kept at about 2°C. above the melting point of paraffin (many prefer a paraffin with a melting point of from 54–56°C. when the section cutting must be done in a warm room and from 52–54°C. when the section cutting is to be done in a cooler room). The nuclei of tissue cells are usually stained with hematoxylin (a basic stain) and the cytoplasm with eosin (an acid stain). Sections may be affixed to slides by means of egg albumin (Mayer's albumin). Tissues may be mounted in Canada balsam (or glycerin jelly, oil of cedarwood, or gum damar may be used for this purpose).

Q. **Will I be Asked to Indicate the Significance of Various Tests?**

A. You may be asked occasional questions. It is therefore important to know that amylase and lipase, for instance, are usually pancreatic function tests; calcium and phosphorus, parathyroid function tests, etc. As you acquire clinical laboratory experience you will become familiar with elementary pathology and this, in turn, will make your tasks more enjoyable. Recommended reading is *Outline of General Pathology* by Krikor Y. Yardumian (Univ. of Pittsburgh Press).

Q. **If I Am not Sure of a Certain Answer, Should I Guess it or Leave the Space Blank?**

A. In tests where the wrong answer counts no more than a point, and there is a 50–50 chance of getting the correct answer, you may wish to guess. If, on the other hand, a correction factor is used (for instance: one point subtracted from the total score for every four incorrectly answered questions) do not guess, unless you are fairly certain that your guess is correct. *This advice is for the test ONLY—be sure you do not carry it over into the lab!*

Q.   **How Much Time and Energy Should I Devote to Time-Consuming Questions?**

A.   The large majority of written medical technology tests are objective tests (multiple choice, T-F, completion, matching, etc.) that can be finished in the time allotted. First answer all the easier questions, then go back and answer those questions which you left unanswered. Review everything if time permits. Should you, on the other hand, be confronted with an objective test so designed that it cannot possibly be completed in the time allotted (you will probably be told about it in this case), work your way through from the beginning, skipping only those questions that give you trouble. Work as fast and (you will not have a chance to go over the material again) as accurately as you can. Do not spend too much time on any given question since, in this type of test, each item is usually worth the same amount of credit.

   Essay Test: Read all the questions, then answer first the easier ones. Do not, on the other hand, spend too much time developing the easier questions. Save yourself enough time and energy to do a good job on the harder ones.

Q.   **What Biochemistry Topics Should I Concentrate Upon?**

A.   Unless you have taken recent courses, you should first review chemistry and physic fundamentals. Then memorize all the important normal values. For every important test you should know, in addition to the normal value, a standard (or acceptable) procedure and the analytical principle upon which the procedure is based. You may also be asked questions concerning specimen collection, reagent preparation, and the common application or applications of a test. Questions on various laboratory instruments, including analytical balance, may also be featured. Clinical laboratory glassware and pipettes is another important subject.

Q.   **Will it be Necessary for me to Learn the 17-Ketosteroid and 17-Hydroxy-corticosteroid Determinations? These tests are not Performed in Our Laboratory.**

A.   You should have an idea of what these tests are for, what material is used for analysis, etc. In an advanced examination you may also be expected to know an acceptable procedure.

Q.   **Will it be Required that I be Familiar with the T_3 Test?**

A.   See the preceding answer.

Q.   **Will I be Required to Know the Life-Cycle of Parasites?**

A.   From the clinical laboratory standpoint, knowledge of the life-cycle of human parasites has, for the most part, a cultural rather than a practical value. The large majority of examination questions center on the things that may actually be seen in the laboratory, i.e., the various eggs, the larva of *Strongyloides,* the cysts and the trophozoites, etc., etc. You must also be familiar with a number of standard techniques, such as flotation and sedimentation. Infections with exotic parasites may occasionally be encountered in the United States. Only eight or nine species however are commonly troublesome:

> *Entamoeba histolytica* (amebic dysentery)
> *Giardia lamblia* (giardiasis)
> *Ascaris lumbricoides* (ascariasis)

Necator americanus (hookworm disease)
Strongyloides stercoralis (strongyloidiasis)
Enterobius vermicularis (pinworm) (enterobiasis)
Trichuris trichiura (whipworm) (trichuriasis)
and various tapeworms, cutaneous and visceral larva migrans.

Q. **What Hematology Topics Should I Review Most?**

A. You should have a clear understanding of the kinds of cells seen on the blood smear, how to estimate their number and judge whether they are normal or abnormal. Next you should know every important normal value. You should also be familiar with standard procedures. The list includes: sedimentation rate and red cell indices, osmotic fragility, L.E. cell preps., sickle cell examinations, bleeding time, platelet and reticulocyte counts and all the coagulation tests. With the more widespread use of electronic cell counters like the Coulter S, red blood cell indices have become more precise and more useful.

Q. **Will I be Asked Questions on Abnormal, as well as Normal, Hematology?**

A Yes. The various hematological procedures used for the diagnosis of infec tions, anemias, leukemoid and leukemias, bleeding disorders, lupus and mononucleosis, etc., have almost constant application. Peripheral and bone marrow smears may be featured in more advanced examinations.

Q. **What Bacterial Species Should I be Familiar with?**
What Bacterial Classifications Should I Follow?

A. You need only be concerned with species that have either medical or public health importance. By far, the classification of bacteria used the most is that of Bergey *(Manual of Determinative Bacteriology*, Williams & Wilkins Company, Baltimore, Md.).

Q. **How Much Should I Know About Gram-Negative Bacteria?**

A. You should know a lot about Gram-negative intestinal bacteria and fastidious Gram-negative rods.

Q. **How Much Should I Know About Acid-Base Balance?**

A. Similar to above.

Q. **Will I be Asked Questions About Water or Milk Bacteriology?**

A. You may, as a rule and unless you are taking an examination for a public health certificate, be asked elementary questions only. The IMViC reactions of *Escherichia coli* and *Enterobacter aerogenes* are a frequent feature; also MPN, presumptive, completed, confirmed tests.

Q. **I Was Told that a Recent California Board Examination Contained Many Questions on the VDRL Test. Should I, Therefore, Spend a Great Deal of Time on This Procedure?**

A. From time to time, examinations may put more emphasis on a certain subject, such as the VDRL test. There is no way of anticipating, on the other hand, what the particular contents of the next examination will be. You should certainly learn the serological tests for syphilis required or recommended by your own state. Also remember that, in carrying out a STS procedure, you should follow *exactly* the directions and recommendations of the author serologist.

Alba's Medical Technology Board Examination Review

You have in your hands "the ultimate" in medical technology review. It contains all the material the serious student needs to acquire a solid technical foundation and to pass fair examinations in his fields. **Volume I** is a complete text, featuring detailed outlines of every clinical laboratory subject plus a substantial number of review questions, with answers, and extensive glossaries. **Volume II** contains thousands of representative questions from actual recent examinations and all questions have been provided with authoritative answers. "Practical Math for Clinical Chemistry," "Board Examination Tips," and other unusual features are also included in this second volume.

HOW TO OBTAIN THESE BOOKS

Alba's Medical Technology Board Examination Review is available as a two-volume set usually obtainable direct from our office or through one of the book dealers listed on the following page. If you are in a hurry to obtain the book(s), we suggest you first phone a dealer in your area. If the books are not available through a dealer in your area or if you prefer to order them direct from the publisher, please remit $17.50 for each copy of Volume I and $15.00 for each copy of Volume II, or authorize us to bill you for this amount plus shipping & postage charges. Books are routinely shipped by special fourth class mail and delivery date depends upon postal conditions. Cost of special mailing services (such as air mail or special delivery) is borne by customer in all cases.

Berkeley Scientific Publications, Drawer 160, Westlake, OR 97493

DEALERS AND DISTRIBUTORS

Affiliated Medical Book Corp.
1355 Nostrand Ave.
Brooklyn NY 11226

South Campus Bookstore
Community College of
  Allegheny County
1750 Clairton Rd.
West Mifflin PA 15122

Barnes & Noble Bookstores
105 Fifth Ave.
New York NY 10003

Bassett Center Book Store
84 Bassett Center
El Paso TX 79925

Beers Book Center
1406 J St.
Sacramento CA 95814

The Book Corner
Stone Plaza Shopping Center
Greenville SC 29609

Bookmaster, Inc.
911 Schindler Dr.
Silver Spring MD 20904

Brown's House of Books
PO Box 30009
Amarillo TX 79120

The College Store
Pemberton-Browns Mills N.J.
Pemberton NJ 08068

UCLA Health Sciences Store
308 Westwood Plaza
Los Angeles CA 90024

Guy S. Milberry Union
Book and Supply Store
500 Parnassus Ave.
San Francisco CA 94143

Campus Book Store
854 N. Vermont Ave.
Los Angeles CA 90029

Chicago Medical Book Co.
7400 North Melvina Ave.
Chicago IL 60648

The Cleveland State Barnes
& Noble Bookstore
2400 Euclid Ave.
Cleveland OH 44115

Bookstore—Univ. of Colo.
Medical Center
4200 E. Ninth Ave.
Denver CO 80220

Delaware Technical &
Community College Bookstore
Georgetown DE 19947

Dodgson's Book Center
2225 West Shaw, Suite 116
Fresno, CA 93705

Dolbey's, Inc.
PO Box 7316
Philadelphia PA 19101

Grace Dworkin
528 Riverside Dr.
New York NY 10027

E B S Book Service
290 Broadway
Lynbrook NY 11563

Ephraim's
80 Franklin St
Worcester MA 01608

Campus Book Store
Univ. of Florida
Gainesville FL 32601

Manoa Campus Bookstore
Univ. of Hawaii
2465 Campus Rd.
Honolulu HI 96822

Login Bros. Book Co., Inc.
1450 W. Randolph St.
Chicago IL 60607

Campus Store
Loma Linda Univ.
11161 Anderson St.
Loma Linda CA 92354

Lou's Books
5647 Atlantic Ave.
Long Beach CA 90805

Univ. of Louisville
Health Sciences Center
Medical-Dental Bookstore
Louisville KY 40201

Macomb County Community
  College Center Campus Store
Warren MI 48093

J.A. Majors Co.
3770 Zip Industrial Blvd.
Atlanta GA 30354

J.A. Majors Co.
8911 Directors Row
Dallas TX 75247

J.A. Majors Co.
1806 Southgate
Houston TX 77025

J.A. Majors Co.
2120 S. Roman St.
New Orleans LA 70125

Bookstore
Marshall Univ.
Huntington WV 25701

The Medical Bibliothec
496 Clarkson Ave.
Brooklyn NY 11203

Medical Book Exchange
730–732 Culbertson Dr.
Oklahoma City OK 73105

The Medical Bookstore Inc.
331 N. Seventh St.
Springfield IL 62701

Bookstore—Univ. of Miami
Coral Gables FL 33124

Med Bookstore—Univ. of Miami
Miami FL 33152

Missouri Book Store
909 Lowry
Columbia MO 65201

Univ. Bookstore in the
T.A. Brady Commons
Columbia MO 65201

Moyer Student Union Bookstore
4505 Maryland Parkway
Las Vegas NV 89154

New England Book Service
Charlotte VT 05445

Univ. of Oregon Health
  Sciences Center
3181 SW Sam Jackson Park Rd.
Portland OR 97201

Reilly's Medical Books
431 MacDade Blvd.
Folsom PA 19033

Rittenhouse Book Distributors
251 S. 24th St
Philadelphia PA 19103

Hornet Book Store
Sacramento State College
Sacramento CA 95819

San Antonio College Bookstore
402 Dewey
San Antonio TX 78284

Sioux City Stationery Co.
4th & Nebraska Sts.
Sioux City IA 51102

USC Health Sciences Store
1969 Zonal Ave.
Los Angeles CA 90033

Stacey's Div. Bro-Dart
405 California Ave.
Palo Alto CA 94306

Technical Book Co.
2056 Westwood Blvd.
Los Angeles CA 90025

Univ. Book & Supply
Univ. Center
Knoxville TN 37916

Univ. Center Store
800 Madison Ave.
Memphis TN 30163

United States Book Co.
1701 Murray Ave.
Pittsburg, PA 15217

Walden Book Co., Inc.
179 Ludlow St.
Stamford CT 06904

Univ. Book Store
4326 University Way NE
Seattle WA 98105

Wayne Medical Bookstore
1036 Beaubien
Detroit MI 48226

The White Shop
College Plaza
New Haven CT 06519

The University Bookstore
711 State St.
Madison WI 53708